The Elements of the Theory of Algebraic Numbers

BY

LEGH WILBER REID
Professor of Mathematics in Haverford College

WITH AN

INTRODUCTION

BY

DAVID HILBERT
Professor of Mathematics in the University of Gottingen

New York
THE MACMILLAN COMPANY
1910

Reprinted 1926

Reprinted 1946

Photo-Lithoprint Reproduction
EDWARDS BROTHERS, INC.
Lithoprinters
ANN ARBOR, MICHIGAN

TO

MY WIFE.

PREFACE.

It has been my endeavor in this book to lead by easy stages a reader, entirely unacquainted with the subject, to an appreciation of some of the fundamental conceptions in the general theory of algebraic numbers. With this object in view, I have treated the theory of rational integers more in the manner of the general theory than is usual, and have emphasized those properties of these integers which find their analogues in the general theory. The same may be said of the general quadratic realm, which has been treated rather as an example of the general realm of the *n*th degree than simply as of the second degree, as little use as was possible, without too great sacrifice of simplicity, being made of the special properties of the quadratic realm in the proofs. The theorems and their proofs have therefore been so formulated as to be readily extendable, in most cases, to the general realm of the *n*th degree, and it is hoped that a student, who wishes to continue the study of the subject, will find the reading of works on the general theory, such as Hilbert's Bericht über die Theorie der Algebraischen Zahlkörper, rendered easier thereby. The realm $k(\sqrt{-1})$ has been discussed at some length with two objects in view; first, to show how exactly the theorems relating to rational integers can be carried over to the integers of a higher realm when once the unique factorization theorem has been established; and second, to illustrate, by a brief account of Gauss' work in biquadratic residues, the advantage gained by widening our field of operation. The proofs of the theorems relating to biquadratic residues have necessarily been omitted but the examples given will make the reader acquainted with their content. The realms $k(\sqrt{-3})$ and $k(\sqrt{2})$ have been briefly discussed in order to introduce the reader to modifications which must be made in our conceptions of integers and units. In $k(\sqrt{-5})$, the failure of the unique factorization law is shown and its restoration in terms of ideal factors is foreshadowed.

References have been given more with a view to aiding the student in continuing his study of the subject than to pointing out the original source of a theorem or concept.

The author has adopted the term "realm" as the equivalent of körper, corpus, campus, body, domain and field, as it has the advantage, he believes, of not having been used in any other branch of mathematics. It is suggested by Gauss' use of the term "Bürgerrecht" in connection with his introduction of the integers of $k(\sqrt{-1})$ as his field of operation (see p. 218).

Many numerical examples have been given, especially in cases involving ideals, and it is hoped that through them the student may attain some familiarity with the methods of reckoning with algebraic numbers. The fact that the earlier discoveries in the theory of numbers were made inductively inspires the belief that such discoveries may also be made in the higher theory, if a sufficient amount of numerical material be at hand.

The following is a list of the principal authorities that have been consulted, the abbreviations used in citation being given. The lectures of Professor Hilbert, mentioned above, the use of which he kindly allowed me. Bachmann: Die Lehre von der Kreistheilung; Elemente der Zahlentheorie; Niedere Zahlentheorie; Allegmeine Arithmetik der Zahlenkörper. Borel et Drach: Lecons sur la Theorie des Nombres et Algebra. Cahen: Elements de la Theorie des Nombres, cited as Cahen. Cayley: Encyclopaedia Britannica, 9th ed., Vol. XVII, pp. 614–624. Chrystal: Algebra. Dirichlet-Dedekind: Vorlesungen über Zahlentheorie, 4th ed, cited as Dirichlet-Dedekind. Gauss: Disquisitiones Arithmeticae, Works, Vol. I; Theoria Residuorum Biquadraticorum, Commentatio Prima, Commentatio Secunda, Works, Vol. II. Hilbert: Bericht über die Theorie der Algebraischen Zahlkörper, Jahresbericht der Deutschen Mathematiker-Vereinigung, Vol. IV, cited as Hilbert: Bericht. Kronecker: Vorlesungen über Zahlentheorie. Laurent: Theorie des Nombres, Ordinaires et Algebriques. Mathews: Theory of Numbers, cited as Mathews; also Encyclopaedia Britannica, Supplement, Vol. XXXI. Minkowski: Geometrie der Zahlen; Diophantische Approximationen. H. J.

S. Smith: Report on the Theory of Numbers, Collected Mathematical Papers, Vol. I, pp. 38–364, cited as H. J. S. Smith. Tschebyscheff: Theorie der Congruenzen. Weber: Algebra. Wertheim; Elemente der Zahlentheorie; Anfangsgründe der Zahlenlehre.

In conclusion, I wish to express my most sincere thanks to Professor Hilbert for having given me my first interest in the subject of the theory of numbers by his lectures, which I attended in the winter semester, 1897–98, at Göttingen, for his continued interest in my work, and for his great kindness in writing an introduction to this book. I desire also to acknowledge my indebtedness to Professor James Harkness of McGill University for many helpful suggestions, and to the late Professor J. Edmund Wright of Bryn Mawr College and my colleague Professor W. H. Jackson for valuable assistance with the proof sheets.

LEGH W. REID.

HAVERFORD COLLEGE.

CONTENTS.

INTRODUCTION.

CHAPTER I.

Preliminary Definitions and Theorems.

CHAPTER II.

The Rational Realm.

Divisibility of Integers.

CHAPTER III.

The Rational Realm.

Congruences.

CHAPTER IV.

The Rational Realm.

Quadratic Residues.

CHAPTER V.

The Realm $k(i)$.

CHAPTER VI.

The Realm $k(\sqrt{-3})$.

CHAPTER VII.

The Realm $k(\sqrt{2})$.

CHAPTER VIII.

The Realm $k(\sqrt{-5})$.

CHAPTER IX.

General Theorems Concerning Algebraic Numbers.

CHAPTER X.

The General Quadratic Realm.

CHAPTER XI.

Ideals of a Quadratic Realm.

CHAPTER XII.

Congruences whose Moduli are Ideals.

CHAPTER XIII.

THE UNITS OF THE GENERAL QUADRATIC REALM.

CHAPTER XIV.

THE IDEAL CLASSES OF A QUADRATIC REALM.

INTRODUCTION.

Die Zahlentheorie ist ein herrlicher Bau, erschaffen und aufgeführt von Männern die zu den glänzendsten Forschern im Bereiche der mathematischen Wissenschaften gehören: Fermat, Euler, Lagrange, Legendre, Gauss, Jacobi, Dirichlet, Hermite, Kummer, Dedekind und Kronecker; Alle diese Männer haben in den begeistersten Worten ihrer hohen Meinung über die Zahlentheorie Ausdruck gegeben und bis heute giebt es wohl keine Wissenschaft, von deren Ruhme ihre Jünger so erfüllt sind, wie von der Zahlentheorie. Man preist an der Zahlentheorie die Einfachheit ihrer Grundlagen, die Genauigkeit ihrer Begriffe und die Reinheit ihrer Wahrheiten; man rühmt sie als das Vorbild für die anderen Wissenschaften, als die tiefste unversiegbare Quelle aller mathematischen Erkenntniss und als reiche Spenderin von Anregungen für andere mathematische Forschungsgebiete wie Algebra, Funktionentheorie, Analysis und Geometrie. Dazu kommt, dass die Zahlentheorie vom Wechsel der Mode unabhängig ist und dort nicht wie oft in anderen Wissensgebieten, bald die eine Auffassung oder Methode übermässig sich aufbauseht, bald zu anderer Zeit unverdiente Zurücksetzung erfährt; in der Zahlentheorie ist oft das älteste Problem noch heute modern, wie ein echtes Kunstwerk aus der Vergangenheit.

Und dennoch ist jetz wie früher wahr, worüber Gauss und Dirichlet klagten, dass nur eine geringe Anzahl von Mathematikern zu einer eingehenden Beschäftigung mit der Zahlentheorie und zu einem vollen und freien Genusse ihrer Schönheit gelangt. Zumal ausserhalb Deutschlands und unter der heran wachsenden mathematischen Jugend ist arithmetisches Wissen nur wenig verbreitet.

Jeder Liebhaber der Zahlentheorie wird wünschen, dass die Zahlentheorie gleichmässig ein Besitz aller Nationen sei und gerade besonders unter der jungen Generation, der die Zukunft gehört, Pflege und Verbreitung finde. Das vorliegende Buch steckt sich dieses Ziel: Möge es dasselbe erreichen, indem es nicht nur dazu beitrage, dass die Elemente der Zahlentheorie Gemeingut aller Mathematiker werden, sondern, indem es auch zugleich als Einführung und Erleichterung zum Studium der darin genannten Originalwerke diene, sowie zur selbständigen Bethätigung der Zahlentheorie anrege. Bei der liebevollen Vertiefung des Verfassers in die Zahlentheorie und bei dem hingebenden Verständniss, mit dem der Verfasser in das Wesen derselben eingedrungen ist, dürfen wir auf die Erfüllung dieses Wunsches bauen.

DAVID HILBERT.

GÖTTINGEN, 10, März, 1907.

TRANSLATION.

The theory of numbers is a magnificent structure, created and developed by men who belong among the most brilliant investigators in the domain of the mathematical sciences: Fermat, Euler, Lagrange, Legendre, Gauss, Jacobi, Dirichlet, Hermite, Kummer, Dedekind and Kronecker. All these men have expressed their high opinion respecting the theory of numbers in the most enthusiastic words and up to the present there is indeed no science so highly praised by its devotees as is the theory of numbers. In the theory of numbers, we value the simplicity of its foundations, the exactness of its conceptions and the purity of its truths; we extol it as the pattern for the other sciences, as the deepest, the inexhaustible source of all mathematical knowledge, prodigal of incitements to investigation in other departments of mathematics, such as algebra, the theory of functions, analysis and geometry.

Moreover, the theory of numbers is independent of the change of fashion and in it we do not see, as is often the case in other departments of knowledge, a conception or method at one time given undue prominence, at another suffering undeserved neglect; in the theory of numbers the oldest problem is often to-day modern, like a genuine work of art from the past. Nevertheless it is true now as formerly, a fact which Gauss and Dirichlet lamented, that only a small number of mathematicians busy themselves deeply with the theory of numbers and attain to a full enjoyment of its beauty. Especially outside of Germany and among the younger mathematicians arithmetical knowledge is little disseminated. Every devotee of the theory of numbers will desire that it shall be equally a possession of all nations and be cultivated and spread abroad, especially among the younger generation to whom the future belongs. Such is the aim of this book. May it reach this goal, not only by helping to make the elements of the theory of numbers the common property of all mathematicians, but also by serving as an introduction to the original works to which reference is made, and by inciting to independent activity in the field of the theory of numbers. On account of the devoted absorption of the author in the theory of numbers and the comprehensive understanding with which he has penetrated into its nature, we may rely upon the fulfilment of this wish.

CHAPTER I.

Preliminary Definitions and Theorems.

§ 1. Algebraic Numbers. Algebraic Integers. Degree of an Algebraic Number.

It will be assumed in this book that the complex number system has been built up and that the laws to which the four fundamental operations of algebra are subject have been demonstrated to hold when these operations are performed upon any numbers of this system.

We shall occupy ourselves with certain properties of a special class of these numbers, known as algebraic numbers, these properties flowing in the greater part from the relation in which two numbers stand to one another when one is said to be a divisor of the other. We proceed to define an algebraic number.

A number, α, is said to be an *algebraic* number when it satisfies an equation of the form

$$x^n + a_1 x^{n-1} + \cdots + a_{n-1} x + a_n = 0 \qquad 1)$$

where $a_1, a_2, \cdots, a_n$ are rational numbers. We shall call an equation of form 1) a rational equation. The simplest algebraic numbers are evidently the rational numbers. An algebraic number is said to be an *algebraic integer* or briefly an *integer*, when it satisfies an equation of the form 1) whose coefficients, a_1, a_2, $\cdots$, a_n, are rational integers. The simplest algebraic integers are the positive and negative natural numbers. An algebraic number, α, evidently satisfies an infinite number of rational equations, for if α satisfy 1), it also satisfies any equation formed by multiplying 1) by an integral function of x of the form

$$x^m + b_1 x^{m-1} + \cdots + b_{m-1} x + b_m,$$

where $b_1, \cdots, b_m$ are rational numbers, and this equation will be of the form 1). There will be however among all these rational equations satisfied by α, one and only one of lowest degree, l. For suppose that α satisfied two different rational equations of the lth degree, l being the degree of the rational equation of lowest degree satisfied by α, and let these equations be

$$x^l + a_1x^{l-1} + \cdots + a_l = 0 \qquad 2)$$

$$x^l + b_1x^{l-1} + \cdots + b_l = 0 \qquad 3)$$

Then α will satisfy the equation formed by subtracting 3) from 2); that is,

$$(a_1 - b_1)x^{l-1} + \cdots + a_l - b_l = 0 \qquad 4)$$

Unless 4) be identically zero, α satisfies a rational equation of degree lower than the lth, which is contrary to our original supposition. Therefore 4) is identically 0, and 2) and 3) are the same equation. Hence α satisfies only one rational equation of the lth degree.

This equation is irreducible; that is, its first member can not be resolved into factors of lower degree in x, with rational coefficients; for if

$$x^l + a_1x^{l-1} + \cdots + a_l = (x^h + b_1x^{h-1} + \cdots + b_h) \times (x^k + c_1x^{k-1} + \cdots + c_k),$$

where $b_1, \cdots, b_h, c_1, \cdots, c_k$ are rational numbers, α would satisfy one of the rational equations

$$x^h + b_1x^{h-1} + \cdots + b_h = 0; \quad x^k + c_1x^{k-1} + \cdots + c_k = 0.$$

This is, however, impossible since both of these equations are of lower degree than the lth. Hence the rational equation of lowest degree, which α satisfies, is irreducible. If l be the degree of this equation, α is said to be an algebraic number of the lth degree.

THEOREM 1. *If α be an algebraic number,*

$$f_1(x) = x^l + a_1x^{l-1} + \cdots + a_l = 0$$

the single rational equation of lowest degree which α satisfies, and

$$f_2(x) = x^m + b_1x^{m-1} + \cdots + b_m = 0$$

any other rational equation satisfied by α, then $f_1(x)$ is a divisor of $f_2(x)$.

We can always put $f_2(x)$ in the form

$$f_2(x) = f_3(x) \cdot f_1(x) + f_4(x) \qquad 2)$$

where $f_2(x)$ and $f_4(x)$ are rational integral functions of x whose coefficients are rational integers and $f_4(x)$ of lower degree than $f_1(x)$. Substituting α for x in 2) we have

$$f_2(\alpha) = f_3(\alpha) \cdot f_1(\alpha) + f_4(\alpha),$$

whence, since $f_2(\alpha) = 0$ and $f_1(\alpha) = 0$, $f_4(\alpha) = 0$; that is, unless $f_4(x)$ is identically 0, α will satisfy a rational equation, $f_4(x) = 0$ of lower degree than the lth. But this is contrary to our original hypothesis. Hence $f_4(x)$ is identically zero, and $f_1(x)$ is therefore a divisor of $f_2(x)$.

We shall see later (Chap. II, Th. 4) that the rational equation of lowest degree which an algebraic number, α, satisfies, determines the question whether or not α is an algebraic integer; that is, that the coefficients of the single rational equation of lowest degree, which an algebraic number, α, satisfies, shall be integers, is a *necessary* as well as sufficient condition for α to be an algebraic integer.

§ 2. Algebraic Number Realms.

A system of algebraic numbers is called a *number realm* or briefly a *realm*, if the sum, difference, product and quotient of every two numbers of the system, excluding division by 0, are numbers of the system; that is, if the system is invariant with respect to these four operations.

The simplest example of a realm is the system of all rational numbers, for evidently the sum, difference, product and quotient of any two rational numbers are rational numbers. Another example is the system of numbers of the form $x + y\sqrt{-1}$, where x and y take all rational values. For the sum, difference, product and quotient of any two of these numbers are numbers of this form.

§ 3. Generation of a Realm.

If α be any algebraic number, the system consisting of all numbers, which can be formed by repeated performance upon α of the four fundamental reckoning operations, that is, the system consisting of all rational functions of α with rational coefficients, will be a realm.

For the sum, difference, product and quotient of any two rational functions of α are rational functions of α and hence numbers of the system.

We say that α *generates* this realm. We say also that α *defines* the realm and denote the latter by $k(\alpha)$. The rational realm can be generated by any rational number, a; for a divided by a gives 1, and from 1 by repeated additions and subtractions of 1, we can obtain all rational integers, and from them by division all rational fractions. As the number defining the rational realm we generally take 1, thus denoting the realm by $k(1)$. More usually, however, the rational realm is denoted by the letter R. The realm given as the second example in the last paragraph can be generated by $\sqrt{-1}$; for $\sqrt{-1}$ divided by $\sqrt{-1}$ gives 1, and from 1 we can generate the rational realm and then by multiplying $\sqrt{-1}$ by all rational numbers in turn and adding to each of these products each rational number in turn, we obtain all numbers of the form $x+y\sqrt{-1}$, where x and y take all rational values. This realm is therefore denoted by $k(\sqrt{-1})$. We have seen in the last example that among the numbers of $k(\sqrt{-1})$ are found all the numbers of the rational realm. It may be easily seen that this is true of every realm; that is, every realm contains R; for if ω be any number, ω divided by ω gives 1, and from 1 we can generate R. It is well to observe that, although $\sqrt{-1}$ is the number which most conveniently defines $k(\sqrt{-1})$ and is indeed the one usually selected, it is not the only number that will serve this purpose. We see, on the contrary, that this realm can be generated by any number of the form $a+b\sqrt{-1}$ where a and b are rational numbers, and $b \neq 0$; that is, $k(\sqrt{-1})$ and $k(a+b\sqrt{-1})$ are identical; for since $k(a+b\sqrt{-1})$ contains R, it contains a and b and hence $\dfrac{a+b\sqrt{-1}-a}{b}, = \sqrt{-1}$. Therefore $k(a+b\sqrt{-1})$ contains all numbers of $k(\sqrt{-1})$. Moreover since $k(\sqrt{-1})$ contains $a+b\sqrt{-1}$, it contains all numbers of $k(a+b\sqrt{-1})$. Hence $k(\sqrt{-1})$ is identical with $k(a+b\sqrt{-1})$. It may be shown similarly that any realm may be defined by any one of an infinite number of its numbers; as, for example, if α be any algebraic number, $k(\alpha)$ and $k(a+b\alpha)$, where a and b are rational numbers, and $b \neq 0$ are identical. A realm may be generated by any number of algebraic numbers. If $\alpha, \beta, \cdots, \lambda$ are a finite number of algebraic numbers, the system consisting of all rational functions of these numbers with rational coefficients is a realm which we denote by $k(\alpha, \beta, \cdots, \lambda)$. It can be shown, however, that in every realm $k(\alpha, \beta, \cdots, \lambda)$ we can find a number θ such that $k(\alpha, \beta, \cdots, \lambda) = k(\theta)$. We shall not prove this, as all realms discussed in this book will be defined by a single number.

§ 4. Degree of a Realm. Conjugate Realms. Conjugate Numbers.

If the rational equation of lowest degree which α satisfies be

$$x^n + a_1 x^{n-1} + \cdots + a_n = 0 \qquad 1)$$

then $k(\alpha)$ is said to be of the nth degree. That is, the degree of a realm is the degree of the number defining the realm. Thus $k(\sqrt{-1})$ is of the second degree, since the rational equation of lowest degree which $\sqrt{-1}$ satisfies is $x^2+1=0$. Likewise $k(\sqrt[3]{2})$ is of the third degree. There is evidently only one realm of the first degree $k(1)$, but an infinite number of all other degrees. If the remaining roots of 1) be $\alpha', \alpha'', \cdots, \alpha^{(n-1)}$, then the realms $k(\alpha'), k(\alpha''), \cdots, k(\alpha^{(n-1)})$ are called the *conjugates* of $k(\alpha)$.

If θ be any number of $k(\alpha)$, it is a rational function of α, which we may denote by $r(\alpha)$. Then $\theta' = r(\alpha')$, $\theta'' = r(\alpha'')$, $\cdots$, $\theta^{(n-1)} = r(\alpha^{(n-1)})$, which are derived from θ by the substitutions $\alpha:\alpha'$, $\alpha:\alpha''$, $\cdots$, $\alpha:\alpha^{(n-1)}$, are called the *conjugates* of θ.

§ 5. Forecast of Remaining Chapters.

We shall consider now several special realms. In each we shall find an infinite number of algebraic integers, the study of whose properties in their mutual relations will be our task. It will be observed that the properties of an integer depend upon the realm in which it is considered to lie. Thus the integer 5 is unfactorable in R and in $k(\sqrt{-3})$, but in $k(\sqrt{-1})$ it is the product of two integers, $2+\sqrt{-1}$ and $2-\sqrt{-1}$.

The realms will be taken up in the order of their degrees. That is, the first to be studied will be R, which is, as has been already said, the only realm of the first degree. We shall then take up in turn four special examples of quadratic realms, $k(\sqrt{-1})$, $k(\sqrt{-3})$, $k(\sqrt{2})$ and $k(\sqrt{-5})$. In the cases of $k(\sqrt{-1})$, $k(\sqrt{-3})$ and $k(\sqrt{2})$, we shall see that, with the introduction of a few new conceptions, the integers of these realms obey in their relations to each other laws almost identical with those governing the integers of R.

In the case of $k(\sqrt{-5})$ we shall observe an important difference, and at first sight it will seem that our old laws have no analogues in this realm. By the introduction, however, of the conception of the ideal number not only will the difficulties of this particular realm be overcome, but we shall be able to establish in terms of these ideal numbers general laws for the mutual relations of the integers of any quadratic realm, which are analogous to those already found for the integers of the special realms examined. Furthermore the larger part of the theorems proved for the integers of the general quadratic realm hold for the integers of a realm of any degree whatever.

CHAPTER II.

The Rational Realm.

DIVISIBILITY OF INTEGERS.

§ 1. The Numbers of the Rational Realm.

The rational realm consists of the system of rational numbers, any one of which, except 0, may be taken to define it. It is usually denoted by $k(1)$ or simply R. The absolute value of a number, m, of R is m taken positively and is denoted by $|m|$. Thus

$$|\pm 5| = 5.$$

The absolute value of a number is used when the result of an enumeration is to be expressed as a function of this number.

§ 2. Integers of the Rational Realm.

The positive and the negative rational integers are evidently integers of R, for they satisfy equations of the form $x+a=0$, where a is a rational integer. The sum, difference and product of any two rational integers are seen to be integers. The question will at once be asked, are these all the numbers of the rational realm which are algebraic integers under the definition given of an algebraic integer (Chap. I, § 1). That is, although a rational fraction, b/c, where b is not divisible by c evidently cannot satisfy an equation of the form $x+a=0$, where a is a rational integer, we have not yet shown that b/c cannot satisfy an equation of higher degree than the first and of the form

$$x^n + a_1x^{n-1} + \cdots + a_n = 0,$$

where $a_1, a_2, \cdots, a_n$ are rational integers.

To show this, it is necessary to prove first that a rational integer can be resolved in one and only one way into prime factors. Therefore, until we have proved this theorem, the integers with which we are dealing should be looked upon as merely the ordinary rational integers. When we have proved the above theorem we shall see that the system of rational integers and the system of integers of R are coextensive.

§ 3. **Definition of Divisibility.**

An integer, a, is said to be divisible by an integer, b, when there exists an integer, c, such that $a=bc$; then b and c are said to be *divisors,* or *factors,* of a and a is said to be a *multiple* of b and c. Furthermore, a is said to be *resolved into the factors* b and c, or to be *factored.*

We have, as direct consequences of the definition of divisibility and the fact that the sum, difference and product of any two integers are integers, the following:

i. *If a be a multiple of b, and b a multiple of c, a is a multiple of c.* For since a is a multiple of b, we have $a=a_1b$, and since b is a multiple of c, $b=b_1c$. From which it follows that $a=a_1b_1c$. Hence a is a multiple of c. In general if each integer of a series $a, b, c, d, \cdots$, be a multiple of the one next following, each integer is a multiple of all that follow it; that is, if a be a multiple of b, b a multiple of c, c a multiple of d, etc., a is a multiple of $b, c, d, \cdots$, b a multiple of $c, d, \cdots$, etc.

ii. *If two integers a and b be multiples of an integer c, $a+b$ and $a-b$ are multiples of c.* If two or more integers $a, b, c, \cdots$ be each divisible by an integer m, m is said to be a *common divisor* or *common factor* of $a, b, c, \cdots$. If an integer, m, be a multiple of two or more integers, $a, b, c, \cdots$, m is said to be a *common multiple* of $a, b, c, \cdots$.[1]

§ 4. **Units of the Rational Realm.**

There are two integers, 1 and -1, which are divisors of every rational integer and they are the only rational integers that enjoy this property.

We call 1 and -1 the *units* of R.

Any integer which is divisible by m is also divisible by $-m$; hence any two integers which differ only by a unit factor are considered as identical in all questions of divisibility. We say

[1] Throughout this book the letters of the Latin alphabet will always denote rational numbers, unless there be a direct statement to the contrary.

that two such integers are associated, and call either one the associate of the other. Two integers, a and b, each of which divides the other, are associates, for if $a = cb$ and $b = da$ where c and d are integers, then $cd = 1$, and hence $c = \pm 1$. Two integers whose absolute values are the same are evidently associates. For the sake of generality we consider an integer as associated with itself.

Thus the associates of 5 are 5 and -5 since

$$5 = 1 \cdot 5 \text{ and } -5 = -1 \cdot 5.$$

The factorizations of 30,

$$\begin{aligned} 30 &= 2 \cdot 3 \cdot 5, \\ &= -2 \cdot -3 \cdot 5, \\ &= -2 \cdot 3 \cdot -5, \\ &= 2 \cdot -3 \cdot -5, \end{aligned}$$

are looked upon as identical, since they differ only by the replacement of one or more of the factors by their associates.

Two integers with no common divisors other than units are said to be *prime to each other.*

Under this definition the units are considered prime to every integer including themselves.

If $$|a| = |b|$$

a and b are associates, and it follows therefore that if a be prime to b $$|a| \neq |b|$$

unless a and b be units.

A system of integers such that no two of them have common divisors other than the units are said to be *prime each to each.*

§ 5. Rational Prime Numbers.

Any integer, p, that is not a unit and that has no divisors other than p and $-p$, 1 and -1, that is, than its associates and the units, is called a prime number or, briefly, a prime.

The units are not considered to be prime numbers, because many of the theorems relating to prime numbers will be found not to hold for them.

Every integer, m, with divisors other than m, $-m$, 1, -1 is called a *composite* number. We can obtain the positive prime numbers less than any given positive integer, m, as follows: The only even one is 2. We write down then the odd integers smaller than m,

$$3, 5, 7, 9, 11, 13, 15, 17, 19, 21, \cdots,$$

and remove from the series those which are composite. To do this strike out, counting from 3, the 3d, 6th, 9th, $\cdots$ integers; that is, 9, 15, 21, $\cdots$. Then counting from 5, strike out the 5th, 10th, $\cdots$ integers; that is, 15, 25, $\cdots$, counting integers already struck out, and in general, if p be the smallest integer not struck out, excluding those whose multiples have been struck out, we strike out the pth, $2p$th, $3p$th, $\cdots$ integers, counting from p; that is, all multiples of p except p. The integers not struck out are the positive primes smaller than m.

This method is known as the Sieve of Eratosthenes. It is, however, not necessary to carry out the process for every prime, p, smaller than m; for every composite number, m_1, smaller than p^2, will have been struck out as a multiple of a prime smaller than p, since if m_1 be less than p^2, it contains as a factor a prime less than p. The greatest value of p for which the process must be carried out is therefore the greatest prime not greater than $\sqrt{m}$.

The positive primes less than 100 are: 2, 3, 5, 7, 11, 13, 17, 19, 23, 29, 31, 37, 41, 43, 47, 53, 59, 61, 67, 71, 73, 79, 83, 89, 97.

Ex. 1. Show that every rational prime, except 2, is either of the form $4n-1$ or $4n+1$.

Ex. 2. Show that every rational prime, except 2 and 3, is either of the form $6n-1$ or $6n+1$.

§ 6. The Rational Primes are Infinite in Number.

The proof of this theorem as given by Euclid (Elements, Book IX, Prop. 20) is the following: Let us suppose that there are only a finite number of positive primes, p being the greatest. Multiply these primes together and add 1 to the product, forming the number

$$N = 2 \cdot 3 \cdot 5 \cdots p + 1.$$

It is evident that N is not divisible by any of the primes 2, 3, 5, $\cdots$, p. Hence N is either a prime itself, or contains as a factor a prime greater than p. In either case there exists a prime greater than p, which contradicts our original assumption. Hence the number of rational primes is infinite.

This proof of Euclid's tells us far more than merely that the rational primes are infinite in number, for if $2, 3, \cdots, p$ be the n smallest positive primes it gives a limit, $p+1$ to $2\cdot 3\cdots p+1$, within which a prime greater than p must lie. To bring out clearly what has been proved we may state the theorem as follows: *If $2, 3, \cdots, p$ be the n smallest positive primes, then there is a prime greater than p among the numbers $p+1, \cdots, 2\cdot 3\cdots p+1$ and consequently the rational primes are infinite in number.* For example, 2, 3, 5, 7, being all the positive rational primes not greater than 7, there is certainly one prime greater than 7 among the numbers $8, 9, \cdots, 2\cdot 3\cdot 5\cdot 7+1$.

After it became known that the rational primes are infinite in number, the attention of investigators was turned to the question whether, if from the positive integers a series be selected which form an arithmetical progression, as for example $1, 5, 9, 13, \cdots$, or $3, 7, 11, 15, \cdots$, there are in every such series an infinite number of primes. Proofs showing that this is true of the two series given will be found in this book.

It is not difficult to prove also that there are an infinite number of primes of each of the forms $6n-1$, $6n+1$, and $8n+5$.[1]

These are, however, only special cases of the general theorem that in every unlimited arithmetical progression, whose general term is $a+nd$, the first term a and the common difference, d, being prime to each other, there occur infinitely many prime numbers. This theorem was first proved by Dirichlet (see D. D., 4th Ed., Sup. VI), but he did not give an interval within which a new prime must lie, as in the case of Euclid's proof. This omission was supplied by Kronecker in 1885. (See above reference.)

Among problems relating to prime numbers which still await solution is first of all that known as the *problem of the frequency of the primes.* It consists in the determination of the number of

[1] Kronecker: Vorlesungen über Mathematik; Part II, Vol. I, p. 438. Cahen: Théorie des Nombres, p. 318.

positive primes less than any given positive number m, that is, in the determination of the law which governs the distribution of the primes among the entire series of positive integers.

Kronecker mentions two interesting theorems which are believed to be true, although no proofs have yet been obtained.

I. *Every positive even integer can be represented as the sum of two positive prime numbers (2 excepted).* This theorem was first stated by Goldbach, then by Waring. Kronecker remarks[1] that after testing this theorem for the even integers from 2 to 2000, it is observed that the number of possible representations of $2n$ in this form increases as n increases, which heightens the probability of correctness; for example, we have

$$4=2+2;\ 6=3+3;\ 8=3+5;\ 10=3+7,\ 5+5;$$
$$12=5+7;\ 14=3+11,\ 7+7;\ 16=3+13,\ 5+11;$$
$$18=5+13,\ 7+11;\ \text{etc.}$$

II. *Every positive even integer can be represented in infinitely many ways as the difference of two positive primes.*

If the truth of this theorem be assumed and it be applied to the integer 2, we obtain the theorem: *However far we may go in the series of positive primes, we shall always find primes which differ only by 2, that is, which lie as close as possible together.* Naturally the frequency of such pairs of primes decreases the farther out we go in the series of positive integers. Among the first one hundred integers there are eight such pairs:

$$3, 5;\ 5, 7;\ 11, 13;\ 17, 19;\ 29, 31;\ 41, 43;\ 59, 61;\ 71, 73;$$

and among the second hundred seven:

$$101, 103;\ 107, 109;\ 137, 139;\ 149, 151;\ 179, 181;\ 191, 193;\ 197, 199.$$

If we go sufficiently far in the series of positive integers we can find as great a number of successive integers as we please, no one of which is a prime, for none of *the integers* $n!+2$, $n!+3$, $\cdots$, $n!+n$ is a prime, since $n!+i$, $i \leq n$, is divisible by i; for example, $5!+2$, $5!+3$, $5!+4$, $5!+5$ are all composite numbers.

§ 7. Unique Factorization Theorem.

According to the definition, every composite number can be

[1] Vorlesungen über Math., Part II, Vol. I, p. 68.

resolved into the product of two factors, neither of which is a unit. One or both of these factors may be composite, and hence in turn resolvable into two factors, neither of which is a unit, and we can continue this process until we reach factors which are primes. It is evident that when one or both of the factors are composite, the resolution is not unique; for example, $210=14\cdot15=10\cdot21=6\cdot35=2\cdot105=3\cdot70=5\cdot42=7\cdot30$. We shall show that, when the resolution is continued until the factors are primes, it will be unique, considering associated factors as the same (see § 4), and that such a resolution is always possible; for example,

$$\begin{aligned} 210 &= 14\cdot15 = 2\cdot7\cdot3\cdot5 \\ &= 10\cdot21 = 2\cdot5\cdot3\cdot7 \\ &= 6\cdot35 = 2\cdot3\cdot5\cdot7 \\ &= 2\cdot105 = 2\cdot3\cdot5\cdot7 \\ &= 3\cdot70 = 3\cdot2\cdot5\cdot7 \\ &= 5\cdot42 = 5\cdot2\cdot3\cdot7 \\ &= 7\cdot30 = 7\cdot2\cdot3\cdot5; \end{aligned}$$

that is, 210 can be represented in only one way as a product of prime numbers.

To prove this theorem, upon which the whole theory of the rational integers depends, that is, that every rational integer can be represented in one and only one way as a product of prime numbers, we require the two following theorems:

THEOREM A. *If a be any integer and b any integer different from 0, there exists an integer m such that*

$$|a-mb|<|b|$$

Let

$$\frac{a}{b}=m+r,$$

where m is the integer nearest to $\frac{a}{b}$ and hence $|r|\leqq\frac{1}{2}$; then m is the required integer, for $\left|\frac{a}{b}-m\right|<1$,
whence, multiplying by $|b|$,

$$|a-mb|<|b|.$$

This theorem is equivalent to saying that we can divide a by b

so as to obtain a remainder less in absolute value than b, the quotient being m. There are, except when a is divisible by b, evidently two integers which satisfy the requirements of the theorem, one selected as above and another differing from the first by 1; for example, if $a = 12$ and $b = -5$, then

$$|12 - (-2)(-5)| < |-5| \text{ and } |12 - (-3)(-5)| < |-5|;$$

and hence both -2 and -3 satisfy the requirements of the theorem, -2 being the integer selected as in the proof.

THEOREM B. *If a and b be any two integers prime to each other, there exist two integers, x and y, such that*

$$ax + by = 1.$$

If either a or b be a unit, the existence of the integers x, y is evident. We shall now show that, if neither a nor b be a unit, the determination of x and y can be made to depend upon the determination of a corresponding pair of integers x_1, y_1 for a pair of integers a_1, b_1 prime to each other and such that one of them is less in absolute value than both a and b.

Assume $|b| < |a|$, which evidently does not limit the generality of the proof.

By Th. A there exists an integer m such that

$$|a - mb| < |b|.$$

Then b and $a - mb$ are a pair of integers, a_1, b_1, prime to each other, and $a - mb$ is less in absolute value than both a and b.

If now two integers x_1, y_1 exist such that

$$a_1x_1 + b_1y_1 = 1;$$

that is, $$bx_1 + (a - mb)y_1 = 1,$$

we have $$ay_1 + b(x_1 - my_1) = 1,$$

and hence $$x = y_1, \quad y = x_1 - my_1.$$

The determination of x_1, y_1 for a_1, b_1 may, if neither a_1 nor b_1 be a unit, be made to depend similarly upon that of x_2, y_2 for a pair of integers a_2, b_2 prime to each other and such that one of them is less in absolute value than both a_1 and b_1. By a continuation of this process, we are able always to make the determination of x and y depend eventually upon that of x_n, y_n for a pair of integers a_n, b_n, one of which is a unit.

Since the existence of x_n and y_n is evident, the existence of x and y is proved.

Ex. Let $a = 14$, $b = 9$; then $a_1 = 9$, $b_1 = 5$, and the determination of x and y, so that

$$14x + 9y = 1 \qquad 2)$$

depends upon the determination of x_1, y_1, so that

$$9x_1 + 5y_1 = 1. \qquad 3)$$

We can make the determination of x_1, y_1 depend upon the determination of x_2, y_2 for the pair of integers $a_2 = 5$, $b_2 = -1$, but it is sufficient here to notice that $x_1 = -1$, $y_1 = 2$ satisfy 3) and hence $x = y_1 = 2$, $y = x_1 - my_1 = -1 - 1 \cdot 2 = -3$ satisfy 2).

The problem of finding the two integers x and y is most easily solved by the method of continued fractions, but the form of proof here used to show the existence of x and y has been adopted as being more easily applicable to realms of higher degree.

The proof given satisfies completely, however, the requirement which Kronecker considered should be imposed upon every existence proof in the Theory of Numbers (see below); that is, it furnishes a method by which in a finite number of steps the desired integers x, y can be found from the given ones a, b.

Hensel says in his preface to Kronecker's "Lectures on the Theory of Numbers," "Kronecker consciously imposed upon the definitions and proofs of the general arithmetic a demand whose rigorous observance essentially distinguishes his exposition of the theory of numbers and algebra from almost all others.

"He considered that one can and must so formulate each definition in this domain that by a finite number of trials it can be determined whether or not it is applicable to any proposed quantity.

"Likewise a proof of the existence of a quantity is to be looked upon as rigorous only when it contains at the same time a method, by which the quantity, whose existence is proved, can be actually found. Kronecker was very far from throwing entirely aside a definition or proof which did not satisfy these high requirements, but he considered that something was still wanting and he held its completion in this direction to be an important task, by which our knowledge would be extended in an essential point.

"He considered, moreover, that a formulation rigorous in this sense was in general of simpler form than another which did not satisfy this demand and he has in many cases shown by his lectures that this is the case."

Cor. *If a and b be any two rational integers, there exists a common divisor d of a and b such that every common divisor* *of a and b divides d, and we can find two integers x and y such that*

$$ax + by = d.$$

Let

$$a = a_1c, \quad b = b_1c,$$

where a_1 and b_1 are prime to each other.

By Theorem B two integers x and y exist such that

$$a_1x + b_1y = 1. \tag{1}$$

Multiplying 1) by c, we have

$$a_1cx + b_1cy = c;$$

that is

$$ax + by = c.$$

Every common divisor of a and b evidently divides c. Hence c is the divisor, d, sought.

We call d the *greatest common divisor of a and b.*

It is evident that two such divisors which are not associates cannot exist; for if d_1, d_2 be two such divisors, then since from the definition d_1 must divide d_2 and d_2 must divide d_1, d_1 and d_2 are associates.

Any number of integers, $a_1, a_2, \cdots, a_n$, possess a common divisor which is divisible by all common divisors of these integers; for let d_1 be the greatest common divisor of a_1, a_2 as defined above. Then two integers, x_1 and x_2, exist such that

$$a_1x_1 + a_2x_2 = d_1.$$

Let now d_2 be the greatest common divisor of d_1 and a_3. It is evident that d_2 is a common divisor of a_1, a_2, a_3, and that two integers, y_1, y_2, exist such that

$$d_1y_1 + a_3y_2 = d_2,$$

or

$$a_1x_1y_1 + a_2x_2y_1 + a_3y_2 = d_2;$$

that is, three integers, z_1, z_2, z_3, exist such that

$$a_1z_1 + a_2z_2 + a_3z_3 = d_2,$$

from which identity it is evident that every common divisor of a_1, a_2, a_3, divides d_2.

Proceeding similarly with d_2 and a_4, then with their greatest common divisor d_3 and a_5, etc., we see finally that there exist n integers $u_1, u_2, \cdots, u_n$ such that

$$a_1u_1 + a_2u_2 + \cdots + a_nu_n = d,$$

where d is a common divisor of $a_1, a_2, \cdots, a_n$.

From this identity it is evident that every common divisor of $a_1, a_2, \ldots a_n$ divides d. We call d therefore the greatest common divisor of the n integers $a_1, a_2, \cdots, a_n$.

The common divisors of a system of integers are evidently the divisors of the greatest common divisor of the system.

To find the greatest common divisor of n integers $a_1, a_2, \cdots, a_n$, we find the greatest common divisor d_1 of a_1 and a_2; then the greatest common divisor of d_1 and a_3, which will evidently be the greatest common divisor of a_1, a_2, a_3.

Proceeding in this manner we arrive finally at an integer d which is the greatest common divisor of all of the integers. In particular, if $a_1, a_2, \cdots, a_n$ have the greatest common divisor 1, we have

$$a_1u_1 + a_2u_2 + \cdots + a_nu_n = 1.$$

This corollary is usually known as the greatest common divisor theorem and can be proved independently of Theorem B which follows easily from it.

The independent proof of the corollary depends upon Theorem A and the following simple theorem whose truth is obvious.

If $a = mb + r$, then every integer which divides both a and b divides both b and r, and vice versa; that is, the common divisors of a and b are identical with the common divisors of b and r.

By virtue of these two theorems we are able to substitute for the problem of finding the integer which is divisible by all common divisors of a and b ($|b| \leqq |a|$) the corresponding problem for the two integers b and r, where $a = mb + r$, and $|r| < |b|$.[1]

From Theorem A, it is evident that we can form a chain of identities,

$$\begin{aligned} a &= mb + r, \\ b &= m_1r + r_1, \\ r &= m_2r_1 + r_2, \\ \vdots \quad & \quad \vdots \quad \vdots \end{aligned}$$

[1] Euclid: Elements, Book VII, Prop. 2.

in which $|r| > |r_1| > |r_2|$, etc., arriving after a finite number of such steps, since the integers less in absolute value than a given integer are finite in number, at a remainder r_{n+1} which is 0, and hence

$$r_{n-1} = m_{n+1} r_n$$

Now from the theorem above it is evident that the common divisors of a and b are identical with the common divisors of b and r, and hence with those of r and r_1, and finally with those of r_{n-1} and r_n.

But r_n is a common divisor of r_{n-1} and r_n and evidently is divisible by every common divisor of r_{n-1} and r_n. Hence r_n is the desired common divisor of a and b; that is, it is divisible by all the common divisors of a and b. Moreover, we can by means of the method of continued fractions express $d, = r_n$, in the form

$$ax + by = d.$$[1]

The greatest common divisor of two or more integers is seen to be the common divisor of greatest absolute value, there being only one such common divisor since, if $|a| = |b|$, then a and b are associates. It is also, as we have seen from the proof of the above corollary, the common divisor such that the quotients obtained by dividing each of the integers by this divisor have no common divisor other than ± 1.

The reason why neither of these properties has been chosen for the definition of the greatest common divisor of two or more integers will appear later (see p. 252).

An objection to the former of the two, which is the one usually employed is, however, immediately evident in that the idea of inequality is introduced, whereas the question is purely one of divisibility.

THEOREM C. *If the product of two integers, a and b, be divisible by a prime number, p, at least one of the integers is divisible by p.*

Let $ab = cp$, and assume a not divisible by p. Then a and p have no common divisor, and there exist two integers, x and y, such that

$$ax + py = 1. \qquad 1)$$

[1] Cahen: p. 60. Bachman: Niedere Zahlentheorie, p. 107. Chrystal: Vol. II, p. 445.

Multiplying 1) by b, we have

$$bax + bpy = b,$$

and therefore

$$(cx + by)p = b,$$

where $cx + by$ is an integer. Hence b is divisible by p.

Cor. 1. *If the product of any number of integers be divisible by a prime number, p, at least one of the integers is divisible by p.*

Cor. 2. *If neither of two integers be divisible by a prime number, p, their product is not divisible by p.*

Cor. 3. *If the product of two integers, a and b, be divisible by an integer c and neither a nor b be divisible by c, then c is a composite number.*

THEOREM 1. *Every rational integer can be represented in one and only one way as the product of prime numbers.*

Let m be a rational integer. If m be a prime, the theorem is evident. Let m be a composite number; m then has some divisor, a, other than $\pm m$ or ± 1. Either a is a prime or it has some divisor, b, other than $\pm a$ or ± 1. If b be not prime, it has some divisor, c, other than ± 1 and $\pm b$. Proceeding in this manner, we must at last arrive at a prime number, for the integers of the series $a, b, c, \cdots$, decrease in absolute value, and since there are only a finite number of integers smaller in absolute value than m, the series can have only a finite number of terms, the last of which will be a prime number; for otherwise the series could be extended. Let this prime be p_1. By §3, I, p_1 is a factor of m and we have $m = p_1 m_1$. If m_1 be a prime, the resolution of m into its prime factors is complete. If m_1 be a composite number, it contains a prime factor, p_2, and we have

$$m_1 = p_2 m_2,$$

or

$$m = p_1 p_2 m_2.$$

If m_2 be not a prime, we can proceed as before until we have resolved m into factors, all of which are primes. That there will be only a finite number of these factors is evident from the fact that the integers of the series, $m, m_1, m_2, \cdots$, decrease in absolute value and hence must be finite in number.

We have now shown that the representation of an integer as a product of a finite number of primes is always possible. It remains to be proved that this representation is unique, regarding representations as identical, which differ only by the substitution for a prime of its associate.

Let $$m = p_1p_2p_3 \cdots p_r = q_1q_2q_3 \cdots q_s$$

be two representations of m as a product of prime numbers.

Since the product $q_1q_2 \cdots q_s$ is divisible by p_1, at least one of its factors, say q_1, must be divisible by p_1. But q_1 has only the divisors $\pm q_1$ and ± 1. Hence $q_1 = \pm p_1$; that is, q_1 is associated with p_1. Then follows

$$p_2p_3 \cdots p_r = \pm q_2q_3 \cdots q_s.$$

In the same manner we can show that some factor of the product $q_2q_3 \cdots q_s$ is associated with p_2, and proceeding similarly we can show that for each prime that occurs once or oftener as a factor of the product, $p_1p_2p_3 \cdots p_r$, there occurs at least as often an associated prime in the product $q_1q_2q_3 \cdots q_s$. In like manner, we can show that for each prime which occurs once or oftener as a factor of the product $q_1q_2q_3 \cdots q_s$, there occurs at least as often an associated prime in the product $p_1p_2p_3 \cdots p_r$. Hence the two representations are identical. We can simplify the representation of a composite number as the product of its prime factors by expressing the product of associated prime factors as a power of one of them. Thus, if of the prime factors of m, e_1 are associated with p_1, e_2 with $p_2, \cdots, e_r$ with p_r, we can write

$$m = \pm p_1^{e_1}p_2^{e_2} \cdots p_r^{e_r}.$$

Cor. 1. *If a and b be prime to each other and c be divisible by both a and b, then c is divisible by their product.*

Cor. 2. *If a and b be each prime to c, then ab is prime to c.*

Cor. 3. *If a be prime to c and ab be divisible by c, b is divisible by c.*

THEOREM 2. If

$$f_1(x) = a_0x^m + a_1x^{m-1} + \cdots + a_m,$$

$$f_2(x) = b_0x^n + b_1x^{n-1} + \cdots + b_n,$$

be any two integral functions of x, whose coefficients are rational integers, having in each case no common divisor, then the coefficients of the product of these functions

$$f(x) = f_1(x) \cdot f_2(x) = c_0x^{m+n} + c_1x^{m+n-1} + \cdots + c_{m+n}$$

are rational integers without a common divisor.

If the coefficients $c_0, c_1, \cdots, c_{m+n}$ of $f(x)$ have a common divisor other than ± 1, there must be at least one prime number which divides all of them.

Let p be such a prime and suppose that p divides

$$a_0, a_1, \cdots, a_{r-1}, \text{ but not } a_r,$$

and

$$b_0, b_1, \cdots, b_{s-1}, \text{ but not } b_s,$$

where in accordance with our original assumption that the coefficients of $f_1(x)$ and $f_2(x)$ have no common divisors,

$$0 \leqq r \leqq m \text{ and } 0 \leqq s \leqq n.$$

We have now

$$c_{r+s} = a_rb_s + a_{r-1}b_{s+1} + a_{r-2}b_{s+2} + \cdots + a_{r+1}b_{s-1} + a_{r+2}b_{s-2} + \cdots.$$

It is evident that c_{r+s} is not divisible by p, for a_rb_s is not divisible by p, neither a_r nor b_s being divisible by p, while all the remaining terms are divisible by p, since each of these terms contains as a factor some one of the coefficients $a_0, a_1, \cdots, a_{r-1}, b_0, b_1, \cdots, b_{s-1}$, which are all divisible by p.

Hence the coefficients of $f(x)$ have no common divisor.

THEOREM 3. *If*

$$f_1(x) = x^m + a_1x^{m-1} + \ldots + a_m,$$

$$f_2(x) = x^n + b_1x^{n-1} + \cdots + b_n$$

be two rational integral functions of x, the coefficients of the *highest powers of x in each case being* 1, *and the remaining coefficients rational numbers, the coefficients,* $c_1, c_2, \cdots, c_{m+n}$ *of their product*

$$f(x) = f_1(x) \cdot f_2(x) = x^{m+n} + c_1 x^{m+n-1} + \cdots + c_{m+n}$$

cannot all be rational integers unless all of the coefficients $a_1, a_2, \cdots, a_m, b_1, b_2, \cdots, b_n$ *are rational integers.*[1]

Let a_0 and b_0 be the least common denominators of the coefficients of $f_1(x)$ and $f_2(x)$ respectively. Then each of the functions $a_0 f_1(x)$ and $b_0 f_2(x)$ has rational integral coefficients without a common divisor. If now the coefficients $c_1, c_2, \cdots, c_{m+n}$ are to be integers, the coefficients of the product,

$$a_0 b_0 f_1(x) \cdot f_2(x) = a_0 b_0 f(x),$$

must all be divisible by $a_0 b_0$.

But by Th. 2 this is impossible unless $a_0 = 1$, $b_0 = 1$; that is, $a_1, a_2, \cdots, a_m, b_1, b_2, \cdots, b_n$ are integers.

THEOREM 4. *A necessary as well as sufficient condition that an algebraic number α shall be an algebraic integer is that the coefficients of the single rational equation of lowest degree of the form*

$$f_1(x) = x^l + a_1 x^{l-1} + \cdots + a_l = 0, \qquad 1)$$

which it satisfies, shall be rational integers.

If α satisfy an equation

$$f_2(x) = x^m + b_1 x^{m-1} + \cdots + b_m = 0,$$

of degree higher than the lth whose coefficients are rational numbers, then by Chap. I, Th. 1,

$$f_2(x) = f_1(x) \cdot f_3(x),$$

where $f_3(x)$ is a rational integral function of x with rational coefficients, the coefficient of its term of highest degree being 1. But by Th. 3 the coefficients of $f_2(x)$ cannot all be rational integers unless the coefficients of $f_1(x)$ are all rational integers. Hence the theorem.

[1] Gauss: Disq. Arith., Art. 42, Works, Vol. I.

We see therefore that the system of rational integers and that of the integers of R are coextensive, and hence that all that has been said in the preceding pages concerning rational integers may now be looked upon as applying to the integers of R. Hereafter the terms *rational integers* and *integers of R* will be used interchangeably.

It is seen from the above theorem that the equation of lowest degree of the form 1) satisfied by an algebraic number, determines not only the degree of the number, but whether it is or is not an algebraic integer.

After having proved the unique factorization theorem we could have shown that no rational fraction a/b, where a and b are prime to each other and $b \neq \pm 1$, can satisfy an equation of the form 1) whose coefficients are rational integers and hence that the only integers of R are the rational integers, but it has seemed better to treat the question in the general manner we have used above.

§ 8. Divisors of an Integer.

We can now exhibit in a very convenient form all divisors of any given integer, m, and deduce therefrom simple expressions for the number and the sum of these divisors. Let m be written in the form

$$m = \pm p_1^{e_1} p_2^{e_2} \cdots p_r^{e_r},$$

where $p_1, p_2, \cdots, p_r$ are the different prime factors of m.

If d be a divisor of m, it can contain as factors only those primes which occur in m, but each of these primes can occur in d to any power not greater than that to which it occurs in m; that is, every divisor of m must have the form

$$d = \pm p_1^{m_1} p_2^{m_2} \cdots p_r^{m_r},$$

where $$0 \leqq m_i \leqq e_i; \; i = 1, 2, \cdots, r,$$

and each of the integers obtained by giving these different values to $m_1, m_2, \cdots, m_r$ is a divisor of m. We can now easily obtain an expression for the number, N, of the different divisors of m, associated divisors being considered as identical. Since there are $e_1 + 1$, $e_2 + 1$, $\cdots$, $e_r + 1$ possible values for m_1, m_2, $\cdots$, m_r respectively, there are $(e_1 + 1)(e_2 + 1) \cdots (e_r + 1)$ different sets of values of m_1, m_2, $\cdots$, m_r and each of these sets gives a different divisor of m. Moreover, these sets of values of $m_1, m_2, \cdots, m_r$ give all the different divisors of m, whence we have

$$N = (e_1 + 1)(e_2 + 1) \cdots (e_r + 1).$$

We can find similarly an expression for the sum, S, of the different positive divisors of m.

On expanding the product

$$(1 + p_1 + p_1^2 + \cdots + p_1^{e_1})(1 + p_2 + p_2^2 + \cdots + p_2^{e_2}) \cdots (1 + p_r + p_r^2 + \cdots p_r^{e_r}),$$

we obtain a series, all of whose terms are positive divisors of m, each positive divisor of m occurring once and but once. The sum of this series is therefore S.

Hence

$$S = (1 + p_1 + p_1^2 + \cdots + p_1^{e_1})(1 + p_2 + p_2^2 + \cdots p_2^{e_2}) \cdots (1 + p_r + p_r^2 + \cdots p_r^{e_r})$$

$$= \frac{p_1^{e_1+1} - 1}{p_1 - 1} \cdot \frac{p_2^{e_2+1} - 1}{p_2 - 1} \cdots \frac{p_r^{e_r+1} - 1}{p_r - 1}.$$

Ex. Let $m = 60 = 2^2 \cdot 3 \cdot 5$.

We have $N = (2+1) \cdot (1+1)(1+1) = 12,$

and $S = \frac{2^3 - 1}{2-1} \cdot \frac{3^2 - 1}{3 - 1} \cdot \frac{5^2 - 1}{5 - 1} = 7 \cdot 4 \cdot 6 = 168,$

results which are easily substantiated by observing that the positive divisors of 60 are 1, 2, 3, 4, 5, 6, 10, 12, 15. 20, 30 and 60.

We observe that N depends only upon the exponents of the powers to which the different prime factors appear in m, while S depends also upon the absolute values of these primes.

We have defined (§ 3) a common divisor and a common multiple of two or more integers. The representation of an integer as a product of its different prime factors leads us to convenient expressions for the common divisors and common multiples of a system of integers.

Let $m_1, m_2, \cdots, m_k$ be any system of integers and suppose each integer of this system expressed as a product of powers of its different prime factors. Let $p_1, p_2, \cdots, p_r$ be the different prime factors of $m_1, m_2, \cdots, m_k$; $l_1, l_2, \cdots, l_r$, the exponents of the lowest powers, and $g_1, g_2, \cdots, g_r$, the exponents of the highest powers to which $p_1, p_2, \cdots, p_r$ occur in any of these integers. Remembering now that every common divisor of $m_1, m_2, \cdots, m_k$, can contain as a factor a prime, p_i, to a power not higher than the lowest to which p_i occurs in any of the integers $m_1, m_2, \cdots, m_k$, we see that every common divisor of $m_1, m_2, \cdots, m_k$, has the form

$$p_1^{d_1} p_2^{d_2} \cdots p_r^{d_r},$$

where $$0 \leqq d_i \leqq l_i;\ i = 1, 2, \cdots, r.$$

When $d_1, d_2, \cdots, d_r$ have their greatest possible values, that is, $l_1, l_2, \cdots, l_r$, the divisor so obtained, is evidently the greatest common divisor of $m_1, m_2, \cdots, m_k$. Denoting the greatest common divisor of $m_1, m_2, \cdots, m_k$, by g, we have therefore

$$g = p_1^{l_1} p_2^{l_2} \cdots p_r^{l_r}.$$

Likewise since every common multiple of $m_1, m_2, \cdots, m_k$, must contain as a factor a prime, p_i, at least to the highest power to which p_i occurs in any one of the integers $m_1, m_2, \cdots, m_k$, we see that every common multiple of $m_1, m_2, \cdots, m_k$ has the form

$$a p_1^{n_1} p_2^{n_2} \cdots p_r^{n_r},$$

where $$n_i \geqq g_i,\ i = 1, 2, \cdots, r,$$

and a is any integer.

When $n_1, n_2, \cdots, n_r$ have their least possible values, that is, $g_1, g_2, \cdots, g_r$, and a is a unit, the multiple obtained is the least common multiple of $m_1, m_2, \cdots, m_k$. Denoting the least common multiple of $m_1, m_2, \cdots, m_k$ by l, we have therefore

$$l = p_1^{g_1} p_2^{g_2} \cdots p_r^{g_r}.$$

We observe that just as the common divisors of a system of integers are the divisors of the greatest common divisor of the system, so every common multiple of all the integers of the system is a multiple of their least common multiple. When two or more of the integers $m_1, m_2, \cdots, m_k$ are prime to each other, the greatest common divisor of the system is evidently a unit, and when the integers $m_1, m_2, \cdots, m_k$ are prime each to each their least common multiple is their product, $m_1 m_2 \cdots m_k$. If an integer be divisible by each one of a system of integers $m_1, m_2, \cdots, m_k$, it is divisible by their least common multiple.

If we have two integers

$$a = p_1^{a_1} p_2^{a_2} \cdots p_r^{a_r},\ b = p_1^{b_1} p_2^{b_2} \cdots p_r^{b_r},$$

and $$g = p_1^{l_1} p_2^{l_2} \cdots p_r^{l_r},\ l = p_1^{g_1} p_2^{g_2} \cdots p_r^{g_r}$$

be respectively their greatest common divisor and least common multiple, it is evident that

$$l_1 + g_1 = a_1 + b_1,\ l_2 + g_2 = a_2 + b_2, \cdots, l_r + g_r = a_r + b_r,$$

and hence that $gl = ab$; that is, the product of two integers is equal to the product of their greatest common divisor and least common multiple; for example

$$12 \cdot 30 = 6 \cdot 60.$$

The representation of an integer m as a product of powers of its different prime factors gives us also a criterion for determining whether m is or is not the kth power of an integer.

Let $$m = \pm p_1^{e_1} p_2^{e_2} \cdots p_r^{e_r}.$$

By putting $m = n^k$, we see immediately that the necessary and sufficient condition that m shall be the kth power of an integer is, if k be odd, that $e_1, e_2, \cdots, e_r$ shall be divisible by k, while if k be even there is the further condition that m shall be positive.

§ 9. Determination of the Highest Power of a Prime, p, by which $m!$ is divisible.

The method employed consists in counting, successively, those integers of this product which are divisible by p, p^2, p^3, etc., respectively. Remembering that those integers which are divisible by p^i have already been counted $i - 1$ times, as among those divisible by $p, p^2, \cdots, p^{i-1}$, the sum of these enumerations is seen to be the exponent of the desired power of p. Denote this exponent by e. Since e will have the same value for $-p$ as for p, we can without loss of generality assume p positive.

Let $[a/b]$ denote the greatest integer contained in the fraction a/b, where a and b are both positive; in particular $[a/b]$ is 0 when a is less than b. Put $[m/p] = m_1$, $[m/p^2] = m_2, \cdots, [m/p^i] = m_i, \cdots$. There are in the product

$$m! = 1 \cdot 2 \cdot 3 \cdots m,$$

the m_1 integers,

$$p, 2p, 3p, \cdots, m_1 p, \qquad 1)$$

divisible by p, and $m!$ is therefore certainly divisible by p^{m_1}; that is, $e \nless m_1$.

In like manner there are in $m!$ the m_2 integers

$$p^2, 2p^2, \cdots, m_2 p^2 \qquad 2)$$

divisible by p^2. We have counted these integers once already among the integers 1), but since they each contain p twice as a factor, and there are m_2 of them, we must add m_2 to the exponent of the power of p which is known to divide $m!$. Hence $m!$ is certainly divisible by $p^{m_1+m_2}$; that is,

$$e \nless m_1 + m_2.$$

Likewise there are m_3 integers of $m!$ divisible by p^3, each of which has been counted twice already. Hence

$$e \nless m_1 + m_2 + m_3.$$

Continuing this process we arrive finally at a fraction m/p^k, which is less than 1, and hence

$$m_k = \left[\frac{m}{p^k}\right] = 0.$$

The highest power of p by which $m!$ is divisible is therefore $p^{m_1+m_2+\cdots+m_{k-1}}$, whose exponent e is $[m/p] + [m/p^2] + \cdots + [m/p^{k-1}]$.

If $p > m$, then $m_1 = 0$, and hence $e = 0$.

Ex. Let $m = 100$, and $p = 3$; then

$$m_1 = [\tfrac{100}{3}] = 33,$$
$$m_2 = [\tfrac{100}{9}] = 11,$$
$$m_3 = [\tfrac{100}{27}] = 3,$$
$$m_4 = [\tfrac{100}{81}] = 1,$$
$$m_5 = [\tfrac{100}{243}] = 0,$$

and

$$e = 33 + 11 + 3 + 1 = 48.$$

It is easily shown that

$$\left[\frac{a}{bc}\right] = \left[\frac{\left[\frac{a}{b}\right]}{c}\right],$$

and hence $$m_i = \left[\frac{m_{i-1}}{p}\right].$$

Using this fact in the example just given we have $m_1 = [\frac{100}{3}] = 33$, $m_2 = [\frac{33}{3}] = 11$, $m_3 = [\frac{11}{3}] = 3$, $m_4 = [\frac{3}{3}] = 1$, $m_5 = [\frac{1}{3}] = 0$.

§ 10. The Quotient $\frac{m!}{a!b!\cdots k!}$, where $m = a + b + \cdots + k$, is an Integer.[1]

This quotient will be recognized as the so-called multinomial coefficient; that is, the coefficient of $x_1^a x_2^b \cdots x_r^k$ in the expansion of $(x_1 + x_2 + \cdots x_r)^m$. When $r = 2$, and $m = a + b$, we have the binomial coefficient; that is, the coefficient of $x_1^a x_2^{m-a}$ in the expansion of $(x_1 + x_2)^m$.

This theorem is easily proved by means of that of the last section. To show that
$$\frac{m!}{a!b!\cdots k!} \qquad 1)$$
is an integer it is necessary and sufficient to show that every prime, p, is contained to as high a power in the numerator as in the denominator. Let $e, a_1, b_1, \cdots, k_1$, be the exponents of the highest powers to which p is contained in $m!, a!, b!, \cdots, k!$, respectively. We must show that
$$e \gtreqless a_1 + b_1 + \cdots + k_1.$$

Since $$m = a + b + \cdots + k,$$

it follows that $$\frac{m}{p} = \frac{a}{p} + \frac{b}{p} + \cdots + \frac{k}{p},$$

and hence $$\left[\frac{m}{p}\right] \geqq \left[\frac{a}{p}\right] + \left[\frac{b}{p}\right] + \cdots + \left[\frac{k}{p}\right].$$

Similarly $$\left[\frac{m}{p^2}\right] \geqq \left[\frac{a}{p^2}\right] + \left[\frac{b}{p^2}\right] + \cdots \left[\frac{k}{p^2}\right],$$
$$\vdots$$
$$\left[\frac{m}{p^i}\right] \geqq \left[\frac{a}{p^i}\right] + \left[\frac{b}{p^i}\right] + \cdots \left[\frac{k}{p^i}\right].$$
$$\vdots$$

[1] The truth of this theorem is at once evident since $\frac{m!}{a!b!\cdots k!}$ is the number of permutations of m things $a, b, \cdots, k$ of which are alike.

Hence, by addition,

$$\left[\frac{m}{p}\right]+\left[\frac{m}{p^2}\right]+\cdots+\left[\frac{m}{p^i}\right]+\cdots$$

$$\geqq\left[\frac{a}{p}\right]+\left[\frac{a}{p^2}\right]+\cdots+\left[\frac{a}{p^i}\right]+\cdots$$

$$+\left[\frac{b}{p}\right]+\left[\frac{b}{p^2}\right]+\cdots+\left[\frac{b}{p^i}\right]+\cdots$$

$$\cdots\cdots\cdots$$

$$+\left[\frac{k}{p}\right]+\left[\frac{k}{p^2}\right]+\cdots+\left[\frac{k}{p^i}\right]+\cdots$$

But

$$e=\left[\frac{m}{p}\right]+\left[\frac{m}{p^2}\right]+\cdots+\left[\frac{m}{p^i}\right]+\cdots,$$

$$a_1=\left[\frac{a}{p}\right]+\left[\frac{a}{p^2}\right]+\cdots+\left[\frac{a}{p^i}\right]+\cdots,$$

$$b_1=\left[\frac{b}{p}\right]+\left[\frac{b}{p^2}\right]+\cdots+\left[\frac{b}{p^i}\right]+\cdots,$$

$$\cdots\cdots\cdots$$

$$k_1=\left[\frac{k}{p}\right]+\left[\frac{k}{p^2}\right]+\cdots+\left[\frac{k}{p^i}\right]+\cdots.$$

Hence $$e \gtreqless a_1+b_1+\cdots+k_1.$$

Therefore p is contained to at least as high a power in the numerator of 1) as in the denominator. But p was any prime; therefore 1) is an integer.

From this it follows that *the product of any m successive positive integers is divisible by $m!$*

For

$$\frac{(a+1)(a+2)\cdots(a+m)}{m!}=\frac{a!(a+1)(a+2)\cdots(a+m)}{a!\,m!}=\frac{(a+m)!}{a!\,m!}$$

which is an integer. From this and the fact that 0 is included among m successive integers which are not all positive or all negative, it follows that the product of any m successive integers is divisible by $m!$

Examples.[1]

1. The sum of two odd squares can not be a square.

2. Every integer of the form $4n-1$ has an odd number of factors of the form $4n-1$.

3. Every prime greater than 5 has the form $30m+n$ where $n=1, 7, 11, 13, 17, 19, 23$ or 29.

4. The square of every prime greater than 3 is of the form $24m+1$, and the square of every integer which is not divisible by 2 or 3 is of the same form.

5. If n differ from the two successive squares between which it lies by x and y respectively, prove that $n-xy$ is a square.

6. The cube of every rational integer is the difference of the squares of two rational integers.

7. Any uneven cube, n^3, is the sum of n consecutive uneven integers, of which n^2 is the middle one.

8. Show that x^3-x is divisible by 6 if x be any integer.

9. Show that $x^4-4x^3+5x^2-2x$ is divisible by 12 if x be any integer.

10. Show that $x^{4m}+x^{2m}+1$ never represents a prime number if x be any integer other than 1.

11. Show that $(mn)!$ is divisible by $(m!)^n n!$

12. Show that $(2m)!(2n)!$ is divisible by $m!\,n!\,(m+n)!$

13. What is the least multiplier that will convert 945 into a complete square?

14. Find the number of the divisors of 2160 and their sum.

15. Find a number of the form $2^n\cdot 3\cdot a$ (a being prime) which shall be equal to half the sum of its divisors (itself excluded).

[1] See Chrystal; Algebra, Part II, pp. 506, 518 and 526 for other examples, also C. Smith, Algebra, and Hall and Knight, Higher Algebra.

CHAPTER III.

The Rational Realm.

CONGRUENCES.

§ 1. Definition. Elementary Theorems.

If the difference of two integers, a and b, be divisible by an integer m, a and b are said to be congruent to each other with respect to the modulus m. This relation is expressed by writing

$$a \equiv b, \bmod m.$$[1]

Similarly, if the difference of a and b be not divisible by m, we say that a and b are incongruent to each other, with respect to the modulus m, and write

$$a \not\equiv b, \bmod m.$$

Ex. We say that 21 is congruent to 15 with respect to the modulus 3, since $21 - 15$ is divisible by 3. In the above notation this fact is expressed by writing $21 \equiv 15, \bmod 3.$

We can express the fact that a is congruent to b by writing

$$a - b = km, \text{ or } a = b + km,$$

where k is an integer, but the notation $a \equiv b, \bmod m$, which is due to Gauss, has the great advantage of placing in evidence the analogy between congruences and equations; and we shall see that most of the transformations to which equations can be subjected are also applicable to congruences.

H. J. S. Smith says: "It will be seen that the definition of a congruence involves only one of the most elementary arithmetical conceptions,—that of the divisibility of one number by another. But it expresses that conception in a form so suggestive of analogies with other parts of analysis, so easily available in calculation and so fertile in new results that its introduction into arith-

[1] The author has adopted a slight variation of Gauss's notation, $a \equiv b \pmod m$, due, he believes, to H. J. S. Smith.

metic (by Gauss) has proved a most important contribution to the progress of the science."

We have as direct consequences of the definition of congruences the following:

i. *If* $a \equiv b, \bmod m,$ 1)

and $b \equiv c, \bmod m,$ 2)

then $a \equiv c, \bmod m;$

for, from 1) and 2), we have respectively

$$a - b = km,$$
$$b - c = k_1 m,$$

where k and k_1 are integers, and by addition

$$a - c = (k + k_1) m;$$

that is, $a \equiv c, \bmod m.$

It is now evident that we can divide all integers into classes with respect to a given modulus, if we put into the same class those and only those integers which are congruent to each other with respect to this modulus. We ask: How many such classes will there be for any given modulus m?

Any integer, a, can be written in the form

$$a = km + r,$$

where k is an integer and r is one of the integers

$$0, 1, 2, 3, \cdots, |m| - 1.$$

But a is congruent to r, mod m, and if we give k all integral values from $-\infty$ to $+\infty$, the resulting values of a will be a series of integers, all of which are congruent to r, and hence by i to each other with respect to the modulus m. By putting for r the $|m|$ different values $0, 1, 2, 3, \cdots, |m| - 1$, we shall get $|m|$ classes and every integer is seen to fall into one or the other of these classes. An integer can not be in two different classes, for then we should have

$$a = km + r = k_1 m + r_1,$$

where $$r \neq r_1,$$
which gives $$(k - k_1)m = r_1 - r.$$

Since the first member of this equation is divisible by m, the second member must be divisible by m also, but since r and r_1 are both positive and less than $|m|$, we have $|r - r_1| < |m|$, and hence $r - r_1$ is not divisible by m, unless $r - r_1 = 0$; that is, $r = r_1$ and hence $k = k_1$.

There are therefore exactly $|m|$ incongruent number classes with respect to the modulus m, each integer being in one and but one of the classes.

The absolute value of an integer, m, may now be defined as *the number of incongruent number classes with respect to the modulus m.*

This definition brings out clearly a reason for the introduction of the absolute value of an integer; that is, to express the result of an enumeration as a function of an integer.

In all theorems relating to congruences we shall think of the entire system of rational numbers as divided into such classes, with respect to some given modulus; and whatever is true of any individual integer with respect to this modulus will be true of the entire class to which it belongs. We shall thus deal rather with the classes than with the individuals in them and it will only be necessary to have a representative of each class.

Such a system of $|m|$ representative integers, each integer being chosen arbitrarily from the class to which it belongs, is called a *complete system of incongruent numbers*, or *a complete residue system, with respect to the modulus m.*

The latter designation is derived from an extension of the ordinary idea of the remainder, which holds when the system chosen is $0, 1, 2, \cdots, |m| - 1$, by calling either one of any two integers, which are congruent to each other with respect to the modulus m, a remainder or residue of the other with respect to m.

Any $|m|$ consecutive integers evidently form a complete residue system with respect to the modulus m.

The most useful systems are, first, that composed of the smallest possible positive residues

$$0, 1, 2, \cdots, |m| - 1,$$

and second, that composed of the residues of smallest possible absolute value, the latter being, when m is odd and $|m| = 2n + 1$,

$$-n, -(n-1), \cdots, -1, 0, 1, \cdots, n-1, n;$$

and, when m is even and $|m| = 2n$

$$-(n-1), \cdots, -1, 0, 1, \cdots, n-1, n,$$

the two residues n and $-n$ being congruent to each other, mod m.

Ex. If $m = 11$, each of the systems

$$0, 1, 2, 3, 4, 5, 6, 7, 8, 9, 10;$$
$$-5, -4, -3, -2, -1, 0, 1, 2, 3, 4, 5;$$
$$50, -15, -25, 20, 32, 22, -10, 13, -19, 4, 16$$

is a complete residue system, mod 11.

ii. *Addition and subtraction of congruences.*

If $$a_1 \equiv b_1, \text{ mod } m, \qquad 3)$$

and $$a_2 \equiv b_2, \text{ mod } m, \qquad 4)$$

then $$a_1 \pm a_2 \equiv b_1 \pm b_2, \text{ mod } m;$$

for we have from 3) and 4), respectively,

$$a_1 - b_1 = k_1 m,$$
$$a_2 - b_2 = k_2 m,$$

whence $$(a_1 \pm a_2) - (b_1 \pm b_2) = (k_1 \pm k_2) m;$$

that is, $$(a_1 \pm a_2) \equiv b_1 \pm b_2, \text{ mod } m.$$

iii. *Multiplication by an integer.*

If $$a \equiv b, \text{ mod } m, \qquad 5)$$

then $$ac \equiv bc, \text{ mod } m;$$

for from 5) we have $a - b = km$;

whence $$ac - bc = kcm;$$

that is, $$ac \equiv bc, \text{ mod } m.$$

iv. *Multiplication of congruences.*

If $$a_1 \equiv b_1, \text{ mod } m, \qquad 6)$$

and $a_2 \equiv b_2$, mod m 7)

then $a_1 a_2 \equiv b_1 b_2$, mod m;

for from 6) we have by iii

$$a_1 a_2 \equiv b_1 a_2, \text{ mod } m;$$

and similarly, from 7) $b_1 a_2 \equiv b_1 b_2$, mod m,

whence by i $a_1 a_2 \equiv b_1 b_2$, mod m.

From this it follows, evidently, that if

$$a \equiv b, \text{ mod } m,$$

then $a^k \equiv b^k$, mod m,

where k is any positive integer.

v. *If $f(x)$ be a polynomial in x with integral coefficients;*

that is, $f(x) = a_0 x^n + a_1 x^{n-1} + \cdots + a_n$,

and if $r \equiv r_1$, mod m,

then $f(r) \equiv f(r_1)$, mod m, 8)

for from $r \equiv r_1$, mod m

it follows by iv and iii that

$$a_i r^{n-i} \equiv a_i r_1^{n-i}, \text{ mod } m, \qquad i = 0, 1, 2, \cdots, n,$$

and by addition we obtain 8).

It may be shown similarly that if $f(x_1, x_2, \cdots, x_n)$ be a polynomial in $x_1, x_2, \cdots, x_n$ with rational integral coefficients, and if

$$\left.\begin{matrix} a_1 \equiv b_1 \\ a_2 \equiv b_2 \\ \vdots \quad \vdots \\ a_n \equiv b_n \end{matrix}\right\}, \text{ mod } m,$$

then $f(a_1, a_2, \cdots, a_n) \equiv f(b_1, b_2, \cdots, b_n)$, mod m.

Ex. Let $f(x) = 2x^3 - x^2 + 5$;

since $-3 \equiv 11$, mod 7,

we have $f(-3) \equiv f(11)$, mod 7;

that is, $-58 \equiv 2546$, mod 7.

vi. *Removal of a common factor.*

We have seen in III that we can multiply both members of a congruence by any integer, without affecting the validity of the congruence; the converse of this, however, is not in general true.

Thus we have $$8 \equiv 14, \text{ mod } 6,$$

but $$4 \not\equiv 7, \text{ mod } 6.$$

To consider this question in general, let

$$a \equiv b, \text{ mod } m,$$

be a congruence in which a and b are both divisible by k; that is,

$$a = a_1 k \text{ and } b = b_1 k.$$

where a_1 and b_1 are integers.

Then from $$a_1 k \equiv b_1 k, \text{ mod } m,$$

it does not necessarily follow that

$$a_1 \equiv b_1, \text{ mod } m;$$

for that $a_1 - b_1$ shall be divisible by m is not a necessary consequence of $k(a_1 - b_1)$ being divisible by m, unless k be prime to m, and all we can say in general is that $a_1 - b_1$ is divisible by those factors of m which are not contained in k; that is, by m/d, where d is the greatest common divisor of k and m.

Hence from $$a_1 k \equiv b_1 k, \text{ mod } m,$$

it follows in general only that

$$a_1 \equiv b_1, \text{ mod } \frac{m}{d}, \qquad 9)$$

where d is the greatest common divisor of k and m.

If k be prime to m, d is 1, and hence from 9) we have

$$a_1 \equiv b_1, \text{ mod } m.$$

Ex. From $8 \equiv 14, \text{ mod } 6,$

it follows that $4 \equiv 7, \text{ mod } 3;$

but from $5 \equiv 35, \text{ mod } 6,$

it follows that $1 \equiv 7, \text{ mod } 6.$

vii. *If*

$$a \equiv b, \bmod m,$$

and d be a divisor of m, then

$$a \equiv b, \bmod d;$$

for since $a - b$ is divisible by m it is divisible by d.

viii. *If* $a \equiv b$ *with respect to each of the moduli* $m_1, m_2, \cdots, m_n$, *then*

$$a \equiv b, \bmod l,$$

where l is the least common multiple of $m_1, m_2, \cdots, m_n$; for since $a - b$ is divisible by each of the integers $m_1, m_2, \cdots, m_n$, it is divisible by their least common multiple. An important special case of this is when $m_1, m_2, \cdots, m_n$ are prime each to each, l being then their product.

ix. *All integers belonging to the same residue class have with the modulus the same greatest common divisor;* for if

$$a \equiv b, \bmod m,$$

then

$$a - b = km,$$

and any integer that divides a and m must also divide b, and any integer that divides b and m must also divide a. Therefore the greatest common divisor of a and m is identical with the greatest common divisor of b and m. In particular *if any integer of a residue class be prime to the modulus m, then all the integers of this class are prime to m.*

§ 2. The Function $\phi(m)$.

By $\phi(m)$[1] *we denote the number of integers of a complete residue system, mod m, which are prime to m.* Such a system of integers is called a *reduced residue system*, or a *reduced system of incongruent numbers, mod m.* That the number of integers in such a system is independent of the complete residue system chosen is obvious from § 1, ix. We can therefore calculate $\phi(m)$ for a particular value of m by writing down any complete residue system, mod m, and removing those integers of this system that are not prime to m. The number of those remaining is evidently $\phi(m)$.

[1] The symbol is due to Gauss: Disq. Arith., § 38, Works, Vol. I. Euler first gave a general expression for $\phi(m)$: Comm. Arith., I, p. 274.

Thus for $m = -10$, take as a complete residue system

$$-10, -19, 2, -7, -16, 5, 16, 17, 18, -1.$$

Striking out the integers $-10, 2, -16, 5, 16, 18$, that are not prime to -10, we have left the four integers $-19, -7, 17, -1$, that constitute a reduced residue system, mod -10.

Hence $\phi(-10) = 4$.

As a second example, let $m = 7$.

A complete residue system, mod 7, is

$$0, 1, 2, 3, 4, 5, 6,$$

and we see that $\phi(7) = 6$.

The last example leads us at once to a general expression for $\phi(p)$, when p is a prime; for the integers $0, 1, \cdots, |p| - 1$ constitute a complete residue system, mod p, and are, with the exception of 0, all prime to p, whence it is evident that

$$\phi(p) = |p| - 1.$$

It should be observed that, since the units are regarded as prime to themselves,

$$\phi(\pm 1) = 1.$$

The first method, which we shall employ to obtain a general expression for $\phi(m)$ in terms of m, is exactly similar to that employed in the examples just given; that is, we write down a complete residue system, mod m, remove those integers of this system which have a common divisor with m, and count those remaining, their number being $\phi(m)$.

The general expression for $\phi(m)$, where m is any integer, is given by the following theorem:

THEOREM I. *If $p_1, p_2, \cdots, p_r$ be the different positive prime factors of m, and $\phi(m)$ denote the number of integers of a complete residue system, mod m, that are prime to m, then*

$$\phi(m) = |m| \left(1 - \frac{1}{p_1}\right)\left(1 - \frac{1}{p_2}\right) \cdots \left(1 - \frac{1}{p_r}\right).$$

Since, evidently,

$$\phi(-m) = \phi(m),$$

we can without loss of generality assume m positive.

Let

$$m = p_1^{e_1} p_2^{e_2} \cdots p_r^{e_r},$$

where $p_1, p_2, \cdots, p_r$ are the different positive prime factors of m. Take as a complete residue system, mod m,

$$1, 2, 3, 4, \cdots, m \qquad S)$$

Our task is to remove from the system S those integers which are divisible by one or more of the primes $p_1, p_2, \cdots, p_r$, and to count the integers left. We shall first remove those divisible by p_1, namely the m/p_1 integers

$$p_1, 2p_1, 3p_1, \cdots, \frac{m}{p_1} p_1.$$

Removing these from S there remains a system, S_1, consisting of $m - m/p_1, = m(1 - 1/p_1)$, integers, none of which is divisible by p_1.

From this system S_1 we must now remove those integers that are divisible by p_2; that is, those integers of S which are not divisible by p_1 but are divisible by p_2. The integers of S which are divisible by p_2 are the m/p_2 integers

$$p_2, 2p_2, 3p_2, \cdots, rp_2, \cdots, \frac{m}{p_2} p_2,$$

and the necessary and sufficient condition that any one, rp_2, of these integers be also divisible by p_1, is that the coefficient, r, of p_2 shall be divisible by p_1.

The number of the integers, which are to be removed from the system S_1 on account of their divisibility by p_2, is therefore the same as the number of the integers

$$1, 2, 3, \cdots, \frac{m}{p_2},$$

which are not divisible by p_1, and this is, since m/p_2 is divisible by p_1, exactly as in the first step of this proof

$$\frac{m}{p_2}\left(1 - \frac{1}{p_1}\right).$$

There remains then of S a system, S_2, of

$$m\left(1-\frac{1}{p_1}\right)-\frac{m}{p_2}\left(1-\frac{1}{p_1}\right)=m\left(1-\frac{1}{p_1}\right)\left(1-\frac{1}{p_2}\right)$$

integers, none of which is divisible by p_1 or p_2. We are now led to conclude by induction that the number of the integers of S, which are divisible by none of the r primes $p_1, p_2, \cdots, p_r$ is

$$m\left(1-\frac{1}{p_1}\right)\left(1-\frac{1}{p_2}\right)\cdots\left(1-\frac{1}{p_r}\right).$$

To prove that this is correct, it is only necessary, since we know that it holds for $r=2$, to show that, if it holds for $r=i$, it holds for $r=i+1$.

Assume then that, having removed from S the integers divisible by one or more of the i primes $p_1, p_2, \cdots, p_i$, there is left a system S_i of

$$m\left(1-\frac{1}{p_1}\right)\left(1-\frac{1}{p_2}\right)\cdots\left(1-\frac{1}{p_i}\right) \qquad 1)$$

integers.

To obtain the number of integers of S that are divisible by none of the primes $p_1, p_2, \cdots, p_{i+1}$, we must remove from S_i those integers which are divisible by p_{i+1} and count those remaining. The integers of S_i that are divisible by p_{i+1} are the same as the integers of S that are divisible by p_{i+1} but are divisible by none of the primes $p_1, p_2, \cdots, p_i$. The integers of S that are divisible by p_{i+1} are

$$p_{i+1},\ 2p_{i+1},\ \cdots,\ rp_{i+1},\ \cdots,\ \frac{m}{p_{i+1}}p_{i+1},$$

and the necessary and sufficient condition that any one rp_{i+1} of these integers shall be divisible by none of the primes $p_1, p_2, \cdots, p_i$ is that the coefficient, r, of p_{i+1} be divisible by none of these primes. The number of integers to be removed from S_i coincides therefore with the number of the integers

$$1, 2, \cdots, \frac{m}{p_{i+1}},$$

that are divisible by none of the primes $p_1, \cdots, p_i$. By formula 1), whose correctness has been assumed, this number is

$$\frac{m}{p_{i+1}}\left(1-\frac{1}{p_1}\right)\left(1-\frac{1}{p_2}\right)\cdots\left(1-\frac{1}{p_i}\right).$$

Subtracting this number from 1) we get

$$m\left(1-\frac{1}{p_1}\right)\left(1-\frac{1}{p_2}\right)\cdots\left(1-\frac{1}{p_i}\right)-\frac{m}{p_{i+1}}\left(1-\frac{1}{p_1}\right)\left(1-\frac{1}{p_2}\right)$$

$$\cdots\left(1-\frac{1}{p_i}\right)=m\left(1-\frac{1}{p_1}\right)\left(1-\frac{1}{p_2}\right)\cdots\left(1-\frac{1}{p_i}\right)\left(1-\frac{1}{p_{i+1}}\right)$$

an expression identical in form with 1), as the number of the integers of S which are divisible by none of the primes

$$p_1, p_2, \cdots, p_i, p_{i+1}.$$

But we have proved the correctness of 1) when $i=2$, hence the theorem holds when $i=3$, and similarly when $i=r$.

If m be any integer, positive or negative, and $p_1, p_2, \cdots, p_r$ be its different prime factors, positive or negative, we have as an absolutely general expression for $\phi(m)$

$$\phi(m)=|m|\left(1-\frac{1}{|p_1|}\right)\cdots\left(1-\frac{1}{|p_r|}\right).$$

Making use of the representation of m as a product of powers of its different prime factors, we obtain another expression for $\phi(m)$; that is,

$$\phi(m)=(|p_1|-1)|p_1|^{e_1-1}\cdots(|p_r|-1)|p_r|^{e_r-1}. \qquad 1_a)$$

If m be a power of a single prime as p^e, we have

$$\phi(\pm p^e)=(|p|-1)|p|^{e-1},$$

and, in particular, when $e=1$,

$$\phi(p)=|p|-1.$$

Ex. Let $m=60=2^2\cdot 3\cdot 5.$

We have $\phi(60)=60(1-\tfrac{1}{2})(1-\tfrac{1}{3})(1-\tfrac{1}{5})$

$=60\cdot\tfrac{1}{2}\cdot\tfrac{2}{3}\cdot\tfrac{4}{5}=16;$

a result seen to be true when we write down the complete residue system, mod 60,

$$1, 2, \cdots, 60.$$

For when we remove those integers which are not prime to 60, there are left the integers

$$1, 7, 11, 13, 17, 19, 23, 29, 31, 37, 41, 43, 47, 49, 53, 59,$$

in number 16.

We observe that $\phi(m)$ is an even number except when $m = \pm 1$, or ± 2; for if $m = \pm 2^e$, we have $\phi(\pm 2^e) = 2^{e-1}$, which is an even number when $e > 1$, and if m contain an odd prime factor p_1, then from 1) it is evident that $\phi(m)$ contains the even number $|p_1| - 1$ as a factor and hence is an even number. This may be proved independently of the formula.[1]

The above proof, which is the one usually given for this theorem, has been used here on account of its great simplicity. It does not, however, admit of extension to the higher realms in the form here given, since a property of rational numbers has been made use of which has no analogue in the case of algebraic numbers of a higher degree. We therefore give below a proof depending upon the same principles as the above but so formulated that it is at once capable of extension to a realm of any degree.[2] In giving these two forms we hope to make clear to the reader some of those conditions which must be satisfied by the form of proof of a theorem regarding rational integers in order that, should the theorem be found to hold for the integers of any algebraic number realm, the same form of proof can be used for it in the general case. The proof of the general theorem (Th. 1) depends directly upon the following simple theorem:

THEOREM 2. *If $a = bc$, where b and c are any integers, there are in a complete residue system, mod a, exactly $|c|$, $= |a/b|$, numbers that are divisible by b.*

Since by § 1, ix, if the theorem be true for any particular residue system, mod a, it is true for all, we shall construct $|c|$ numbers which are divisible by b and incongruent each to each, mod a, and shall then show that no other number of a complete

[1] Cahen: p. 33. [2] See p. 44.

residue system, mod a, of which these numbers are a portion, can be divisible by b.

Let
$$c_1, c_2, \cdots, c_c, \qquad 2)$$
be any complete residue system, mod c. The integers
$$bc_1, bc_2, \cdots, bc_c \qquad 3)$$
are incongruent, mod a, for if
$$bc_h \equiv bc_i, \text{ mod } a,$$
then
$$c_h \equiv c_i, \text{ mod } c,$$
which is impossible.

Moreover, every integer, bd, divisible by b is congruent, mod a, to some one of the numbers 3), for d is congruent, mod c, to some one, say c_i, of the integers 2), and from
$$d \equiv c_i, \text{ mod } c,$$
it follows that $bd \equiv bc_i$, mod a, and bc_i is one of the integers 3). Hence the integers 3) comprise all those integers of a complete residue system, mod a, of which they are a portion, that are divisible by b. They are $|c|$ in number and the theorem is therefore proved.

If we select the particular residue system
$$1, 2, \cdots, |m|,$$
and observe that the integers of this system, that are divisible by b, are, considering b positive,
$$b, 2b, \cdots, \left|\frac{m}{b}\right| b,$$
the truth of the theorem is at once evident. The form of proof used above has, however, been chosen on account of its immediate adaptability to the higher realms.

From the above theorem we obtain at once the following:

THEOREM 3. *If p be any prime*
$$\phi(p^e) = |p^e|\left(1 - \frac{1}{|p|}\right)$$

There are in a complete residue system, mod p^e, exactly $|p^e/p|$ numbers that are divisible by p and therefore $|p^e| - |p^e/p|$ that are prime to p. Hence the theorem.

We shall now prove again Theorem 1, placing no restriction upon either m or its prime factors as to sign.

THEOREM 1. *If $p_1, p_2, \cdots, p_r$ be the different prime factors of m, and $\phi(m)$ denote the number of integers of a complete residue system, mod m, that are prime to m, then*

$$\phi(m) = |m|\left(1 - \frac{1}{|p_1|}\right)\left(1 - \frac{1}{|p_2|}\right)\cdots\left(1 - \frac{1}{|p_r|}\right).$$

Second Proof.[1]

Denote by S a complete residue system, mod m, and let

$$S_1 = \frac{|m|}{|p_1|} + \frac{|m|}{|p_2|} + \cdots + \frac{|m|}{|p_r|},$$

$$S_2 = \frac{|m|}{|p_1||p_2|} + \frac{|m|}{|p_1||p_3|} + \cdots + \frac{|m|}{|p_{r-1}||p_r|},$$

. . . .

$$S_r = \frac{|m|}{|p_1||p_2|\cdots|p_r|}.$$

Consider now the sum

$$N = |m| - S_1 + S_2 - \cdots + (-1)^r S_r.$$

Making use of Theorem 2, we see that an integer of S, which is divisible by i of the p's but not by $i+1$ of them, is counted once in $|m|$, i times in S_1, $i(i-1)/1\cdot 2$ in $S_2, \cdots$, and finally once in S_i. Hence this integer contributes to N the number

$$1 - i + \frac{i(i-1)}{1\cdot 2} - \cdots + (-1)^i = (1-1)^i = 0.$$

Therefore every integer of S that is not prime to m contributes 0 to N, while every integer of S that is prime to m contributes 1 to N, since it is counted once in $|m|$ and is not counted in $S_1, S_2, \cdots, S_r$. Hence N is the number of those integers of S which are prime to m; that is,

$$N = \phi(m).$$

[1] Mathews: § 7.

Therefore

$$\phi(m)=|m|-S_1+S_2-\cdots+(-1)^rS_r$$

$$=|m|\left(1-\frac{1}{|p_1|}\right)\left(1-\frac{1}{|p_2|}\right)\cdots\left(1-\frac{1}{|p_n|}\right).$$

§ 3. **The Product Theorem for the ϕ-Function.**

THEOREM 4. *If $m=m_1m_2$, where m_1 and m_2 are prime to each other, then* $\phi(m)=\phi(m_1)\phi(m_2)$.

Let $m_1=\pm p_1^{e_1}p_2^{e_2}\cdots p_r^{e_r}$,

and $m_2=\pm q_1^{f_1}q_2^{f_2}\cdots q_s^{f_s}$,

where $p_1, p_2, \cdots, p_r, q_1, q_2, \cdots, q_s$ are different primes.

Then $m=\pm p_1^{e_1}\cdots p_r^{e_r}q_1^{f_1}\cdots q_s^{f_s}$,

and

$$\phi(m)=|m|\left(1-\frac{1}{|p_1|}\right)\cdots\left(1-\frac{1}{|p_r|}\right)\left(1-\frac{1}{|q_1|}\right)\cdots\left(1-\frac{1}{|q_s|}\right)$$

$$=|m_1|\left(1-\frac{1}{|p_1|}\right)\cdots\left(1-\frac{1}{|p_r|}\right)\cdot|m_2|\left(1-\frac{1}{|q_1|}\right)\cdots\left(1-\frac{1}{|q_s|}\right)$$

$$=\phi(m_1)\phi(m_2).$$

Ex. Since $60=4\cdot 15$, and 4 is prime to 15, we have

$$\phi(60)=\phi(4)\phi(15)=2\cdot 8=16$$

The above result can evidently be extended to a product of any number of factors, which are prime each to each; that is, if $m=m_1m_2\cdots m_r$, where $m_1, m_2, \cdots m_r$ are prime each to each, then $\phi(m)=\phi(m_1)\phi(m_2)\cdots\phi(m_r)$.

This theorem is useful in the calculation of $\phi(m)$.

Ex. Since $315=3^2\cdot 5\cdot 7$, we have

$$\phi(315)=\phi(3^2)\phi(5)\phi(7)=6\cdot 4\cdot 6=144.$$

This property of the function $\phi(m)$ can be derived without the use of Theorem I. This having been done and having shown that

$$\phi(p^e)=|p^e|\left(1-\frac{1}{|p|}\right),$$

we can derive the general expression for $\phi(m)$ in terms of m. This is the method adopted by Gauss.[1]

§ 4. The Summation Theorem for the ϕ-Function.

THEOREM 5. *If d be any divisor of m and $m=nd$, the number of integers of a complete residue system, mod m, which have with m the greatest common divisor d is $\phi(n)$.*

Since by § 1, ix, if the theorem be true for any particular residue system, mod m, it is true for all, we may take the system used in Theorem 2. We have shown there that the system of integers

$$dn_1, dn_2, \cdots, dn_n, \qquad 1)$$

where $n_1, n_2, \cdots, n_n$ is a complete residue system, mod n, comprises all those and only those integers of a complete residue system, mod m, which are divisible by d.

Hence the integers of this complete residue system, mod m, which have with d the greatest common divisor d are those of the system 1) in which the coefficient of d is prime to n. Since $n_1, n_2, \cdots, n_n$ is a complete residue system, mod n, the number of these integers is $\phi(n)$ and the theorem is proved.

THEOREM 6. *If $d_1, d_2, \cdots, d_r$ be the different divisors of m, we have*

$$\sum_{i=1}^{r}\phi(d_i)=|m|.$$

The proof of this theorem follows easily from the last. Write down all the different divisors, $d_1, d_2, \cdots, d_r$, of the integer m, and let

$$m=m_1d_1=m_2d_2=\cdots=m_rd_r,$$

observing that both 1 and m are included among the divisors of m. Separate the integers of a complete residue system, mod m, into classes in the following manner. Place in the first class those integers of the system that have with m the greatest common divisor d_1; by Theorem 5 they will be $\phi(m_1)$ in number. Place in the second class those integers of the system that have with m the greatest common divisor d_2; they will be similarly $\phi(m_2)$

[1] Disq. Arith., Art. 38. Works, Vol. I. See also p. 75.

in number. Proceeding in this way it is evident that we shall have r classes and that each integer of the system will occur in one and but one of these classes. But the number of integers in a complete residue system, mod m, is $|m|$. Hence the total number of integers in these classes is $|m|$. Since, however, the total number of integers in the classes is also

$$\phi(m_1)+\phi(m_2)+\cdots+\phi(m_r),$$

and $m_1, m_2, \cdots, m_r$

are merely $d_1, d_2, \cdots, d_r$

in different order, we have

$$\sum_{i=1}^{r}\phi(d_i)=|m|.$$

Ex. Let $m=30$. The different divisors of m are

$$1,\ 2,\ 3,\ 5,\ 6,\ 10,\ 15,\ 30.$$

We have then

$$\phi(1)+\phi(2)+\phi(3)+\phi(5)+\phi(6)+\phi(10)+\phi(15)+\phi(30)=30,$$

a result which may be verified by calculating the values of $\phi(1)$, $\phi(2)$, $\cdots$, $\phi(30)$, and taking their sum. We have

$$1+1+2+4+2+4+8+8=30.$$

The above property of the function $\phi(m)$ has been derived immediately from the original definition of the function, no use having been made of the expression found for $\phi(m)$ in terms of m. It completely defines $\phi(m)$ and from it we can derive all the properties of the function, in particular the expression for $\phi(m)$ in terms of m.[1]

We shall give now another proof of this property of $\phi(m)$ making use of Theorems 3 and 4.

In order to bring out clearly the analogy which exists between this proof and that of the corresponding theorem in the higher realms which will be given later we shall put no restriction upon either m or its prime factors as to their sign, although so far as this proof is concerned merely with rational integers, they may evidently all be assumed positive without limiting its generality.

[1] Dirichlet-Dedekind: § 138.

Let
$$m = \pm p_1^{e_1} p_2^{e_2} \cdots p_r^{e_r}$$
where $p_1, p_2, \cdots, p_r$ are different primes.

Every divisor of m has the form
$$d_i = \pm p_1^{f_1} p_2^{f_2} \cdots p_r^{f_r} \qquad 1)$$
where f_1 is one of the numbers $0, 1, \cdots e_1$,

f_2 is one of the numbers $0, 1, \cdots e_2$,

. . . .

f_r is one of the numbers $0, 1, \cdots e_r$.

We have by Theorem 4
$$\phi(d_i) = \phi(p_1^{f_1})\phi(p_2^{f_2}) \cdots \phi(p_r^{f_r}). \qquad 2)$$

If we let $f_1, f_2, \cdots, f_r$ run through the values $0, 1, \cdots, e_1; 0, 1, \cdots, e_2; \cdots; 0, 1, \cdots, e_r$, respectively, we obtain from 1) all the divisors of m, and from 2) the corresponding values of $\phi(d_i)$ whose sum is
$$\sum_{i=1}^{r} \phi(d_i).$$
We see therefore that the terms of the series obtained by multiplying out the product
$$P = [\phi(1) + \phi(p_1) + \phi(p_1^2) + \cdots + \phi(p_1^{e_1})] \cdots$$
$$[\phi(1) + \phi(p_r) + \phi(p_r^2) + \cdots + \phi(p_r^{e_r})] \qquad 3)$$
are identical with the terms of
$$\sum_{i=1}^{r} \phi(d_i);$$
that is,
$$P = \sum_{i=1}^{r} \phi(d_i).$$
But
$$\phi(1) = 1,\ \phi(p_1) = |p_1| - 1, \cdots, \phi(p_1^{e_1}) = |p_1|^{e_1 - 1}(|p_1| - 1),$$
whence
$$\phi(1) + \phi(p_1) + \cdots + \phi(p_1^{e_1}) = |p_1|^{e_1},$$
and similarly for the other factors of 3).

Therefore
$$P = |p_1|^{e_1} |p_1|^{e_2} \cdots |p_r|^{e_r} = |m|,$$

and hence

$$\sum_{i=1}^{r}\phi(d_i) = |m|.$$

§ 5. Discussion of Certain Functional Equations and Another Derivation of the General Expression for $\phi(m)$.

THEOREM 7. *If m be any integer other than ± 1, whose different prime factors are $p_1, p_2, \cdots, p_r$, and d any divisor of m other than $\pm m$, and if we separate all integers of the form*

$$\frac{m}{p_1, p_2 \cdots p_i},$$

no p being repeated, into two classes, I and II, putting in class I those such that m is divided by none or by the product of an even number of the p's, and in class II those such that m is divided by the product of an odd number of the p's, then exactly as many integers of the one class are divisible by d as of the other.[1]

Before proving this theorem it will be well to illustrate its content by an example.

Let

$$m = 60 = 2^2.3.5.$$

Forming the above mentioned numbers we have the following:

Class I: $60, \frac{60}{2.3}, \frac{60}{2.5}, \frac{60}{3.5}$; that is, 60, 10, 6, 4.

Class II: $\frac{60}{2}, \frac{60}{3}, \frac{60}{5}, \frac{60}{2.3.5}$; that is, 30, 20, 12, 2.

If now $d = 10$, we see that two numbers of each class are divisible by 10; that is, 60 and 10 of I, and 30 and 20 of II.

We proceed to prove the theorem, observing that since we are concerned here only with questions of divisibility and since in such questions what is true of one associate of an integer is true of both of its associates, we may without limiting the generality of our proof assume $m, p_1, \cdots, p_r$ and d to be positive.

Making this assumption, we see that the positive and negative terms of the developed product

[1] Dirichlet-Dedekind: § 138.

$$m\left(1-\frac{1}{p_1}\right)\left(1-\frac{1}{p_2}\right)\cdots\left(1-\frac{1}{p_r}\right) \qquad 1)$$

coincide respectively with the integers of I and II. That is, denoting by Σm_1, Σm_2, respectively, the sums of the numbers of these classes, we have

$$m\left(1-\frac{1}{p_1}\right)\left(1-\frac{1}{p_2}\right)\cdots\left(1-\frac{1}{p_r}\right)=\Sigma m_1-\Sigma m_2.$$

Let

$$m=p_1^{e_1}p_2^{e_2}\cdots p_r^{e_r};$$

we shall first prove the theorem for the case in which

$$e_1=e_2=\cdots=e_r=1;$$

that is, m is not divisible by a higher power than the first of any prime.

Setting $p_1p_2\cdots p_r=a$, we have

$$a\left(1-\frac{1}{p_1}\right)\left(1-\frac{1}{p_2}\right)\cdots\left(1-\frac{1}{p_r}\right)=(p_1-1)(p_2-1)\cdots(p_r-1)$$
$$=\Sigma a_1-\Sigma a_2,$$

where Σa_1, Σa_2 have meanings corresponding to those of Σm_1, Σm_2.

If now b be any positive divisor of a other than a, the number of the a_1 terms that are divisible by b is exactly equal to the number of a_2 terms that are divisible by b, for, if we put

$$a=bq_1q_2\cdots q_s$$

where $q_1, q_2, \cdots, q_s$ are those prime factors of a which do not divide b, then the a_1 terms and the a_2 terms that are divisible by b are respectively the positive and negative terms of the developed product

$$b(q_1-1)(q_2-1)\cdots(q_s-1). \qquad 2)$$

Moreover, since $b\neq a$ there is at least one prime, q, that divides a but not b; that is, there is at least one q. Hence there are exactly as many positive as negative terms in the developed product 2) and consequently as many of the a_1's as of the a_2's are divisible by b.

The theorem is therefore proved for the case in which m is not divisible by a higher power than the first of any prime.

We proceed now to prove the theorem for the general case.

Let a, a_1, a_2 retain the meanings assigned above. We have

$$m = p_1^{e_1-1} p_2^{e_2-1} \cdots p_r^{e_r-1} p_1 p_2 \cdots p_r = na,$$

and it is evident that the integers m_1, m_2 coincide respectively with the products na_1, na_2. Now let d be any positive divisor of m other than m and let g be the greatest common divisor of the two integers

$$d = gb, \quad n = gc.$$

We see that b is a divisor of a; for ca/b is an integer since

$$\frac{ca}{b} = \frac{gca}{gb} = \frac{na}{d} = \frac{m}{d}, \qquad 3)$$

which is an integer, and c is prime to b.

From 3) it follows, since c is prime to b, that, if $d = m$, then $c = 1$ and $b = a$. Conversely, if b be equal to a, and hence be divisible by all prime factors of m, then c must be 1, since it is a divisor of m but prime to b, and hence $d = m$.

Excluding, therefore, the case $d = m$, so that we have always $b \neq a$, there are among the integers a_1 exactly as many that are divisible by b as there are among the integers a_2.

Since, moreover, the necessary and sufficient condition that an integer m_1, or m_2, where

$$m_1 = na_1 = gca_1,$$

or

$$m_2 = na_2 = gca_2,$$

shall be divisible by $d = gb$, is that a_1, or a_2, shall be divisible by b, there are exactly as many of the integers m_1 divisible by d as of the integers m_2.

The theorem is therefore proved.

Many interesting applications may be made of this theorem; among them are the two following:

THEOREM[1] 8. A) *If $f(m)$ and $F(m)$ be two functions of an integer m that are connected by the relation*

$$\Sigma f(d) = F(m), \qquad 4)$$

where d runs through all divisors of m including m, then

$$f(m) = \Sigma F(m_1) - \Sigma F(m_2), \qquad 5)$$

where m_1, m_2, run through the values defined in the last theorem.

B) *If $f(m)$ and $F(m)$ be connected by the relation*

$$\Pi f(d) = F(m) \qquad 6)$$

where the product relates to the values of the function corresponding to all the values of d, then

$$f(m) = \frac{\Pi F(m_1)}{\Pi F(m_2)}. \qquad 7)$$

To prove A it is sufficient to observe that if d be any divisor of m other than $\pm m$, it is a divisor of exactly as many of the m_1's as of the m_2's (Theorem 7), and hence, when in 5) we replace the F's by their values in terms of the f's from 4), $f(d)$ will occur exactly as often with the plus sign as with the minus sign.

Hence all terms in the second member of 5) will cancel except $f(m)$ which occurs once only. We shall illustrate this by a numerical example.

Let $m = 15$. We have

$$15(1-\tfrac{1}{3})(1-\tfrac{1}{5}) = 1 - 3 - 5 + 15 = 1 + 15 - (3 + 5),$$

whence $$\Sigma m_1 = 1 + 15,$$

and $$\Sigma m_2 = 3 + 5.$$

Also from 4)

$$\begin{aligned} f(1) + f(3) + f(5) + f(15) &= F(15), \\ f(1) + f(5) &= F(5), \\ f(1) + f(3) &= F(3), \\ f(1) &= F(1). \end{aligned}$$

[1] This theorem holds also in the case $m = 1$, which was excluded in Th. 7, if we assume that in this case there is only a single $m_1, = 1$, and no m_2.

We have now from 5)

$$f(15) = \Sigma F(m_1) - \Sigma F(m_2);$$

for

$$\begin{aligned} f(15) &= F(1) + F(15) - [F(3) + F(5)] \\ &= f(1) + f(1) + f(3) + f(5) + f(15) \\ &\qquad - (f(1) + f(3) + f(1) + f(5)) \\ &= f(15). \end{aligned}$$

The proof of B is evidently exactly like that of A. It will suffice if we illustrate it by a numerical example.

Let $m = 15$; we have from 6)

$$\begin{aligned} f(1)f(3)f(5)f(15) &= F(15), \\ f(1)f(5) &= F(5), \\ f(1)f(3) &= F(3), \\ f(1) &= F(1). \end{aligned}$$

From 7)

$$\begin{aligned} f(15) &= \frac{\Pi F(m_1)}{\Pi F(m_2)}, \\ &= \frac{F(1)F(15)}{F(3)F(5)}, \\ &= \frac{f(1)\cdot f(1)f(3)f(5)f(15)}{f(1)f(3)\cdot f(1)f(5)}, \\ &= f(15). \end{aligned}$$

From Theorem 8, A, we can easily deduce by the aid of Theorem 6 the general expression for $\phi(m)$.

From Theorem 6 we have

$$\Sigma\phi(d) = |\,m\,|,$$

where d runs through all divisors of m.

Applying Theorem 8, we have

$$f(m) = \phi(m) \text{ and } F(m) = |\,m\,|,$$

and hence

$$\phi(m) = \Sigma m_1 - \Sigma m_2 = |m| \left(1 - \frac{1}{|p_1|}\right)\left(1 - \frac{1}{|p_2|}\right) \cdots \left(1 - \frac{1}{|p_r|}\right)$$

As an example of the use of Theorem 8, B, we give the following:

Let $f(m) = p$, when m is a power of the prime number p, and $f(m) = 1$, when $m = 1$ or is divisible by two or more different prime numbers.

We have

$$\Pi f(d) = m,$$

where d runs through all divisors of m, from which it follows by Theorem 8, B, that the quotient

$$\frac{\Pi m_1}{\Pi m_2} = f(m)$$

is different from 1 only when m is a power of a prime number, in which case it is equal to this prime.

For a derivation by another method of the other properties of the ϕ functions from the single one that

$$\Sigma\phi(d) = |m|,$$

see Kronecker, Vorlesungen über Zahlentheorie, Vol. I, pp. 245, 246.

Also for another independent proof that

$$\phi(ab) = \phi(a)\phi(b),$$

if a be prime to b, see the same, p. 125.

§ 6. **ϕ-Functions of Higher Order.**[1]

The theory of the ϕ-function may be generalized as follows:

By $\phi_n(m)$ we denote the number of sets of n integers of a complete residue system, mod m, such that the greatest common divisor of the integers of each set is prime to m, two sets being different if the order of the integers in them be different.

For example, let $m = 6$; then

$$1, 2, 3, 4, 5, 6 \qquad 1)$$

[1] Cahen: pp. 36, 37. Bachman: Niedere Zahlentheorie, pp. 91, 93.

will be a complete residue system, mod 6. All possible sets of two numbers each that can be formed from the numbers 1) are

1, 1	1, 2	1, 3	1, 4	1, 5	1, 6
2, 1	2, 2	2, 3	2, 4	2, 5	2, 6
3, 1	3, 2	3, 3	3, 4	3, 5	3, 6
4, 1	4, 2	4, 3	4, 4	4, 5	4, 6
5, 1	5, 2	5, 3	5, 4	5, 5	5, 6
6, 1	6, 2	6, 3	6, 4	6, 5	6, 6

Of these there are twelve sets the greatest common divisor of the numbers of each of which is not prime to 6; they are

2, 2; 2, 4; 2, 6; 3, 3; 3, 6; 4, 2; 4, 4; 4, 6; 6, 2; 6, 3; 6, 4; 6, 6.

There are therefore twenty-four sets, the greatest common divisor of the numbers of each of which is prime to 6. Hence

$$\phi_2(6)=24.$$

It can be shown that

$$\phi_n(m)=|m|^n\left(1-\frac{1}{|p_1|^n}\right)\left(1-\frac{1}{|p_2|^n}\right)\cdots\left(1-\frac{1}{|p_r|^n}\right),$$

where $p_1, p_2, \cdots, p_r$ are the different prime factors of m.

The following theorems can also be proved:

i. *If $m=p$, a prime number, then*

$$\phi_n(p)=|p|^n-1.$$

ii. *If $|m|>2$, $\phi_n(m)$ is even.*

iii. *If m_1 and m_2 be two integers prime to each other, then*

$$\phi_n(m_1m_2)=\phi_n(m_1)\phi_n(m_2).$$

iv. *If d run through all divisors of m,*

$$\Sigma\phi_n(d)=|m|^n.$$

Ex. Let $m=6$, and $n=2$; then

$$\phi_2(6)=6^2(1-\tfrac{1}{2^2})(1-\tfrac{1}{3^2})=24.$$

§ 7. Residue Systems Formed by Multiplying the Numbers of a Given System by an Integer Prime to the Modulus.

THEOREM 9. *If* $m_1, m_2, \cdots, m_m$ *be a complete residue system, mod* m, *and* a *be prime to* m, *then* $am_1, am_2, \cdots, am_m$ *is also a complete residue system, mod* m.

The integers $am_1, am_2, \cdots, am_m$ are incongruent each to each, mod m, for from

$$am_i \equiv am_j, \text{ mod } m,$$

it would follow that, since a is prime to m,

$$m_i \equiv m_j, \text{ mod } m,$$

which is contrary to the hypothesis that $m_1, m_2, \cdots, m_m$ form a complete residue system, mod m. The integers $am_1, \cdots, am_m$ are, moreover, $|m|$ in number. They form, therefore, a complete residue system, mod m.

Cor. If $r_1, r_2, \cdots, r_{\phi(m)}$ *form a reduced residue system, mod* m, *and* a *be prime to* m, *then* $ar_1, \cdots, ar_{\phi(m)}$ *is also a reduced residue system, mod* m; for $ar_1, \cdots, ar_{\phi(m)}$ are incongruent each to each, mod m, prime to m and $\phi(m)$ in number.

Ex. Since

$$-9,\ 2,\ -17,\ 14,\ 15,\ -4,\ -13,\ 8,\ 19,\ 20$$

constitute a complete residue system, mod 10, and 3 is prime to 10,

$$-27,\ 6,\ -51,\ 42,\ 45,\ -12,\ -39,\ 24,\ 57,\ 60$$

is also a complete residue system, mod 10. Likewise since

$$-9,\ -17,\ -13,\ 19$$

is a reduced residue system, mod 10.

$$-27,\ -51,\ -39,\ 57$$

is also a reduced residue system, mod 10.

If p be any prime number and a any integer prime to p, it is evident from the above that there exists an integer a_1 such that

$$aa_1 \equiv 1, \text{ mod } p.$$

We call a_1 the *reciprocal of* a, *mod* p.

§ 8. Fermat's Theorem as Generalized by Euler.

THEOREM 10. *If m be any rational integer and a any rational integer prime to m, then $a^{\phi(m)} \equiv 1$, mod m.*

Let

$$r_1, r_2, \cdots, r_{\phi(m)} \tag{1}$$

be a reduced residue system, mod m. Then since

$$ar_1, ar_2, \cdots, ar_{\phi(m)} \tag{2}$$

is also a reduced residue system, mod m, each integer of 2) is congruent to some integer of 1), mod m, that is, we have

$$\left.\begin{array}{l} ar_1 \equiv r_{j_1}, \\ ar_2 \equiv r_{j_2}, \\ \cdot \quad \cdot \quad \cdot \quad \cdot \quad \cdot \quad \cdot \\ ar_{\phi(m)} \equiv r_{j_{\phi(m)}} \end{array}\right\}, \text{ mod } m, \tag{3}$$

where $r_{j_1}, r_{j_2}, \cdots, r_{j_{\phi(m)}}$ are the integers 1), though perhaps in a different order. Since $r_{j_1}, r_{j_2}, \cdots, r_{j_{\phi(m)}}$ are the integers 1), we have

$$r_1 r_2 \cdots r_{\phi(m)} = r_{j_1} r_{j_2} \cdots r_{j_{\phi(m)}} = P.$$

Multiplying the congruences 3) together, we have

$$a^{\phi(m)} P \equiv P, \text{ mod } m, \tag{4}$$

where P is prime to m, since each of its factors is prime to m.

Hence, dividing both members of 4) by P, we have

$$a^{\phi(m)} \equiv 1, \text{ mod } m. \tag{5}$$

If $m = \pm p^n$, where p is a prime, we have

$$a^{(|p|-1)|p|^{n-1}} \equiv 1, \text{ mod } p^n, \tag{6}$$

and, in particular, when $m = p$

$$a^{|p|-1} \equiv 1, \text{ mod } p. \tag{7}$$

If p be positive, 7) becomes

$$a^{p-1} \equiv 1, \text{ mod } p; \tag{8}$$

that is, *if p be a positive prime number, and a an integer not divisible by p, $a^{p-1} - 1$ is divisible by p.* This is the form in which the theorem was enunciated by Fermat.[1]

[1] This theorem was published by Fermat in 1670, without proof. Euler was the first to give a proof. He gave two: Comm. Acad. Petrop. VIII, 1741, and Comm. Nov. Acad. Petrop. VII, p. 74, 1761.

Ex. 1. Let $m = 15;\ a = 2;$ then $\phi(15) = 8.$

From 5) it follows that

$$2^{\phi(m)} = 2^8 \equiv 1, \bmod 15;$$

that is, $$256 \equiv 1, \bmod 15.$$

Ex. 2. Let $$p = 7;\ a = -3.$$

From 7) it follows that $(-3)^6 \equiv 1, \bmod 7;$

that is, $$729 \equiv 1, \bmod 7.$$

Ex. 3. Let

$$m = p^n = 3^2;\ a = 2;\ \text{then } \phi(3^2) = 2 \cdot 3 = 6.$$

From 6) it follows that

$$2^6 \equiv 1, \bmod 9;$$

that is, $$64 \equiv 1, \bmod 9.$$

On account of the great importance of Fermat's theorem, we shall give for the form 8) a second proof, depending upon the binomial theorem. If
$$a^p \equiv a, \bmod p, \tag{9}$$
where p is a positive prime, hold for every integral value of a, then
$$a^{p-1} \equiv 1, \bmod p$$
holds when a is prime to p.

We shall show now that 9) holds for all integral values of a. We see that 9) holds when $a = 1$. If, therefore, we can show that a sufficient condition that 9) shall hold for $a = a_1 + 1$ is that it shall hold for $a = a_1$, 9) will hold for all positive integral values of a. We have by the binomial theorem

$$(a+1)^p = a^p + pa^{p-1} + \frac{p(p-1)}{1 \cdot 2} a^{p-2} + \cdots + \frac{p(p-1)\cdots 2}{1 \cdot 2 \cdots (p-1)} a + 1.$$

From § 10 we know that all coefficients in this expansion are integers. Hence since p occurs as a factor in the numerator of the coefficient of every term except the first and last, and, since the denominators of these terms contain only factors that are prime to p, the coefficient of every term except the first and last is divisible by p, and we have

$$(a+1)^p \equiv a^p + 1, \bmod p,$$

for every integral value of a.

Therefore $(a_1+1)^p \equiv a_1^p + 1, \bmod p,$

whence assuming that 9) holds for $a = a_1$; that is,

$$a_1^p \equiv a_1, \bmod p,$$

we have $(a_1+1)^p \equiv a_1 + 1, \bmod p;$

that is, 9) holds for $a = a_1 + 1$, if it holds for $a = a_1$. But 9) holds for $a = 1$. Hence 9) holds for every positive integral value of a. Moreover, since every negative integer is congruent to some positive integer, mod p, 9) holds also for all negative integral values of a.

Fermat's theorem in the form 8) is an immediate consequence of the theorem that we have just proved.

§ 9. Congruences of Condition. Preliminary Discussion.

The congruences which we have so far considered may be compared to arithmetical equalities, the values of the quantities involved being given and the congruence simply expressing the fact that the difference of the two numbers is divisible by the modulus.

We shall now consider congruences which hold only when special values are given to certain of the quantities involved; that is, the values of these "unknown" quantities are determined by the condition imposed by the congruence; for example, let x be determined by the condition that its square is to be congruent to 2, mod 7. We have $x^2 \equiv 2, \bmod 7,$

and see easily that we must have

$$x \equiv 3 \text{ or } -3, \bmod 7.$$

To develop the theory of congruences of condition, it is necessary to introduce the conception of the congruence of two polynomials with respect to a given modulus; thus, *if* $f(x_1, x_2, \cdots, x_n)$ *be a polynomial*[1] *in the undetermined quantities* $x_1, x_2, \cdots, x_n$ *with rational integral coefficients, we say that* $f(x_1, x_2, \cdots, x_n)$ *is identically congruent to* 0 *with respect to the modulus* m, *if all its coefficients be divisible by* m.

[1] We shall understand by a polynomial in n undetermined quantities $x_1, x_2, \cdots, x_n$ a rational integral function of $x_1, x_2, \cdots, x_n$ whose coefficients, unless the contrary be expressly stated, are rational integers.

This relation is expressed symbolically by

$$f(x_1, x_2, \cdots, x_n) \equiv 0, \text{ mod } m.\text{[1]}$$

Two polynomials $f(x_1, x_2, \cdots, x_n)$ *and* $\phi(x_1, x_2, \cdots, x_n)$ *are said to be identically congruent to each other, mod m, if their difference be identically congruent to* 0, *mod m, or what is the same thing if the coefficients of corresponding terms in the two polynomials be congruent; that is, in symbols*

$$f(x_1, x_2, \cdots, x_n) \equiv \phi(x_1, x_2, \cdots, x_n), \text{ mod } m,$$

if $$f(x_1, x_2, \cdots, x_n) - \phi(x_1, x_2, \cdots, x_n) \equiv 0, \text{ mod } m.$$

For example, we have

$$8x^2 - 2xy + 6y + 1 \equiv 2x^2 + xy - 2, \text{ mod } 3,$$

since $$6x^2 - 3xy + 6y + 3 \equiv 0, \text{ mod } 3,$$

or, in other words, since

$$8 \equiv 2, \quad -2 \equiv 1, \quad 6 \equiv 0, \text{ and } 1 \equiv -2, \text{ mod } 3.$$

If $f(x_1, x_2, \cdots, x_n) \equiv \phi(x_1, x_2, \cdots, x_n)$, mod m, and $a_1, a_2, \cdots, a_n$ be any n integers, then evidently

$$f(a_1, a_2, \cdots, a_n) \equiv \phi(a_1, a_2, \cdots, a_n). \text{ mod } m.$$

If, however, all the coefficients of $f(x_1, x_2, \cdots, x_n)$ be not congruent, mod m, to the corresponding coefficients of $\phi(x_1, x_2, \cdots, x_n)$, we do not have in general

$$f(a_1, a_2, \cdots, a_n) \equiv \phi(a_1, a_2, \cdots, a_n), \text{ mod } m, \qquad 1)$$

for every set of integers $a_1, a_2, \cdots, a_n$. The demand that $x_1, x_2, \cdots, x_n$ shall have such values and only such that 1) will hold is expressed by writing

$$f(x_1, x_2, \cdots, x_n) \equiv \phi(x_1, x_2, \cdots, x_n), \text{ mod } m. \qquad 2)$$

Any set of integers satisfying 1) is called a *solution* of 2). The determination of all such sets, or the proof that none exist, is called *solving the congruence* 2). It is customary to say, that a congruence is *solvable* or *unsolvable* according as it has or has not solutions. We call 2) a *congruence of condition.*

[1] The symbol $\equiv$ is read "is identically congruent to."

If $a_1, a_2, \cdots, a_n$ and $b_1, b_2, \cdots, b_n$ be two sets of n rational integers and

$$\left.\begin{array}{l} a_1 \equiv b_1 \\ a_2 \equiv b_2 \\ \cdot\ \cdot\ \cdot\ \cdot \\ \cdot\ \cdot\ \cdot\ \cdot \\ a_n \equiv b_n \end{array}\right\}, \bmod m, \qquad 3)$$

then by § 1, v,

$$f(a_1, a_2, \cdots, a_n) \equiv f(b_1, b_2, \cdots, b_n), \bmod m,$$

and $$\phi(a_1, a_2, \cdots, a_n) \equiv \phi(b_1, b_2, \cdots, b_n), \bmod m.$$

Hence, if $a_1, a_2, \cdots, a_n$ be a solution of 2), $b_1, b_2, \cdots, b_n$ is also a solution. Two solutions so related are, however, looked upon as identical.

In order that two solutions may be counted as different, it is necessary and sufficient that there shall be in the one solution a value of at least one unknown which is incongruent, mod m, to the value of the same unknown in the other solution; that is, the n relations 3) must not hold simultaneously.

It is evident from the above that in order to solve any congruence, as 2), it is sufficient to substitute for the unknowns the $|m|^n$ sets of values obtained by putting for each unknown the $|m|$ numbers of a complete residue system, mod m, and observe which values of $f(x_1, x_2, \cdots, x_n)$ so obtained are congruent to the corresponding values of $\phi(x_1, x_2, \cdots, x_n)$, mod m. There being only a finite number, $|m|^n$, of possible solutions, we can by this process always completely solve any given congruence. If the congruence have the form

$$f(x_1, x_2, \cdots, x_n) \equiv 0, \bmod m,$$

and $a_1, a_2, \cdots, a_n$ be a solution, then $f(x_1, x_2, \cdots, x_n)$ is said to be *zero, mod m*, for these values of $x_1, x_2, \cdots, x_n$.

Ex. Let us consider the congruence

$$f(x, y) = 2x^2 - xy + y - 2y^2 + 1 \equiv 0, \bmod 3.^1 \qquad 4)$$

[1] In order to avoid confusion, we shall use throughout this book the symbol $=$ instead of $\equiv$ to denote algebraic identity.

Putting for x and y, the numbers $-1, 0, 1$ of a complete residue system, mod 3, we obtain nine values of $f(x, y)$.

$$\begin{array}{lll} f(0,-1)=-2, & f(1,-1)=1, & f(-1,-1)=-1, \\ f(0,0)=1, & f(1,0)=3, & f(-1,0)=3, \\ f(0,1)=0, & f(1,1)=1, & f(-1,1)=3, \end{array}$$

Four of these values $f(0,1)$, $f(1,0)$, $f(-1,0)$, and $f(-1,1)$ are congruent to 0, mod 3. Hence the solutions of 4) are:

$$\left.\begin{array}{ll} x\equiv 0, & y\equiv 1, \\ x\equiv 1, & y\equiv 0, \\ x\equiv -1, & y\equiv 0, \\ x\equiv -1, & y\equiv 1, \end{array}\right\} \text{mod } 3.$$

By the *degree of a polynomial, mod m*, we shall understand *the degree of the term, or terms, of highest degree, whose coefficient, or coefficients, are not divisible by m.*

A *reduced* polynomial, mod p, is one whose coefficients are all numbers of the residue system, $0, 1, \cdots, p-1$.

§ 10. **Equivalent Congruences.**

Addition and Multiplication Transformations. Two congruences

$$f_1(x_1, x_2, \cdots, x_n) \equiv f_2(x_1, x_2, \cdots, x_n), \text{ mod } m, \qquad 1)$$

and

$$\phi_1(x_1, x_2, \cdots, x_n) \equiv \phi_2(x_1, x_2, \cdots, x_n), \text{ mod } m, \qquad 2)$$

are said to be equivalent when every solution of the first is a solution of the second, and every solution of the second is a solution of the first.

In solving a congruence, as in the case of algebraic equations, we proceed under the assumption that a solution exists and look upon the congruence as an identity in the values of $x_1, x_2, \cdots, x_n$ that satisfy it, though as yet unknown. Looking then upon 1) as an identity in these unknown values of $x_1, x_2, \cdots, x_n$, we consider what operations can be performed upon 1) that will produce another identity 2) such that each of these identities is a necessary consequence of the other. Operations of which this is true we shall call *reversible operations.*

Referring to § 1, we see that there are two such operations: first, if 1) be the given congruence and

$$F_1(x_1, x_2, \cdots, x_n) \equiv F_2(x_1, x_2, \cdots, x_n), \text{ mod } m, \qquad 3)$$

be any identical congruence, mod m, in $x_1, x_2, \cdots, x_n$, we can add 3) member by member to 1), obtaining

$$f_1(x_1, x_2, \cdots, x_n) + F_1(x_1, x_2, \cdots, x_n) \equiv f_2(x_1, x_2, \cdots, x_n) + F_2(x_1, x_2, \cdots, x_n), \text{ mod } m,$$

a congruence equivalent to 1).

By means of this transformation, we can transpose any term with its sign changed from one member of a congruence to the other, and can thus reduce any congruence, as 1), to an equivalent congruence of the form

$$f(x_1, x_2, \cdots, x_n) \equiv 0, \text{ mod } m, \qquad 4)$$

whose second member is 0. We shall hereafter assume the congruences with which we deal to have been reduced to this form.

We may also by this transformation reduce the coefficients of $f(x_1, x_2, \cdots, x_n)$ to their smallest possible absolute values, mod m, and thus lessen the labor of solving the congruence.

Ex. The congruence

$$14x^4 - 10x^3 + 2x^2 + 7x - 12 \equiv 0, \text{ mod } 7, \qquad 5)$$

is equivalent to the congruence

$$-3x^3 + 2x^2 + 2 \equiv 0, \text{ mod } 7,$$

which has two roots $x \equiv -1$ or 2, mod 7, and these are therefore the roots of 5).

A second operation which, when performed upon any congruence, as 1) or 4), yields an equivalent congruence, is the multiplication of both members of the congruence by any integer, a, prime to the modulus; that is, the congruences

$$f(x_1, x_2, \cdots, x_n) \equiv 0, \text{ mod } m,$$

and

$$af(x_1, x_2, \cdots, x_n) \equiv 0, \text{ mod } m,$$

where a is prime to m, are equivalent.

Conversely, we may divide all the coefficients of a congruence by any integer prime to the modulus, obtaining an equivalent congruence.

Ex. The congruences

$$15x^2y - 21xy + 3y^2 + 9 \equiv 0, \text{ mod } 35$$

and $5x^2y - 7xy + y^2 + 3 \equiv 0$, mod 35

are equivalent.

As a special case of the *multiplication transformation,* as we shall call the second of the above transformations, we have the multiplication of the congruence

$$f(x_1, x_2, \cdots, x_n) \equiv 0, \text{ mod } m,$$

by -1; that is, *the change of sign of each of its coefficients.*

§ 11. **Systems of Congruences.**[1] **Equivalent Systems.**

So far we have considered only single congruences; that is, the unknown quantities are subjected to a single condition. We can, however, as in the case of algebraic equations, subject them to two or more conditions simultaneously; that is, $x_1, x_2, \cdots, x_n$ may be required to satisfy simultaneously the congruences

$$f_1(x_1, x_2, \cdots, x_n) \equiv 0, \text{ mod } m_1,$$
$$f_2(x_1, x_2, \cdots, x_n) \equiv 0, \text{ mod } m_2,$$
$$\cdot \quad \cdot \quad \cdot \quad \cdot \quad \cdot \quad \cdot \quad \cdot \quad \cdot$$
$$\cdot \quad \cdot \quad \cdot \quad \cdot \quad \cdot \quad \cdot \quad \cdot \quad \cdot$$
$$f_r(x_1, x_2, \cdots, x_n) \equiv 0, \text{ mod } m_r.$$

By a *solution* of such a system of congruences we understand a set of values of $x_1, x_2, \cdots, x_n$ which satisfy simultaneously all the congruences.

Two solutions, $a_1, a_2, \cdots, a_n$ and $b_1, b_2, \cdots, b_n$, are considered different when and only when the nr congruences

$$\left.\begin{matrix} a_1 \equiv b_1 \\ a_2 \equiv b_2 \\ \cdot \quad \cdot \\ \cdot \quad \cdot \\ a_n \equiv b_n \end{matrix}\right\}, \text{mod } m_1, \text{ mod } m_2, \cdots, \text{ mod } m_r,$$

are not satisfied simultaneously.

Two systems of congruences are said to be equivalent when each solution of the first system is a solution of the second and each solution of the second is a solution of the first. It is evident that any one of the congruences of the system can be transformed

[1] See Stieltjes: Essai sur la theorie des Nombres.

into an equivalent congruence by the transformations of the last article and the system so obtained will be equivalent to the original system. If the moduli be the same, we can obtain an equivalent system by adding two congruences and taking the new congruence together with the $r-2$ of the original ones not used and either one of those used. Thus the system

$$\left.\begin{aligned} f_1(x_1, x_2, \cdots, x_n) &\equiv 0, \bmod m, \\ f_2(x_1, x_2, \cdots, x_n) &\equiv 0, \bmod m, \end{aligned}\right\} \qquad 1)$$

is equivalent to the system

$$f_1(x_1, x_2, \cdots, x_n) \equiv 0, \bmod m,$$
$$f_1(x_1, x_2, \cdots, x_n) + f_2(x_1, x_2, \cdots, x_n) \equiv 0, \bmod m,$$

or, more generally, if a_1, a_2 be any two integers prime to m, 1) is equivalent to the system

$$f_1(x_1, x_2, \cdots, x_n) \equiv 0, \bmod m,$$
$$a_1 f_1(x_1, x_2, \cdots, x_n) + a_2 f_2(x_1, x_2, \cdots, x_n) \equiv 0, \bmod m.$$

Ex. Let the given system be

$$\left.\begin{aligned} 4x - 3y + 7z &\equiv 5 \\ 5x + y - 3z &\equiv 2 \\ x - 4y - z &\equiv 1 \end{aligned}\right\}, \bmod 17. \qquad 2)$$

Multiplying the third congruence first by -4 and then by -5, and adding it to the first and second respectively, we obtain the system

$$\left.\begin{aligned} 13y + 11z &\equiv 1 \\ 21y + 2z &\equiv -3 \\ x - 4y - z &\equiv 1 \end{aligned}\right\}, \bmod 17, \qquad 3)$$

that is equivalent to 2).

Adding the first and second congruences of 3), we obtain the equivalent system

$$\left.\begin{aligned} 13z &\equiv -2 \\ 21y + 2z &\equiv -3 \\ x - 4y - z &\equiv 1 \end{aligned}\right\}, \bmod 17.$$

The congruence $\qquad 13z \equiv -2, \bmod 17,$

has the single solution $\qquad z \equiv -8, \bmod 17,$

that substituted in $\qquad 21y + 2z \equiv -3, \bmod 17,$

gives $\qquad y \equiv -1, \bmod 17.$

Substituting these values of y and z in

$$x - 4y - z \equiv 1, \bmod 17,$$

we have $$x \equiv 6, \mod 17.$$

We obtain therefore as a solution of the given system

$$x \equiv 6,\ y \equiv -1,\ z \equiv -8, \mod 17,$$

a result easily verified by substitution in the original system. The method of solution shows that this is the only solution (see § 13).

§ 12. Congruences in One Unknown. Comparison with Equations.

The general congruence in one unknown has the form

$$f(x) = a_0x^n + a_1x^{n-1} + \cdots + a_n \equiv 0, \mod m. \qquad 1)$$

If r be a rational integer such that

$$f(r) \equiv 0, \mod m,$$

r is called a *root* of 1).

The degree of 1) is, as has been said, the degree of the term of highest degree whose coefficient is not divisible by m.

Such a congruence presents many analogies to the equation

$$a_0x^n + a_1x^{n-1} + \cdots + a_n = 0; \qquad 2)$$

for example, to the addition to both members of the equation of the same function of the unknown corresponds the addition to the members of the congruence of any functions of the unknown which are identically congruent with respect to the modulus, and to the multiplication of the equation by any quantity not a function of the unknown corresponds the multiplication of the congruence by any integer prime to the modulus.

If m be a prime number the congruence presents still other striking analogies with algebraic equations, these analogies being absent in the case of a composite modulus.

For example, consider the two congruences of the second degree

$$(x-1)(x-3) \equiv 0, \mod 7, \qquad 3)$$

and $$(x-1)(x-3) \equiv 0, \mod 12. \qquad 4)$$

We see that 3) has two roots, 1 and 3, while 4) has four roots, 1, 3, 7 and 9; that is, 3) has a number of roots equal to its degree, while 4) has more roots than its degree.

The analogy with algebraic equations in the case of the prime modulus is as evident as is the lack of analogy in the case of the composite modulus. We shall see later that no congruence of the form 1) with prime modulus can have *more* roots than its degree.

The reason for this difference in the case of the above example is seen to be that, if a be any integer, the product $(a-1)(a-3)$ is divisible by a prime number, as 7, when and only when one of its factors is divisible by this prime, a statement no longer true when the modulus is composite; that is, a product is zero, mod m, when and only when one of its factors is zero, mod m, if m be a prime number, but not otherwise. We shall, therefore, in the discussion of the general congruence of the form 1) confine ourselves first to the case in which the modulus is a prime and shall then show that the solution of any congruence of the form 1) with composite modulus can be reduced to the solution of a series of congruences of the same form with prime moduli.

Although striking analogies between congruences and algebraic equations have already been pointed out, while others will be observed later, it is important to note an essential difference between them.

In the case of an algebraic equation it is the same thing to say that all the coefficients of an equation are zero or that it is satisfied by every value of the unknown quantity, each of these properties implying the other.

In the case of congruences, however, although, if the coefficients be all congruent to zero with respect to the modulus, the congruence is, of course, satisfied by any integral value of the unknown, on the other hand, it is not true in general that, if a congruence be satisfied by all integral values of the unknown, that all of its coefficients are divisible by the modulus.

For example, as is easily seen from Fermat's theorem, the congruence

$$x^p - x \equiv 0, \text{ mod } p,$$

where p is a prime, is satisfied by every integral value of x; but its coefficients are not all divisible by p. The reason for the difference will be shown later. We shall see also that, although a congruence of the form 1) with prime modulus can not have more roots than its degree, it can have less; for example, the three congruences

$$x^3 - 2x^2 - x + 2 \equiv 0, \bmod 5,$$

$$x^3 + 2x^2 - 2x + 1 \equiv 0, \bmod 5,$$

$$x^3 + 4x^2 + x + 1 \equiv 0, \bmod 5,$$

that are all of the third degree and have the same prime modulus, 5, have respectively three roots, 1, −1, and 2, one root, −2, and no root.

Before taking up the general congruence in one unknown, we shall consider that of the first degree.

§ 13. Congruences of the First Degree in One Unknown.

The most general congruence of the first degree can be written in the form

$$ax \equiv b, \bmod m.$$

We shall consider first the case where a is prime to m.

THEOREM 11. *The congruence*

$$ax \equiv b, \bmod m,$$

where a is prime to m, has always one and but one root.

If we put for x successively the $|m|$ integers $m_1, m_2, \cdots, m_m$ of a complete residue system, mod m, we obtain $|m|$ integers $am_1, am_2, \cdots, am_m$, that also constitute a complete residue system (Th. 9), and it is evident that one and but one of these integers, say am_i, will be congruent to b, mod m. Hence the congruence has always one and but one root, m_i. We can evidently solve any congruence of this form by this method.

Ex. Let the given congruence be

$$3x \equiv -5, \bmod 14. \qquad 1)$$

Taking as a complete residue system, mod 14, the integers 0, 1, 2, 3, $\cdots$, 13, and putting x equal to these values in succession, we have

$$3x = 0,\ 3,\ 6,\ 9,\ 12,\ 15,\ 18,\ 21,\ 24,\ 27,\ 30,\ 33,\ 36,\ 39.$$

The only one of these integers that is congruent to −5, mod 14, is 9; that is,

$$3 \cdot 3 \equiv -5, \bmod 14.$$

Hence $x \equiv 3$, mod 14, is the single root of 1)

By means of Fermat's theorem we can find a general expression for the root of a congruence of the above form.

Since a is prime to m, we have

$$a^{\phi(m)} \equiv 1, \bmod m,$$

which multiplied by b gives

$$ba^{\phi(m)} \equiv b, \bmod m,$$

or

$$aba^{\phi(m)-1} \equiv b, \bmod m.$$

Hence $ba^{\phi(m)-1}$ is the root of the congruence

$$ax \equiv b, \bmod m,$$

where a is prime to m.

This is one of the few cases in the theory of numbers where the quantity sought can be expressed as an explicit function of the given quantities.

Ex. The root of

$$3x \equiv -5, \bmod 14,$$

is

$$x \equiv -5 \cdot 3^{\phi(14)-1}, \bmod 14;$$

that is,

$$x \equiv -5 \cdot 3^5 \equiv -11 \equiv 3, \bmod 14.$$

We shall now consider the general case where a is any integer that may or may not be prime to m.

THEOREM 12. *The necessary and sufficient condition for the solvability of the congruence*

$$ax \equiv b, \bmod m,$$

is that b shall be divisible by the greatest common divisor, d, of a and m, and when this condition is fulfilled, the congruence has exactly $|d|$ incongruent roots.

Let $a = a_1 d$ and $m = m_1 d$, where a_1 is prime to m_1. From

$$ax \equiv b, \bmod m, \qquad 2)$$

we have

$$a_1 dx = b + km_1 d.$$

Hence b must be divisible by d; that is, $b = b_1 d$ is a necessary condition that 2) can be solved. This gives

$$a_1 dx = b_1 d + km_1 d, \qquad 3)$$

or

$$a_1 x \equiv b_1, \bmod m_1. \qquad 4)$$

Since a_1 is prime to m_1, 4) has a root (Th. 11). Moreover, all roots of 4) are also roots of 2); for from 4) follows 3) and hence 2). Therefore the divisibility of b by d is a sufficient as well as necessary condition for the solvability of 2). We see also that not only are all roots of 4) roots of 2), but all roots of 2) satisfy 4) and are therefore integers of the form $r + km_1$, where r is a root of 4). We ask now how many of these roots are incongruent to each other, mod m; that is, how many incongruent roots has 2)? Any two roots, $r + k_1 m_1$, $r + k_2 m_1$, of 4) are congruent, mod m, when and only when

$$r + k_1 m_1 - (r + k_2 m_1) = nm,$$

where n is an integer; that is, if

$$(k_1 - k_2) m_1 = n m_1 d,$$

or

$$k_1 - k_2 = nd,$$

or

$$k_1 \equiv k_2, \text{ mod } d.$$

Hence, in order that the roots of 2) shall be incongruent, it is necessary and sufficient that the values of k shall be incongruent, mod d. If we put, therefore, for k the $|d|$ integers of a complete residue system, mod d, for example, 0, 1, 2, $\cdots$, $|d| - 1$, we shall obtain all the incongruent roots of 2), namely

$$r, r + m_1, r + 2m_1, \cdots, r + (|d| - 1) m_1.$$

They are evidently $|d|$ in number.

Ex. Consider the congruence

$$12x \equiv -20, \text{ mod } 56. \qquad 5)$$

Here $d = 4$. Dividing by 4 we have

$$3x \equiv -5, \text{ mod } 14,$$

a congruence whose root has already been found to be -11. Therefore the roots of 5) have the form $-11 + 14k$, and are four in number. They are -11, 3, 17 and 31.

§ 14. Determination of an integer that has certain residues with respect to a given series of moduli.

Let us consider first the case in which the required integer has to satisfy two such conditions; that is, we are to determine x so that we have simultaneously

$$x \equiv a_1, \bmod m_1, \tag{1}$$

and
$$x \equiv a_2, \bmod m_2. \tag{2}$$

All integers satisfying 1) have the form $x = a_1 + m_1 y$, where y is an integer. Since x must also satisfy 2), y must satisfy the condition

$$m_1 y \equiv a_2 - a_1, \bmod m_2. \tag{3}$$

By Th. 12 for 3) to have a solution, it is necessary and sufficient that $a_2 - a_1$ shall be divisible by the greatest common divisor, d, of m_1 and m_2. If this requirement be fulfilled and y_0 be one root of 3), every root, y, of 3) must satisfy the condition

$$y \equiv y_0, \bmod \frac{m_2}{d};$$

that is,
$$y = y_0 + \frac{m_2}{d} y_1,$$

where y_1 is any integer. All integers satisfying both 1) and 2) have therefore the form

$$x = a_1 + m_1 y_0 + \frac{m_1 m_2}{d} y_1;$$

that is,
$$x \equiv a_1 + m_1 y_0, \bmod \frac{m_1 m_2}{d}.$$

Hence if x_0 be any integer satisfying both 1) and 2), all and only those integers satisfy both 1) and 2) that are congruent to x_0 with respect to the least common multiple of the moduli of 1) and 2).

By an easy extension of this method we obtain the common solution, if any exist, of the n congruences

$$\left.\begin{array}{l} x \equiv a_1, \bmod m_1, \\ x \equiv a_2, \bmod m_2, \\ \vdots \\ \vdots \\ x \equiv a_n, \bmod m_n, \end{array}\right\} \tag{4}$$

and we see that, if x_0 be an integer satisfying all these congruences and l the least common multiple of the moduli,

$$x \equiv x_0, \bmod l,$$

gives all the common solutions of the system 4). The general problem of determining whether any given system of congruences of the form $ax \equiv b$, mod m, have common solutions and of finding them, if they exist, can be solved by the above method. When the coefficients of x are prime to the moduli the congruences can evidently be reduced to the form $x \equiv c$, mod m, and we have the case just treated. If the moduli be prime each to each,

$$l = m_1 m_2 \cdots m_n$$

and the congruences 4) always have a common solution.

We shall now give another solution of this problem for the special case last mentioned. This solution is interesting on account both of its symmetry and some important deductions that can be made from its form. We have then to determine the common solutions of the congruences 4), the moduli $m_1, m_2, \cdots, m_n$ being prime each to each.

We determine first for each modulus, m_i, an auxiliary integer, b_i, such that b_i is congruent to 1 with respect to the modulus m_i and is divisible by each of the other moduli, and hence by their product; that is, we determine $b_1, b_2, \cdots, b_n$ so that

$$\begin{array}{llll} b_1 \equiv 1, & \text{mod } m_1, & \text{and } b_1 \equiv 0, & \text{mod } m_2 m_3 \cdots m_n, \\ b_2 \equiv 1, & \text{mod } m_2, & \text{and } b_2 \equiv 0, & \text{mod } m_1 m_3 \cdots m_n, \\ \vdots & \vdots \quad \vdots & \vdots & \vdots \\ \vdots & \vdots \quad \vdots & \vdots & \vdots \\ b_n \equiv 1, & \text{mod } m_n, & \text{and } b_n \equiv 0, & \text{mod } m_1 m_2 \cdots m_{n-1}. \end{array}$$

It is evident that this can always be done, for we have in the case of b_1 from the second condition $b_1 = m_2 m_3 \cdots m_n c_1$, and it only remains to determine a value for c_1 in accordance with the condition

$$m_2 m_3 \cdots m_n c_1 \equiv 1, \text{ mod } m_1,$$

that is always possible since $m_2 m_3 \cdots m_n$ is prime to m_1.

Having found these auxiliary integers, we put

$$r = a_1 b_1 + a_2 b_2 + \cdots + a_n b_n,$$

and shall show that the common solutions of 4) are the integers satisfying the congruence

$$x \equiv r, \text{ mod } m_1 m_2 \cdots m_n. \qquad 5)$$

If x satisfy 5), then

$$x \equiv r, \text{ mod } m_i, \qquad 6)$$

and, since all the auxiliary integers except b_i are divisible by m_i, from 6) it follows that

$$x \equiv a_i b_i, \text{ mod } m_i,$$

and hence, since $b_i \equiv 1, \text{ mod } m_i,$

we see that $x \equiv a_i, \text{ mod } m_i.$

Hence every integer, that satifies 5), satisfies each of the congruences 4). Moreover, every integer, that satisfies each of the congruences 4), satisfies 5), for, if x_0 be such an integer, then from

$$x_0 \equiv a_i, \text{ mod } m_i,$$

and $r \equiv a_i, \text{ mod } m_i,$

we see that $x_0 - r \equiv 0, \text{ mod } m_i;$

that is, $x_0 - r$ is divisible by each one of the moduli $m_1, m_2, \cdots, m_n$, and hence, since they are prime to each other, by their product.

Therefore $x_0 \equiv r, \text{ mod } m_1 m_2 \cdots m_n$. Hence the integers satisfying 5) are all the common solutions of 4). It will be observed that the auxiliary integers $b_1, b_2, \cdots, b_n$ are entirely independent of $a_1, a_2, \cdots, a_n$, being dependent only on the moduli.

Ex. It is required to find the common solutions of the congruences

$$x \equiv 2, \text{ mod } 11, \quad x \equiv 4, \text{ mod } 15, \quad x \equiv 9, \text{ mod } 14.$$

To calculate the auxiliary integers b_1, b_2, b_3, we have

$$b_1 = 210 c_1 \equiv 1, \text{ mod } 11,$$
$$b_2 = 154 c_2 \equiv 1, \text{ mod } 15,$$
$$b_3 = 165 c_3 \equiv 1, \text{ mod } 14,$$

and hence

$$c_1 \equiv 1, \text{ mod } 11, \quad b_1 = 210,$$
$$c_2 \equiv 4, \text{ mod } 15, \quad b_2 = 616,$$
$$c_3 \equiv 9, \text{ mod } 14, \quad b_3 = 1485.$$

Therefore $r = 420 + 2464 + 13365 = 16249,$

whence $x \equiv 16249$, mod 2310,

or $x \equiv 79$, mod 2310,

a result that is easily verified.

We observe now two important facts concerning r, that are direct consequences of the symmetrical method of its formation.

First, if for $a_1, a_2, \cdots, a_n$ be put the integers of complete residue systems with respect to the moduli $m_1, m_2, \cdots, m_n$, respectively, the resulting values of r form a complete residue system, mod l, for we obtain thus $|l|$ values of r and they are incongruent each to each, mod l. To show this, let two values of r be

$$r' = a_1'b_1 + a_2'b_2 + \cdots + a_n'b_n,$$

and

$$r'' = a_1''b_1 + a_2''b_2 + \cdots + a_n''b_n,$$

where we do not have simultaneously

$$a_1' \equiv a_1'', \text{ mod } m_1, \ a_2' \equiv a_2'', \text{ mod } m_2, \cdots, a_n' \equiv a_n'', \text{ mod } m_n;$$

that is, in order that the two values of r be different we must have at least one of the a''s, such as a_i', in r' incongruent, mod m_i, to the corresponding a'', a_i'', in r''.

Let $a_i' \not\equiv a_i''$, mod m_i.

If $r' \equiv r''$, mod l,

it would follow that $r' \equiv r''$, mod m_i,

and hence also $a_i'b_i \equiv a_i''b_i$, mod m_i,

or, since $b_i \equiv 1$, mod m_i,

$$a_i' \equiv a_i'', \text{ mod } m_i,$$

that is contrary to our supposition. The two values of r are therefore incongruent with respect to the modulus l.

In the second place, if we select from the system of values of r just formed those which are formed by putting for $a_1, a_2, \cdots, a_n$, the integers of reduced residue systems with respect to the moduli $m_1, m_2, \cdots, m_n$ respectively, the resulting values of r form a reduced residue system, mod l. We have already shown that these values of r are incongruent each to each, mod l. It remains to be shown that all and only those values of r that are prime to l occur in the system as formed. If one of these values of r, as r', $= a_1'b_1 + \cdots + a_n'b_n$, have a prime factor, p, in common with l, then some one of the moduli, as m_i, must have this factor in common with r, and since

$$r' \equiv a_i', \text{ mod } m_i,$$

a_i' and m_i would have the common factor p, which is contrary to the hypothesis that a_i' is an integer of a reduced residue system, mod m_i.

Hence all values of r obtained above are prime to l. Moreover, when a value of r, as r', is prime to l, $a_1', a_2', \cdots, a_n'$ are each prime to their respective moduli, for, if any a, as a_i', have a factor p in common with its modulus, then since

$$r' \equiv a_i', \text{ mod } m_i,$$

r' would have the factor p in common with m_i, and hence with l. Hence all values of r, that are prime to l, occur in the above system, and it is therefore a reduced residue system, mod l.

Ex. Let $m_1 = 6, \quad m_2 = 5,$

we have $b_1 = 5c_1 \equiv 1, \text{ mod } 6,$

and $b_2 = 6c_2 \equiv 1, \text{ mod } 5,$

whence $c_1 \equiv 5, \text{ mod } 6,$

and $c_2 \equiv 1, \text{ mod } 5.$

Then $b_1 = 25, \text{ and } b_2 = 6,$

whence $r = 25a_1 + 6a_2.$

Putting for a_1 the values 1, 5 and for a_2 the values 1, 2, 3, 4, that is, the integers of reduced residue systems, mod 6, mod 5, respectively, we have for the resulting values of r 31, 37, 43, 49, 131, 137, 143, 149, that, being all prime to 30 and in number $\phi(30), = 8$, constitute a reduced residue system, mod 30.

This method of forming a reduced residue system shows us at once that the number of integers in such a system, mod $m_1 m_2 \cdots m_n$, where $m_1, m_2, \cdots, m_n$ are prime each to each, is equal to the product of the numbers of the integers in the reduced residue systems for each of the moduli $m_1, m_2, \cdots, m_n$.

We obtain therefore a new proof of Th. 4; that is, that

$$\phi(m_1 m_2 \cdots m_n) = \phi(m_1)\phi(m_2) \cdots \phi(m_n),$$

where $m_1, m_2, \cdots, m_n$ are prime each to each.

We shall proceed to the discussion of the general congruence of the nth degree in one unknown with prime modulus and shall first develop briefly the theory of the divisibility of polynomials with respect to a prime modulus.

§ 15. **Divisibility of one Polynomial by another with respect to a Prime Modulus. Common Divisors. Common Multiples.**

If p be any rational prime number we have the following definition: *A polynomial, $f(x)$, is said to be divisible with respect to the modulus p by a polynomial $\phi(x)$ when there exists a polynomial $Q(x)$ such that*

$$f(x) \equiv Q(x)\phi(x), \text{ mod } p.$$

We say that $\phi(x)$ and $Q(x)$ are *divisors* or *factors*, mod p, of $f(x)$, and that $f(x)$ is a *multiple*, mod p, of $\phi(x)$ and $Q(x)$. We also say that $f(x)$ is *resolved*, mod p, into the factors $\phi(x)$ and $Q(x)$. The degree of a polynomial, mod p, is the degree of the term of highest degree whose coefficient is not divisible by p. The sum of the degrees of the factors of $f(x)$ is evidently equal to the degree of $f(x)$.

Ex. It is easily seen that

$$x^5 + 3x^4 - 4x^3 + 2 \equiv (2x^2 - 3)(3x^3 - x^2 + 1), \text{ mod } 5.$$

Hence $2x^2 - 3$ and $3x^3 - x^2 + 1$ are divisors, mod 5, of $x^5 + 3x^4 - 4x^3 + 2$.

We have as direct consequences of the definition of divisibility:

i. *If $f_1(x)$ be a multiple, mod p, of $f_2(x)$ and $f_2(x)$ be a multiple, mod p, of $f_3(x)$, then $f_1(x)$ is a multiple, mod p, of $f_3(x)$, or more generally, if each polynomial of the series $f_1(x)$, $f_2(x)$, $\cdots$, $f_n(x)$ be a multiple, mod p, of the one immediately following, then each polynomial of the series is a multiple, mod p, of all that follow.*

ii. *If $f_1(x)$ and $f_2(x)$ be multiples, mod p, of $f(x)$, then $f_1(x) + f_2(x)$ and $f_1(x) - f_2(x)$ are multiples, mod p, of $f(x)$, or more generally, if $f_1(x)$ and $f_2(x)$ be multiples, mod p, of $f(x)$, and $F_1(x)$, $F_2(x)$ be any two polynomials, then $F_1(x)f_1(x) + F_2(x)f_2(x)$ is a multiple of $f(x)$.*

If two or more polynomials $f_1(x), f_2(x), \cdots, f_n(x)$ be divisible, mod p, by a polynomial $\phi(x)$, $\phi(x)$ is said to be a *common divisor*, mod p, of $f_1(x), f_2(x), \cdots, f_n(x)$. If a polynomial $f(x)$ be a multiple, mod p, of two or more polynomials $\phi_1(x), \phi_2(x), \cdots, \phi_n(x)$, $f(x)$ is said to be a *common multiple*, mod p, of $\phi_1(x), \phi_2(x), \cdots, \phi_n(x)$.

§ 16. **Unit and Associated Polynomials with Respect to a Prime Modulus. Primary Polynomials.**

We ask now whether there exist polynomials that with respect to a modulus p divide all polynomials. Evidently those have this property that are of degree 0 and are $\not\equiv 0$, mod p; that is, the rational integers not divisible by p, for they are divisors, mod p, of 1 and 1 divides every polynomial. Furthermore, these are the only polynomials having this property, for no polynomial, $f(x)$, of degree higher than the 0th can divide, mod p, all polynomials, for it can not divide 1, since then the sum of the degrees of the divisor and the quotient, mod p, would be greater than 0, the degree of 1.

We call the rational integers, excluding those divisible by p, the *unit polynomials*, mod p, or briefly, *units*, mod p, and since two polynomials that are congruent, mod p, are considered as identical, we can take as the units, mod p, the integers of any reduced residue system, mod p, for example, $1, 2, \cdots, |p| - 1$.

Thus the unit polynomials, mod 7, are 1, 2, 3, 4, 5, 6.

Two polynomials which differ only by a unit factor, mod p, are called *associated polynomials* and are looked upon as identical in all questions of divisibility, mod p.

If two polynomials, $f_1(x)$, $f_2(x)$, are each associated, mod p, with a third polynomial, they are associated with each other; for if

$$f_1(x) \equiv af_3(x), \text{ mod } p, \tag{1}$$

and

$$f_2(x) \equiv bf_3(x), \text{ mod } p, \tag{2}$$

where a and b are units, mod p, then, multiplying 2) by b_1, the reciprocal, mod p, of b, we have

$$b_1 f_2(x) \equiv f_3(x), \text{ mod } p,$$

and hence from 1)

$$f_1(x) \equiv ab_1 f_2(x), \text{ mod } p,$$

where ab_1 is a unit, mod p.

Two polynomials, that are associated, mod p, are evidently of the same degree and each is a divisor, mod p, of the other.

Conversely, if two polynomials be each divisible, mod p, by the other, they are associated.

Two polynomials that have no common divisor, mod p, other than the units are said to be prime to each other, mod p.

Any polynomial, $f(x)$, has $|p|-1$ associates, mod p. Of these one and only one has as the coefficient of its term of highest degree 1. This one is called the ***primary*** associate, mod p, of $f(x)$. For example, the six polynomials

$$x^3+2x-3,\quad 2x^3+4x-6,\quad 3x^3+6x-2,$$
$$4x^3+\ x-5,\quad 5x^3+3x-1,\quad 6x^3+5x-4,$$

are associated, mod 7, and x^3+2x-3 is the primary one.

§ 17. Prime Polynomials with respect to a Prime Modulus. Determination of the Prime Polynomials, mod p, of any Given Degree.

A polynomial that is not a unit, mod p, and that has no divisors, mod p, other than its associates and the units, is called a prime polynomial, mod p.

If it has divisors, mod p, other than these it is said to be *composite*, mod p.

To find the primary prime polynomials, mod 3, of any given degree we may proceed as follows, considering all polynomials to be reduced. All polynomials of the first degree are evidently prime. Hence primary prime polynomials of the first degree, mod 3, are three in number, namely

$$x,\quad x+1,\quad x+2.$$

The reduced primary polynomials, mod 3, of the second degree are nine in number, namely

$$\begin{array}{lll} x^2, & x^2+x, & x^2+2x, \\ x^2+1, & x^2+x+1, & x^2+2x+1, \\ x^2+2, & x^2+x+2, & x^2+2x+2. \end{array}$$

From the three primary polynomials of the first degree, we can form the six composite polynomials of the second degree

$$\left.\begin{array}{ll} x^2 \equiv x^2, & x(x+1) \equiv x^2 + x, \\ (x+1)^2 \equiv x^2+2x+1, & x(x+2) \equiv x^2+2x, \\ (x+2)^2 \equiv x^2+x+1, & (x+1)(x+2) \equiv x^2+2, \end{array}\right\}, \bmod 3.$$

These being the primary composite, polynomials, mod 3, of the second degree, we see that

$$x^2+1, \quad x^2+x+2, \quad x^2+2x+2,$$

are the primary prime polynomials, mod 3, of the second degree.

In like manner we see that there are nineteen composite polynomials of the third degree, mod 3, and hence eight prime polynomials of the third degree, mod 3, since there are in all twenty-seven reduced primary polynomials of the third degree, mod 3.

It can be shown that, when n is greater than 1, the number of prime polynomials, mod p, of the nth degree is

$$\frac{1}{n}\left(p^n - \Sigma p^{\frac{n}{q_1}} + \Sigma p^{\frac{n}{q_1 q_2}} - \Sigma p^{\frac{n}{q_1 q_2 q_3}} + \cdots\right),$$

where $q_1, q_2, q_3, \cdots$, are the different prime factors of n.

This expression being always different from 0, it follows that there exist prime polynomials, mod p, of any given degree.[1]

§ 18. **Division of one Polynomial by Another with Respect to a Prime Modulus.**

THEOREM 13. *If $f(x)$ be any polynomial and $\phi(x)$ be any polynomial not identically congruent to 0, mod p, there exists a polynomial $Q(x)$, such that the polynomial*

$$f(x) - Q(x)\phi(x) \equiv R(x), \bmod p, \qquad 1)$$

is of lower degree than $\phi(x)$.

The operation of determining the polynomials $Q(x)$ and $R(x)$ is called dividing $f(x)$ by $\phi(x)$, mod p. We call $Q(x)$ the quotient, and $R(x)$ the remainder in the division, mod p, of $f(x)$ by $\phi(x)$. We shall prove the existence of $Q(x)$ and $R(x)$ by giving a method for their determination.

[1] H. J. S. Smith: p. 153. Borel et Drach: pp. 49, 50. Bachmann: Niedere Zahlentheorie, pp. 372, 373.

Let
$$f(x) = a_0x^n + a_1x^{n-1} + \cdots + a_n,$$
$$\phi(x) = b_0x^m + b_1x^{m-1} + \cdots + b_m$$

be any two polynomials and let

$$b_0 \not\equiv 0, \mod p.$$

We shall consider first the case in which b_0 is 1, and shall then show that the general case can be reduced to this one. Since b_0 is 1, we can divide $f(x)$ by $\phi(x)$ as in ordinary division until we get a remainder $R(x)$ of lower degree than $\phi(x)$, the quotient being $Q(x)$. We have then

$$f(x) - Q(x)\phi(x) = R(x),$$

from which follows at once 1).

We can now reduce to this particular case the general case in which b_0 has any value not divisible by p. Let c_0 be the reciprocal, mod p, of b_0; then

$$c_0\phi(x) \equiv \phi_1(x), \mod p, \qquad 2)$$

where $\phi_1(x)$ is a polynomial the coefficient of whose term of highest degree is 1 when reduced, mod p. Dividing $f(x)$ by $\phi_1(x)$ as above, we have

$$f(x) \equiv Q(x)\phi_1(x) + R(x), \mod p,$$

and hence, making use of 2),

$$f(x) \equiv c_0Q(x)\phi(x) + R(x), \mod p,$$

where $c_0Q(x)$ and $R(x)$ are the quotient and remainder required.[1]

The above theorem plays the same rôle in the theory of the divisibility of polynomials with respect to a prime modulus that Th. A does in that of rational integers.

Ex. Let it be required to divide, mod 7,

$$f(x) = 5x^5 - 2x^4 + 2x^3 - 5x^2 + 2x + 1,$$

by
$$\phi(x) = 3x^3 + x^2 - 5x - 2.$$

[1] See also Cahen: p. 70, Borel et Drach: p. 33, and Bachmann: Niedere Zahlentheorie, p. 368, concerning the division of one polynomial by another with respect to a prime modulus.

Since 5 is the reciprocal, mod 7, of 3, we have

$$\phi_1(x) \equiv 5\phi(x) \equiv x^3 + 5x^2 + 3x - 3, \text{ mod } 7. \qquad 3)$$

Dividing $f(x)$ by $\phi_1(x)$ as in ordinary algebraic division, we have

$$5x^5 - 2x^4 + 2x^3 - 5x^2 + 2x + 1 - (5x^2 - 27x + 122)(x^3 + 5x^2 + 3x - 3)$$
$$= -519x^2 - 445x + 367,$$

whence, reducing coefficients, mod 7,

$$5x^5 - 2x^4 + 2x^3 - 5x^2 + 2x + 1 - (-2x^2 + x + 3)(x^3 + 5x^2 + 3x - 3)$$
$$\equiv -x^2 + 3x + 3, \text{ mod } 7,$$

or, making use of 3),

$$5x^5 - 2x^4 + 2x^3 - 5x^2 + 2x + 1 - 5(-2x^2 + x + 3)(3x^3 + x^2 - 5x - 2)$$
$$\equiv -x^2 + 3x + 3, \text{ mod } 7;$$

that is,

$$5x^5 - 2x^4 + 2x^3 - 5x^2 + 2x + 1 - (-3x^2 - 2x + 1)(3x^3 + x^2 - 5x - 2)$$
$$\equiv -x^2 + 3x + 3, \text{ mod } 7,$$

where $-3x^2 - 2x + 1$ and $-x^2 + 3x + 3$ are the required polynomials $Q(x)$ and $R(x)$.

§ 19. Congruence of two Polynomials with Respect to a Double Modulus.

Two polynomials, $f_1(x)$, $f_2(x)$, are said to be identically congruent to each other with respect to the double modulus p, $\phi(x)$, where p is a prime number and $\phi(x)$ a polynomial, if their difference, $f_1(x) - f_2(x)$, is divisible, mod p, by $\phi(x)$; that is, in symbols

$$f_1(x) \equiv f_2(x), \text{ modd } p,\ \phi(x), \qquad 1)$$

if $$f_1(x) - f_2(x) \equiv Q(x)\phi(x), \text{ mod } p, \qquad 2)$$

or, in other words, if

$$f_1(x) - f_2(x) = Q(x)\phi(x) + F(x)\cdot p, \qquad 3)$$

where $Q(x)$ and $F(x)$ are polynomials.

It should be observed that 1), 2) and 3) all express exactly the same relation between the polynomials $f_1(x)$, $f_2(x)$ and $\phi(x)$ and the prime number p, but, just as in the case of congruences between integers, 1) places this relation before us in a more illuminating manner than does either 2) or 3).

The fact that $f(x)$ is divisible, mod p, by $\phi(x)$ is expressed in the above notation by writing

$$f(x) \equiv 0, \text{ modd } p, \ \phi(x).$$

Ex. From § 15, Ex., we have

$$x^5 + 3x^4 - 4x^3 + 2 \equiv 0, \text{ modd } 5, \ 2x^2 - 3.$$

We have as consequences of the above definition just as in the case of integers, the double modulus p, $\phi(x)$ being understood, throughout.

i. *If* $$f_1(x) \equiv f_2(x)$$
and $$f_2(x) \equiv f_3(x),$$
then $$f_1(x) \equiv f_3(x).$$

ii. *If* $$f_1(x) \equiv f_2(x)$$
and $$F_1(x) \equiv F_2(x),$$
then $$f_1(x) \pm F_1(x) \equiv f_2(x) \pm F_2(x).$$

iii. *If* $$f_1(x) \equiv f_2(x).$$
and $F(x)$ *be any polynomial,*
then $$F(x)f_1(x) \equiv F(x)f_2(x).$$

iv. *If* $$f_1(x) \equiv f_2(x)$$
and $$F_1(x) \equiv F_2(x),$$
then $$f_1(x) \cdot F_1(x) \equiv f_2(x) \cdot F_2(x),$$
and, in particular,
if $$f_1(x) \equiv f_2(x),$$
then $$(f_1(x))^k \equiv (f_2(x))^k.$$

The results corresponding to v, ⋯, ix, § 1, follow easily.

§ 20. Unique Factorization Theorem for Polynomials with respect to a Prime Modulus.

We shall now show that a polynomial can be resolved in one and but one way with respect to a prime modulus, p, into prime factors, considering always associated factors as the same. The proof will be closely analogous to that of the corresponding theorem for rational integers. We begin by stating the following theorem which is an immediate consequence of the definition of divisibility.

THEOREM 14. *If* $f(x) \equiv Q(x)\phi(x) + R(x)$, *mod* p, *every polynomial that divides, mod* p, *both* $f(x)$ *and* $\phi(x)$ *divides both* $\phi(x)$ *and* $R(x)$, *and vice versa; that is, the common divisors, mod* p, *of* $f(x)$ *and* $\phi(x)$ *are identical with the common divisors, mod* p, *of* $\phi(x)$ *and* $R(x)$.

By means of this theorem and Th. 13 we can now prove the theorem which is the basis of the unique factorization theorem.

THEOREM 15. *If* $f_1(x)$, $f_2(x)$ *be any two polynomials and* p *a rational prime, there exists a common divisor,* $D(x)$, *mod* p, *of* $f_1(x)$, $f_2(x)$ *such that* $D(x)$ *is divisible, mod* p, *by every common divisor, mod* p, *of* $f_1(x)$, $f_2(x)$, *and there exist two polynomials* $\phi_1(x)$, $\phi_2(x)$, *such that*

$$f_1(x)\phi_1(x) + f_2(x)\phi_2(x) \equiv D(x), \text{ mod } p.$$

We may evidently assume $f_2(x)$ of degree not higher than $f_1(x)$.

Dividing $f_1(x)$ by $f_2(x)$, mod p, we can find two polynomials $Q_1(x)$, $f_3(x)$, such that

$$f_1(x) \equiv Q_1(x)f_2(x) + f_3(x), \text{ mod } p,$$

$f_3(x)$ being of lower degree than $f_2(x)$.

Dividing $f_2(x)$ by $f_3(x)$, mod p, we have

$$f_2(x) \equiv Q_2(x)f_3(x) + f_4(x), \text{ mod } p,$$

where $f_4(x)$ is of lower degree than $f_3(x)$, and similarly

$$f_3(x) \equiv Q_3(x)f_4(x) + f_5(x), \text{ mod } p,$$

$$\vdots \qquad \vdots \qquad \vdots$$

$$\vdots \qquad \vdots \qquad \vdots$$

$$f_{n-2}(x) \equiv Q_{n-2}(x)f_{n-1}(x) + f_n(x), \text{ mod } p,$$

$$f_{n-1}(x) \equiv Q_{n-1}(x)f_n(x), \text{ mod } p,$$

a chain of identical congruences in which we must after a finite number of steps reach one in which the remainder, $f_{n+1}(x)$, is 0, mod p, since the degrees of the remainders continually decrease.

By Th. 14 the common divisors, mod p, of $f_n(x)$ and $f_{n-1}(x)$ are identical with those of $f_{n-1}(x)$ and $f_{n-2}(x)$, those of $f_{n-1}(x)$, $f_{n-2}(x)$ with those of $f_{n-2}(x)$, $f_{n-3}(x)$, and finally those of $f_3(x)$, $f_2(x)$ with those of $f_2(x)$, $f_1(x)$.

But $f_n(x)$ is a common divisor, mod p, of $f_n(x)$ and $f_{n-1}(x)$ and is evidently divisible by every common divisor of $f_n(x)$ and $f_{n-1}(x)$. Hence $f_n(x)$ is the desired common divisor $D(x)$, mod p, of $f_1(x)$ and $f_2(x)$.

If now we substitute the value of $f_3(x)$ in terms of $f_1(x)$, $f_2(x)$ obtained from the first of these congruences in the second and the values of $f_3(x)$ and $f_4(x)$ in terms of $f_1(x)$, $f_2(x)$ in the third and continue until the congruence

$$f_{n-2}(x) \equiv Q_{n-2}(x) f_{n-1}(x) + f_n(x), \text{ mod } p,$$

is reached, we shall obtain the congruence

$$f_1(x)\phi_1(x) + f_2(x)\phi_2(x) \equiv D(x), \text{ mod } p.$$

Cor. If $f_1(x)$, $f_2(x)$ be two polynomials prime to each other, mod p, there exist two polynomials $\phi_1(x)$, $\phi_2(x)$ such that

$$f_1(x)\phi_1(x) + f_2(x)\phi_2(x) \equiv 1, \text{ mod } p.$$

In this case $D(x)$ is an integer α not divisible by p, and we have two polynomials $\Phi_1(x)$, $\Phi_2(x)$ such that

$$f_1(x)\Phi_1(x) + f_2(x)\Phi_2(x) \equiv \alpha, \text{ mod } p,$$

whence, multiplying by the reciprocal of α, mod p, we obtain

$$f_1(x)\phi_1(x) + f_2(x)\phi_2(x) \equiv 1, \text{ mod } p.$$

It will be noticed that this corollary corresponds to Th. B, while Th. 15 corresponds to the corollary to Th. B, the order of proof here being reversed. The corollary could have been proved first as before.[1]

THEOREM 16. *If the product of two polynomials, $f_1(x), f_2(x)$, be divisible, mod p, by a prime polynomial, $P(x)$, at least one of the polynomials, $f_1(x)$, $f_2(x)$, is divisible, mod p, by $P(x)$.*

Let $$f_1(x) f_2(x) \equiv Q(x) P(x), \text{ mod } p, \qquad 1)$$

[1] Laurent: Theorie des Nombres Ordinaires et Algebriques, p. 120.

where $Q(x)$ is a polynomial, and assume $f_1(x)$ not divisible, mod p, by $P(x)$. Then $f_1(x)$ and $P(x)$ are prime, mod p, to each other and by the last theorem there exist two polynomials, $\phi_1(x)$, $\phi_2(x)$, such that

$$f_1(x)\phi_1(x) + P(x)\phi_2(x) \equiv 1, \text{ mod } p. \qquad 2)$$

Multiplying 2) by $f_2(x)$, we have

$$f_1(x)f_2(x)\phi_1(x) + f_2(x)P(x)\phi_2(x) \equiv f_2(x), \text{ mod } p,$$

and therefore, making use of 1),

$$P(x)(Q(x)\phi_1(x) + f_2(x)\phi_2(x)) \equiv f_2(x), \text{ mod } p,$$

where $Q(x)\phi_1(x) + f_2(x)\phi_2(x)$ is a polynomial. Hence $f_2(x)$ is divisible, mod p, by $P(x)$. Expressed in the double modulus notation this theorem is:

If $f_1(x), f_2(x)$ be any two polynomials and $P(x)$ a prime polynomial, mod p, and if

$$f_1(x)f_2(x) \equiv 0, \text{ modd } p, P(x),$$

then either $\quad f_1(x) \equiv 0, \text{ modd } p, P(x),$

or $\quad f_2(x) \equiv 0, \text{ modd } p, P(x).$

Cor. 1. *If the product of any number of polynomials be divisible, mod p, by a prime polynomial $P(x)$, then at least one of the polynomials is divisible, mod p, by $P(x)$.*

Cor. 2. *If neither of two polynomials be divisible, mod p, by a prime polynomial $P(x)$, their product is not divisible, mod p, by $P(x)$.*

THEOREM 17. *A polynomial, $f(x)$, can be resolved in one and but one way into a product of prime polynomials, mod p.*

Let $f(x)$ be any polynomial. We shall take $f(x)$ in its reduced form, mod p, for the sake of convenience, this assumption in no wise limiting the generality of the proof. Let the degree, mod p, of $f(x)$ be n. If $f(x)$ be prime, mod p, the theorem is evident. If $f(x)$ be not prime, it has a divisor, $\phi(x)$, mod p, and we have

$$f(x) \equiv \phi(x)\Psi(x), \text{ mod } p,$$

where $\phi(x)$, $\Psi(x)$ are polynomials neither of which is a unit and the sum of whose degrees is n.

If $\phi(x)$ be not a prime polynomial, mod p, then

$$\phi(x) \equiv \phi_1(x)\Psi_1(x), \text{ mod } p,$$

where $\phi_1(x)$, $\Psi_1(x)$ are polynomials that are not units and that have degrees whose sum is equal to the degree of $\phi(x)$.

If $\phi_1(x)$ be not a prime polynomial, mod p, we proceed in the same manner and, since the degrees of the factors form a decreasing series of positive rational integers, we must after a finite number of such factorizations reach in the series $\phi(x)$, $\phi_1(x)$, $\phi_2(x)$, $\cdots$ a prime polynomial $P_1(x)$, mod p. We have then

$$f(x) \equiv P_1(x)f_1(x), \text{ mod } p.$$

Proceeding similarly with $f_1(x)$ in case it be not prime, mod p, we obtain

$$f_1(x) \equiv P_2(x)f_2(x), \text{ mod } p,$$

where $P_2(x)$ is prime, mod p, and hence

$$f(x) \equiv P_1(x)P_2(x)f_2(x), \text{ mod } p.$$

Continuing this process, we must after a finite number of such factorizations reach in the series $f(x)$, $f_1(x)$, $f_2(x)$, $\cdots$ a prime polynomial $P_n(x)$, mod p. We have then

$$f(x) \equiv P_1(x)P_2(x) \cdots P_n(x), \text{ mod } p,$$

where $P_1(x), P_2(x), \cdots, P_n(x)$ are all prime, mod p; that is, $f(x)$ can be resolved, mod p, into a finite number of prime factors.

It remains to be shown that this resolution is unique. Suppose that

$$f(x) \equiv Q_1(x)Q_2(x) \cdots Q_m(x), \text{ mod } p,$$

be a second resolution of $f(x)$ into prime factors, mod p. Then

$$P_1(x)P_2(x) \cdots P_n(x) \equiv Q_1(x)Q_2(x) \cdots Q_m(x), \text{ mod } p, \quad 3)$$

and it follows from Th. 16, Cor. 1 that at least one of the $Q(x)$'s, say $Q_1(x)$, is divisible, mod p, by $P_1(x)$ and hence is associated, mod p, with $P_1(x)$; that is,

$$Q_1(x) \equiv a_1 P_1(x), \text{ mod } p,$$

where a_1 is a unit, mod p.

Dividing 3) by $P_1(x)$, mod p, we have

$$P_2(x) \cdots P_n(x) \equiv a_1 Q_2(x) \cdots Q_n(x), \text{ mod } p. \qquad 4)$$

From 4) it follows that at least one of the remaining $Q(x)$'s must be associated, mod p, with $P_2(x)$. Dividing 4) by $P_2(x)$, mod p, and proceeding as before, we see that with each $P(x)$ there is associated, mod p, at least one $Q(x)$ and, if two or more $P(x)$'s are associated, mod p, with one another, at least as many $Q(x)$'s are associated, mod p, with these $P(x)$'s and hence with one another.

In exactly the same manner, we can prove that with each $Q(x)$ there is associated, mod p, at least one $P(x)$ and, if two or more $Q(x)$'s are associated, mod p, with one another, at least as many $P(x)$'s are associated, mod p, with these $Q(x)$'s and hence with one another.

Hence, considering two associated factors as the same, the resolutions are identical; that is, if in the one resolution there occur e factors associated, mod p, with a certain prime polynomial, there will be in the other resolution exactly e factors associated, mod p, with the same prime polynomial.

We can now evidently write any polynomial, $f(x)$, in the form

$$f(x) \equiv a(P_1(x))^{e_1}(P_2(x))^{e_2} \cdots (P_n(x))^{e_n}, \text{ mod } p,$$

where $P_1(x), P_2(x), \cdots, P_n(x)$ are the unassociated prime factors, mod p, of $f(x)$.

If we take $P_1(x), P_2(x), \cdots, P_n(x)$ primary, the resolution is absolutely unique. The representations of the greatest common divisor and least common multiple given for rational integers are easily extended to polynomials.

§ 21. **Resolution of a Polynomial into its Prime Factors with respect to a Prime Modulus.**

The resolution of a polynomial, $f(x)$, into its prime factors, mod p, may be effected by dividing, mod p, $f(x)$ by each of the prime polynomials of the first degree $x, x-1, \cdots, x-p+1$, (p being taken positive) in turn until either a polynomial is found that divides $f(x)$, or it is determined that $f(x)$ is divisible by none of them.

Suppose that $f(x)$ is divisible, mod p, by $x-a_1$ and that the quotient is $f_1(x)$. We proceed in the same way with $f_1(x)$ until we have found all the prime, mod p, factors of the first degree of $f(x)$.

Suppose that

$$f(x) \equiv (x-a_1)(x-a_2)\cdots(x-a_n)f_2(x), \text{ mod } p,$$

where $f_2(x)$ has no factor, mod p, of degree lower than the second.

The prime factors, mod p, of the second degree of $f_2(x)$ can next be determined in the same manner, then those of the third degree, etc. In case, however, we do not know the prime, mod p, polynomials of the second degree, we can simply determine whether $f_2(x)$ is divisible, mod p, by any polynomial of the second degree. If it is, such a polynomial is evidently a prime, mod p, polynomial, for $f_2(x)$ contains no factors, mod p, of degree lower than the second. The same method can be applied to the determination of the prime factors of higher degree.[1]

§ 22. **The General Congruence of the nth Degree in one Unknown and with Prime Modulus.**

THEOREM 18. *If r be a root of the congruence*

$$f(x) = a_0x^n + a_1x^{n-1} + \cdots + a_n \equiv 0, \text{ mod } p, \qquad 1)$$

$f(x)$ is divisible, mod p, by $x-r$, and conversely, if $f(x)$ be divisible, mod p, by $x-r$, r is a root of 1).

Dividing, mod p, $f(x)$ by $x-r$, we have

$$f(x) \equiv (x-r)\phi(x) + f(r), \text{ mod } p,$$

whence, since r is a root of 1),

$$f(r) \equiv 0, \text{ mod } p,$$

and hence $\qquad f(x) \equiv (x-r)\phi(x), \text{ mod } p;$

that is, $f(x)$ is divisible, mod p, by $x-r$. The converse is evident.

If $f(x)$ be prime, mod p, the congruence 1) evidently has no roots. The converse is, however, not true; that is, $f(x)$ may be

[1] Borel et Drach: p. 36.

composite, mod p, but 1) have no roots, for the prime, mod p, factors of $f(x)$ may all be of higher degree than the first. This theorem gives us another method for determining the factors, mod p, of the first degree of any polynomial in x. Some of these factors may be alike and we are led therefore to say that *r is a multiple root of order e* of 1), if $f(x)$ be divisible, mod p, by $(x-r)^e$, but not by $(x-r)^{e+1}$.

If therefore $r_1, r_2, \cdots, r_m$ be the incongruent roots of 1) of orders $e_1, e_2, \cdots, e_m$ respectively, we have

$$f(x) \equiv (x-r_1)^{e_1}(x-r_2)^{e_2} \cdots (x-r_m)^{e_m} f_1(x), \text{ mod } p,$$

where $f_1(x)$ is a polynomial having no linear factor, mod p, and whose degree, s, is such that

$$e_1 + e_2 + \cdots + e_m + s = n,$$

where n is the degree of $f(x)$.

Counting a multiple root of order e of 1) as e roots, we see that 1) has exactly as many roots as $f(x)$ has linear factors, mod p, and obtain the following important theorem:

THEOREM 19. *The number of roots of the congruence*

$$f(x) = a_0 x^n + a_1 x^{n-1} + \cdots + a_n \equiv 0, \text{ mod } p,$$

where p is a prime number, is not greater than its degree.

Cor. 1. If the number of incongruent roots of a congruence with prime modulus be greater than its degree the congruence is an identical one.

Cor. 2. If the congruence

$$f(x) \equiv 0, \text{ mod } p, \qquad 2)$$

have exactly as many roots as its degree and $\phi(x)$ be a divisor, mod p, of $f(x)$, then the congruence

$$\phi(x) \equiv 0, \text{ mod } p,$$

has exactly as many roots as its degree; for

$$f(x) \equiv \phi(x) Q(x), \text{ mod } p,$$

where $Q(x)$ is a polynomial in x, and every root of the congruence 2) is a root of either the congruence

$$\phi(x) \equiv 0, \text{ mod } p, \qquad 3)$$

or of the congruence

$$Q(x) \equiv 0, \bmod p. \qquad 4)$$

Moreover, the sum of the degrees of 3) and 4) is equal to the degree of 2). If, therefore, $\phi(x)$ had fewer roots than its degree, then $Q(x)$ must have more roots than its degree, which is impossible. Hence the corollary.

§ 23. **The Congruence $x^{\phi(m)} - 1 \equiv 0$, mod m.**

Although in the case of congruences of degree higher than the first the theorem just given tells all that we know in general regarding the number of their roots, still there is one important case in which the number of roots is always exactly equal to the degree of the congruence.

THEOREM 20. *The congruence*

$$x^{\phi(m)} - 1 \equiv 0, \bmod m, \qquad 1)$$

has exactly as many roots as its degree.

The $\phi(m)$ integers of a reduced residue system, mod m, evidently satisfy 1). Moreover, since by §1, ix, two integers congruent, mod m, have with m the same greatest common divisor, and the greatest common divisor of 1 and m is 1, every root of 1) must have with m the greatest common divisor 1, that is, be prime to m. Hence the number of roots of 1) is exactly equal to $\phi(m)$, its degree.

Ex. The congruence

$$x^{\phi(10)} - 1 \equiv 0, \bmod 10,$$

or

$$x^4 - 1 \equiv 0, \bmod 10,$$

has the four roots 1, 3, 7, and 9.

Cor. If d be a positive divisor of $p-1$, the congruence

$$x^d - 1 \equiv 0, \bmod p,$$

where p is a prime, has exactly d roots; for $x^d - 1$ is a divisor of $x^{p-1} - 1$ and hence by Th. 19, Cor. 2, we have the corollary.

Since the congruence

$$x^p - x \equiv 0, \bmod p,$$

has the p roots $0, 1, 2, \cdots, p-1$ equal in number to its degree, we have the identical congruence

$$x^p - x \equiv x(x-1)(x-2)\cdots(x-\overline{p-1}), \text{ mod } p.$$

Ex. $x^7 - x \equiv x(x-1)(x-2)(x-3)(x-4)(x-5)(x-6), \text{ mod } 7.$

§ 24. **Wilson's Theorem.**

The result just obtained gives us a proof of the following interesting theorem.

THEOREM 21. *If p be a prime number and $r_1, r_2, \cdots, r_{\phi(p)}$ be a reduced residue system, mod p, then*

$$r_1 r_2 \cdots r_{\phi(p)} + 1 \equiv 0, \textit{ mod } p.$$

By the previous section we have evidently

$$x^{\phi(p)} - 1 \equiv (x-r_1)(x-r_2)\cdots(x-r_{\phi(p)}), \text{ mod } p,$$

from which, putting $x=0$, we have

$$-1 \equiv (-r_1)(-r_2)\cdots(-r_{\phi(p)}), \text{ mod } p,$$

whence, since $\phi(p)$ is even except when $p=2$,

$$r_1 r_2 \cdots r_{\phi(p)} + 1 \equiv 0, \text{ mod } p,$$

which evidently holds also when $p=2$.[1]

Ex. Let $p=5$, and take as a reduced residue system, mod 5, the integers $-2, -1, 1, 2$. Then

$$(-2)(-1)\cdot 1\cdot 2+1=5\equiv 0, \text{ mod } 5.$$

This theorem is a particular case of the following more general theorem that is due to Gauss.[2]

If $r_1, r_2, \cdots, r_{\phi(m)}$ be a reduced residue system, mod m, the product $r_1 r_2 \cdots r_{\phi(m)}$ is congruent to -1, mod m, when $m=4$, p^n or $2p^n$, where p is an odd prime, and is congruent to 1, mod m, when m has any other value.

The two following examples will illustrate this theorem; for its proof see references given above.

Ex. 1. Let $m=3^2$, and take as a reduced residue system, mod 3^2, -4, -2, -1, 1, 2, 4; then

$$(-4)(-2)(-1)\cdot 1\cdot 2\cdot 4=-64\equiv -1, \text{ mod } 3^2.$$

[1] See Matthews, § 16, for another proof of this theorem.

[2] Gauss: Disq. Arith., Art. 78. Dirichlet-Dedekind: § 38. Bachmann: Niedere Zahlentheorie, p. 170. Cahen: p. 103.

Ex. 2. Let $m = 15$, and take as a reduced residue system, mod 15, -7, -4, -2, -1, 1, 2, 4, 7; then

$$(-7)(-4)(-2)(-1)\cdot 1\cdot 2\cdot 4\cdot 7 = 3136 \equiv 1, \text{ mod } 15.$$

As a special case of Th. 21 we have the following:

If p be a positive prime number and the product of all positive integers less than p be increased by 1, the result is divisible by p; that is,

$$(p-1)! + 1 \equiv 0, \text{ mod } p.$$

The theorem was first stated in this form by Waring in his "Meditationes Algebraicae" (1770) and ascribed to its author, Sir John Wilson.

The converse of the original form is true; that is, *If the product of all positive integers less than a given integer, m, be increased by 1 and the result be divisible by m, then m is a prime number.* This is easily seen to be true; for, if $m = ab$, where neither a nor b is a unit, then $(m-1)!$ is divisible by a, whence we have

$$(m-1)! + 1 \not\equiv 0, \text{ mod } m.$$

For example $\quad 5! + 1 = 121 \not\equiv 0, \text{ mod } 6.$

Wilson's theorem gives therefore an unfailing method for determining whether any given integer is a prime number. It is, however, obviously of no practical use on account of the immense labor of the numerical reckoning when m is large.

§ 25. Common Roots of Two Congruences.

The common roots of two congruences

$$f_1(x) \equiv 0, \text{ mod } p, \text{ and } f_2(x) \equiv 0, \text{ mod } p,$$

are evidently the roots of the congruence

$$\phi(x) \equiv 0, \text{ mod } p,$$

where $\phi(x)$ is the greatest common divisor, mod p, of $f_1(x)$ and $f_2(x)$. Since the congruence

$$x^p - x \equiv 0, \text{ mod } p,$$

has for its roots the numbers of a complete residue system, mod p, the incongruent roots of any congruence

$$f(x) \equiv 0, \text{ mod } p,$$

will be the roots of the congruence

$$\phi(x) \equiv 0, \text{ mod } p, \qquad 2)$$

where $\phi(x)$ is the greatest common divisor, mod p, of $x^p - x$ and $f(x)$. This gives us another method of determining all the incongruent roots of any given congruence with prime modulus. The congruence 2) will always have as many roots as its degree, since the congruence 1) has as many roots as its degree and $\phi(x)$ is a divisor, mod p, of $x^p - x$.

Ex. To find the roots of the congruence

$$x^4 - 3x^3 - x^2 + 2x - 6 \equiv 0, \text{ mod } 7, \qquad 3)$$

by the above method, since 0 is not a root of the congruence, we need only find the greatest common divisor, mod 7, of $x^4 - 3x^3 - x^2 + 2x - 6$ and $x^6 - 1$.

This greatest common divisor is $x^2 - 3x + 2$, and the congruence

$$x^2 - 3x + 2 \equiv 0, \text{ mod } 7,$$

has the roots 1 and 2, that are therefore the incongruent roots of 3).

§ 26. **Determination of the Multiple Roots of a Congruence with Prime Modulus.**

The multiple roots of the congruence

$$f(x) \equiv 0, \text{ mod } p, \qquad 1)$$

may be determined by a method exactly analogous to that employed for determining the multiple roots of an algebraic equation. Thus let $P(x)$ be a prime function, mod p, and let $f(x)$ be divisible, mod p, by $(P(x))^e$ but not by $(P(x))^{e+1}$; then

$$f(x) \equiv (P(x))^e Q(x), \text{ mod } p,$$

or, what is the same thing,

$$f(x) = (P(x))^e Q(x) + pF(x), \qquad 2)$$

where $F(x)$ and $Q(x)$ are polynomials in x and $Q(x)$ is prime, mod p, to $P(x)$.

Differentiating 2), we have

$$f'(x) = (P(x))^{e-1}(eP'(x)Q(x) + P(x)Q'(x)) + pF'(x),$$

where $P'(x)$, $Q'(x)$ and $F'(x)$ are polynomials in x. Hence

$$f'(x) \equiv (P(x))^{e-1}Q_1(x), \text{ mod } p,$$

where $Q_1(x)$ is a polynomial in x and is moreover not divisible, mod p, by $P(x)$, for

$$Q_1(x) = eP'(x)Q(x) + P(x)Q'(x),$$

where $P'(x)$ is of lower degree than $P(x)$ and $Q(x)$ is prime, mod p, to $P(x)$. Therefore $f'(x)$ is divisible, mod p, by the prime factor $P(x)$ exactly once less than $f(x)$ is divisible by $P(x)$. In particular, if $f(x)$ be divisible, mod p, by $(x-r)^e$, but not by $(x-r)^{e+1}$, then $f'(x)$ is divisible, mod p, by $(x-r)^{e-1}$ but not by $(x-r)^e$. Hence the theorem:

THEOREM 22. *If the congruence*

$$f(x) \equiv 0, \text{ mod } p,$$

have a multiple root r of order e, the congruence

$$f'(x) \equiv 0, \text{ mod } p,$$

has the multiple root r of order $e-1$.

If the greatest common divisor, mod p, of $f(x)$ and $f'(x)$ be $\phi(x)$, then the roots of the congruence

$$\phi(x) \equiv 0, \text{ mod } p, \tag{3}$$

if it have any, will be the multiple roots of 1) and each root of 3) will occur once oftener as a root of 1) than as a root of 3).

It may happen, of course, that $f(x)$ and $f'(x)$ have a common divisor, $\phi(x)$, mod p, and yet 1) has no multiple roots. In this case the repeated prime factors, mod p, of $f(x)$ are of higher degree than the first, and $\phi(x)$ therefore contains no factor of the first degree, mod p.

Ex. Let the given congruence be

$$f(x) = 2x^3 - x + 1 \equiv 0, \text{ mod } 5. \tag{4}$$

We have $$f'(x) = 6x^2 - 1 \equiv x^2 - 1, \text{ mod } 5,$$

and the greatest common divisor, mod 5, of $f(x)$ and $f'(x)$ is $x+1$.

The congruence

$$x + 1 \equiv 0, \text{ mod } 5,$$

has the root -1.

Hence the congruence 4) has two roots -1. Dividing $f(x)$ by $(x+1)^2$,

we have $$f(x) \equiv 2(x+1)^2(x-2), \text{ mod } 5,$$

and see that $f(x)$ has the third root 2.

§ 27. Congruences in One Unknown and with Composite Modulus.

The solution of a congruence of the form

$$f(x) = a_0x^n + a_1x^{n-1} + \cdots + a_n \equiv 0, \text{ mod } m, \qquad 1)$$

where
$$m = m_1 m_2 \cdots m_t,$$

$m_1, m_2, \cdots m_t$ being integers prime each to each, can be reduced to the solution of the system of t congruences,

$$\left.\begin{array}{l} f(x) \equiv 0, \text{ mod } m_1, \\ f(x) \equiv 0, \text{ mod } m_2, \\ \vdots \qquad \vdots \\ \vdots \qquad \vdots \\ f(x) \equiv 0, \text{ mod } m_t. \end{array}\right\} \qquad 2)$$

Every root of 1) is evidently a root of each of the congruences 2), and conversely any integer, that is simultaneously a root of each of the congruences 2), is a root of 1).

If therefore $a_1, a_2, \cdots, a_t$ be roots of the congruences 2) and r be chosen so that

$$\left.\begin{array}{l} r \equiv a_1, \text{ mod } m_1, \\ r \equiv a_2, \text{ mod } m_2, \\ \vdots \quad \vdots \qquad \vdots \\ \vdots \quad \vdots \qquad \vdots \\ r \equiv a_t, \text{ mod } m_t, \end{array}\right\} \qquad 3)$$

then r is a root of 1).

Since $m_1, m_2, \cdots, m_t$ are prime each to each, it is, by §14, always possible to find r so as to satisfy the conditions 3).

Let $b_1, b_2, \cdots, b_t$ be auxiliary integers selected as in § 14; then

$$r \equiv a_1b_1 + a_2b_2 + \cdots + a_tb_t, \text{ mod } m \qquad 4)$$

is a root of 1), and, if the congruences 2) have respectively $l_1, l_2, \cdots, l_t$ incongruent roots, then by § 14 1) has $l_1 l_2 \cdots l_t$ incongruent roots, that are obtained by putting in 4) for $a_1, a_2, \cdots, a_t$ respectively the $l_1, l_2, \cdots, l_t$ roots of the congruences 2).

In particular, if any one of the congruences 2) have no root, then 1) has no root.

Ex. The solution of the congruence

$$x^4 + 3x^3 + 3x^2 + 3x + 2 \equiv 0, \text{ mod } 30, \qquad 5)$$

can be reduced to the solution of the two congruences

$$x^4+3x^3+3x^2+3x+2\equiv 0, \text{ mod } 6, \qquad 6)$$

and

$$x^4+3x^3+3x^2+3x+2\equiv 0, \text{ mod } 5. \qquad 7)$$

The roots of 6) are $-2, -1, 1, 2$ and those of 7) are $-2, -2, -1, 2$. The roots of 5) are then

$$r\equiv 25a_1+6a_2, \text{ mod } 30. \begin{cases} a_1=-2,-1,1,2.^1 \\ a_2=-2,-1,2. \end{cases}$$

that gives as the roots of 5), $-13, -11, -8, -7, -2, -1, 2, 4, 7, 8, 13, 14$.

If now we suppose m to be resolved into a product of powers of its different prime factors, that is,

$$m=p_1^{e_1}p_2^{e_2}\cdots p_r^{e_r},$$

where $p_1, p_2, \cdots, p_r$ are different primes, then the solution of 1) is reduced to the solution of r congruences of the form

$$f(x)\equiv 0, \text{ mod } p^e. \qquad 8)$$

We shall now show that the solution of 8) can be made to depend upon the solution of the congruence

$$f(x)\equiv 0, \text{ mod } p^{e-1}, \qquad 9)$$

where the modulus is a power of p one degree lower than that of the modulus of 8), and thus be made to depend eventually upon the solution of the congruence

$$f(x)\equiv 0, \text{ mod } p,$$

whose modulus is a prime.

Let x_0 be a root of 9); then all integers of the form $x_0+p^{e-1}y$, where y is an integer, are roots of 9). Furthermore, since all roots of 8) are roots of 9), if 8) have roots they must be of this form.

Putting in 8) $$x=x_0+p^{e-1}y, \qquad 10)$$

we have $$f(x_0+p^{e-1}y)\equiv 0, \text{ mod } p^e,$$

or, expanding $f(x_0+p^{e-1}y)$,

$$f(x_0)+f'(x_0)p^{e-1}y+\frac{f''(x_0)}{2!}p^{2e-2}y^2+\cdots\equiv 0, \text{ mod } p^e. \qquad 11)$$

Since $$f(x_0)\equiv 0, \text{ mod } p^{e-1},$$

[1] See Example § 14.

we have $$f(x_0) = cp^{e-1},$$

and hence, dividing each term of 11) by p^{e-1},

$$c + f'(x_0)y + \frac{f''(x_0)}{2!}p^{e-1}y^2 + \cdots \equiv 0, \bmod p,$$

whence we have

$$c + f'(x_0)y \equiv 0, \bmod p, \qquad 12)$$

as a necessary and sufficient condition that y must satisfy in order that the root, $x_0 + p^{e-1}y$, of 9) may also be a root of 8).

There are three cases to be considered:

i. If $$f'(x_0) \not\equiv 0, \bmod p,$$

there is always one and but one value, y_0, of y that satisfies 12) and this gives one value only of $x_0 + p^{e-1}y_0$ that satisfies 8).

ii. If $$f'(x_0) \equiv 0, \bmod p, \text{ and } c \not\equiv 0, \bmod p,$$

there is no value of y satisfying 12) and hence no value of x of the form $x_0 + p^{e-1}y$ satisfying 8); that is, 8) has no root.

iii. If $$f'(x_0) \equiv 0, \bmod p, \text{ and } c \equiv 0, \bmod p,$$

then 12) is an identical congruence and consequently 12) has $|p|$ solutions, mod p, from which by substitution in 10) we obtain $|p|$ solutions of 8).[1]

Ex. The roots of the congruence

$$x^4 - 8x^3 + 9x^2 + 9x + 14 \equiv 0, \bmod 5^2, \qquad 13)$$

if any exist, must satisfy the congruence

$$x^4 - 8x^3 + 9x^2 + 9x + 14 \equiv 0, \bmod 5,$$

whose roots are 1 and 2, and hence be of the form

$$1 + 5y \quad \text{or} \quad 2 + 5y.$$

Substituting $1 + 5y$ and $2 + 5y$ in 13), we obtain respectively

$$5 + 7y \equiv 0, \bmod 5, \qquad 14)$$

and $$4 - 19y \equiv 0, \bmod 5. \qquad 15)$$

From 14) we have $$y \equiv 0, \bmod 5,$$

and from 15) $$y \equiv 1, \bmod 5,$$

that give 1 and 7 as the roots of 13).

[1] See Cahen: pp. 96–103.

§ 28. **Residues of Powers.**

If a be prime to m, and $b \equiv a^t$, *mod m, where t is a positive integer, b is said to be a power residue of a with respect to the modulus m.*

For example, since $4 \equiv 3^2$, mod 5, we say that 4 is a power residue of 3 with respect to the modulus 5.

Two power residues of *a* which are congruent to each other, and hence to the same power of *a*, mod *m*, are looked upon as the same.

A system of integers such that every power residue of a, mod m, is congruent to one and only one integer of the system, mod m, is called a complete system of power residues of a with respect to the modulus m.

Ex. Every power of 5 is congruent, mod 6, to 1 or 5. Hence 1, 5 constitute a complete system of power residues of 5, with respect to the modulus 6.

These integers may evidently be selected from among the integers of any reduced residue system, mod *m*. For convenience they are usually taken from the system $1, 2, \cdots, |m|$ and we may indeed define a complete system of power residues of *a*, mod *m*, as being the smallest positive residues that the successive powers of *a*, $a^0 = 1, a^1, a^2, a^3, \cdots, a^t, \cdots$ give when divided by *m*.

The more general definition given above will, however, serve our purposes better as it will admit of direct extension to realms of higher degree than the first, while the latter does not.

We shall now investigate certain questions relating to power residues, and, in particular, the important one as to when a complete system of power residues of an integer *a*, mod *m*, is also a reduced residue system, mod *m*.

The following table gives the power residues of all numbers of a reduced residue system, mod 13, with respect to this modulus. In order to calculate the residue of a^k, it is not necessary to raise *a* to the *k*th power, but only to multiply the residue of a^{k-1} by *a* and then take the residue of the product with respect to *m*.

$$m = 13.$$

a^0	a^1	a^2	a^3	a^4	a^5	a^6	a^7	a^8	a^9	a^{10}	a^{11}	a^{12}
1	1	1	1	1	1	1	1	1	1	1	1	1
1	2	4	8	3	6	12	11	9	5	10	7	1
1	3	9	1	3	9	1	3	9	1	3	9	1
1	4	3	12	9	10	1	4	3	12	9	10	1
1	5	12	8	1	5	12	8	1	5	12	8	1
1	6	10	8	9	2	12	7	3	5	4	11	1
1	7	10	5	9	11	12	6	3	8	4	2	1
1	8	12	5	1	8	12	5	1	8	12	5	1
1	9	3	1	9	3	1	9	3	1	9	3	1
1	10	9	12	3	4	1	10	9	12	3	4	1
1	11	4	5	3	7	12	2	9	8	10	6	1
1	12	1	12	1	12	1	12	1	12	1	12	1

We ask now, what is the smallest value t_a of t other than 0 for which we have

$$a^t \equiv 1, \text{ mod } m.$$

That t_a always exists and is $\leqq \phi(m)$ is evident from Fermat's theorem, that gives, since a is prime to m,

$$a^{\phi(m)} \equiv 1, \text{ mod } m.$$

Giving t_a the above meaning, we say that the integer a *appertains to the exponent t_a with respect to the modulus m.* We see from the table that

$$\left.\begin{array}{rl} 2, 6, 7, 11 \text{ appertain} & \text{to the exponent } 12; \text{ that is, } \phi(13). \\ 4, 10 \text{ appertain} & \text{to the exponent } 6 \\ 5, 8 \text{ appertain} & \text{to the exponent } 4 \\ 3, 9 \text{ appertain} & \text{to the exponent } 3 \\ 12 \text{ appertains} & \text{to the exponent } 2 \end{array}\right\}, \text{ mod } 13.$$

It is evident that, if $a \equiv b$, mod m, then a and b appertain to the same exponent, mod m.

THEOREM 23. *If the integer a appertain to the exponent t_a, mod m, then the t_a powers of a,*

$$1, a, a^2, \cdots, a^{t_a - 1}, \tag{1}$$

are incongruent each to each, mod m.

Let a^s and a^{s+r} be any two of the powers 1). If

$$a^{s+r} \equiv a^s, \text{ mod } m, \tag{2}$$

then, since a is prime to m,

$$a^r \equiv 1, \text{ mod } m. \tag{3}$$

But $r < t_a$ and hence 3) is impossible, since a appertains to t_a. Therefore 2) is impossible.

THEOREM 24. *If a appertain to the exponent t_a, mod m, any two powers of a with positive exponents are congruent or incongruent to each other, mod m, according as their exponents are congruent or incongruent, mod t_a.*

Let a^{s_1}, a^{s_2} be any two powers of a, s_1, s_2 being positive integers, and let

$$s_1 = q_1 t_a + r_1, \quad s_2 = q_2 t_a + r_2,$$

where q_1, q_2 are positive integers and

$$0 \leqq r_1 < t_a, \quad 0 \leqq r_2 < t_a, \quad r_1 \geqq r_2. \qquad 4)$$

If $$a^{q_1 t_a + r_1} \equiv a^{q_2 t_a + r_2}, \text{ mod } m, \qquad 5)$$

then $$a^{r_1} \equiv a^{r_2}, \text{ mod } m, \qquad 6)$$

whence, since a is prime to m,

$$a^{r_1 - r_2} \equiv 1, \text{ mod } m.$$

But from 4) we have

$$0 \leqq r_1 - r_2 < t_a,$$

and hence, since a appertains to t_a, mod m,

$$r_1 = r_2. \qquad 7)$$

Therefore $$s_1 \equiv s_2, \text{ mod } t_a, \qquad 8)$$

is a necessary condition for

$$a^{s_1} \equiv a^{s_2}, \text{ mod } m. \qquad 9)$$

Moreover, from 8) follow in turn 7), 6) and 5).

Hence 8) is also a sufficient condition for the existence of 9). We have therefore

$$\left.\begin{array}{l} a^0 \equiv a^{t_a} \equiv a^{2t_a} \equiv a^{3t_a} \equiv \cdots \\ a^1 \equiv a^{t_a+1} \equiv a^{2t_a+1} \equiv a^{3t_a+1} \equiv \cdots \\ a^2 \equiv a^{t_a+2} \equiv a^{2t_a+2} \equiv a^{3t_a+2} \equiv \cdots \\ \cdot \quad \cdot \quad \cdot \quad \cdot \quad \cdot \quad \cdot \quad \cdot \quad \cdot \quad \cdot \quad \cdot \quad \cdot \\ a^{t_a-1} \equiv a^{2t_a-1} \equiv a^{3t_a-1} \equiv a^{4t_a-1} \equiv \cdots \end{array}\right\}, \text{ mod } m.$$

This is known as the *law of the periodicity of the power residues*. It can be verified by an examination of the table, p. 99, where we see, for example, that 5 appertains to the exponent 4, mod 13, and we have

$$\left.\begin{matrix} 5^0 \equiv 5^4 \equiv 5^8 \equiv 5^{12} \\ 5^1 \equiv 5^5 \equiv 5^9 \\ 5^2 \equiv 5^6 \equiv 5^{10} \\ 5^3 \equiv 5^7 \equiv 5^{11} \end{matrix}\right\}, \text{ mod } 13, \qquad \left.\begin{matrix} 0 \equiv 4 \equiv 8 \equiv 12 \\ 1 \equiv 5 \equiv 9 \\ 2 \equiv 6 \equiv 10 \\ 3 \equiv 7 \equiv 11 \end{matrix}\right\}, \text{ mod } 4.$$

THEOREM 25. *The exponent, t_a, to which an integer a appertains with respect to the modulus m, is always a divisor of $\phi(m)$.*[1]

Since $$a^{\phi(m)} \equiv 1 \equiv a^0, \text{ mod } m,$$
we have by Th. 24,
$$\phi(m) \equiv 0, \text{ mod } t_a.$$

THEOREM 26. *If two integers, a_1, a_2, appertain, mod m, to two exponents, t_1, t_2, that are prime to each other, then their product, a_1a_2, appertains, mod m, to the exponent, t_1t_2.*

Let a_1a_2 appertain, mod m, to an exponent t, then

$$(a_1a_2)^t \equiv 1, \text{ mod } m. \tag{10}$$

Raising both members of 10) to the t_1 power, we have

$$a_1^{t_1t}a_2^{t_1t} \equiv 1, \text{ mod } m.$$

But $$a_1^{t_1t} \equiv 1, \text{ mod } m,$$

and hence $$a_2^{t_1t} \equiv 1, \text{ mod } m,$$

and therefore, since a_2 appertains to the exponent t_2, mod m, t_1t must be a multiple of t_2 (Th. 24). Whence, since t_1 and t_2 are prime to each other, it follows that t is a multiple of t_2. In like manner we can show that t is a multiple of t_1.

Therefore t, being a multiple of t_1 and t_2, that are prime to each other, is a multiple of their product t_1t_2. Hence the smallest possible value of t for which 10) will hold is t_1t_2, and a_1a_2 appertains to this exponent, mod m.

Ex. We see from the table, p. 99, that 12 and 3 appertain, mod 13, to the exponents 2 and 3 respectively, and that their product $36 (\equiv 10, \text{ mod } 13)$ appertains to the exponent 6.

Limiting ourselves now to the case in which the modulus is a

[1] For a proof of this theorem not dependent upon Fermat's theorem, see Mathews, p. 18.

prime number, p, we ask whether there are integers appertaining to every positive divisor of $\phi(p)$ and, if so, how many. Before proving the theorem, that will answer this question in its entirety, let us examine the table, p. 99, and see how matters stand when $p=13$. The positive divisors of $\phi(13)$, $=12$, are 1, 2, 3, 4, 6 and 12.

$$\left.\begin{array}{l} \text{To 1 appertains the single integer } 1, \\ \text{To 2 appertains the single integer } 12, \\ \text{To 3 appertain the two integers } 3,\ 9, \\ \text{To 4 appertain the two integers } 5,\ 8, \\ \text{To 6 appertain the two integers } 4,\ 10, \\ \text{To 12 appertain the four integers } 2,\ 6,\ 7,\ 11, \end{array}\right\}, \text{ mod } 13.$$

THEOREM 27. *To every positive divisor, t, of $\phi(p)$, there appertain $\phi(t)$ integers*[1] *with respect to the modulus p.*

Assume that to every positive divisor, t, of $\phi(p)$, there appertains at least one integer, a. We shall show that, if this assumption be true, there appertain to t $\phi(t)$ integers; that is, to every positive divisor, t, of $\phi(p)$ there appertain either $\phi(t)$ integers or no integers. Let $\psi(t)$ denote the number of integers appertaining to t. Each of the integers

$$a^0=1, a, a^2, \cdots, a^{t-1} \qquad 11)$$

is a root of the congruence

$$x^t \equiv 1, \text{ mod } p, \qquad 12)$$

for, if a^r be one of these integers, then

$$(a^r)^t=(a^t)^r \equiv 1, \text{ mod } p,$$

since $$a^t \equiv 1, \text{ mod } p.$$

The integers 11) are moreover by Th. 23 incongruent each to each, mod p, and, being t in number, are therefore all the roots of 12), since 12) can not have more than t incongruent roots. But every integer appertaining to t must evidently be a root of 12) and we need look therefore only among the integers 11) to find all integers appertaining to t. Let a^r be any one of the integers 11). If a^r appertain to t, we must have $a^r, a^{2r}, \cdots, a^{(t-1)r}$

[1] We, of course, consider only incongruent integers; see p. 99.

each incongruent to 1, mod p. By Th. 24 the necessary and sufficient condition for this is

$$ir \not\equiv 0, \mod t, \qquad 13)$$

where i runs through the values $1, 2, \cdots, t-1$. In order now that 13) may hold, we must have r prime to t; for suppose that the contrary is true and that d is the greatest common divisor of r and t, assuming for convenience d to be positive. We have

$$r = r_1 d, \quad t = t_1 d,$$

and, since $t_1 < t$ and i runs through all values from 1 to $t-1$, one of the values of t will be t_1 and we shall have for this value

$$t_1 r_1 d \equiv 0, \mod t_1 d;$$

that is, 13) does not hold.

But, since $i < t$, 13) holds whenever r is prime to t. Hence the necessary and sufficient condition that any one, a^r, of the integers $1, a, a^2, \cdots, a^{t-1}$ shall appertain to t, is that its exponent, r, shall be prime to t. This condition is fulfilled by $\phi(t)$ of these integers, and we have proved therefore that

$$\psi(t) = \text{either } \phi(t) \text{ or } 0.$$

We shall now prove that the latter case can never occur. We separate the $\phi(p)$ integers of a reduced residue system, mod p, into classes according to the divisor of $\phi(p)$ to which they appertain; that is, if $t_1, t_2, \cdots, t_n$ be the positive divisors of $\phi(p)$, we put in one class the $\psi(t_1)$ integers of the above system that appertain to t_1, in another class the $\psi(t_2)$ integers that appertain to t_2, etc. It is evident that no integer can belong to two different classes and that every integer must belong to some one of these classes.

The integers of a reduced residue system, mod p, being $\phi(p)$ in number, we have therefore

$$\psi(t_1) + \psi(t_2) + \cdots + \psi(t_n) = \phi(p).$$

But by Th. 6, $\phi(p)$ taking the place of m, we have

$$\phi(t_1) + \phi(t_2) + \cdots + \phi(t_n) = \phi(p),$$

whence

$$\psi(t_1)+\psi(t_2)+\cdots+\psi(t_n)=\phi(t_1)+\phi(t_2)+\cdots+\phi(t_n). \quad 14)$$

Since, however, every term in the first member of 14) is equal either to the corresponding term in the second member or 0, if even a single term in the first member were 0, 14) would not hold. Hence no term in the sum $\psi(t_1)+\psi(t_2)+\cdots+\psi(t_n)$ is 0.

Therefore $$\psi(t)=\phi(t).$$

§ 29. **Primitive Roots.**

An integer, that appertains to the exponent $\phi(m)$ with respect to the modulus m, is said to be a primitive root of m.

For example; 2, 6, 7 and 11 appertain, mod 13, to the exponent $\phi(13)$, $=12$, and are therefore primitive roots of 13. It can be shown that such integers exist only when $m=2$, 4, p^n or $2p^n$, where p is an odd prime.[1] We shall discuss however only the case where m is a prime number.

It having been proved in Th. 27 that, if p be a prime, there appertain $\phi(\phi(p))$ integers to the exponent $\phi(p)$, mod p, we see that p has always $\phi(\phi(p))$ incongruent primitive roots. If r be a primitive root of p, then by Th. 23 the $\phi(p)$ powers of r $r, r^2, \cdots, r^{\phi(p)}$ form a reduced residue system, mod p. Hence every integer, that is not divisible by p, is congruent to one of these powers of r, mod p. This property, upon which depends the usefulness of a primitive root, may be used to define it as follows: *An integer, a complete system of whose power residues, mod m, constitute a reduced residue system, mod m, is called a primitive root of m.*

For example; $2, 2^2, 2^3, 2^4, 2^5, 2^6, 2^7, 2^8, 2^9, 2^{10}, 2^{11}, 2^{12}$ constitute a reduced residue system, mod 13. Hence 2 is a primitive root of 13.

We shall illustrate the advantage of this representation of a reduced residue system by a second proof of the generalized form of Wilson's theorem (Th. 21). Let p be an odd prime, r a primi-

[1] Gauss: Disq. Arith., Arts. 57–93. Dirichlet-Dedekind: §§ 127–131. Bachmann: Elemente der Zahlentheorie, pp. 89–104. Bachmann: Niedere Zahlentheorie, pp. 322–348. Mathews: §§ 19–29. Wertheim: §§ 48–69.

tive root of p, and $q_1, q_2, \cdots, q_{\phi(p)}$ any reduced residue system, mod p. Since the integers $r, r^2, \cdots, r^{\phi(p)}$ constitute a reduced residue system, mod p, each of the q's must be congruent to some one of these powers of r, mod p; that is,

$$\left.\begin{array}{l} q_1 \equiv r^{l_1}, \\ q_2 \equiv r^{l_2}, \\ \cdot\ \cdot\ \cdot\ \cdot\ \cdot\ \cdot \\ q_{\phi(p)} \equiv r^{l_{\phi(p)}}, \end{array}\right\} \text{mod } p,$$

where $l_1, l_2, \cdots, l_{\phi(p)}$ are the numbers $1, 2, \cdots, \phi(p)$ in some order. Multiplying these congruences together, we have

$$q_1 q_2 \cdots, q_{\phi(p)} \equiv r^{1+2+\cdots+\phi(p)}, \text{ mod } p.$$

$$\equiv r^{[1+\phi(p)]\frac{\phi(p)}{2}}, \text{ mod } p.$$

But

$$r^{1+\phi(p)} \equiv r, \text{ mod } p,$$

and hence

$$q_1 q_2 \cdots, q_{\phi(p)} \equiv r^{\frac{\phi(p)}{2}}, \text{ mod } p. \qquad 1)$$

We have also

$$r^{\phi(p)} - 1 = (r^{\phi(p)/2} - 1)(r^{\phi(p)/2} + 1) \equiv 0, \text{ mod } p,$$

and hence, since

$$r^{\phi(p)/2} - 1 \not\equiv 0, \text{ mod } p,$$

r being a primitive root of p,

$$r^{\phi(p)/2} + 1 \equiv 0, \text{ mod } p. \qquad 2)$$

Therefore from 1) and 2) it follows that

$$q_1 q_2 \cdots q_{\phi(p)} + 1 \equiv 0, \text{ mod } p.$$

When $p = 2$, this proof does not hold as $\phi(p)$ is then odd.

§ 30. **Indices.**

If $q \equiv r^i$, mod p, r being a primitive root of p and i one of the numbers $0, 1, \cdots, \phi(p) - 1$, i is said to be *the index of q to the base r, mod p*, and we write $i = \text{ind}_r\, q$, mod p.

The subscript r is often omitted, in which case it is understood that all indices are to be taken to a certain given base.

The relation of an integer to its index is evidently very similar to that of a number to its logarithm and indices play a part in the theory of numbers similar to that of logarithms in arithmetic. It can be easily shown that they obey the following laws:

Let p be the modulus, and r a primitive root of p.

i. *The index of the product of two integers is congruent to the sum of the indices of the factors, mod* $\phi(p)$, that is,

$$\text{ind}_r\, ab \equiv \text{ind}_r\, a + \text{ind}_r\, b, \mod \phi(p).$$

This result can evidently be extended to the product of any number of integers; that is,

$$\text{ind}_r\,(a_1 a_2 \cdots a_n) \equiv \text{ind}_r\, a_1 + \text{ind}_r\, a_2 + \cdots + \text{ind}_r\, a_n, \mod \phi(p).$$

ii. *The index of the nth power of an integer is congruent to n times the index of the integer, mod* $\phi(p)$, *n being a positive integer;* that is,

$$\text{ind}_r\, a^n \equiv n\, \text{ind}_r\, a, \mod \phi(p).$$

To prove i, from which ii at once follows, let

$$\text{ind}_r\, a = i_1, \quad \text{ind}_r\, b = i_2, \quad \text{ind}_r\, ab = i.$$

Then $\quad a \equiv r^{i_1}, \mod p, \quad b \equiv r^{i_2}, \mod p, \quad ab \equiv r^{i}, \mod p,$

and hence $\quad r^{i} \equiv r^{i_1+i_2}, \mod p.$

Therefore by Th. 24 $\quad i \equiv i_1 + i_2, \mod \phi(p)$;

that is $\quad \text{ind}_r\, ab \equiv \text{ind}_r\, a + \text{ind}_r\, b, \mod \phi(p).$

We observe that in every system $\text{ind}_r\, 1 \equiv 0$. By means of the following tables, we can verify these results and illustrate the use of indices. Table A gives for the modulus 13 the index to the base 2 of each integer of a reduced residue system, and Table B gives the residue corresponding to any index for the same base and modulus. It is evident that two integers congruent to each other, mod p, have the same index in any system of indices, mod p.

Jacobi has given in his Canon Arithmeticus, Berlin, 1839, such tables for all primes less than 1000. See also for such tables for all numbers less than 100 that have primitive roots Wertheim, Elemente der Zahlentheorie, also Cahen for list of primitive roots and tables of indices for every prime number less than 200.

A.

Residue...	1	2	3	4	5	6	7	8	9	10	11	12
Index......	0	1	4	2	9	5	11	3	8	10	7	6

B.

Index......	0	1	2	3	4	5	6	7	8	9	10	11
Residue...	1	2	4	8	3	6	12	11	9	5	10	7

Ex. Using the above tables, where the modulus is 13 and the base 2, we have $\text{ind}_2 5 = 9$, $\text{ind}_2 9 = 8$.

Therefore $\text{ind}_2 45 \equiv \text{ind}_2 5 + \text{ind}_2 9 \equiv 17$, mod 12, and hence $\text{ind}_2 45 = 5$. This result may be verified by observing that

$$45 \equiv 6, \text{ mod } 13,$$

whence $$\text{ind}_2 45 \equiv \text{ind}_2 6, \text{ mod } 12;$$

that is, $$\text{ind}_2 45 = 5.$$

We can pass from a system of indices with base r_1, mod p, to one with the base r_2 and the same modulus by a process similar to that employed in passing from one system of logarithms to another.

Let p be the modulus, a any integer not divisible by p, and

$$i_1 = \text{ind}_{r_1} a, \quad i_2 = \text{ind}_{r_2} a, \quad i = \text{ind}_{r_2} r_1.$$

Then we have $$a \equiv r_1^{i_1}, \text{ mod } p, \qquad 2)$$

and also $$a \equiv r_2^{i_2}, \text{ mod } p.$$

But $$r_1 \equiv r_2^{i}, \text{ mod } p, \qquad 3)$$

and hence from 2) and 3) it follows that

$$a \equiv r_2^{ii_1}, \text{ mod } p,$$

whence $$\text{ind}_{r_2} a \equiv ii_1, \text{ mod } \phi(p);$$

that is, $$\text{ind}_{r_2} a \equiv \text{ind}_{r_2} r_1 \cdot \text{ind}_{r_1} a, \text{ mod } \phi(p). \qquad 4)$$

Therefore, *to obtain a system of indices to the base r_2 for a given modulus p, from one to the base r_1, we have only to multiply each index of the latter system by $\text{ind}_{r_2} r_1$ and take the smallest positive residue of the products with respect to the modulus $\phi(p)$.*

If r_1, r_2 be any two primitive roots of p, then

$$\text{ind}_{r_1} r_2 \cdot \text{ind}_{r_2} r_1 \equiv 1, \text{ mod } \phi(p).$$

This follows at once from 4) by putting $a = r_2$.

Ex. To obtain for the modulus 13 a system of indices to the base 7 from one to the base 2, we have first to find $\text{ind}_7\, 2$.

We have $$\text{ind}_2 7 \cdot \text{ind}_7 2 \equiv 1, \text{ mod } 12,$$

and from table A $$\text{ind}_2 7 = 11,$$

whence $$11\, \text{ind}_7 2 \equiv 1, \text{ mod } 12.$$

Therefore $$\text{ind}_7 2 = 11.$$

Multiplying by 11 each index to the base 2 and taking the least positive residues of these products with respect to the modulus 12, we obtain for the modulus 13 the following system of indices to the base 7.

Residue...	1	2	3	4	5	6	7	8	9	10	11	12
Index......	0	11	8	10	3	7	1	9	4	2	5	6

THEOREM 28. *If* $\text{ind}_r a$, *mod* p, *be* i *and* d *be the greatest common divisor of* i *and* $p-1$, *then* a *appertains to the exponent* $(p-1)/d$.

We have $$a \equiv r^i, \text{ mod } p.$$

We ask what is the smallest value of m for which

$$a^m \equiv r^{mi} \equiv 1, \text{ mod } p. \qquad 5)$$

By Th. 24 we must have

$$mi \equiv 0, \text{ mod } p-1,$$

and hence $$m\frac{i}{d} \equiv 0, \text{ mod } \frac{p-1}{d}. \qquad 6)$$

But i/d is prime to $(p-1)/d$ and $(p-1)/d$ is therefore the smallest value of m greater than zero, that will satisfy 6). Hence $(p-1)/d$ is the smallest value of m that will satisfy 5); that is, a appertains, mod p, to the exponent $(p-1)/d$.

Cor. *If* r *be a primitive root of* p, *then the* $\phi(p-1)$ *primitive roots of* p *are those* $\phi(p-1)$ *incongruent powers of* r *whose exponents are prime to* $p-1$.

Ex. One primitive root of 13 is 2. Hence the 4, $=\phi(12)$, primitive roots of 13 are $2, 2^5, 2^7, 2^{11}$.

§ 31. Solution of Congruences by means of Indices.

If we have a table of indices to any base for a given modulus p, we can solve any congruence of the form

$$ax \equiv b, \bmod p, \tag{1}$$

where a is not divisible by p;
for from 1) it follows that

$$\text{ind}\, a + \text{ind}\, x \equiv \text{ind}\, b, \bmod \phi(p),$$

which gives

$$\text{ind}\, x \equiv \text{ind}\, b - \text{ind}\, a, \bmod \phi(p),$$

from which we can determine ind x and then x.

Ex. From the congruence

$$7x \equiv 4, \bmod 13,$$

we have $\quad \text{ind}\, x \equiv \text{ind}\, 4 - \text{ind}\, 7 \equiv 2 - 11 \equiv -9, \bmod 12.$

Hence $\quad \text{ind}\, x = 3,$

and therefore $\quad x \equiv 8, \bmod 13.$

The solution of the congruence

$$ax^n \equiv b, \bmod p, \tag{2}$$

where a is not divisible by p, can be reduced by the use of indices to the solution of a congruence of the first degree, mod $\phi(p)$.

For from 2) we have

$$\text{ind}\, a + n\, \text{ind}\, x \equiv \text{ind}\, b, \bmod \phi(p),$$

and hence

$$n\, \text{ind}\, x \equiv \text{ind}\, b - \text{ind}\, a, \bmod \phi(p), \tag{3}$$

that is, a congruence of the first degree in the unknown ind x. By Th. 12 the necessary and sufficient condition that 3) shall be solvable is that ind b — ind a shall be divisible by the greatest common divisor, d, of n and $\phi(p)$. When this condition is satisfied 3) gives $|d|$ values of ind x, corresponding to which we find $|d|$ values of x, that satisfy 2) and are incongruent, mod p.

In the following examples 2 is understood throughout to be the base of the system of indices employed, tables A and B being used.

Ex. 1. From the congruence

$$5x^7 \equiv 4, \bmod 13,$$

we have $\quad 7\, \text{ind}\, x \equiv \text{ind}\, 4 - \text{ind}\, 5 \equiv 2 - 9 \equiv -7, \bmod 12.$

whence, upon removal of the factor 7, that is prime to the modulus 12, we have

$$\text{ind}\, x \equiv -1, \bmod 12.$$

Therefore $\text{ind}\, x = 11,$

and $x \equiv 7, \text{ mod } 13.$

Ex. 2. From the congruence

$$4x^{15} \equiv 5, \text{ mod } 13, \qquad 4)$$

we have $15 \text{ ind}\, x \equiv \text{ind}\, 5 - \text{ind}\, 4 \equiv 9 - 2 \equiv 7, \text{ mod } 12.$

The greatest common divisor of 15 and 12 does not divide 7. Hence 4) has no roots.

Ex. 3. From the congruence

$$x^9 \equiv 8, \text{ mod } 13,$$

we have $9 \text{ ind}\, x \equiv \text{ind}\, 8 \equiv 3, \text{ mod } 12. \qquad 5)$

The greatest common divisor of 9 and 12 is 3 and it divides the second member, 3, of 5). Hence 5) has 3 roots, that we find by the method of Th. 12.

From 5) we have $3 \text{ ind}\, x \equiv 1, \text{ mod } 4,$

whence $\text{ind}\, x \equiv 3, \text{ mod } 4,$

and consequently $\text{ind}\, x \equiv 3, 7, 11, \text{ mod } 12.$

Therefore $\text{ind}\, x = 3, 7, \text{ or } 11;$

and $x \equiv 8, 11, \text{ or } 7, \text{ mod } 13.$

§ 32. Binomial Congruences.

The subject of power residues and in particular that portion relating to primitive roots may be treated from another point of view, that of the binomial congruence

$$x^n - 1 \equiv 0, \text{ mod } p.^{1} \qquad 1)$$

We see by § 25 that all roots of 1) are roots of the congruence

$$\phi(x) \equiv 0, \text{ mod } p,$$

where $\phi(x)$ is the greatest common divisor, mod p, of $x^n - 1$ and $x^{p-1} - 1$.

It is easily seen that

$$\phi(x) = x^d - 1,$$

where d is the positive greatest common divisor of n and $p - 1$.

The congruence

$$x^n - 1 \equiv 0, \text{ mod } p,$$

[1] Cahen: p. 77. Bachmann: Niedere Zahlentheorie, p. 318. H. J. S. Smith: pp. 140–145.

has therefore d incongruent roots, that are the roots of

$$x^d - 1 \equiv 0, \bmod p. \qquad 2)$$

We can now confine ourselves to congruences of the form 2), where d is a divisor of $p-1$.

The roots of 1) fall into two classes, those which satisfy no congruence of the same form and of lower degree, these being called *primitive* roots, and those which satisfy congruences of this form and of lower degree, these being called *imprimitive* roots.

It is easily seen that every integer that is a root of a congruence

$$x^{d_1} - 1 \equiv 0, \bmod p, \qquad 3)$$

where d_1 is a divisor of d, is also a root of 2), and conversely that every imprimitive root of 2) is the root of a congruence of the form 3), where d_1 is a divisor of d smaller than d.

The primitive roots of 2) are evidently, in the language of power residues, those integers that appertain to the exponent d, mod p. They are evidently $\phi(d)$ in number (Th. 27). The primitive roots of p are the primitive roots of the congruence

$$x^{p-1} - 1 \equiv 0, \bmod p.$$

The product of any number of roots of 2) is a root of 2) and, in particular, any positive integral power of a root of 2) is a root of 2).

If r be any primitive root of 2), then the d roots of 2) are by Th. 23

$$1, r, r^2, \cdots, r^{d-1}.$$

If a_1, a_2 be roots of the congruences

$$x^{d_1} - 1 \equiv 0, \bmod p, \qquad 3)$$

and

$$x^{d_2} - 1 \equiv 0, \bmod p, \qquad 4)$$

respectively, then $a_1 a_2$ is a root of the congruence

$$x^{d_1 d_2} - 1 \equiv 0, \bmod p. \qquad 5)$$

In particular, if a_1, a_2 be primitive roots of 3) and 4) respectively and d_1, d_2 be prime to each other, then a_1a_2 is a primitive root of 5) (Th. 26).

The close analogy between the theory of binomial congruences and that of binomial equations will be easily seen.

§ 33. **Determination of a Primitive Root of a Given Prime Number.**[1]

The method, which is due to Gauss, depends upon the determination of a series of integers each of which appertains to a higher exponent with respect to the given prime, p, than any of the preceding ones.

In such a series we must evidently reach an integer which appertains to the exponent $p-1$, mod p; that is, which is a primitive root of p.

Take any positive integer, a_1, less than p and greater than 1, and form a complete system of its power residues, mod p.

Let us suppose that a_1 appertains to the exponent t_1, mod p. If $t_1 = p-1$, then a_1 is the primitive root required.

If $t_1 \neq p-1$, it is evident that none of the power residues of a_1 can be a primitive root of p, for they are the roots of the congruence

$$x^{t_1} - 1 \equiv 0, \text{ mod } p, \qquad 1)$$

and hence appertain, mod p, to exponents not greater than t_1.

Suppose that $t_1 \neq p-1$. We proceed to determine an integer appertaining, mod p, to an exponent greater than t_1. Select any positive integer, a_2, less than p and not contained among the power residues of a_1, mod p, and form a complete system of its power residues, mod p. Let t_2 be the exponent to which a_2 appertains, mod p. If $t_2 = p-1$, a_2 is a primitive root of p and the problem is solved. Suppose that $t_2 \neq p-1$; then t_2 can not be a divisor of t_1, for a_2 would in that case be a root of the congruence 1) and hence a power residue of a_1, mod p, which is contrary to our hypothesis.

If t_2 be a multiple of t_1 but $\neq p-1$, we have found an integer,

[1] Gauss: Disq. Arith., Art. 73 Cahen: pp. 90–95. Mathews: pp. 20–22. H. J. S. Smith: pp. 49–54.

a_2, appertaining to a higher exponent than a_1, mod p, although not a primitive root of p. We then select a positive integer less than p and not contained among the power residues of a_2, form its power residues, mod p, and proceed as before. Suppose, however, that t_2 is not a multiple of t_1, and let m be the least common multiple of t_1 and t_2. It is evident that m is greater than t_1, since t_2 is not a divisor of t_1. We shall show how to determine an integer appertaining to the exponent m, mod p.

We first resolve m into two factors, m_1, m_2, prime to each other and divisors of t_1 and t_2 respectively. This may be accomplished as follows.

Let p_1 be a prime that occurs to the power e_1 as a factor of t_1 and to the power e_2 as a factor of t_2. We take $p_1^{e_1}$ as a factor of m_1, or $p_1^{e_2}$ as a factor of m_2, according as e_1 is greater or less than e_2. If $e_1 = e_2$, then $p_1^{e_1}$ may be taken as a factor of either m_1 or m_2. We have then $m = m_1 m_2 = t_1/d_1 \cdot t_2/d_2$, where d_1, d_2 are respectively the product of primes that occur in the case of d_1 to a lower power in t_1 than in t_2, and in the case of d_2 to a lower power in t_2 than in t_1.

Consider now the residues, mod p, of $a_1^{d_1}$, and $a_2^{d_2}$. These integers appertain respectively to the exponents t_1/d_1, t_2/d_2, that are prime to each other.

Hence their product $a_1^{d_1} a_2^{d_2}$ appertains to the exponent m, that is the product of these exponents (Th. 26).

Ex. To find a primitive root of 157. The power residues of 2, mod 157, are

2,	4,	8,	16,	32,	64,	128,	99,	41,	82,
7,	14,	28,	56	112,	67,	134,	111,	65,	130,
103,	49,	98,	39,	78,	156,				
−2,	−4,	−8,	−16,	−32,	−64,	−128,	−99,	−41,	−82,
−7,	−14,	−28,	−56,	−112,	−67,	−134,	−111,	−65,	−130,
−103,	−49,	−98,	−39,	−78,	$-156 \equiv 1$.				

The work is shortened by observing that the residue of 2^{26} is -1, and consequently the remaining 26 residues are the negatives of the first 26. We see that 2 appertains to the exponent 52, mod 157. The integer 3, not being contained among the residues of 2, we form its power residues, mod 157, and find that it appertains to the exponent 78.

We have $$52 = 2^2 \cdot 13,$$
and $$78 = 2 \cdot 3 \cdot 13.$$

The least common multiple of 52 and 78 is 156, that can be resolved into two factors prime to each other and divisors of 52 and 78 respectively.

Thus $$156 = \frac{2^2 \cdot 13}{13} \times \frac{2 \cdot 3 \cdot 13}{2} = \frac{52}{13} \times \frac{78}{2}.$$

The integers 2^{13} and 3^2 appertain to the exponents $\frac{52}{13}$ and $\frac{78}{2}$ respectively, and hence their product $2^{13}3^2$ appertains to the exponent 156; that is, $2^{13}3^2$ is a primitive root of 157. But we have seen that

$$2^{13} \equiv 28, \text{ mod } 157.$$

Hence $$2^{13} \cdot 3^2 \equiv 28 \cdot 9 \equiv 252 \equiv 55, \text{ mod } 157.$$

We have therefore 55 as a primitive root of 157.

We could have resolved 156 in another way, since 13 occurs to the same power in 52 and 78.

Thus $$156 = \frac{2^2 \cdot 13}{1} \times \frac{2 \cdot 3 \cdot 13}{2 \cdot 13} = \frac{52}{1} \times \frac{78}{26}.$$

Then 2 and 3^{26} appertain to the exponents 52 and 3 respectively, and their product $2 \cdot 3^{26}$ appertains to the exponent 156; that is, $2 \cdot 3^{26}$ is a primitive root of 157.

We have $$2 \cdot 3^{26} \equiv 2 \cdot 144 \equiv 288 \equiv 131, \text{ mod } 157,$$

and hence 131 is a primitive root of 157. For this example and a table of the power residues of 55, mod 157, see Cahen: pp. 92, 93.

§ 34. The Congruence $x^n \equiv b$, mod p. Euler's Criterion.

The congruence

$$a_1 x^n \equiv b_1, \text{ mod } p,$$

where a_1 is not divisible by p, can always be reduced to the form

$$x^n \equiv b, \text{ mod } p,$$

and in this form it has a special interest. In what follows we consider

$$b \not\equiv 0, \text{ mod } p.$$

From what has been said in § 31, the truth of the following theorem is at once evident.

Theorem 29. *The necessary and sufficient condition that the congruence* $$x^n \equiv b, \text{ mod } p, \qquad 1)$$

shall be solvable, is that ind b *shall be divisible by the greatest common divisor,* d*, of* n *and* $\phi(p)$*; this condition being satisfied the congruence has exactly* $|d|$ *incongruent roots.*

See § 31, Ex. 3.

Since ind b varies with the primitive root taken as base of the system of indices used, this condition for the solvability of 1) appears to depend upon the primitive root selected.

It is evident, however, that in reality the solvability of 1) is in no way dependent upon this selection, and it must be possible therefore to find a criterion for the solvability of this congruence that is independent of indices.

Such a criterion is that first given by Euler and known as Euler's criterion. It is contained in the following theorem.

THEOREM 30. *If* d *be the positive greatest common divisor of* n *and* $\phi(p)$*, the necessary and sufficient condition that the congruence*

$$x^n \equiv b, \bmod p, \tag{2}$$

shall be solvable is

$$b^{\phi(p)/d} \equiv 1, \bmod p. \tag{3}$$

This condition being satisfied, the congruence has exactly d *incongruent roots.*

Let r be any primitive root of p, and let

$$\text{ind}_r\, b = c.$$

Suppose 2) to be solvable, then c is divisible by d.

Let

$$c = md.$$

Then

$$b \equiv r^{md}, \bmod p,$$

and

$$b^{\phi(p)/d} \equiv r^{m \cdot \phi(p)}, \bmod p,$$

whence

$$b^{\phi(p)/d} \equiv 1, \bmod p.$$

Therefore 3) is a necessary condition for the solvability of 2).

Conversely, if b satisfy 3), the index of b in every system of indices, mod p, must be divisible by d; for, if

$$b \equiv r^c, \bmod p,$$

then

$$b^{\phi(p)/d} \equiv r^{c\phi(p)/d}, \bmod p,$$

and hence $$r^{c\phi(p)/d} \equiv 1, \text{ mod } p.$$

Since r, being a primitive root of p, appertains to the exponent $\phi(p)$, $c\phi(p)/d$ must be divisible by $\phi(p)$.

Therefore c/d is an integer; that is, c is divisible by d. Hence 3) is a sufficient as well as necessary condition for the solvability of 2). That the congruence when solvable has d roots is evident from the preceding paragraph.

All incongruent integers b, for which the congruence 2) is solvable may be obtained by observing that they are the roots of the congruence

$$x^{\phi(p)/d} \equiv 1, \text{ mod } p. \qquad 4)$$

This congruence has $\phi(p)/d$ incongruent roots, since $\phi(p)/d$ is a divisor of $\phi(p)$. These roots are the incongruent, mod p, values of b for which 2) is solvable. Such numbers congruent to the nth power of an integer, mod p, are called the n-ic residues of p, and we have the following theorem.

THEOREM 31. *The number of incongruent n-ic residues, mod p, is $\phi(p)/d$, where d is the positive greatest common divisor of n and $\phi(p)$, and these residues are the roots of the congruence*

$$x^{\phi(p)/d} \equiv 1, \text{ mod } p.$$

Thus, if $p = 7$, we have for

$n=2$, 3 incongruent quadratic residues of 7,

$n=3$, 2 incongruent cubic residues of 7,

$n=4$, 3 incongruent biquadratic residues of 7,

$n=5$, 6 incongruent quintic residues of 7,

$n=6$, 1 incongruent sextic residue of 7,

and so on.

We may obtain the above results and also the residues themselves by raising each number of a reduced residue system, mod p, to the nth power and determining the number of the reduced residue system to which each of these nth powers is congruent, mod p. Thus for $p=7$, we take as a reduced residue system 1, 2, 3, 4, 5, 6, and have for

$$\left.\begin{array}{lllllll} n=2, & 1^2\equiv 1, & 2^2\equiv 4, & 3^2\equiv 2, & 4^2\equiv 2, & 5^2\equiv 4, & 6^2\equiv 1,\\ n=3, & 1^3\equiv 1, & 2^3\equiv 1, & 3^3\equiv 6, & 4^3\equiv 1, & 5^3\equiv 6, & 6^3\equiv 6,\\ n=4, & 1^4\equiv 1, & 2^4\equiv 2, & 3^4\equiv 4, & 4^4\equiv 4, & 5^4\equiv 2, & 6^4\equiv 1,\\ n=5, & 1^5\equiv 1, & 2^5\equiv 4, & 3^5\equiv 5, & 4^5\equiv 2, & 5^5\equiv 3, & 6^5\equiv 6,\\ n=6, & 1^6\equiv 1, & 2^6\equiv 1, & 3^6\equiv 1, & 4^6\equiv 1, & 5^6\equiv 1, & 6^6\equiv 1, \end{array}\right\}\bmod 7.$$

Hence the incongruent quadratic residues of 7 are 1, 2 and 4, the cubic residues 1 and 6, the biquadratic residues 1, 2 and 4, the quintic residues 1, 2, 3, 4, 5 and 6, the sextic residue 1.

An integer is therefore a quadratic residue of 7 when and only when it is congruent to one of the integers 1, 2, 4, mod 7, and likewise for the other values of n.

In the next chapter we shall discuss fully the subject of quadratic residues.

Investigations concerning the properties of cubic and biquadratic residues have led to important developments in the theory of numbers, that will be noticed later.

EXAMPLES.

1. Show that $x^{13}-x$ is divisible by 2730, x being any integer.

2. If x be a prime greater than 13, $x^{12}-1$ is divisible by 21840.

3. If p be a prime and a prime to p, then either $a^{\frac{p(p-1)}{2}}-1$ or $a^{\frac{p(p-1)}{2}}+1$ is divisible by p^2.

4. No number of form m^4+4 except 5 is prime. $m\not\equiv 0$, mod 5.

5. The product of numbers of the form $mx+1$ is a number of the same form.

6. The cube of any integer not divisible by 3 is congruent to ± 1, mod 9.

7. Solve the congruences

a) $$x^3-8x+1\equiv 0, \bmod 5.$$

b) $$x^4+6x^3-8x^2+13x+5\equiv 0, \bmod 7.$$

c) $$x^4+2x^3-13x^2+5x+13\equiv 0, \bmod 11.$$

8. The congruence

$$8x^5+4x^4-3x^3+3x^2+3x+6\equiv 0, \bmod 7,$$

has a multiple root; solve the congruence.

9. Solve the system of congruences

$$\left.\begin{aligned} 3x-4y+5z-9u &\equiv 1 \\ 2x+3y+4z+5u &\equiv 8 \\ x+5y+6z+2u &\equiv 1 \\ 7x-3y-10z+2u &\equiv 10 \end{aligned}\right\}, \bmod 15.$$

10. Solve the congruence

$$x^5-8x^4+5x^3-5x^2+4x+3\equiv 0, \bmod 27.$$

11. Solve the congruence

$$x^5-6x^4+8x^3-4x^2+7x+2\equiv 0, \bmod 2[illegible].$$

12. Prove Th. 30 without the use of indices.

13. Find the prime polynomials of the third degree, mod 5.

14. If a appertain to the exponent t_a, mod p, then

$$1+a+a^2+\cdots+a^{t_a-1}\equiv 0, \bmod p,$$

(Gauss: Disq. Arith., Art. 79.)

15. The product of all incongruent primitive roots, mod p, is congruent to 1, mod p, except when $p=3$. (*Ibid.*: Art. 80.)

16. If $r_1, r_2, \cdots, r_{\phi(m)}$ be a reduced residue system, mod m, then all primes are contained in the forms

$$km+r_1,\ km+r_2,\ \cdots,\ km+r_{\phi(m)}.$$

17. If p be a prime of the form $4n-1$ and a appertain, mod p, to the exponent $(p-1)/2$, then $-a$ is primitive root of p.

18. Use theorem in Ex. 17 to determine a primitive root of 191. (Cahen: p. 94.)

19. Determine a primitive root of 73 (Gauss: Disq. Arith., Art. 74), also one of 97 (Mathews: p. 20).

20. If p be a prime and $r_1, r_2, \cdots, r_{\phi(p)}$ a reduced residue system, mod p, every rational integral symmetric function of the r's, whose degree is not a multiple of $\phi(p)$, is divisible by p. (Cahen: p. 109.)

21. Solve the congruences

a) $$x^{20}\equiv 3, \bmod 13.$$

b) $$x^9\equiv 10, \bmod 13.$$

CHAPTER IV.

THE RATIONAL REALM.

QUADRATIC RESIDUES.[1]

§ 1. The General Congruence of the Second Degree with One Unknown.

The most general congruence of the second degree with one unknown has the form

$$ax^2 + bx + c \equiv 0, \text{ mod } m. \qquad 1)$$

We have seen (Chap. III, § 27) that the solution of 1) when m is a composite number can be reduced to the solution of a system of congruences of the same form but with prime moduli. We shall therefore confine ourselves to the case in which m is a prime number, p, and furthermore, since for $p=2$ the congruence is easily solvable by trial, we shall suppose p odd.

We consider then the congruence

$$ax^2 + bx + c \equiv 0, \text{ mod } p, \qquad 2)$$

where a is not divisible by the odd prime p, for if it were, the congruence would not be of the second degree. Multiplying 2) by the reciprocal, a_1, mod p, of a, we obtain the congruence

$$x^2 + a_1bx + a_1c \equiv 0, \text{ mod } p. \qquad 3)$$

If now the coefficient of x in 3) be not even, we make it so by putting a_1b+p for a_1b. Having done this, if necessary, 3) is transformed into the equivalent congruence

$$x^2 + 2b_1x + c_1 \equiv 0, \text{ mod } p. \qquad 4)$$

Adding b_1^2 to both members of 4), we obtain

$$(x+b_1)^2 \equiv b_1^2 - c_1, \text{ mod } p,$$

or putting

$$x + b_1 \equiv z, \text{ mod } p, \qquad 5)$$

$$b_1^2 - c_1 \equiv d, \text{ mod } p,$$

[1] Gauss: Disq. Arith., pp. 73–119. Wertheim: pp. 170–236. Cahen: pp. 113–143. Bachmann: Niedere Zahlentheorie: pp. 180–317. Dirichlet-Dedekind: pp. 75–127.

we see that the solution of 2) can be reduced to the solution of a binominal congruence

$$z^2 \equiv d, \text{ mod } p. \qquad 6)$$

If

$$d \not\equiv 0, \text{ mod } p, \qquad 7)$$

the congruence 6) has either *no* roots or two *incongruent* roots, for if r be a root, then $-r$ is also a root, and if

$$r \equiv -r, \text{ mod } p,$$

then

$$2r \equiv 0, \text{ mod } p,$$

and hence

$$r \equiv 0, \text{ mod } p,$$

which is impossible from 7).

The solutions of 4), or what is the same thing 3), being connected with those of 6) by the relation 5), we see that 4) has two incongruent roots or no roots according as 6) has two incongruent or no roots.

If

$$d \equiv 0, \text{ mod } p,$$

then 6) has the two equal roots

$$z \equiv 0, \text{ mod } p,$$

and 4) has the two equal roots[1]

$$x \equiv -b_1, \text{ mod } p,$$

$x^2 + 2b_1x + c_1$ being a perfect square, mod p. The solutions in the case of equal roots being obvious, we shall exclude this case and confine ourselves therefore to the consideration of binomial congruences of the form 6), where

$$d \not\equiv 0, \text{ mod } p.$$

The analogy shown here between quadratic equations and congruences of the same degree with prime modulus should be noticed, the vanishing of the discriminant $b^2 - 4ac$ of $ax^2 + bx + c$ being in the one case the condition that the equation

$$ax^2 + bx + c = 0,$$

shall have equal roots, and the divisibility of $b^2 - 4ac$ by the modulus being in the other case the condition that the congruence

[1] Wertheim: p. 170.

$$ax^2 + bx + c \equiv 0, \text{ mod } p,$$

shall have equal roots.

Ex. Let $$5x^2 - 11x - 12 \equiv 0, \text{ mod } 23,$$

be the proposed congruence. Multiplying it by 14, the reciprocal, mod 23, of 5, we obtain the equivalent congruence.

$$70x^2 - 154x - 168 \equiv 0, \text{ mod } 23,$$

or $$x^2 - 16x - 7 \equiv 0, \text{ mod } 23,$$

or $$(x-8)^2 \equiv 2, \text{ mod } 23.$$

Putting $$x - 8 \equiv z, \text{ mod } 23, \tag{8}$$

we have $$z^2 \equiv 2, \text{ mod } 23,$$

which has the roots $$z \equiv 5 \text{ or } -5, \text{ mod } 23.$$

These substituted in 8) give the two roots of the original congruence

$$x \equiv 13 \text{ or } 3, \text{ mod } 23.$$

§ 2. Quadratic Residues and Non-residues.

An integer, a, prime to the modulus m, is said to be a quadratic residue or non-residue of m, according as the congruence

$$x^2 \equiv a, \text{ mod } m,$$

has or has not roots; that is, a is said to be a quadratic residue of m, if it be a residue, mod m, of some square number, and a quadratic non-residue of m, if it be a residue, mod m, of no square number.

Ex. 1. The congruence $x^2 \equiv 2, \text{ mod } 7$,
has the roots 3 and -3; hence 2 is a quadratic residue of 7.

Ex. 2. The congruence $x^2 \equiv 5, \text{ mod } 7$,
has no roots, as may be seen by trying the integers -3, -2, -1, 0, 1, 2, 3 (also see Chap. III, § 34); hence 5 is a quadratic non-residue of 7.

If there be no danger of misunderstanding, the word quadratic is omitted. The behavior of the integer a in this relation is called its *quadratic character with respect to the modulus m.* It is evident that all integers belonging to the same residue class, mod m, have the same quadratic character with respect to m. We have now two principal questions to answer concerning the congruence

$$x^2 \equiv a, \text{ mod } m.$$

I. *What integers are quadratic residues of a given modulus m?*

II. *Of what moduli is a given integer, a, a quadratic residue?*

We shall confine ourselves now to the case in which m is a prime, p. Furthermore, we may suppose p to be odd, since the case $p=2$ is at once disposed of by observing that all odd integers are quadratic residues of 2, and all even integers, being not prime to 2, are excluded from consideration. For convenience, we also suppose p to be positive.

We have as a special case of Th. 30, Chap. III, the following:

Euler's Criterion.

THEOREM 1. *The necessary and sufficient condition that a shall be a quadratic residue of p; that is, that the congruence*

$$x^2 \equiv a, \bmod p,$$

shall have roots, is $\quad a^{(p-1)/2} \equiv 1, \bmod p.$

COR. 1. *The integer a is a quadratic residue or non-residue of p according as we have*

$$a^{(p-1)/2} \equiv 1, \text{ or } -1, \bmod p;$$

for since $\quad a^{p-1} - 1 \equiv 0, \bmod p,$

then $\quad (a^{(p-1)/2} - 1)(a^{(p-1)/2} + 1) \equiv 0, \bmod p;$

whence it follows that either

$$a^{(p-1)/2} - 1 \equiv 0, \bmod p,$$

or $$a^{(p-1)/2} + 1 \equiv 0, \bmod p.$$

Therefore if $a^{(p-1)/2} \equiv 1, \bmod p$, a is a quadratic residue of p, and if $a^{(p-1)/2} \equiv -1, \bmod p$, a is a quadratic non-residue of p.

COR. 2. *The product of two quadratic residues or of two quadratic non-residues of p is a quadratic residue of p, and the product of a quadratic residue and a quadratic non-residue of p is a quadratic non-residue of p.*

Let a_1, a_2 be quadratic residues, and a_3, a_4 quadratic non-residues of p.

Then since $\quad a_1^{(p-1)/2} \equiv 1, \bmod p,$

and $$a_2^{(p-1)/2} \equiv 1, \bmod p,$$

it follows that $$(a_1a_2)^{(p-1)/2} \equiv 1, \bmod p.$$

Hence a_1a_2 is a quadratic residue of p.

Since $$a_3^{(p-1)/2} \equiv -1, \bmod p,$$

and $$a_4^{(p-1)/2} \equiv -1, \bmod p,$$

it follows that $$(a_3a_4)^{(p-1)/2} \equiv 1, \bmod p.$$

Hence a_3a_4 is a quadratic residue of p.

Since $$a_1^{(p-1)/2} \equiv 1, \bmod p,$$

and $$a_3^{(p-1)/2} \equiv -1, \bmod p,$$

it follows that $$(a_1a_3)^{(p-1)/2} \equiv -1, \bmod p.$$

Hence a_1a_3 is a quadratic non-residue of p. From Cor. 2 follows at once:

Cor. 3. *The product of several integers is a quadratic residue or non-residue of p, according as an even or odd number of the integers are quadratic non-residues of p.*

It is therefore only necessary to be able to determine the quadratic character of all prime numbers with respect to any modulus p.

Ex. 1. $$x^2 \equiv 3, \bmod 13. \qquad 1)$$

We have $$3^{(13-1)/2} = 3^6 \equiv 1, \bmod 13.$$

Hence 3 is a quadratic residue of 13, the roots of 1) being 4 and -4.

Ex. 2. $$x^2 \equiv 7, \bmod 13.$$

We have $$7^{(13-1)/2} = (7^2)^3 \equiv (-3)^3 \equiv -1, \bmod 13.$$

Hence 7 is a quadratic non-residue of 13.

We can verify the result by substituting the numbers, ± 1, ± 2, ± 3, ± 4, ± 5, ± 6, which give

$$\left.\begin{matrix} 1 \not\equiv 7 & 9 \not\equiv 7 & 25 \not\equiv 7 \\ 4 \not\equiv 7 & 16 \not\equiv 7 & 36 \not\equiv 7 \end{matrix}\right\}, \bmod 13.$$

This also follows from the fact that $\text{ind}_2\, 7$, mod 13, is not divisible by 2.

Ex. 3. Since $$21 = 3 \cdot 7$$

and 3 is a residue of 13, and 7 a non-residue of 13, 21 is by Cor. 2 a non-residue of 13, which is verified by

$$\begin{aligned} 21^{(13-1)/2} &\equiv (-5)^6, \bmod 13, \\ &\equiv ((-5)^2)^3 \equiv (-1)^3 \equiv -1, \bmod 13. \end{aligned}$$

§ 3. Determination of the Quadratic Residues and Non-residues of a Given Odd Prime Modulus.

THEOREM 2. *If p be an odd prime, one half the integers of a reduced residue system, mod p, are quadratic residues of p, and the other half non-residues.*

First Proof:

Take as a reduced residue system, mod p, the integers

$$-\frac{p-1}{2}, -\frac{p-3}{2}, \ldots, -2, -1, 1, 2, \ldots, \frac{p-3}{2}, \frac{p-1}{2} \qquad 1)$$

The squares of the integers

$$1, 2, 3, \ldots, \frac{p-3}{2}, \frac{p-1}{2} \qquad 2)$$

are incongruent each to each, mod p, for if $(p-r)/2$ and $(p-s)/2$ be any two of these integers, r and s being integers of the series $1, 3, \cdots, p-2$, and unequal, and

$$\left(\frac{p-r}{2}\right)^2 \equiv \left(\frac{p-s}{2}\right)^2, \text{ mod } p,$$

then $$\left(\frac{p-r}{2}+\frac{p-s}{2}\right)\left(\frac{p-r}{2}-\frac{p-s}{2}\right) \equiv 0, \text{ mod } p,$$

whence either $$\frac{p-r}{2}+\frac{p-s}{2} \equiv 0, \text{ mod } p, \qquad 3)$$

or $$\frac{p-r}{2}-\frac{p-s}{2} \equiv 0, \text{ mod } p, \qquad 4)$$

Both 3) and 4) are, however, impossible, since $(p-r)/2$ and $(p-s)/2$ are unequal and both positive and less than $p/2$.

The squares of the $\frac{1}{2}(p-1)$ integers 2) give, therefore, $\frac{1}{2}(p-1)$ incongruent residues, mod p, and these are all the incongruent quadratic residues of p, for the squares of the remaining integers of 1) give evidently the same residues.

Hence the theorem.

Second Proof:

Let r be a primitive root of p. Then

$$r, r^2, \cdots, r^i, \cdots, r^{p-1}$$

is a reduced residue system, mod p.

From Chap. III, Th. 29, it follows at once that every power of r with an even exponent is a residue of p, and every power of r with an odd exponent is a non-residue.

Hence there are $\frac{1}{2}(p-1)$ residues of p and $\frac{1}{2}(p-1)$ non-residues of p.

We can express this also by saying that those of the integers of a reduced residue system which have even indices are residues of p, while those which have odd indices are non-residues. The residues of any prime for which we have a table of indices can evidently be easily thus determined.

Th. 1, Cor. 3, can be deduced from the second proof given above in a very elegant manner; for if

$$a = a_1 a_2 \cdots a_n,$$

then $\qquad \operatorname{ind} a \equiv \operatorname{ind} a_1 + \operatorname{ind} a_2 + \cdots + \operatorname{ind} a_n, \bmod \phi(p),$

and hence, since $\phi(p)$ is even, ind a is odd or even according as ind a_1 + ind a_2 + $\cdots$ + ind a_n is odd or even. But ind a_1 + ind a_2 + $\cdots$ + ind a_n, and hence ind a, is odd or even according as an odd or even number of the indices of $a_1, a_2, \cdots, a_n$ are odd. Hence a is a quadratic residue or non-residue of p according as an even or odd number of its factors $a_1, a_2, \cdots, a_n$ are quadratic non-residues of p.

We can now answer fully the first of our two questions concerning the congruence

$$x^2 \equiv a, \bmod p,$$

where p is an odd prime; for suppose that we have any reduced residue system, mod p, and that those residues of this system which are quadratic residues of p, are $r_1, r_2, \cdots, r_{\frac{1}{2}\phi(p)}$ and those which are quadratic non-residues of p are $n_1, n_2, \cdots, n_{\frac{1}{2}\phi(p)}$, this having been determined by any of the methods given above. Then all those and only those integers included in the forms

$$kp + r_1, \; kp + r_2, \cdots, \; kp + r_{\frac{1}{2}\phi(p)}$$

are quadratic residues of p, and all and only those integers included in the forms $kp+n_1,\ kp+n_2, \cdots,\ kp+n_{\frac{1}{2}\phi(p)}$

are quadratic non-residues of p, k taking all integral values.

Ex. 1. Let $p=17$, and take as a reduced residue system,

$$-8, -7, -6, -5, -4, -3, -2, -1, 1, 2, 3, 4, 5, 6, 7, 8$$

We have

$$\left.\begin{array}{l}(\pm 1)^2 \equiv 1,\ (\pm 3)^2 \equiv 9,\ (\pm 5)^2 \equiv 8,\ (\pm 7)^2 \equiv 15, \\ (\pm 2)^2 \equiv 4,\ (\pm 4)^2 \equiv 16,\ (\pm 6)^2 \equiv 2,\ (\pm 8)^2 \equiv 13,\end{array}\right\} \bmod 17.$$

Hence 1, 2, 4, 8, 9, 13, 15, 16 are the incongruent quadratic residues of 17, and all those and only those integers which are included in the forms $17k+1$, $17k+2$, $17k+4$, $17k+8$, $17k+9$, $17k+13$, $17k+15$, $17k+16$, are quadratic residues of 17.

The incongruent quadratic non-residues of 17 are

$$3, 5, 6, 7, 10, 11, 12, 14,$$

and hence all and only those integers which are included in the forms $17k+3$, $17k+5$, $17k+6$, $17k+7$, $17k+10$, $17k+11$, $17k+12$, $17k+14$, are quadratic non-residues of 17.

Ex. 2. Let $$p=13.$$

From table A, Chap. IV, § 30, we see that the indices of 1, 3, 4, 9, 10 and 12 are even, and the indices of 2, 5, 6, 7, 8 and 11 are odd.

Hence 1, 3, 4, 9, 10 and 12 are the incongruent quadratic residues of 13, and 2, 5, 6, 7, 8, and 11 are the incongruent quadratic non-residues of 13.

We see then, as above, that the quadratic residues of 13 are integers of the forms

$$13k+1,\ 13k+3,\ 13k+4,\ 13k+9,\ 13k+10,\ 13k+12,$$

and the quadratic non-residues of 13 of the forms

$$13k+2,\ 13k+5,\ 13k+6,\ 13k+7,\ 13k+8,\ 13k+11.$$

We have now answered fully the first question concerning the congruence $$x^2 \equiv a, \bmod p;$$

that is, we are able, as shown in the two examples above, to give for any value of p a finite system of forms, $kp+r$, where r is a known integer and k any integer, such that all and only those integers obtained from these forms by letting k take all integral values, are quadratic residues of p.

A similar series of forms may, as was shown above, be given for the non-residues of p.

Before considering the second question, that is, of what odd prime moduli is a a quadratic residue, we shall introduce a symbolic notation which will greatly simplify the discussion.

§ 4. **Legendre's Symbol.**

The quadratic character of an integer a with respect to a prime p, can be expressed in a very convenient manner by means of the following symbol introduced by Legendre.

Let (a/p) denote $+1$ or -1, according as a is a quadratic residue or non-residue of p; that is, $(a/p)=1$ denotes that a is a quadratic residue of p and $(a/p)=-1$ denotes that a is a quadratic non-residue of p. In what follows, p is assumed first of all to be odd, and secondly, for the sake of convenience, positive. This last assumption is not necessary, but simply to avoid the trouble of writing $|p|$ when the absolute value of p is to be taken. Combining this with Euler's criterion, we see that

$$\left(\frac{a}{p}\right) \equiv a^{\frac{p-1}{2}}, \text{ mod } p,$$

expresses the quadratic character of a, with respect to p.

From Th. I, Cor. 3, it is evident that

$$\left(\frac{ab \cdots l}{p}\right) = \left(\frac{a}{p}\right)\left(\frac{b}{p}\right)\cdots\left(\frac{l}{p}\right)$$

If

$$a \equiv b, \text{ mod } p,$$

then

$$\left(\frac{a}{p}\right) = \left(\frac{b}{p}\right).$$

Also

$$\left(\frac{a}{p}\right) = \left(\frac{b}{p}\right), \text{ or } \left(\frac{a}{p}\right)\left(\frac{b}{p}\right) = 1,$$

denotes that the quadratic character of a with respect to p is the same as the quadratic character of b with respect to p, and

$$\left(\frac{a}{p}\right) = -\left(\frac{b}{p}\right), \text{ or } \left(\frac{a}{p}\right)\left(\frac{b}{p}\right) = -1,$$

denotes that the quadratic character of a with respect to p is opposite to the quadratic character of b with respect to p.

If $a = k^2 a_1$, then since $(k^2/p) = 1$,

$$\left(\frac{a}{p}\right) = \left(\frac{k^2}{p}\right)\left(\frac{a_1}{p}\right) = \left(\frac{a_1}{p}\right).$$

In determining the value of (a/p) we may therefore suppose all square factors to have been removed from a.

§ 5. Determination of the Odd Prime Moduli of which a Given Integer is a Quadratic Residue.

To answer the second question: of what odd prime moduli is a a quadratic residue, of what a non-residue, we notice first that if

$$a = \pm q_1 q_2 \cdots q_n,$$

where $q_1, q_2, \cdots, q_n$ are the positive prime factors of a we have

$$\left(\frac{a}{p}\right) = \left(\frac{\pm 1}{p}\right)\left(\frac{q_1}{p}\right)\left(\frac{q_2}{p}\right)\cdots\left(\frac{q_n}{p}\right)$$

Hence $(a/p) = 1$ or -1 according as an even or an odd number of the symbols $(\pm 1/p), (q_1/p), \cdots, (q_n/p)$ have the value -1; that is, a will be a quadratic residue of all primes of which an even number or none of the factors $\pm 1, q_1, \cdots, q_n$ are non-residues. To determine for what values of p the value of (a/p) is 1, for what -1, it is therefore only necessary to determine for what values of p the value of each of the symbols in the second member of 1) is $+1$, for what -1. The problem may be reduced therefore to the following three simpler ones:

To determine

1. Of what odd prime moduli -1 is a quadratic residue?
2. Of what odd prime moduli 2 is a quadratic residue?
3. Of what odd prime moduli is another positive odd[1] prime a quadratic residue?

§ 6. Prime Moduli of which -1 is a Quadratic Residue.

By trial -1 is seen to be a residue of 5, 13, 17, 29 and a non-residue of 3, 7, 11, 19, 23, and we are led by induction to the following theorem:

[1] Primary prime. See p. 193.

THEOREM 3. *The unit -1 is a quadratic residue of all positive primes of the form $4n+1$ and a quadratic non-residue of all positive primes of the form $4n-1$.*[2]

We have (§ 4)

$$\left(\frac{-1}{p}\right) \equiv (-1)^{\frac{p-1}{2}}, \text{ mod } p,$$

whence, since $$(-1)^{(p-1)/2} = 1 \text{ or } -1,$$

$$\left(\frac{-1}{p}\right) = (-1)^{\frac{p-1}{2}}$$

Now p has either the form $4n+1$ or $4n-1$, and it is easily seen

that when $$p = 4n+1,\ (-1)^{(p-1)/2} = 1,$$

and when $$p = 4n-1,\ (-1)^{(p-1)/2} = -1,$$

Therefore $$\left(\frac{-1}{p}\right) = 1 \text{ when } p = 4n+1,$$

and $$\left(\frac{-1}{p}\right) = -1 \text{ when } p = 4n-1.$$

Ex. 1. We have $(-1/13) = 1$ since $13 = 4\cdot 3 + 1$; that is, the congruence $$x^2 \equiv -1, \text{ mod } 13,$$
has roots. These roots are easily seen to be 5 and -5.

Ex. 2. We have $(-1/23) = -1$, since $23 = 4\cdot 6 - 1$; that is, the congruence $$x^2 \equiv -1, \text{ mod } 23,$$
has no roots; a result easily verified.

§ 7. Determination of a root of the congruence $x^2 \equiv -1$, mod p, ($p = 4n + 1$) by means of Wilson's Theorem.

Write down the following congruences, which are evidently true:

$$2n+1 \equiv -2n, \text{ mod } p,$$
$$2n+2 \equiv -(2n-1), \text{ mod } p,$$
$$2n+3 \equiv -(2n-2), \text{ mod } p,$$
$$\cdot \quad \cdot \quad \cdot \quad \cdot \quad \cdot \quad \cdot \quad \cdot \quad \cdot \quad \cdot \quad \cdot$$
$$\cdot \quad \cdot \quad \cdot \quad \cdot \quad \cdot \quad \cdot \quad \cdot \quad \cdot \quad \cdot \quad \cdot$$
$$4n \equiv -1, \text{ mod } p,$$

[2] First given by Fermat; first proved by Euler.

and the identical congruence

$$(2n)! \equiv (2n)!, \bmod p.$$

Multiplying these congruences together, we obtain

$$(4n)! \equiv (-1)^{2n}[(2n)!]^2, \bmod p,$$

or

$$(p-1)! \equiv \left[\left(\frac{p-1}{2}\right)!\right]^2, \bmod p,$$

But by Wilson's Theorem

$$(p-1)! \equiv -1, \bmod p,$$

whence

$$\left[\left(\frac{p-1}{2}\right)!\right]^2 \equiv -1, \bmod p,$$

and therefore

$$x \equiv \left(\frac{p-1}{2}\right)!, \bmod p,$$

is a root of

$$x^2 \equiv -1, \bmod p.$$

Ex. By the above theorem the congruence

$$x^2 \equiv -1, \bmod 13,$$

has a root

$$x \equiv \left(\frac{13-1}{2}\right)! \equiv 6! \equiv 5, \bmod 13;$$

that is,

$$5^2 \equiv -1, \bmod 13.$$

§ 8. Gauss's Lemma.

The following theorem known as Gauss's Lemma, will enable us to determine $(2/p)$ and (q/p).

THEOREM 4. *If m be any integer not divisible by p and if among the residues of smallest absolute value, mod p, of the products $1m$, $2m$, $3m$, $\cdots$, $\frac{1}{2}(p-1)m$, there be an even number of negative ones, m is a quadratic residue of p, if an odd number, m is a quadratic non-residue; that is, if μ be the number of negative residues, $(m/p) = (-1)^\mu$.*

We shall illustrate the content of this theorem by a numerical example.

Let $p = 13$ and $m = 3$. The residues of smallest absolute value, mod 13, of the integers

$$3, 6, 9, 12, 15, 18$$

are

$$3, 6, -4, -1, 2, 5,$$

two of which are negative. Hence 3 is a residue of 13; that is,

$$\left(\frac{3}{13}\right)=(-1)^2=1.$$

This is seen to be true since the congruence

$$x^2\equiv 3, \text{ mod } 13,$$

has the roots 4 and -4.

To prove the theorem we proceed as follows:

Since m is prime to p, the $(p-1)/2$ multiples of m

$$1m,\ 2m, \ldots, \frac{p-1}{2}m \tag{1}$$

are incongruent each to each, mod p. Their residues of smallest absolute value, mod p, are therefore different integers of the system

$$-\frac{p-1}{2}, -\frac{p-3}{2}, \ldots, -2, -1, 1, 2, \ldots, \frac{p-3}{2}, \frac{p-1}{2}.$$

Those which are positive and belong therefore to the system

$$1, 2, \ldots, \frac{p-1}{2}, \tag{2}$$

we shall denote by $b_1, b_2, \cdots, b_\lambda$. Those which are negative, and belong therefore to the system

$$-1, -2, \ldots, -\frac{p-1}{2},$$

we shall denote by $-a_1, -a_2, \cdots, -a_\mu$.

Evidently $a_1, a_2, \cdots, a_\mu$ belong to the system 2). Moreover

$$\lambda+\mu=\frac{p-1}{2}.$$

We shall now prove that

$$a_1, a_2, \cdots, a_\mu, b_1, b_2, \cdots, b_\lambda$$

are the integers

$$1, 2, \ldots, \frac{p-1}{2}$$

in some order. To do this it will be sufficient to show that no two of these integers are congruent to each other, mod p. It is evident that no two a's are congruent to each other, mod p, and the same is true of the b's. Also no a is congruent to a b, mod p.

For if $$a_i \equiv b_j, \text{ mod } p,$$

and if hm and km be the integers of 1), of which $-a_i$ and b_j are the residues of smallest absolute value, mod p, then

$$-hm \equiv km, \text{ mod } p,$$

and hence $$(h+k)m \equiv 0, \text{ mod } p,$$

which is impossible, for m being prime to p, and h and k both positive and $< p/2$, neither of the factors m or $h+k$ is divisible by p. Therefore the $(p-1)/2$ integers,

$$a_1, a_2, \cdots, a_\mu, b_1, b_2, \cdots, b_\lambda,$$

are incongruent each to each, mod p, and being, moreover, all positive and $< p/2$, must be the integers

$$1, 2, \cdots, \frac{p-1}{2}$$

in some order.

Since $$-a_1, -a_2, \cdots, -a_\mu, b_1, b_2, \cdots, b_\lambda$$
are residues of

$$1m, 2m, 3m, \cdots, \frac{p-1}{2}m, \text{ mod } p,$$

we have

$$1 \cdot 2 \cdots \frac{p-1}{2} m^{\frac{p-1}{2}} \equiv (-1)^\mu a_1 a_2 \cdots a_\mu b_1 b_2 \cdots b_\lambda, \text{ mod } p,$$

whence, since

$$1 \cdot 2 \cdots \frac{p-1}{2} = a_1 a_2 \cdots a_\mu b_1 \cdots b_\lambda,$$

and this product is prime to p, we have

$$m^{\frac{p-1}{2}} \equiv (-1)^\mu, \text{ mod } p.$$

But

$$\left(\frac{m}{p}\right) \equiv m^{\frac{p-1}{2}}, \text{ mod } p,$$

and

$$(-1)^\mu = 1 \text{ or } -1.$$

Therefore

$$\left(\frac{m}{p}\right) = (-1)^\mu.$$

We call μ Gauss's Characteristic.

§ 9. Prime Moduli of which 2 is a Quadratic Residue.

We see by any one of the several methods given, that 2 is a residue of the primes 7, 17, 23, 31, 41, 47, which are of the form $8n \pm 1$, and a non-residue of the primes

$$3, 5, 11, 13, 19, 29, 37,$$

which are of the form $8n \pm 3$.

Now every odd prime is of the one or the other of these forms, and the truth of the following theorem seems at once probable.

THEOREM 4a *The integer 2 is a quadratic residue of all primes of the form $8n \pm 1$, and a quadratic non-residue of all primes of the form $8n \pm 3$.*[1]

From Gauss's Lemma we have

$$\left(\frac{2}{p}\right) = (-1)^\mu,$$

where p is an odd prime, and μ is the number of the integers

$$2, 4, 6, \cdots, p-1, \qquad 1)$$

whose residues of least absolute value, mod p, are negative. To determine when μ is even and when odd we notice that these μ integers are those greater than $p/2$. If we suppose the series 1) to be formed by continued subtraction of 2 from $p-1$ and write it in the form

$$p-1, p-3, \cdots, p-1-2(\mu-1), p-1-2\mu, \cdots, 4, 2,$$

[1] First given by Fermat; first proved by Lagrange.

we see that, since there are μ of its terms, beginning with $p-1$ and going backwards, whose residues of least absolute value, mod p, are negative, the smallest one of these terms will be

$$p-1-2(\mu-1).$$

The greatest term whose residue of least absolute value, mod p, is positive is therefore $p-1-2\mu$.

Hence we have

$$p-1-2(\mu-1)>\frac{p}{2}>p-1-2\mu, \qquad 2)$$

From 2) we obtain

$$\frac{p+2}{4}>\mu>\frac{p+2}{4}-1$$

and therefore μ is the greatest integer contained in the fraction $(p+2)/4$. Hence we have, when

$$p=8n\pm 1,\ \mu=2n,$$

and when $$p=8n\pm 3,\ \mu=2n\pm 1;$$

that is, μ is even when p has the form $8n\pm 1$, and odd when p has the form $8n\pm 3$.

Hence

$$\left(\frac{2}{p}\right)=1, \text{ when } p=8n\pm 1,$$

and

$$\left(\frac{2}{p}\right)=-1, \text{ when } p=8n\pm 3,$$

and the theorem is proved.

We can express this result very conveniently in the following manner. We observe that

when $$p=8n\pm 1,\ \frac{p^2-1}{8}=8n^2\pm 2n$$

and when $$p=8n\pm 3,\ \frac{p^2-1}{8}=8n^2\pm 6n+1;$$

that is, when $$p=8n\pm 1,\ \frac{p^2-1}{8} \text{ is even,}$$

and when $p = 8n \pm 3, \frac{p^2 - 1}{8}$ is odd.

Hence
$$\left(\frac{2}{p}\right) = (-1)^{\frac{p^2-1}{8}}$$

Ex. 1. We have $\left(\frac{2}{17}\right) = (-1)^{\frac{17^2-1}{8}} = (-1)^{36} = 1.$

Therefore 2 is a quadratic residue of 17.

Ex. 2. We have $\left(\frac{2}{11}\right) = (-1)^{\frac{11^2-1}{8}} = (-1)^{15} = -1.$

Therefore 2 is a quadratic non-residue of 11.

§ 10. Law of Reciprocity for Quadratic Residues.

It remains now to answer the question: of what odd primes is a positive odd prime q a residue, of what a non-residue? This is answered by means of a theorem which expresses the quadratic character of q with respect to p in terms of the quadratic character of p with respect to q; thus making the answer depend upon that to our first question, § 2. This theorem, which Gauss has called the "Gem of the Higher Arithmetic," is known as the "Law of Reciprocity of Quadratic Residues," or more briefly as the "Quadratic Reciprocity Law." It is the following:

THEOREM 5. *Law of Reciprocity of Quadratic Residues.*[1] *If p and q be two different positive odd primes, the quadratic character of q with respect to p is the same as or different from the quadratic character of p with respect to q, according as at least one of the primes is of the form $4n+1$, or both are of the form $4n-1$; that is, if*

$$\left.\begin{array}{ll} & p = 4h+1 \text{ and } q = 4k+1, \\ \text{or} & p = 4h+1 \text{ and } q = 4k-1, \\ \text{or} & p = 4h-1 \text{ and } q = 4k+1, \end{array}\right\} \left(\frac{p}{q}\right)\left(\frac{q}{p}\right) = 1,$$

while if $p = 4h-1$ and $q = 4k-1$, $\left(\frac{p}{q}\right)\left(\frac{q}{p}\right) = -1.$

[1] See Bachmann: Niedere Zahlentheorie, pp. 194–318, for a very full discussion of this theorem, a list of all proofs being given.

This theorem can be expressed in a very elegant form, if we observe that the expression $(p-1)/2\cdot(q-1)/2$ is even when one or both of the primes are of the form $4n+1$, but odd when both are of the form $4n-1$. We have, therefore,

$$\left(\frac{p}{q}\right)\left(\frac{q}{p}\right)=(-1)^{\frac{p-1}{2}\cdot\frac{q-1}{2}}$$

The proof which follows is due to Pfarrer Zeller,[2] and depends solely on Gauss's Lemma.

We have by Gauss's Lemma

$$\left(\frac{q}{p}\right)=(-1)^{\mu},$$

where μ is the number of the products

$$1q, 2q, \cdots, \frac{p-1}{2}q, \qquad 1)$$

whose residues of least absolute value, mod p, are negative; likewise

$$\left(\frac{p}{q}\right)=(-1)^{\nu},$$

where ν is the number of the products

$$1p, 2p, \cdots, \frac{q-1}{2}p, \qquad 2)$$

whose residues of least absolute value, mod q, are negative.

Hence $$\left(\frac{p}{q}\right)\left(\frac{q}{p}\right)=(-1)^{\mu+\nu}$$

The problem is therefore resolved into the determination of those cases in which $\mu+\nu$ is even and those in which it is odd. Denote the residues of least absolute value, mod p, of the products 1) by

$$-a_1, -a_2, \cdots, -a_\mu, b_1, b_2, \cdots, b_\lambda,$$

and those of the products 2), mod q, by

$$-c_1, -c_2, \cdots, -c_\nu, d_1, d_2, \cdots, d_\rho,$$

[2] Monatsbericht der Berliner Akademie, December, 1872.

the a's, b's, c's and d's all being positive. Since p and q are different from each other, one must be the greater. Assume $q > p$. We divide now the integers $c_1, c_2, \cdots, c_\nu$, all of which being residues of least absolute value, mod q, belong to the system

$$1, 2, \cdots, \frac{q-1}{2},$$

into two classes according as they are greater or less than $p/2$. The system of those which are $< p/2$ we denote by C_1 and the system of those $> p/2$ by C_2.

Let ν_1 denote the number of the integers C_1, and ν_2 that of the integers C_2.

The proof now falls naturally into the following four parts:

i. That the integers, C_1, are identical with the b's and therefore together with the a's make up the system

$$1, 2, \cdots, \frac{p-1}{2},$$

whence
$$\mu + \nu = \frac{p-1}{2} + \nu_2.$$

ii. That the number, ν_2, of the integers C_2 is odd or even according as the number $(p+q)/4$ is or is not found among them.

iii. That $(p+q)/4$ occurs among the integers C_2, and hence ν_2 is odd, when and only when we have simultaneously

$$p = 4h - 1 \text{ and } q = 4k + 1.$$

iv. That therefore $\mu + \nu$ is odd when and only when simultaneously
$$p = 4h - 1 \text{ and } q = 4k - 1.$$

The proof will be rendered more intelligible if we consider first the relation between the four parts into which we have divided it.

Suppose that we have proved i, then

$$\left(\frac{p}{q}\right)\left(\frac{q}{p}\right) = (-1)^{\frac{p-1}{2}+\nu_2},$$

and to prove our theorem it is sufficient to show that $(p-1)/2 + \nu_2$ is odd when and only when

$$p=4h-1,\ q=4k-1.$$

It is evident, however, that since $(p-1)/2$ is even or odd according as $p=4h+1$ or $4h-1$, to show that $(p-1)/2+\nu_2$ is odd when and only when $p=4h-1$, $q=4k-1$, it is sufficient to show that ν_2 is odd when and only when $p=4h-1$, $q=4k+1$. Now the number $(p+q)/4$ is less than $q/2$ and greater than $p/2$ and hence, *if an integer,* is either one of the integers C_2 or one of the d's.

But $(p+q)/4$ is an integer only when $p=4h+1$, $q=4k-1$ or $p=4h-1$, $q=4k+1$, and hence can therefore evidently never be among the integers C_2 in the cases $p=4h+1, q=4k+1$; and $p=4h-1$, $q=4k-1$. If now we can show that $(p+q)/4$ always occurs among the integers C_2 when $p=4h-1$, $q=4k+1$, and never when $p=4h+1$, $q=4k-1$, then to show that ν_2 is odd when and only when $p=4h-1$, $q=4k+1$, it will be sufficient to show that ν_2 is odd when and only when $(p+q)/4$ occurs among the integers C_2. Therefore to show that $(p-1)/2 + \nu_2$ is odd when and only when $p=4h-1$, $q=4k-1$, it will be sufficient to show that $(p+q)/4$ occurs among the integers C_2 when and only when $p=4h-1$, $q=4k+1$. Our idea is therefore to show that the three conditions

$$p=4h-1,\ q=4k+1,$$

$$\nu_2 \text{ odd},$$

$$\frac{p+q}{4} \text{ one of the integers } C_2,$$

are equivalent, whence it will follow that $(p-1)/2+\nu_2$ is odd when and only when $p=4h-1$, $q=4k-1$.

i. If any integer of the system

$$1, 2, \cdots, \frac{p-1}{2}$$

be not an a it must be a b; for as we have already shown (Th. 4), the a's and b's together make up this system. The integers C_1

belong, however, also to this system, hence each of the integers C_1 must be either an a or a b. We shall show that each b is identical with one of the integers C_1; also that no a is identical with any of the integers C_1 and hence the b's and the integers C_1 coincide. Let b_i be any one of the b's, and $h_i q$ that product of the system 1) whose residue of least absolute value, mod p, is b_i.

We have then $\quad h_i q \equiv b_i$, mod p; $0 < h_i < \frac{p}{2}$;

that is, $$h_i q = k_i p + b_i, \tag{3}$$

where k_i is an integer such that

$$0 < k_i p < h_i q < \frac{p}{2} q,$$

and hence $$0 < k_i < \frac{q}{2}.$$

Therefore $k_i p$ is one of the products of the system 2).

But from 3), we have

$$k_i p \equiv - b_i, \text{ mod } q,$$

where $$0 < b_i < \frac{p}{2}.$$

Hence b_i is one of the integers C_1.

But b_i is any one of the b's; hence each b is identical with one of the integers C_1. Let now a_j be any one of the a's and $h_j q$ that product of the system 1) whose residue of least absolute value, mod p, is $-a_j$. We have then

$$h_j q \equiv - a_j, \text{ mod } p;$$

that is, $$h_j q = k_j p - a_j, \tag{4}$$

where k_j is an integer > 0 and $< q/2$; for from 4)

$$k_j = \frac{h_j q + a_j}{p},$$

and hence, since $\quad 0 < a_j < \frac{p}{2}$, and $0 < h_j < \frac{p}{2}$,

we have
$$0 < k_j < \frac{\frac{p}{2}q + \frac{p}{2}}{p};$$

that is,
$$0 < k_j < \frac{q+1}{2},$$

which gives, since k_j and $(q+1)/2$ are integers,
$$0 < k_j < \frac{q}{2}.$$

Hence k_jp is one of the products 2), and since from 4) it follows that
$$k_jp \equiv a_j, \bmod q,$$

a_j is a d and therefore not one of the integers C_1. But a_j is any one of the a's; hence no a can be identical with one of the integers C_1. Hence the b's and the integers C_1 coincide, and therefore the a's and the integers C_1 make up the system
$$1, 2, \cdots, \frac{p-1}{2}.$$

Therefore
$$\mu + \nu = \frac{p-1}{2} + \nu_2.$$

ii. To prove now that the number, ν_2, of the integers C_2 is odd or even according as the number $(p+q)/4$ is or is not found among them, let c_i be one of the integers C_2 and
$$k_ip \equiv -c_i, \bmod q.$$

Here k_i can not be $(q-1)/2$, for we have
$$\frac{q-1}{2}p = \frac{p-1}{2}q + \frac{q-p}{2};$$

that is,
$$\frac{q-1}{2}p \equiv \frac{q-p}{2}, \bmod q,$$

where $(q-p)/2$ is evidently positive and less than $q/2$, and hence one of the d's.

Therefore to each product, k_ip, of the system 2), whose residue of least absolute value, mod q, taken positively is an integer of C_2, there corresponds, since

$$k_i \mp \frac{q-1}{2},$$

a product $k_j p$, $(k_j \mp (q-1)/2)$, of the same system, such that

$$k_j = \frac{q-1}{2} - k_i. \qquad 5)$$

We shall show now that the residue of least absolute value, mod q, of $k_j p$, taken positively, is also one of the integers C_2.

Multiplying 5) by p, we have

$$k_j p = \frac{q-1}{2} p - k_i p,$$

whence $$k_j p = \frac{p-1}{2} q + \frac{q-p}{2} - k_i p,$$

or $$k_j p \equiv \frac{q-p}{2} - k_i p, \text{ mod } q,$$

and hence $$k_j p \equiv -\frac{p+q}{2} - k_i p, \text{ mod } q.$$

Moreover, since $$k_i p \equiv -c_i, \text{ mod } q,$$

we have $$k_j p \equiv -\frac{p+q}{2} + c_i, \text{ mod } q.$$

But since $$\frac{p}{2} < c_i < \frac{q}{2},$$

we have $$\frac{p}{2} < \frac{p+q}{2} - c_i < \frac{q}{2}.$$

Hence $\frac{p+q}{2} - c_i$ is one of the integers C_2.

Putting $$\frac{p+q}{2} - c_i = c_j, \qquad 6)$$

we see that if $k_i p$, $k_j p$, be two products of the system 2), such that k_i and k_j are connected by the relation 5), and if the residue of least absolute value of $k_i p$, mod q, be $-c_i$, where c_i is one of the integers C_2, then the residue of least absolute value of $k_j p$, mod q, is $-c_j$, where c_j is also one of the integers C_2.

Hence to each integer c_i of C_2 there corresponds in this manner another integer c_j of C_2 and it is evident that unless it should happen that there is one (or any odd number) of these pairs whose integers are identical, the number, ν_2, of the integers C_2 will be even, but if the two integers composing each of any odd number of these pairs be identical, ν_2 is odd.

If $c_i = c_j$, then from 6) it follows that

$$c_i = c_j = \frac{p+q}{4}.$$

Hence there is at most one pair whose integers are identical and this case will occur when and only when $(p+q)/4$ is one of the integers C_2. Hence ν_2 is odd or even according as $(p+q)/4$ does or does not occur among the integers C_2.

iii. To prove now that $(p+q)/4$ occurs among the integers C_2, and hence ν_2 is odd, when and only when we have simultaneously

$$p = 4h - 1,\quad q = 4k + 1,$$

we observe first that

$$\frac{p}{2} < \frac{p+q}{4} < \frac{q}{2}$$

and hence, if $(p+q)/4$ be an integer, it is either one of the integers C_2 or a d.

In order now that $(p+q)/4$ may be one of the integers C_2 it is necessary and sufficient that there shall be one, kp, of the products 2) such that

$$kp \equiv -\frac{p+q}{4}, \text{ mod } q;$$

that is, it is necessary and sufficient that there shall exist two integers h and k such that

$$kp = hq - \frac{p+q}{4}, \qquad 7)$$

and $$k < \frac{q}{2}$$

From 7) it follows that we must have

$$(4k+1)p = (4h-1)q, \qquad 8)$$

and hence $4k+1$ divisible by q.

But we have $$k < \frac{q}{2},$$

and hence $$4k+1 < 2q.$$

Therefore $$q = 4k+1,$$

and consequently from 8) it follows that

$$p = 4h-1;$$

that is, in order that the required integers h and k may exist, p and q must have these forms. Moreover, when p and q have these forms the required integers h and k evidently do exist.

Hence $p=4h-1$, $q=4k+1$ is a necessary and sufficient condition that $(p+q)/4$ shall be one of the integers C_2.

Therefore ν_2 is odd when and only when we have simultaneously

$$p = 4h-1, \text{ and } q = 4k+1.$$

iv. To prove now that $\mu+\nu$ is odd when and only when we have simultaneously $p=4h-1$, $q=4k-1$, we examine the equation

$$\mu + \nu = \frac{p-1}{2} + \nu_2$$

and observe that

$p=4h+1$, $q=4k+1$ gives $\frac{p-1}{2}$ even, ν_2 even, $\mu+\nu$ even,

$p=4h+1$, $q=4k-1$ gives $\frac{p-1}{2}$ even, ν_2 even, $\mu+\nu$ even,

$p=4h-1$, $q=4k+1$ gives $\frac{p-1}{2}$ odd, ν_2 odd, $\mu+\nu$ even,

$p=4h-1$, $q=4k-1$ gives $\frac{p-1}{2}$ odd, ν_2 even, $\mu+\nu$ odd.

Therefore $$\left(\frac{p}{q}\right)\left(\frac{q}{p}\right) = 1$$

when at least one of the positive primes p and q has the form

$4n + 1$, and $$\left(\frac{p}{q}\right)\left(\frac{q}{p}\right) = -1$$

when both have the form $4n - 1$.

§ 11. **Determination of the Value of (a/p) by means of the Quadratic Reciprocity Law, a being any Given Integer and p a Prime.**

Before discussing the question of what odd prime moduli is a given positive odd prime a quadratic residue, which we shall be able to answer by means of the Quadratic Reciprocity Law, we shall illustrate upon an example how greatly the use of this law simplifies the determination of the value of (a/p), where a and p are both given integers and p an odd positive prime; that is, the determination whether the congruence

$$x^2 \equiv a, \bmod p,$$

has or has not roots.

Let $$x^2 \equiv 365, \bmod 1847, \qquad 1)$$

be the congruence under discussion, 1847 being a prime.[1]

We have

$$\left(\frac{365}{1847}\right) = \left(\frac{5}{1847}\right)\left(\frac{73}{1847}\right).$$

Then since 5 is a prime of the form $4n + 1$, we have

$$\left(\frac{5}{1847}\right) = \left(\frac{1847}{5}\right)$$

and since $$1847 \equiv 2, \bmod 5,$$

$$\left(\frac{1847}{5}\right) = \left(\frac{2}{5}\right) = -1,$$

5 being of the form $8n - 3$.

Hence $$\left(\frac{5}{1847}\right) = -1.$$

[1] Dirichlet-Dedekind: p. 103.

Likewise since 73 is of the form $4n+1$,

and $$1847 \equiv 22, \text{ mod } 73,$$

we have

$$\left(\frac{73}{1847}\right) = \left(\frac{1847}{73}\right) = \left(\frac{22}{73}\right) = \left(\frac{2}{73}\right)\left(\frac{11}{73}\right)$$

But $$\left(\frac{2}{73}\right) = 1,$$

since 73 is of the form $8n+1$, and therefore

$$\left(\frac{73}{1847}\right) = \left(\frac{11}{73}\right)$$

Again since 73 is of the form $4n+1$ and $73 \equiv 7$, mod 11,

we have $$\left(\frac{11}{73}\right) = \left(\frac{73}{11}\right) = \left(\frac{7}{11}\right)$$

Since 7 and 11 are both of the form $4n-1$,

$$\left(\frac{7}{11}\right) = -\left(\frac{11}{7}\right) = -\left(\frac{4}{7}\right) = -\left(\frac{2}{7}\right)\left(\frac{2}{7}\right) = -1.$$

Therefore $$\left(\frac{365}{1847}\right) = (-1)(-1) = 1;$$

that is, 1) is solvable.

Its roots can be shown to be ± 496.

§ 12. Determination of the Odd Prime Moduli of which a Given Positive Odd Prime is a Quadratic Residue.

Let q be an odd positive prime.

We are to determine for what positive odd prime values of p the value of (q/p) is 1, for what -1.

By means of the Quadratic Reciprocity Law we are able to make the solution of this problem depend on that of the simpler one, which we have already solved; that is, the division of all rational integers into two classes, one of which contains all residues of q and the other all non-residues.

Let $r_1, r_2, \cdots, r_t$ and $n_1, n_2, \cdots, n_t$ be respectively the incongruent quadratic residues and non-residues of q. Then an integer is a residue or non-residue of q according as it is contained in one of the forms

$$r_1 + kq, r_2 + kq, \cdots, r_t + kq, \qquad 1)$$

or in one of the forms

$$n_1 + kq, n_2 + kq, \cdots, n_t + kq. \qquad 2)$$

It is necessary now to distinguish two cases according as q has the form $4n + 1$ or $4n - 1$.

i. $q = 4n + 1$.

Then
$$\left(\frac{q}{p}\right) = \left(\frac{p}{q}\right);$$

that is, q is a quadratic residue or non-residue of p according as p is a quadratic residue or non-residue of q. Hence q is a residue of all positive odd primes contained in the forms 1) and a non-residue of all positive odd primes contained in the forms 2).

Ex. Let $q = 13$.

The residues of 13 are 1, 3, 4, 9, 10 and 12, the non-residues 2, 5, 6, 7, 8 and 11.

Hence 13 is a residue of all primes of the forms

$$1 + 13k,\ 3 + 13k,\ 4 + 13k,\ 9 + 13k,\ 10 + 13k,\ 12 + 13k,$$

and a non-residue of all primes of the forms

$$2 + 13k,\ 5 + 13k,\ 6 + 13k,\ 7 + 13k,\ 8 + 13k,\ 11 + 13k.$$

ii. $q = 4n - 1$.

We must further divide this case into two parts according as p has the form $4m + 1$ or $4m - 1$.

a) $p = 4m + 1$.

Then
$$\left(\frac{q}{p}\right) = \left(\frac{p}{q}\right)$$

and q is seen to be a quadratic residue of all primes of the form $4m + 1$ contained in the forms 1) and a non-residue of all primes of the form $4m + 1$ contained in the forms 2).

b) $p = 4m - 1$.

Then
$$\left(\frac{q}{p}\right) = -\left(\frac{p}{q}\right)$$

and q is seen to be a quadratic residue of all positive primes of the form $4m - 1$ contained in the forms 2) and a quadratic non-residue of all positive primes of the form $4m - 1$ contained in the forms 1).

The primes p are in this case seen to be subjected to two conditions, first that they shall give with respect to the modulus 4 the residues 1 or -1, and secondly with respect to modulus q the residues $r_1, r_2, \cdots, r_t$ or $n_1, n_2, \cdots, n_t$.

By Chap. III, § 14, we can find the forms which the numbers must have in order to satisfy both of these conditions

Ex.[1] Let $$q = 19.$$

The residues of 19 are

$$1, 4, 5, 6, 7, 9, 11, 16 \text{ and } 17,$$

and the non-residues

$$2, 3, 8, 10, 12, 13, 14, 15 \text{ and } 18.$$

Hence 19 is a residue of all positive primes of the form $4m + 1$ contained in the forms

$$19k + 1,\ 19k + 4,\ 19k + 5,\ 19k + 6,\ 19k + 7,$$
$$19k + 9,\ 19k + 11,\ 19k + 16,\ 19k + 17, \qquad 3)$$

and of all positive primes of the form $4m - 1$ contained in the forms

$$19k + 2,\ 19k + 3,\ 19k + 8,\ 19k + 10,\ 19k + 12,$$
$$19k + 13,\ 19k + 14,\ 19k + 15,\ 19k + 18. \qquad 4)$$

On the other hand 19 is a non-residue of all positive primes of the form $4m - 1$ contained in the forms 3) and of all positive primes of the form $4m + 1$ contained in the forms 4). By Chap. III, § 14, we may combine the two conditions thus imposed upon p into a single one and say that 19 is a quadratic residue of all primes of the forms

$$76k + 1, 3, 5, 9, 15, 17, 25, 27, 31, 45, 49, 51, 59, 61, 67, 71, 73, 75,$$

and a quadratic non-residue of all primes of the forms,

$$76k + 7, 11, 13, 21, 23, 29, 33, 35, 37, 39, 41, 43, 47, 53, 55, 63, 65, 69.$$

§ 13. Determination of the Odd Prime Moduli of which any Given Integer is a Quadratic Residue.

It was shown in § 10 that the solution of this problem could be made to depend upon the solution of the three simpler problems, to determine:

[1] Wertheim: p. 220.

i. Of what odd prime moduli -1 is a quadratic residue.

ii. Of what odd prime moduli 2 is a quadratic residue.

iii. Of what odd prime moduli another positive odd prime is a quadratic residue.

These problems have all been solved and we are now prepared to solve the general question proposed originally in § 2; that is, to determine for what odd prime values of p the value of (a/p) is 1 and for what -1, a being any given integer. Assuming that a contains no square factor and by p_i denoting -1 or any positive prime factor of a, we have for each p_i two systems of forms, one of which contains all positive odd primes of which p_i is a residue, the other all positive odd primes of which p_i is a non-residue.

The positive odd primes of which a is a residue will be those which are contained in none or an even number of the second set of forms. Having obtained for each p_i these two systems of forms the solution of the problem reduces to that of finding an integer which gives certain residues with respect to each one of a series of moduli (Chap. III, § 14). A single example must suffice here to illustrate the application of this method. For an extended discussion of it with numerous examples see Wertheim, pp. 221, and for the solution of this problem as well as the more general one, where the modulus is also composite, see Dirichlet-Dedekind, Bachmann and Mathews, where by an extension of Legendre's symbol a simplification is effected.

Ex. Let $$a = -15.$$

We have $$\left(\frac{-15}{p}\right) = \left(\frac{-1}{p}\right)\left(\frac{3}{p}\right)\left(\frac{5}{p}\right)$$

Two cases must now be distinguished according as p has the form $4k_1 + 1$ or $4k_1 + 3$.

If $p = 4k_1 + 1$, $\left(\frac{-1}{p}\right) = 1$,

and $$\left(\frac{3}{p}\right) = \left(\frac{p}{3}\right) = \quad 1 \text{ when } p = 3k_2 + 1,$$

and $$= -1 \text{ when } p = 3k_2 + 2$$

If $p = 4k_1 + 3$, $\left(\frac{-1}{p}\right) = -1$,

and $\left(\frac{3}{p}\right) = -\left(\frac{p}{3}\right) = \quad 1$ when $p = 3k_2 + 2$,

and $= -1$ when $p = 3k_2 + 1$.

In both cases

$$\left(\frac{5}{p}\right) = \left(\frac{p}{5}\right) = \quad 1 \text{ when } p = 5k_3 + 1 \text{ or } 5k_3 + 4,$$

and $= -1$ when $p = 5k_3 + 2$ or $5k_3 + 3$.

In order now that -15 shall be a residue of p, p must have such a form that either none or two of the symbols $(-1/p)$, $(3/p)$, $(5/p)$ have the value -1.

Hence -15 is a residue of all primes which are contained simultaneously in the forms of one of the following sets:

$4k_1 + 1$, $3k_2 + 1$, $5k_3 + 1$, which give $p = 60k + 1$, 1)

$4k_1 + 1$, $3k_2 + 1$, $5k_3 + 4$, which give $p = 60k + 49$, 2)

$4k_1 + 1$, $3k_2 + 2$, $5k_3 + 2$, which give $p = 60k + 17$, 3)

$4k_1 + 1$, $3k_2 + 2$, $5k_3 + 3$, which give $p = 60k + 53$, 4)

$4k_1 + 3$, $3k_2 + 1$, $5k_3 + 1$, which give $p = 60k + 31$, 5)

$4k_1 + 3$, $3k_2 + 1$, $5k_3 + 4$, which give $p = 60k + 19$, 6)

$4k_1 + 3$, $3k_2 + 2$, $5k_3 + 2$, which give $p = 60k + 47$, 7)

$4k_1 + 3$, $3k_2 + 2$, $5k_3 + 3$, which give $p = 60k + 23$. 8)

We can easily combine 1) and 5), 2) and 6), 3) and 7), 4) and 8), and obtain as the forms of the positive odd primes of which -15 is a residue

$$30k + 1, 17, 19, 23.$$

Similarly we find that -15 is a non-residue of all positive primes contained in the forms

$$30k + 7, 11, 13, 29.$$

§ 14. Other Applications of the Quadratic Reciprocity Law.

We shall now give a few theorems in the proof of which the Quadratic Reciprocity Law and its two subsidiary theorems will be found useful.

THEOREM 6. *There are an infinite number of positive primes of each of the forms $4n + 1$ and $4n - 1$.*[1]

Observing that every prime is of one of these forms, we pro-

[1] See Chap. II, § 6.

ceed to prove that there is an infinite number of primes of the form $4n+1$.

Suppose that there is only a finite number of positive primes $p_1, p_2, \cdots, p_s$, of the form $4n+1$. Form the integer

$$(2p_1p_2\cdots p_s)^2+1=a,$$

which is of the form $4n+1$.

It is divisible by no prime q of the form $4n-1$, for, if this were the case, we should have

$$(2p_1p_2\cdots p_s)^2\equiv -1, \text{ mod } q;$$

that is, -1 would be a quadratic residue of q which is impossible because q is of the form $4n-1$.

Moreover, a is not divisible by any of the primes $2, p_1, p_2, \cdots, p_s$. Hence a is itself a prime of the form $4n+1$, different from each of the primes $p_1, p_2, \cdots, p_s$, or is a product of such primes. But this is contrary to our assumption that there are no primes of the form $4n+1$ other than $p_1, p_2, \cdots, p_s$. Therefore the number of positive primes of the form $4n+1$ is infinite.

To prove now that there is an infinite number of positive primes of the form $4n-1$, we assume as before the contrary to be true; that is, that there are only a finite number of positive primes $q_1, q_2, \cdots, q_t$ of the form $4n-1$, q_t being the greatest.

Form the integer $$2q_1q_2\cdots q_t+1=b.$$

It is greater than q_t and is not divisible by any of the primes $2, q_1, q_2, \cdots, q_t$. Hence, if it be not prime, its prime factors must all be of the form $4n+1$.

Let $$2q_1q_2\cdots q_t+1=p_1p_2\cdots p_r, \qquad 1)$$

where $$\left.\begin{array}{l} p_1\equiv 1 \\ p_2\equiv 1 \\ \vdots \quad \vdots \\ p_r\equiv 1 \end{array}\right\}, \text{ mod } 4.$$

Multiplying these congruences together, we have

$$p_1p_2\cdots p_r\equiv 1, \text{ mod } 4,$$

whence $$2q_1q_2 \cdots q_t + 1 \equiv 1, \bmod 4,$$

and hence $$q_1q_2 \cdots q_t \equiv 0, \bmod 2. \qquad 2)$$

But 2) is impossible since $q_1, q_2, \cdots, q_t$ are all primes of the form $4n-1$.

Hence 1) is impossible and b is either itself a prime of the form $4n-1$ or is a product of primes of this form, all of which are greater than q_t. Therefore the number of positive primes of the form $4n-1$ is infinite.

THEOREM 7. *Every prime of the form $2^{2^n}+1$ has a primitive root 3.*

Let $$p = 2^{2^n} + 1.$$

If 3 be a primitive root of p, then each of the $(p-2)$ powers of 3

$$3, 3^2, \cdots, 3^{p-2}$$

must be incongruent to 1, mod p.

If, however, $3^t \equiv 1$, mod p, where $0 < t < p-1$, p being positive, then by Chap. III, Th. 25, it follows that

$$p - 1 \equiv 0, \bmod t,$$

and, since $$p - 1 = 2^{2^n},$$

$$t = 2^m,$$

and the greatest possible value of t will be 2^{2^n-1}. In order, therefore, that 3 may be a primitive root of p, it is necessary and sufficient that the following $2^n - 1$ incongruences should hold

$$\left.\begin{array}{l} 3 \not\equiv 1, \\ 3^2 \not\equiv 1, \\ 3^{2^2} \not\equiv 1, \\ \vdots \quad \vdots \\ 3^{2^{2^n-1}} \not\equiv 1, \end{array}\right\}, \bmod p.$$

A sufficient condition for this is that the last of these incongruences should hold, for, if any one of the previous ones did not hold, none of the following ones would hold.

We have therefore only to prove

$$3^{2^{2^n-1}} \not\equiv 1, \bmod p;$$

that is $$3^{\frac{p-1}{2}} \not\equiv 1, \bmod p. \qquad 3)$$

But when 3) is satisfied, 3 is a quadratic non-residue of p, and vice versa. Hence we have only to prove $(3/p) = -1$.

Since p is of the form $4n+1$, we have

$$\left(\frac{3}{p}\right) = \left(\frac{p}{3}\right). \qquad 4)$$

But $$2 \equiv -1, \bmod 3,$$

whence $$2^{2^n} \equiv (-1)^{2^n} \equiv 1, \bmod 3.$$

Therefore $$2^{2^n} + 1 \equiv 2, \bmod 3,$$

and $$\left(\frac{p}{3}\right) = \left(\frac{2}{3}\right) = -1,$$

whence from 4) it follows that

$$\left(\frac{3}{p}\right) = -1.$$

Therefore 3 is a primitive root of every prime of the form $2^{2^n}+1$.

The theorem just proved bears an interesting relation to the problem of the construction of regular polygons of a prime number of sides with ruler and compasses; the construction is possible only when p is a prime of the form $2^{2^n}+1$, and can be accomplished by means of a primitive root of p.[1]

THEOREM 8. *Every positive prime p of the form $4q+1$, where q is a positive prime, has 2 as a primitive root.*

If 2 be a primitive root of p, then each of the $p-2$ powers of 2

$$2, 2^2, \cdots, 2^{p-2}$$

must be incongruent to 1, mod p.

If, however, 2 appertains to an exponent t, mod p, less than $p-1$, then $$2^t \equiv 1, \bmod p, \qquad 5)$$

[1] See Klein: Ausgewählte Fragen der Elementar Geometrie, p. 13. Gauss: Disq. Arith., Sect. Sept. Works, Vol. I, p. 412. Bachmann: Die Lehre von der Kreisteilung, p. 57 and Vor. 7th.

and by Chap. III, Th. 25,

$$p - 1 \equiv 0, \bmod t,$$

whence $$4q \equiv 0, \bmod t.$$

Hence, since q is a prime, we can have as possible values of t only $2, 4, q$ or $2q$.

It is necessary and sufficient to show that

$$2^4 \not\equiv 1, \bmod p, \text{ and } 2^{2q} \not\equiv 1, \bmod p,$$

for, if $$2^2 \equiv 1, \bmod p, \text{ then } 2^4 \equiv 1, \bmod p,$$

and, if $$2^q \equiv 1, \bmod p, \text{ then } 2^{2q} \equiv 1, \bmod p.$$

To prove $$2^4 \not\equiv 1, \bmod p;$$

that is, $$15 \not\equiv 0, \bmod p,$$

it is sufficient to notice that the only primes which divide 15 are 3 and 5, neither of which is of the form $4q + 1$, when q is a prime.

Hence $$2^4 \not\equiv 1, \bmod p.$$

To prove $$2^{2q} \not\equiv 1, \bmod p;$$

that is, $$2^{(p-1)/2} \not\equiv 1, \bmod p,$$

we need only show that

$$\left(\frac{2}{p}\right) = -1.$$

we have $$\left(\frac{2}{p}\right) = (-1)^{\frac{p^2-1}{8}} = (-1)^{2q^2+q} = -1,$$

for if $q = 2$, $p, = 4q + 1$, is not a prime and therefore q is always odd, whence it is evident that $2q^2 + q$ is an uneven integer.

Hence $$2^{2q} \not\equiv 1, \bmod p.$$

Therefore 5) holds for no value of t less than $p - 1$.

Hence 2 is a primitive root of every positive prime of the form $4q + 1$ when q is a positive prime.

EXAMPLES.

1. Determine the prime moduli of which 30 is a quadratic residue.

2. Has the congruence

$$x^2 \equiv 1135, \text{ mod } 2311,$$

roots?

3. Solve the congruences:[1]

a)	$5x^2 - 8x - 3 \equiv 0$, mod 23.	$x \equiv 8$ or 12, mod 23.
b)	$3x^2 + 4x + 5 \equiv 0$, mod 20.	$x \equiv -3, -5, 7, 5$, mod 20.
c)	$7x^2 - 3x + 11 \equiv 0$, mod 19.	$x \equiv 5, 9$, mod 19.
d)	$5x^2 - 3x - 2 \equiv 0$, mod 12.	$x \equiv -2, 1, 2, 5$, mod 12.
e)	$3x^2 + 4x + 9 \equiv 0$, mod 12.	$x \equiv -3, 3$, mod 12.
f)	$3x^2 + x - 4 \equiv 0$, mod 10.	$x \equiv 1, 2, 6, 7$, mod 10.

4. Show that among the numbers of a reduced residue system, mod p^n, where p is a prime different from 2, there are exactly as many quadratic residues as non-residues of p^n.[2]

5. Show that every quadratic residue of p is also a quadratic residue of p^n, and that every non-residue of p is also a non-residue of p^n.[3]

6. The numbers a and $p - a$, where p is a prime, have the same or opposite quadratic characters, mod p, according as p is of the form $4n + 1$ or $4n - 1$.

[1] Wertheim: Anfangsgründe der Zahlenlehre, 1902, pp. 320–322. This book contains many numerical examples and should be consulted by every one interested in such work. It also contains many interesting historical notes and some useful tables, and is in many ways a good book for a beginner to read.

[2] Gauss: Disq. Arith., Art. 100; Works, Vol. I.

[3] *Ibid.*, Art. 101.

CHAPTER V.

THE REALM $k(i)$.[1]

§ 1. Numbers of $k(i)$. Conjugate and Norm of a Number.

The number $\sqrt{-1}$, that we shall as usual denote by i, is defined by the equation

$$x^2 + 1 = 0 \tag{1}$$

which it satisfies.

Every number of $k(i)$ is a rational function of i with rational coefficients (Chap. I, § 3), and since by means of the relation $i^2 = -1$ the degree of any rational function of i may be reduced so as to be not higher than the first, every number, α, of $k(i)$ has the form

$$\alpha = \frac{a_1 + b_1 i}{a_2 + b_2 i},$$

where a_1, b_1, a_2, b_2 are rational numbers, or, multiplying the numerator and denominator of this fraction by $a_2 - b_2 i$, we have

$$\alpha = \frac{a_1 a_2 + b_1 b_2}{a_2^2 + b_2^2} + \frac{a_2 b_1 - a_1 b_2}{a_1^2 + b_2^2} i;$$

that is, every number, α, of $k(i)$ has the form

$$\alpha = a + bi,$$

where a and b are rational numbers.[2]

The other root $-i$ of the equation 1) defines the realm $k(-i)$ conjugate to $k(i)$ (Chap. I, § 4). These two realms are identical,

[1] Gauss: Th. Res. Biquad. Com. Sec., Works, Vol. 2, p. 95, f. f. Dirichlet-Dedekind: § 139. Weber: Algebra, Vol. J § 173. Dedekind: Sur la theorie des nombres entiers algebraiques; Bulletin des Sc. Math., 1st Ser., Vol. XI, and 2d Ser., Vol. I. Bachmann: Die Lehre von der Kreisteilung, 12th Vor. Cahen: pp. 354–367.

[2] Throughout the remainder of this book letters of the Latin alphabet will always denote rational numbers (except in $k(i)$, where $i = \sqrt{-1}$) while letters of the Greek alphabet will denote the general numbers of the realm under discussion, which may or may not be rational numbers.

for i is a number of $k(-i)$ and $-i$ is a number of $k(i)$ (Chap. I, § 3). The number $a-bi$, obtained by putting $-i$ for i in any number $\alpha, =a+bi$, of $k(i)$, is the conjugate of α and is denoted by α'; for example, $3+2i$ and $3-2i$ are conjugate numbers (Chap. I, § 4).

A rational number considered as a number of $k(i)$ is evidently its own conjugate.

It is easily seen that the conjugate of a product of two or more numbers of $k(i)$ is equal to the product of the conjugates of its factors; that is, if $\mu=\alpha\beta$, then $\mu'=\alpha'\beta'$. The product of any number, α, of $k(i)$ by its conjugate is called the *norm* of α and is denoted by $n[\alpha]$; that is,

$$n[a+bi]=(a+bi)(a-bi)=a^2+b^2$$

For example:

$$n[3+2i]=(3+2i)(3-2i)=13,$$

and $$n[5]=5\cdot 5=25.$$

We observe that the norms of all numbers of $k(i)$ are positive rational numbers.

THEOREM 1. *The norm of a product is equal to the product of the norms of its factors; that is,* $n[\alpha\beta]=n[\alpha]\cdot n[\beta]$.

For $$\begin{aligned} n[\alpha\beta] &= \alpha\beta\cdot\alpha'\beta' \\ &= \alpha\alpha'\cdot\beta\beta' \\ &= n[\alpha]\cdot n[\beta]. \end{aligned}$$

Every number, α, of $k(i)$ satisfies a rational equation whose degree is the same as that of the realm, that is, the second, and whose remaining root is the conjugate of α, for the equation having for its roots $\alpha, =a+bi$, and $\alpha', =a-bi$, where a and b are rational numbers, is

$$x^2-2ax+a^2+b^2=0; \qquad 2)$$

and this is of the form

$$x^2+px+q=0, \qquad 3)$$

where p and q are rational numbers.

If $b=0$, that is, if $\alpha=\alpha'$, the equation 2) is reducible, becoming

$$(x-a)^2=0,$$

and the rational equation of lowest degree that α satisfies is

$$x-a=0$$

If $b\neq 0$, that is, if $\alpha\neq\alpha'$, the equation 2) is irreducible, and hence is the single rational equation of lowest degree and of the form 3) satisfied by α (Chap. I, § 2).

We observe, therefore, that the numbers of $k(i)$ fall into two classes according as the irreducible equations of lowest degree satisfied by them are of the first or second degree. Those of the second class, that is, those which satisfy irreducible rational equations of the same degree as that of the realm, are called *primitive numbers* of $k(i)$.

The numbers of the first class, that is, those which satisfy irreducible rational equations of a degree lower than that of the realm, are called *imprimitive numbers* of $k(i)$.

The imprimitive numbers of $k(i)$ are evidently the rational numbers.

All numbers of the realm R being included among those of the realm $k(i)$, R is said to be a *sub-realm* of $k(i)$. It is easily seen that $k(i)$ may be defined by any one of its primitive numbers, but by none of its imprimitive numbers.

The constant term of the rational equation of the form 3) whose roots are α and α' is seen to be $n[\alpha]$.

In general, each number α, of a realm, $k(\theta)$, of the nth degree satisfies a rational equation whose degree is the same as that of the realm and whose remaining roots are the $n-1$ conjugates of α (see Chap. VIII, Th. 4).

§ 2. Integers of $k(i)$.

To ascertain what numbers of $k(i)$ are algebraic integers we may consider separately the two classes of numbers of the realm, the imprimitive numbers being at once disposed of by remembering that a rational number is an algebraic integer when and only when it is a rational integer.

To determine when a primitive number α is an algebraic integer, we observe that the necessary and sufficient condition that α shall be an algebraic integer is that the coefficients of the single rational equation of lowest degree,

$$x^2 + px + q = 0,$$

satisfied by α shall be integers (Chap. II, Th. 4).

But $$-p = \alpha + \alpha', \text{ and } q = \alpha\alpha'$$

and hence the necessary and sufficient conditions that α shall be an algebraic integer are that $\alpha + \alpha'$ and $\alpha\alpha'$ shall be rational integers.[2]

If we write α in the form $a + bi$, where $a = a_1/c_1$, and $b = b_1/c_1$, a_1, b_1, c_1 being rational integers with no common factor, these conditions become

$$\frac{a_1 + b_1 i}{c_1} + \frac{a_1 - b_1 i}{c_1} = \frac{2a_1}{c_1} = \text{a rational integer,} \qquad 1)$$

$$\left(\frac{a_1 + b_1 i}{c_1}\right)\left(\frac{a_1 - b_1 i}{c_1}\right) = \frac{a_1^2 + b_1^2}{c_1^2} = \text{a rational integer.} \qquad 2)$$

One at least of the three following cases must occur:

i. $c_1 \neq 2$ or 1; ii. $c_1 = 2$; iii. $c_1 = 1$.

We shall show that i and ii are impossible.

i. If $c_1 \neq 2$ or 1, then by virtue of 1) a_1 and c_1 would have a common factor that by virtue of 2) would be contained in b_1 also. But this is contrary to our hypothesis that a_1, b_1, c_1 have no common factor. Hence i is impossible.

ii. If $c_1 = 2$, then by virtue of 2) $a_1^2 + b_1^2$ would be divisible by 2^2 and hence a_1 and b_1 each by 2; that is, a_1, b_1, c_1 would have the common factor 2, which is contrary to our hypothesis. Hence ii is impossible.

Hence $c_1 = 1$; that is, a and b are rational integers.

[2] This is a special case of the general theorem that a necessary and sufficient condition for an algebraic number α to be an integer is that all the elementary symmetric functions of α and its conjugates shall be rational integers.

Thus all integers[1] of $k(i)$ have the form $a+bi$, where a and b are rational integers, and all numbers of this form are integers of $k(i)$. If $b=0$, we obtain the rational integers. The conjugate of any integer of $k(i)$ is evidently also an integer, and the norm of any integer of $k(i)$ is a positive rational integer. We observe that in $k(i)$, as in R, the sum, difference and product of any two integers are integers.[2]

§ 3. Basis of $k(i)$.

Any two integers ω_1, ω_2 of $k(i)$ are said to form a basis of the realm if every integer of the realm can be represented in the form $a_1\omega_1+a_2\omega_2$, where a_1, a_2 are rational integers.[3]

It is evident that all numbers of the form $a_1\omega_1+a_2\omega_2$ are integers of $k(i)$. We have already seen that 1 and i form a basis of $k(i)$; that they are not the only integers of $k(i)$ having this property is easily shown.

For example: $1+i$, $3+2i$ is also a basis; for if $a+bi$ be any integer of $k(i)$, then from

$$a+bi=a_1(1+i)+a_2(3+2i),$$

we have

$$a_1+3a_2=a,$$

$$a_1+2a_2=b,$$

giving

$$a_1=-2a+3b,$$

$$a_2=a-b,$$

which are rational integers since a and b are rational integers.

We have

$$a+bi=(-2a+3b)(1+i)+(a-b)(3+2i).$$

[1] Throughout the discussion of $k(i)$ the term integer will be used to denote any integer of the realm either complex or rational.

[2] It is true, in general, that the sum, difference, and product of any two algebraic integers is an algebraic integer (see chap. IX, Th. 8, Cor. 2).

[3] There exist in every realm of the nth degree n integers $\omega_1, \omega_2, \cdots, \omega_n$, such that every integer θ of the realm has the form

$$\theta=a_1\omega_1+a_2\omega_2+\cdots+a_n\omega_n,$$

where $a_1, a_2, \cdots, a_n$ are rational integers. In the definition here given I have followed Hilbert (see H. B., § 4). The basis defined above is sometimes called a minimal basis of the realm (see Weber: Algebra, Vol. II, § 145).

For example; $8+5i=-(1+i)+3(3+2i)$.

Every integer of the realm is therefore expressible in the form

$$a_1(1+i)+a_2(3+2i),$$

where a_1 and a_2 are rational integers.

Hence $1+i$, $3+2i$ is a basis.

We observe that the determinant of the coefficients[1] of $1+i$ and $3+2i$ is

$$\begin{vmatrix} 1 & 1 \\ 3 & 2 \end{vmatrix} = -1,$$

this being a particular case of the following theorem.

THEOREM 2. *If ω_1, ω_2 be a basis of $k(i)$, the necessary and sufficient condition that*

$$\left.\begin{aligned} \omega_1^* &= a_1\omega_1 + a_2\omega_2, \\ \omega_2^* &= b_1\omega_1 + b_2\omega_2, \end{aligned}\right\} \tag{1}$$

where a_1, a_2, b_1, b_2 are rational integers, shall be also a basis of $k(i)$ is

$$\begin{vmatrix} a_1 & a_2 \\ b_1 & b_2 \end{vmatrix} = \pm 1. \tag{2}$$

This condition is necessary; for, if ω_1^*, ω_2^* be a basis, we have

$$\begin{aligned} \omega_1 &= a_1^*\omega_1^* + a_2^*\omega_2^*, \\ \omega_2 &= b_1^*\omega_1^* + b_2^*\omega_2^*, \end{aligned} \tag{3}$$

where $a_1^*, a_2^*, b_1^*, b_2^*$ are rational integers, and substituting the values of ω_1^*, ω_2^* from 1) in 3), we have

$$\omega_1 = (a_1^*a_1 + a_2^*b_1)\omega_1 + (a_1^*a_2 + a_2^*b_2)\omega_2, \tag{4}$$

$$\omega_2 = (b_1^*a_1 + b_2^*b_1)\omega_1 + (b_1^*a_2 + b_2^*b_2)\omega_2, \tag{5}$$

From 4) and 5) it follows that

$$a_1^*a_1 + a_2^*b_1 = 1, \quad a_1^*a_2 + a_2^*b_2 = 0,$$

$$b_1^*a_1 + b_2^*b_1 = 0, \quad b_1^*a_2 + b_2^*b_2 = 1,$$

whence

$$\begin{vmatrix} a_1^* & a_2^* \\ b_1^* & b_2^* \end{vmatrix} \cdot \begin{vmatrix} a_1 & a_2 \\ b_1 & b_2 \end{vmatrix} = \begin{vmatrix} a_1^*a_1 + a_2^*b_1 & b_1^*a_1 + b_2^*b_1 \\ a_1^*a_2 + a_2^*b_2 & b_1^*a_2 + b_2^*b_2 \end{vmatrix}$$

$$= \begin{vmatrix} 1 & 0 \\ 0 & 1 \end{vmatrix} = 1.$$

[1] We call a, b the coefficients of the number $a\omega_1 + b\omega_2$, where ω_1, ω_2 is a basis.

Therefore $$\begin{vmatrix} a_1 & a_2 \\ b_1 & b_2 \end{vmatrix} = \pm 1.$$

The condition is also sufficient; for, solving 1) for ω_1 and ω_2, we have, if 2) be satisfied,

$$\omega_1 = \pm (b_2\omega_1^* - a_2\omega_2^*),$$
$$\omega_2 = \pm (b_1\omega_1^* - a_1\omega_2^*),$$

and hence, if $\omega, = c_1\omega_1 + c_2\omega_2$, be any integer of the realm,

$$\omega = \pm (c_1b_2 + c_2b_1)\omega_1^* \mp (c_1a_2 + c_2a_1)\omega_2^*;$$

that is, $$\omega = d_1\omega_1^* + d_2\omega_2^*,$$

where d_1 and d_2 are rational integers. Since there is an infinite number of different sets of rational integers a_1, a_2, b_1, b_2 which satisfy the relation

$$\begin{vmatrix} a_1 & a_2 \\ b_1 & b_2 \end{vmatrix} = \pm 1,$$

there is an infinite number of bases of $k(i)$.

§ 4. **Discriminant of $k(i)$.**

The squared determinant

$$\begin{vmatrix} \omega_1 & \omega_2 \\ \omega_1' & \omega_2' \end{vmatrix}^2$$

formed from any basis numbers and their conjugates is called the discriminant of the realm, and is denoted by d.

That d is the same, no matter what basis is taken, is evident from the last paragraph.

For if ω_1, ω_2 and $\omega_1^*, = a_1\omega_1 + a_2\omega_2, \omega_2^*, = b_1\omega_1 + b_2\omega_2$, be any two bases, then

$$\begin{vmatrix} \omega_1^* & \omega_2^* \\ \omega_1^{*\prime} & \omega_2^{*\prime} \end{vmatrix}^2 = \begin{vmatrix} a_1\omega_1 + a_2\omega_2, & b_1\omega_1 + b_2\omega_2 \\ a_1\omega_1' + a_2\omega_2', & b_1\omega_1' + b_2\omega_2' \end{vmatrix}^2$$
$$= \begin{vmatrix} a_1 & a_2 \\ b_1 & b_2 \end{vmatrix}^2 \begin{vmatrix} \omega_1 & \omega_2 \\ \omega_1' & \omega_2' \end{vmatrix}^2 = \begin{vmatrix} \omega_1 & \omega_2 \\ \omega_1' & \omega_2' \end{vmatrix}^2$$

Hence, since $1, i$ is a basis of $k(i)$,

$$d = \begin{vmatrix} 1 & i \\ 1 & -i \end{vmatrix}^2 = -4.$$

It is easily seen that if ω_1, ω_2 be any two integers of $k(i)$ such that

$$\begin{vmatrix} \omega_1 & \omega_2 \\ \omega_1' & \omega_2' \end{vmatrix}^2 = d,$$

then ω_1, ω_2 is a basis of $k(i)$.

For example:

$$\begin{vmatrix} 1+i & 3+2i \\ 1-i & 3-2i \end{vmatrix}^2 = -4;$$

Hence $1+i$, $3+2i$ is a basis of $k(i)$ as we have already seen.

§ 5. Divisibility of Integers of $k(i)$.

Any integer, α, is said to be divisible by an integer, β, when there exists an integer, γ, such that

$$\alpha = \beta\gamma.$$

We say that β and γ are *divisors* or *factors* of α, and that α is a *multiple* of β and γ.

Ex. 1. We see that $8+i$ is divisible by $3+2i$, since

$$8+i = (3+2i)(2-i).$$

Ex. 2. On the other hand $5+2i$ is not divisible by $1+3i$, for there exists no integer of $k(i)$ which multiplied by $1+3i$ gives $5+2i$.

This can be shown as follows:

If we set $$5+2i = (1+3i)(x+yi), \qquad 1)$$

we obtain $$x = \tfrac{11}{10},\ y = -\tfrac{13}{10};$$

that is, there are no integral values of x and y for which 1) will hold.

Hence $5+2i$ is not divisible by $1+3i$.

This can also be shown as follows:

$$\frac{5+2i}{1+3i} = \frac{(5+2i)(1-3i)}{(1+3i)(1-3i)} = \tfrac{11}{10} - \tfrac{13}{10}i$$

As immediate consequences of the above definition we have the following:

i. *If α be a multiple of β and β be a multiple of γ, α is a multiple of γ*, or more generally

ii. *If each integer of a series $\alpha, \beta, \gamma, \delta, \cdots$, be a multiple of the one next following, each integer is a multiple of all that follow it.*

iii. *If two integers, α and β, be multiples of γ, then $\alpha\xi+\beta\eta$ is a multiple of γ, where ξ and η are any integers of the realm.*

It will be observed that iii depends not only upon the above definition but upon the fact that the sum, difference and product of any two integers of $k(i)$ is an integer of $k(i)$. If α be divisible by β, then α' is divisible by β'; for, if $\alpha=\beta\gamma$, then $\alpha'=\beta'\gamma'$. In particular, if a rational integer be divisible by any integer of $k(i)$, it is divisible by its conjugate.

THEOREM 3. *If α be divisible by β, $n[\alpha]$ is divisible by $n[\beta]$.*
For, if $\alpha=\beta\gamma$, it follows from Th. 1 that

$$n[\alpha]=n[\beta]n[\gamma],$$

and hence that $n[\alpha]$ is divisible by $n[\beta]$.

The converse of this theorem is not in general true, as may be seen from the following example:

If $\alpha=8+i$ and $\beta=3-2i$, $n[\alpha]$, $=65$, is divisible by $n[\beta]$, $=13$, but α is not divisible by β; for putting

$$8+i=(3-2i)(x+yi),$$

we obtain fractional values for x and y.

The determination of the conditions under which $n[\alpha]$ divisible by $n[\beta]$ is a sufficient as well as necessary condition for α to be divisible by β must be postponed until the unique factorization theorem has been proved for the integers of $k(i)$.

If two or more integers, $\alpha, \beta, \gamma, \cdots$, of $k(i)$ be each divisible by an integer μ of $k(i)$, μ is said to be a *common divisor* of $\alpha, \beta, \gamma, \cdots$.

§ 6. Units of $k(i)$. Associated Integers.

We have seen that in the rational realm there are certain integers, ± 1, called units, which are divisors of every integer of the realm. Evidently ± 1 have this property in $k(i)$, and are therefore called units of $k(i)$. We ask now whether there are any other integers of $k(i)$ which enjoy this property. If there be such integers they must be divisors of 1, and conversely every divisor of 1 is a unit. Let ϵ, $=x+yi$, be a unit of $k(i)$; then

$$\alpha\epsilon=1, \qquad 1)$$

where α is an integer of $k(i)$. It follows that

$$n[\alpha]n[\epsilon]=1,$$

and hence $n[\epsilon]=1$; that is,

$$x^2+y^2=1. \qquad 2)$$

That $n[\epsilon]=1$ is not only a necessary but also a sufficient condition that ϵ shall be a unit, is evident from the fact that from it follows

$$\epsilon\epsilon'=1,$$

and hence that ϵ is a divisor of 1.

From 2) it follows that

$$x=\pm 1,\ y=0;\ x=0,\ y=\pm 1,$$

and hence

$$\epsilon=1, -1, i \text{ or } -i,$$

Therefore $1, -1, i, -i$ are the units of $k(i)$. That all these integers are units of $k(i)$ may easily be verified, since, if $a+bi$ be any integer of $k(i)$, we have

$$\begin{aligned} a+bi &= 1(a+bi) \\ &= -1(-a-bi) \\ &= i(-ai+b) \\ &= -i(ai-b) \end{aligned}$$

Starting with the original definition of a unit as *an integer which is a divisor of every integer of the realm,* we obtain therefore the three following equivalent definitions for the units of $k(i)$:

i. *They are the divisors of 1.*

ii. *They are those integers whose reciprocals are integers.* Hence the reciprocal of a unit is a unit.

iii. *They are those integers whose norms are 1.* Hence the conjugate of a unit is a unit.

Two integers, α and β, with no common divisor other than the units are said to be *prime to each other.*

It is customary also to say that two integers, whose common divisors are units, *have no common divisor.* A system of integers, $\alpha_1, \alpha_2, \cdots, \alpha_n$, such that no two of them have a common divisor other than the units are said to be *prime each to each.*

As in the rational realm, two integers, m and $-m$, that differ only by a unit factor, are said to be *associated,* so in $k(i)$ the four integers, α, $-\alpha$, $i\alpha$ and $-i\alpha$, obtained by multiplying any integer, α, by the four units in turn, are called *associated integers.* For example, the four integers $3+2i$, $-3-2i$, $-2+3i$, $2-3i$ are associated. We say also that α, $-\alpha$, $i\alpha$, $-i\alpha$ are the *associates* of α. Any integer that is divisible by α is also divisible by $-\alpha$, $i\alpha$ and $-i\alpha$. Hence in all questions of divisibility associated integers are considered as identical. It will be understood from now on that when two factors, α, β, of an integer of $k(i)$ are said to be the same, they are merely associated; that is, $\alpha = \epsilon\beta$, where ϵ is a suitable unit. They may or may not be equal, equality being understood in the ordinary sense; that is,

$$a_1 + b_1 i = a_2 + b_2 i,$$

when and only when $a_1 = a_2$, and $b_1 = b_2$.

If each of two integers be divisible by the other, they are associated, for let $\alpha/\beta = \gamma$, then $\beta/\alpha = 1/\gamma$. If now both γ and $1/\gamma$ be integers, then γ is a unit and α and β are associated.

§ 7. Prime Numbers of $k(i)$.

An integer of $k(i)$, that is not a unit and that has no divisors other than its associates and the units, is called a prime number of $k(i)$.

An integer of $k(i)$ with divisors other than its associates and the units is called a *composite number.*

It will be observed that these definitions are identical with the corresponding ones in the rational realm. To ascertain whether any integer α, not a unit, is a composite or prime number, we have only to determine whether or not α can be resolved into two factors neither of which is a unit.

We put therefore $\alpha = (a+bi)(c+di)$ and determine for what sets of integral values of a, b, c and d this equation is satisfied. If any one of these sets of values be such that neither $a+bi$ nor $c+di$ is a unit, α is a composite number; but, if for every set of values one of these factors be a unit, α is a prime.

Ex. 1. To determine whether 3 is a prime or composite number of $k(i)$.

Put $$3=(a+bi)(c+di);$$
then $$9=(a^2+b^2)(c^2+d^2),$$
whence we have either

$$\left.\begin{array}{l}a^2+b^2=3\\c^2+d^2=3\end{array}\right\}1) \quad\text{or}\quad \left.\begin{array}{l}a^2+b^2=1\\c^2+d^2=9\end{array}\right\}2)$$

Remembering that a, b, c and d must be rational integers, we see that 1) is impossible, while from 2) $a+bi$ is a unit. Therefore 3 is a prime number of $k(i)$.

Ex. 2. To determine whether $7+4i$ is a prime or composite number of $k(i)$.

Put $$7+4i=(a+bi)(c+di);$$
then $$65=(a^2+b^2)(c^2+d^2),$$
whence we have either

$$\left.\begin{array}{l}a^2+b^2=5\\c^2+d^2=13\end{array}\right\}1) \quad\text{or}\quad \left.\begin{array}{l}a^2+b^2=1\\c^2+d^2=65\end{array}\right\}2)$$

From 2) it would follow that $a+bi$ is a unit, but 1) gives

$$\left.\begin{array}{l}a=\pm 2,\ b=\pm 1,\\c=\pm 3,\ d=\pm 2,\end{array}\right\} \quad\text{or}\quad \left.\begin{array}{l}a=\pm 1,\ b=\pm 2,\\c=\pm 2,\ d=\pm 3,\end{array}\right\}$$

whence $$a+bi=\pm(2+i) \quad\text{or}\quad \pm(1-2i), \qquad 3)$$
or $$a+bi=\pm(2-i) \quad\text{or}\quad \pm(1+2i), \qquad 4)$$
and $$c+di=\pm(3+2i) \quad\text{or}\quad \pm(2-3i), \qquad 5)$$
or $$c+di=\pm(3-2i) \quad\text{or}\quad \pm(2+3i), \qquad 6)$$

the four integers after each sign of equality being associated.

It will be observed that this process gives us not only the divisors of $7+4i$ and its associates, but also the divisors of every other integer whose norm is 65; that is, of $7-4i$, $8+i$, $8-i$, and their associates.

Each one of the eight values of $a+bi$ multiplied by any one of the eight values of $c+di$ gives an integer whose norm is 65, and these sixty-four integers fall into four classes of sixteen each according to the one of the integers $7+4i$, $7-4i$, $8+i$, $8-i$, with which they are associated. Each associate of each one of these four integers will be repeated exactly four times.

Selecting by trial the divisors of $7+4i$, we see that any integer from 4), multiplied by a suitable one from 6), gives $7+4i$.

Thus $$7+4i=(2-i)(2+3i). \qquad 7)$$

Hence $7+4i$ is a composite number.

We have also, $$\begin{aligned} 7+4i &= (-2+i)(-2-3i), \\ &= (1+2i)(3-2i), \\ &= (-1-2i)(-3+2i), \end{aligned}$$

but these factorizations are looked upon as in no way different from 7) since the corresponding factors are associated. Hence $7+4i$ can be factored in only one way into two factors, neither of which is a unit. If now we attempt to factor $2-i$ and $2+3i$, we find that they are prime numbers, and hence we say that $7+4i$ has been resolved into its prime factors.

Ex. 3. Resolution of $-23+41i$ into prime factors.

If we endeavor to resolve $-23+41i$ into two factors neither of which is a unit, we find that it can be done in seven different ways; that is,

$$\left.\begin{aligned} -23+41i &= (1+3i)(10+11i), \\ &= (1+5i)(7+6i), \\ &= (3+5i)(4+7i), \\ &= (1+i)(9+32i), \\ &= (2+i)(-1+21i), \\ &= (3+2i)(1+13i), \\ &= (4+i)(-3+11i). \end{aligned}\right\} \qquad 8)$$

We find, however, that in each case either one or both of the factors is composite and we resolve the composite ones into the following factors all of which can easily be proved to be prime:

$$1+3i=(1+i)(2+i);\ 1+5i=(1+i)(3+2i);$$
$$3+5i=(1+i)(4+i);\ 10+11i=(3+2i)(4+i);$$
$$7+6i=(2+i)(4+i);\ 4+7i=(2+i)(3+2i).$$

when these values are substituted in 8) we have in all seven cases

$$-23+41i=(1+i)(2+i)(3+2i)(4+i);$$

that is, if $-23+41i$ be resolved into factors all of which are prime, the resolution can be affected in only one way.

It is now evident that we can, as in the case of the rational integers, represent every integer of $k(i)$ as a product of its prime factors, and the last example renders it probable that the representation will be unique. We shall proceed to prove three theorems which will enable us to show that the integers of $k(i)$ have indeed this all-important property.

§ 8. Unique Factorization Theorem for $k(i)$.

THEOREM A. *If α be any integer of $k(i)$, and β any integer of*

$k(i)$ different from 0, there exists an integer μ of $k(i)$ such that

$$n[\alpha-\mu\beta]<n[\beta].$$

Let $$\alpha/\beta=a+bi,$$

where $a=r+r_1$, $b=s+s_1$, r and s being the rational integers nearest to a and b respectively, and hence

$$|r_1|\leqq \tfrac{1}{2},\ |s_1|\leqq \tfrac{1}{2}.$$

We shall show that μ, $=r+si$, will fulfill the required conditions.

Since $$\alpha/\beta-\mu=r_1+s_1 i,$$

$$n[\alpha/\beta-\mu]=r_1^2+s_1^2\leqq \tfrac{1}{2};$$

whence $$n[\alpha/\beta-\mu]<1;$$

or, multiplying by $n[\beta]$,

$$n[\alpha-\mu\beta]<n[\beta].$$

Ex. If $$\alpha=5+2i, \text{ and } \beta=1+3i,$$

then $$\frac{\alpha}{\beta}=\frac{5+2i}{1+3i}=\tfrac{11}{10}-\tfrac{13}{10}i,$$

and $$\mu=1-i,$$

therefore $$\alpha-\mu\beta=5+2i-(1-i)(1+3i)=1,$$

and $$n[1]<n[1+3i].$$

The method given above for selecting μ evidently determines it uniquely unless either one or both of the quantities $|r_1|$, $|s_1|$ be $\tfrac{1}{2}$, in which cases there are respectively 2 or 4 integers which satisfy equally the method of selection.

There are, however, values of μ that satisfy the requirements of the theorem other than the one selected as above. In the example given above it would serve as well to take

$$\mu=2-i \text{ or } 1-2i;$$

for $$5+2i-(2-i)(1+3i)=-3i,$$

and $$n[-3i]<n[1+3i];$$

likewise $$5+2i-(1-2i)(1+3i)=-2+i,$$

and $$n[-2+i]<n[1+3i].$$

It can be easily shown that there are in general (including the one selected as in the proof) two, three or four values of μ which satisfy the requirements of the theorem. The particular value of μ selected as above may be called the *nearest* integer to α/β.

The other possible values of μ are found among the integers r_2+s_2i such that r_2, s_2 differ respectively from r_1, s_1 by 1.

This will be made clearer by a graphical proof of the theorem to which we are led by its statement in the following form:

If α/β be any number of $k(i)$, there exists an integer μ of $k(i)$ such that $$n[\alpha/\beta-\mu]<1.$$

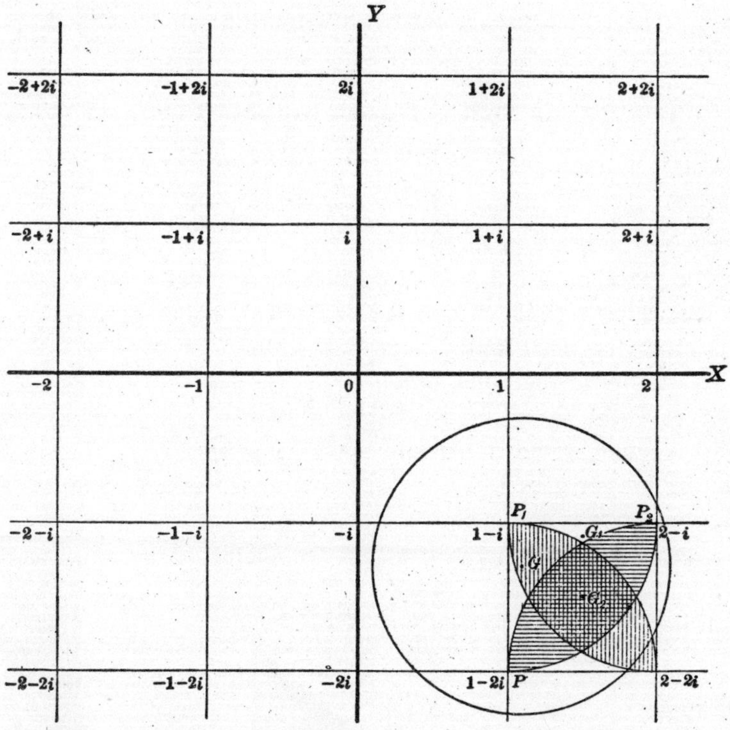

Representing as is usual the number $x+yi$ by a point whose coördinates referred to rectangular axes are x and y, we see that the integers of $k(i)$ are the points of intersection of a lattice formed by two systems of straight lines parallel respectively to the axes of x and y, and at the distance 1 apart.[1]

Our problem is, given any number γ of $k(i)$, we are required to find all integers, μ, of $k(i)$ such that

$$n[\gamma-\mu] < 1. \qquad 1)$$

Let G and N be points representing the numbers $\gamma, = a+bi$, and $\nu, = c+di$, respectively; then every number, ν, of $k(i)$ such that

$$n[\gamma-\nu] < 1$$

is represented by a point lying within the circle of radius 1 described about G as a center, and conversely every number, ν, of the realm represented by a point lying within this circle satisfies 1); for

$$(x-a)^2 + (y-b)^2 = 1$$

is the equation of a circle of radius 1 with center at G, and we have

$$(c-a)^2 + (d-b)^2 < 1;$$

that is

$$n[\gamma-\nu] < 1$$

when and only when the point (c, d) lies within this circle.

The graphical solution of our problem consists therefore merely in describing a circle of radius 1 around the point representing γ and observing what lattice points fall within it.

In the figure the point G represents the number $\gamma = \frac{11}{10} - \frac{13}{10}i$ (see example above), and a circle of radius 1 described around G as a center is seen to enclose the three points P_1, P_2, P_3, representing the integers $1-i$, $2-i$, $1-2i$. Moreover, no other integer point falls within this circle.

The integers $1-i$, $2-i$, $1-2i$ are all the values of μ which satisfy the condition

$$n[\gamma-\mu] < 1,$$

the integer $1-i$, which is the one given by the method of selection used in the proof, being represented by the lattice point nearest to G.

It is evident that the only possible values of μ are those represented by the vertices of the lattice square in which the point G, representing γ, lies.

[1] Cahen: p. 357.

We see that two, three or four of these vertices will satisfy the required condition according as G lies in the unshaded, lightly shaded or heavily shaded portions of the square, the square being thus partitioned by describing from each vertex as a center an arc of a circle of radius 1.

G_1, G and G_2 illustrate respectively the first, second and third cases. G_1 and G_2 illustrate also the cases in which there are respectively two or four equally near lattice points (original method of selection is not unique).

Returning once more to the theorem in its original form, we observe that it is equivalent to saying that *for every integer β, different from* 0, *considered as a modulus there exists a complete residue system such that the norms of all the integers composing this system are less than $n[\beta]$*.

This interpreted graphically implies that if we describe around the origin a circle with radius equal to $\sqrt{n[\beta]}$, that is, passing through the point representing β, there will be among the integers represented by the lattice points lying inside this circle a complete residue system, modulus β.

Theorem A is equivalent to saying that we can divide α by β so as to obtain a remainder whose norm is less than $n[\beta]$, the quotient being μ. In this form its analogy with Theorem A in R is even more clearly brought out. It enables us to do for $k(i)$ exactly what we did in R by means of Theorem A; that is, by an algorithm strictly analogous to that used in R to find a common divisor, δ, of any two integers α and β, such that every common divisor of α and β divides δ. In other words, it enables us to prove that any two integers of $k(i)$ have a *greatest common divisor* and to find it.[1]

For example; let the two integers be $112+i$ and $-57+79i$.

We have $\dfrac{112+i}{-57+79i} = \dfrac{-6305-8905i}{9490}$, whence $\mu = -1-i$,

and $$112+i-(-1-i)(-57+79i) = -24+23i.$$

[1] See Dirichlet-Dedekind: p. 439.

Likewise $\quad \dfrac{-57+79i}{-24+23i}=\dfrac{3185-585i}{1105}$, whence $\mu_1=3-i$,

and $\quad -57+79i-(3-i)(-24+23i)=-8-14i.$

Likewise $\quad \dfrac{-24+23i}{-8-14i}=\dfrac{-130-520i}{260}$, whence $\mu_2=-1-2i$,

and $\quad -24+23i-(-1-2i)(-8-14i)=-4-7i.$

Finally $\quad \dfrac{-8-14i}{-4-7i}=2$, whence $\mu_3=2$

and $\quad -8-14i-(2)(-4-7i)=0.$

Therefore $-4-7i$ is the greatest common divisor of $112+i$ and $-57+79i$.

Instead, however, of proving the existence of a greatest common divisor of any two integers of $k(i)$, we shall proceed as in R, and shall prove the following theorem of which the greatest common divisor theorem is an immediate consequence.

THEOREM B. *If α and β be any two integers of $k(i)$ prime to each other, there exist two integers, ξ and η, of $k(i)$ such that*

$$\alpha\xi+\beta\eta=1.$$

If either α or β be a unit, the existence of the required integers, ξ, η, is evident. We shall now show that, if neither α nor β be a unit, the determination of ξ and η can be made to depend upon the determination of a corresponding pair of integers ξ_1, η_1, for a pair of integers, α_1, β_1, prime to each other and such that the norm of one of them is less than both $n[\alpha]$ and $n[\beta]$.

Assume $n[\beta]\leqq n[\alpha]$, which evidently does not limit the generality of the proof.

By Th. A there exists an integer μ such that

$$n[\alpha-\mu\beta]<n[\beta].$$

Then β and $\alpha-\mu\beta$ are a pair of integers, α_1, β_1, prime to each other and $n[\alpha-\mu\beta]$ is less than both $n[\alpha]$ and $n[\beta]$.

If, now, two integers, ξ_1, η_1, exist such that

$$\alpha_1\xi_1+\beta_1\eta_1=1;$$

that is, $\quad \beta\xi_1+(\alpha-\mu\beta)\eta_1=1,$

we have $$\alpha\eta_1 + \beta(\xi_1 - \mu\eta_1) = 1,$$

and hence $$\xi = \eta_1, \quad \eta = \xi_1 - \mu\eta_1.$$

The determination of ξ_1, η_1 for α_1, β_1 may, if neither α_1 nor β_1 be a unit, be made to depend similarly upon that of ξ_2, η_2 for a pair of integers α_2, β_2 prime to each other and such that the norm of one of them is less than both $n[\alpha_1]$ and $n[\beta_1]$.

By a continuation of this process, we are able always to make the determination of ξ and η depend eventually upon that of ξ_n, η_n for a pair of integers α_n, β_n, one of which is a unit.

Since the existence of ξ_n and η_n is evident, the existence of ξ and η is proved.

We shall see later that, although the proof here given of the unique factorization theorem depends upon Th. A, there are realms in which the unique factorization theorem holds but Th. A does not hold. However, we shall see also that each of the three theorems B, C and the unique factorization theorem is necessary and sufficient for the validity of the other two.

Cor. 1. *If α and β be any two integers of $k(i)$, there exists a common divisor, δ, of α and β such that every common divisor of α and β divides δ, and there exist two integers, ξ and η, of $k(i)$ such that* $$\alpha\xi + \beta\eta = \delta.$$

The proof is the same as in *R*.

We call δ the *greatest common divisor* of α and β.

Cor. 2. *If $\alpha_1, \alpha_2, \cdots, \alpha_n$ be any n integers of $k(i)$, there exists a common divisor, δ, of $\alpha_1, \alpha_2, \cdots, \alpha_n$ such that every common divisor of $\alpha_1, \alpha_2, \cdots, \alpha_n$ divides δ, and there exist n integers $\xi_1, \xi_2, \cdots, \xi_n$ such that*

$$\alpha_1\xi_1 + \alpha_2\xi_2 + \cdots + \alpha_n\xi_n = \delta.$$

Theorem C. *If the product of two integers, α and β, of $k(i)$ be divisible by a prime number, π, at least one of the integers is divisible by π.*

Let $\alpha\beta = \gamma\pi$, where γ is an integer of $k(i)$, and assume α not to be divisible by π. Then α and π are prime to each other and there exist two integers, ξ and η, of $k(i)$ such that

$$\alpha\xi + \pi\eta = 1. \tag{2}$$

Multiplying 2) by β, we have

$$\beta\alpha\xi + \beta\pi\eta = \beta,$$

and therefore

$$\pi(\gamma\xi + \beta\eta) = \beta,$$

where $\gamma\xi + \beta\eta$ is an integer of $k(i)$; hence β is divisible by π.

Cor. 1. *If the product of any number of integers of $k(i)$ be divisible by a prime number, π, at least one of the integers is divisible by π.*

Cor. 2. *If neither of two integers be divisible by a prime number, π, their product is not divisible by π.*

Cor. 3. *If the product of two integers, α and β, be divisible by an integer, γ, and neither α nor β be divisible by γ, then γ is a composite number.*

THEOREM 4. *Every integer of $k(i)$ can be represented in one and only one way as the product of prime numbers.*

Let α be an integer of $k(i)$. If α be not itself a prime number, we have

$$\alpha = \beta\gamma, \tag{3}$$

where β and γ are integers of $k(i)$ neither of which is a unit.

From 3) it follows that $n[\alpha] = n[\beta]n[\gamma]$, whence, since $n[\beta] \neq 1$ and $n[\gamma] \neq 1$, we have $n[\beta]$ and $n[\gamma] < n[\alpha]$.

If β be not a prime number, we have as before

$$\beta = \beta_1\gamma_1,$$

where β_1 and γ_1 are integers neither of which is a unit, and hence $n[\beta_1]$ and $n[\gamma_1] < n[\beta]$. If β_1 be not a prime number, we proceed in the same manner, and, since $n[\beta], n[\beta_1], n[\beta_2], \cdots$ form a decreasing series of positive rational integers, we must after a finite number of such factorizations reach in the series $\beta, \beta_1, \beta_2, \cdots$ a prime number π_1. Thus α has the prime factor π_1, and we have

$$\alpha = \pi_1\alpha_1.$$

Proceeding similarly with α_1, in case it be not a prime number, we obtain

$$\alpha_1 = \pi_2 \alpha_2,$$

where π_2 is a prime number, and hence

$$\alpha = \pi_1 \pi_2 \alpha_2.$$

Continuing this process we must reach in the series $\alpha, \alpha_1, \alpha_2, \cdots$ a prime number π_n, since $n[\alpha], n[\alpha_1], n[\alpha_2], \cdots$ form a decreasing series of positive rational integers. We have thus

$$\alpha = \pi_1 \pi_2 \pi_3 \cdots \pi_n,$$

where the π's are all prime numbers; that is, *α can be represented as a product of a finite number of factors all of which are prime numbers.*

It remains to be proved that this representation is unique. Suppose that

$$\alpha = \rho_1 \rho_2 \rho_3 \cdots \rho_m$$

is a second representation of α as a product of prime factors. It follows by Th. C, Cor. 1 from

$$\pi_1 \pi_2 \pi_3 \cdots \pi_n = \rho_1 \rho_2 \rho_3 \cdots \rho_m, \qquad 4)$$

that at least one of the ρ's, say ρ_1, is divisible by π_1, and hence associated with π_1; that is, $\rho_1 = \epsilon_1 \pi_1$, where ϵ_1 is a unit. Dividing 4) by π_1, we have $\pi_2 \pi_3 \cdots \pi_n = \epsilon_1 \rho_2 \rho_3 \cdots \rho_m.$

From this it follows that at least one of the remaining ρ's, say ρ_2, is divisible by π_2, and hence associated with it. Thus $\rho_2 = \epsilon_2 \pi_2$, where ϵ_2 is a unit, and hence

$$\pi_3 \cdots \pi_n = \epsilon_1 \epsilon_2 \rho_3 \cdots \rho_m.$$

Proceeding in this manner, we see that with each π there is associated at least one ρ, and, if two or more π's be associated with one another, at least as many ρ's are associated with these π's, and hence with one another.

In exactly the same manner we can prove that with each ρ there is associated at least one π, and, if two or more ρ's be associated with one another, at least as many π's are associated with these ρ's, and hence with one another.

Hence considering, as we always shall, two associated factors as the same, the two representations are identical; that is, if in the one representation there occur e factors associated with a certain prime, there will be in the other representation exactly e factors associated with the same prime.

We can now evidently write every integer, α, of $k(i)$ in the form

$$\alpha = \epsilon\pi_1^{e_1}\pi_2^{e_2}\cdots\pi_n^{e_n},$$

where $\pi_1, \pi_2, \cdots, \pi_n$ are the unassociated prime factors of α, and ϵ a suitable unit. Moreover, this representation is unique.

Cor. 1. *If α and β be prime to each other and γ be divisible by both α and β, then γ is divisible by their product.*

Cor. 2. *If α and β be each prime to γ, then $\alpha\beta$ is prime to γ.*

Cor. 3. *If α be prime to γ and $\alpha\beta$ be divisible by γ, β is divisible by γ.*

We have seen that the divisibility of $n[\alpha]$ by $n[\beta]$ is a necessary condition for the divisibility of α by β. We shall now show that it is only when either α or β is a rational integer that the condition is also sufficient.

Let $$\alpha = \eta_\alpha\pi_1^{p_1}\pi_2^{p_2}\cdots\pi_k^{p_k},\quad \beta = \eta_\beta\rho_1^{r_1}\rho_2^{r_2}\cdots\rho_l^{r_l}$$

be representations of α and β as products of powers of their different prime factors, η_α and η_β being units.

From $$n[\alpha] = m\cdot n[\beta],$$

where m is a positive rational integer, it follows that

$$\pi_1^{p_1}\pi_2^{p_2}\cdots\pi_k^{p_k}\cdot\pi_1'^{p_1}\pi_2'^{p_2}\cdots\pi_k'^{p_k} = m\cdot\rho_1^{r_1}\rho_2^{r_2}\cdots\rho_l^{r_l}\cdot\rho_1'^{r_1}\rho_2'^{r_2}\cdots\rho_l'^{r_l},$$

from which we see that each prime, ρ_i, of the set $\rho_1, \rho_2, \cdots, \rho_l$ is associated with one of the π's or with one of the π''s, say π_j or π_j', and that $r_i \ngtr p_j$. In order that α may be divisible by β we must have every ρ associated with an unaccented π, which will not be in general the case. When, however, α is a rational integer we have $\alpha = \alpha'$, and this condition is satisfied, and hence β divides α.

If β be a rational integer it is easy to see likewise that, when $n[\alpha]$ is divisible by $n[\beta]$, α is divisible by β.

§ 9. Classification of the Prime Numbers of $k(i)$.

Every prime, π, of $k(i)$ divides an infinite number of positive rational integers; for example, $n[\pi]$ and its multiples. Among these positive rational integers there will be a smallest one, p, and p will be a rational prime number, for if p be not a prime, that is, if $p=p_1p_2$, π would divide either p_1 or p_2, and hence p would not be the smallest rational integer that π divides. In order, therefore, to find all primes of $k(i)$ we need only examine the divisors of all rational prime numbers considered as integers of $k(i)$.

Moreover it is evident that no prime of $k(i)$ can divide two different rational primes, for then it would divide their rational greatest common divisor, 1, and hence be a unit. Therefore every prime of $k(i)$ occurs once and but once among the divisors of the rational primes considered as integers of $k(i)$.

We have seen already that there are rational primes, as 3, which are also primes of $k(i)$, and other rational primes, as 5, which are factorable in $k(i)$. Denoting then by p the positive rational prime that π divides, we have

$$p=\pi\alpha, \qquad 1)$$

and hence
$$p^2=n[\pi]n[\alpha].$$

We have then two cases

i. $\begin{cases} n[\pi]=p, \\ n[\alpha]=p. \end{cases}$ ii. $\begin{cases} n[\pi]=p^2, \\ n[\alpha]=1. \end{cases}$

i. From $n[\pi]=\pi\pi'=p$ and 1) it follows that $\alpha=\pi'$. If $\pi=a+bi$, we have then

$$p=a^2+b^2.$$

Assume $p\neq 2$; then either a or b must be odd and the other even and therefore
$$p\equiv 1, \bmod 4.$$

Hence when a positive rational prime other than 2 is the product of two conjugate primes of $k(i)$, it has the form $4n+1$.

When $p=2$, we have

$$2=(1+i)(1-i),$$

and hence $$2 = i(1-i)^2;$$

that is, *2 is associated with, and hence divisible by, the square of a prime of* $k(i)$.

ii. Since $n[\alpha] = 1$, α is a unit and hence p is associated with the prime π; that is, p is a prime in $k(i)$. Hence a rational prime p is either a prime of $k(i)$ or the product of two conjugate primes of $k(i)$.

When p is a prime of the form $4n-1$ it is always a prime in $k(i)$, for we have seen that p is factorable into two conjugate primes of $k(i)$ only when it is 2 or of the form $4n+1$.

To prove now that every rational prime of the form $4n+1$ can be represented as the product of two conjugate primes of $k(i)$ we observe that from

$$p \equiv 1, \bmod 4,$$

it follows that the congruence

$$x^2 \equiv -1, \bmod p,$$

has roots. Let a be a root. Then

$$a^2 \equiv -1, \bmod p,$$

and hence $$(a+i)(a-i) \equiv 0, \bmod p.$$

Since $a+i$ and $a-i$ are integers of $k(i)$, the integer p, if a prime of $k(i)$, must divide either $a+i$ or $a-i$. This is however impossible, for from

$$a \pm i = p(c+di),$$

where $c+di$ is an integer of $k(i)$, it would follow that $pd = \pm 1$, which can not hold since p and d are both rational integers and $p > 1$. Hence p is not a prime in $k(i)$, and since the only way in which a rational prime can be factored in $k(i)$ is into two conjugate prime factors, p is factorable in this manner.

Collecting the above results, we see that the primes of $k(i)$ may be classified in the following manner, according to the rational primes of which they are factors.

1) *All positive rational primes of the form $4n+1$ are factorable in $k(i)$ into two conjugate primes, called primes of the first degree.*

2) *All positive rational primes of the form $4n-1$ are primes in $k(i)$, called primes of the second degree.*

3) *The number 2 is associated with the square of a prime of the first degree.*

It will be observed that the norm of every prime π of $k(i)$ is a power (first or second) of a rational prime and that the degree of π is the exponent of this power.

Moreover, we notice that 2 is the only rational prime that is divisible by the *square* of a prime of $k(i)$; for, if this were true of any other rational prime of the form $4n+1$, we should have π associated with π', and hence

$$a+bi=a-bi,\ -a+bi,\ b+ai \text{ or } -b-ai,$$

which give $a=0$, $b=0$, or $a=\pm b$, all of which are seen to be incompatible with $p=a^2+b^2$.

§ 10. Factorization of a Rational Prime in $k(i)$ determined by the value of (d/p).

The rational primes may be classified with regard to their factorization in $k(i)$ in the following manner:

1) *Those of which the discriminant is a quadratic residue are factorable into two conjugate primes in $k(i)$, called primes of the first degree.* For $(d/p)=1$ implies $p=4n+1$, since $d=-4$, and we have seen that all rational primes of this form are thus factorable in $k(i)$.

2) *Those of which the discriminant is a quadratic non-residue remain primes in $k(i)$, called primes of the second degree.* For $(d/p)=-1$ implies $p=4n+3$, and we have seen that all rational primes of this form remain primes in $k(i)$.

3) *Those which divide the discriminant (expressed symbolically by $(d/p)=0$) are associated with the squares of primes of the first degree in $k(i)$.*

Evidently 2 is the only rational prime which divides the discriminant of $k(i)$ and we have seen that $2=i(1-i)^2$. The following table expresses the above results:

1) $$\left(\frac{d}{p}\right)=1,\ p=\pi\pi',$$

2) $$\left(\frac{d}{p}\right) = -1, \; p = p,$$ [1]

3) $$\left(\frac{d}{p}\right) = 0, \; p = \epsilon\pi^2.$$

Ex. Show that, if α, $= a + bi$, be any integer of $k(i)$, such that a and b have no common rational divisor, and c be any rational integer divisible by α, then c is divisible by $n[\alpha]$.

§ 11. **Congruences in $k(i)$.**

Exactly as in the case of rational integers, we say that *two integers α, β, of $k(i)$ are congruent with respect to the modulus, μ, if their difference be divisible by μ*, and write

$$\alpha \equiv \beta, \text{ mod } \mu.$$

The laws of combination that were proved for congruences in R hold here.

We can now divide all integers of $k(i)$ into classes with respect to a given modulus, μ, putting two integers in the same class or different classes, according as they are or are not congruent to each other, mod μ. We shall show that for any given modulus μ there will be $n[\mu]$ such classes. To do this we shall need the following theorem:

THEOREM 5. *There exist among the multiples of any integer μ, of $k(i)$ two, $\iota_1, = a\omega_1, \iota_2, = b\omega_1 + c\omega_2$, such that every multiple of μ can be expressed in the form*

$$l_1\iota_1 + l_2\iota_2,$$

where a, b, c, l_1, l_2 are rational integers and ω_1, ω_2 is a basis of $k(i)$.

Suppose all multiples of μ to be written in the form

$$\iota = a_1\omega_1 + a_2\omega_2,$$

and consider those in which $a_2 \neq 0$.

Among them must be some in which a_2 is smaller in absolute value than in any of those remaining.

Let ι_2, $= b\omega_1 + c\omega_2$, be one of these; then c will divide the coefficient a_2 in every multiple of μ; for, if this be not the case,

[1] This indicates that p is unfactorable in the realm under discussion.

let $\beta, = b_1\omega_1 + c_1\omega_2$, be a multiple of μ such that c_1 is not divisible by c, and let d be the greatest common divisor of c and c_1. There exist two rational integers e, e_1, such that

$$ec + e_1c_1 = d,$$

and hence $\gamma = e\iota_2 + e_1\beta = (eb + e_1b_1)\omega_1 + d\omega_2$

is a multiple of μ in which a_2 is less in absolute value than c, but not 0. But this is contrary to our original hypothesis. Hence we have $$a_2 = l_2c,$$

where l_2 is a rational integer, and hence

$$\iota - l_2\iota_2 = (a_1 - l_2b)\omega_1.$$

Consider now those multiples of μ in which $a_2 = 0$, but $a_1 \neq 0$.

There will be some among them in which a_1 is less in absolute value than in any of those remaining.

Let $\iota_1, = a\omega_1$, be one of these.

It is seen as above that a is a divisor of the coefficient a_1 in every multiple of μ in which $a_2 = 0$, $a_1 \neq 0$. We have, therefore, since $(a_1 - l_2b)\omega_1$ is a multiple of μ belonging to this class,

$$\iota - l_2\iota_2 = (a_1 - l_2b)\omega_1 = l_1\iota_1,$$

where l_1 is a rational integer, and hence

$$\iota = l_1\iota_1 + l_2\iota_2.$$

Any pair, μ_1, μ_2, of multiples of μ, such that every multiple of μ can be written in the form

$$m_1\mu_1 + m_2\mu_2,$$

where m_1, m_2 are rational integers, we call a *basis of the multiples of* μ.

The pair of multiples of μ, $a\omega_1$, $b\omega_1 + c\omega_2$, selected as above, and in which in addition a and c are positive, is called a *canonical basis of the multiples of* μ.

THEOREM 6. *If* μ_1, μ_2 *be a basis of the multiples of* μ, *the necessary and sufficient condition that*

$$\mu_1^* = a_1\mu_1 + a_2\mu_2,$$

$$\mu_2^* = b_1\mu_1 + b_2\mu_2,$$

where a_1, a_2, b_1, b_2 *are rational integers, shall be also a basis of the multiples of* μ *is*

$$\begin{vmatrix} a_1 & a_2 \\ b_1 & b_2 \end{vmatrix} = \pm 1.$$

The proof of the theorem is the same as that of Th. 2.

THEOREM 7. *If*

$$\mu_1 = a_1\omega_1 + a_2\omega_2,$$

$$\mu_2 = b_1\omega_1 + b_2\omega_2,$$

be any basis of the multiples of μ, *then*

$$\left\|\begin{matrix} a_1 & a_2 \\ b_1 & b_2 \end{matrix}\right\| = n[\mu].$$

It is evident from the last theorem (see proof of Th. 2) that the absolute value of the determinant

$$\begin{vmatrix} a_1 & a_2 \\ b_1 & b_2 \end{vmatrix}$$

is the same for every set of basis numbers of the multiples of μ. Hence we need only determine its value for some particular basis.

The integers
$$\mu = a_1 + a_2 i,$$

$$\mu i = -a_2 + a_1 i,$$

constitute a basis of the multiples of μ, and

$$\begin{vmatrix} a_1 & a_2 \\ -a_2 & a_1 \end{vmatrix} = a_1^2 + a_2^2 = n[\mu].$$

Hence the theorem is proved.

THEOREM 8. *If* μ *be any integer of* $k(i)$, *the number of numbers in a complete residue system, mod* μ, *is* $n[\mu]$.

Let $a\omega_1, b\omega_1 + c\omega_2$ be a canonical basis of the multiples of μ and consider the system of integers

$$u\omega_1 + v\omega_2 \begin{cases} u = 0, 1, \cdots, a-1, \\ v = 0, 1, \cdots, c-1, \end{cases} \qquad 1)$$

which are evidently ac, $= n[\mu]$, in number.

We shall show that the integers 1) constitute a complete residue system, mod μ.

First, each of them is incongruent to all the others, mod μ, for if $u_1\omega_1 + v_1\omega_2$, $u_2\omega_1 + v_2\omega_2$ be any two of them, and

$$u_1\omega_1 + v_1\omega_2 \equiv u_2\omega_1 + v_2\omega_2, \text{ mod } \mu,$$

then
$$(u_1 - u_2)\,\omega_1 + (v_1 - v_2)\omega_2 \equiv 0, \text{ mod } \mu,$$

and hence, since c is the greatest common divisor of the coefficients of ω_2 in all multiples of μ,

$$v_1 - v_2 \equiv 0, \text{ mod } c.$$

But v_1 and v_2 are both less than c; hence

$$v_1 = v_2.$$

It follows that $\omega_1(u_1 - u_2) \equiv 0, \text{ mod } \mu,$

and hence, since a is the greatest common divisor of the coefficient of ω_1 in all multiples of μ in which the coefficient of ω_2 is 0,

$$u_1 - u_2 \equiv 0, \text{ mod } a.$$

But u_1 and u_2 are both less than a; hence

$$u_1 = u_2.$$

Thus
$$u_1\omega_1 + v_1\omega_2 = u_2\omega_1 + v_2\omega_2,$$

and the numbers 1) are seen to be incongruent each to each, mod μ. Moreover, every integer of the realm is congruent to one of the integers 1), mod μ. For, let

$$\omega = t_1\omega_1 + t_2\omega_2$$

be any integer of $k(i)$, and let

$$t_2 = mc + r_2,$$

where m and r_2 are rational integers and r_2 satisfies the condition

$$0 \leqq r_2 < c.$$

Also let
$$t_1 - mb = na + r_1,$$

where n and r_1 are rational integers and r_1 satisfies the condition

$$0 \leqq r_1 < a.$$

Then
$$t_1\omega_1 + t_2\omega_2 = (mb + na + r_1)\omega_1 + (mc + r_2)\omega_2$$
$$= na\omega_1 + m(b\omega_1 + c\omega_2) + r_1\omega_1 + r_2\omega_2;$$

and hence $$t_1\omega_1 + t_2\omega_2 \equiv r_1\omega_1 + r_2\omega_2, \bmod \mu,$$

where $r_1\omega_1 + r_2\omega_2$ is one of the integers 1). Hence every integer of the realm is congruent, mod μ, to one and but one of the integers 1).

The integers 1) constitute, therefore, a complete residue system, mod μ, and being $n[\mu]$ in number the theorem is proved.

We can construct a complete residue system for any modulus, μ, by means of the method employed in the above proof. Taking $1, i$ as a basis, we let $$\mu = m(p + qi),$$

where m is the largest rational integer that divides μ, p and q being consequently prime to each other.

It is easily seen that $m(p^2 + q^2)$ is the rational integer of smallest absolute value divisible by μ; that is,

$$a = m(p^2 + q^2).$$

Since $$ac = n[\mu] = m^2(p^2 + q^2),$$

we have therefore $c = m$.

Hence the $n[\mu]$ integers

$$u + vi, \begin{cases} u = 0, 1, \cdots, m(p^2 + q^2) - 1, \\ v = 0, 1, \cdots, m - 1, \end{cases}$$

is a complete residue system, mod μ.

Ex. Let $$\mu = 3 + 6i = 3(1 + 2i).$$

Then $$m = 3, \; a = 15, \; c = 3.$$

The following 45 integers constitute a complete residue system, mod $3 + 6i$,

0	1	2	3	4	5	6	7
i	$1+i$	$2+i$	$3+i$	$4+i$	$5+i$	$6+i$	$7+i$
$2i$	$1+2i$	$2+2i$	$3+2i$	$4+2i$	$5+2i$	$6+2i$	$7+2i$

8	9	10	11	12	13	14
$8+i$	$9+i$	$10+i$	$11+i$	$12+i$	$13+i$	$14+i$.
$8+2i$	$9+2i$	$10+2i$	$11+2i$	$12+2i$	$13+2i$	$14+2i$.

We can thus obtain a complete residue system with respect to any modulus by means of the method employed in the above theorem.

There are two important special cases which deserve mention.

i. *If $\mu = p + qi$, where p and q have no common divisor, the* *integers* $1, 2, \cdots, p^2+q^2, =n[\mu]$, *form a complete residue system, mod* μ.

ii. *If* $\mu = m$, *a rational integer, the* m^2 *integers*

$$x + yi, \begin{cases} x = 0, 1, \cdots, |m| - 1, \\ y = 0, 1, \cdots, |m| - 1, \end{cases}$$

form a complete residue system, mod m.

Ex. 1. Prove i and ii without making use of Th. 8.
Ex. 2. Show that $\alpha \equiv \beta$, mod γ, implies $\alpha' \equiv \beta'$, mod γ'.

All integers belonging to the same residue class, mod μ, have with μ the same greatest common divisors; for from

$$\alpha \equiv \beta, \text{ mod } \mu,$$

it follows that

$$\alpha = \beta + \nu\mu,$$

and hence every common divisor of β and μ is also a divisor of α and every common divisor of α and μ is a divisor of β.

In particular, if one number of a residue class be prime to the modulus, μ, all other numbers of the class are prime to μ.

A system of integers incongruent each to each with respect to a given modulus, μ, and prime to μ is called *a reduced system of incongruent numbers*, mod μ, or a *reduced residue system*, mod μ. Thus the numbers 1, 2, 3, 4, 5, 6, 7, 8, 9, 10 constitute a complete system of incongruent numbers, mod $1+3i$, and 1, 3, 7, 9 constitute a reduced system to the same modulus.

§ 12. The ϕ-Function in $k(i)$.

Just as in R, we understand by $\phi(\mu)$, where μ is an integer of $k(i)$, *the number of integers in a reduced residue system, mod* μ.

We have

$$\phi(\epsilon) = 1,$$

where ϵ is any unit of $k(i)$, and, as may be easily seen,

$$\phi(\pi) = n[\pi] - 1,$$

where π is a prime of $k(i)$; for example, $\phi(2+i) = 4$, since 1, 2, 3, 4, 5 constitute a complete residue system, mod $2+i$, and all these integers except 5 are prime to $2+i$. Likewise

$$\phi(1+3i) = 4,$$

since 1, 2, 3, 4, 5, 6, 7, 8, 9, 10 constitute a complete residue system, mod $1+3i$, and of these integers only 1, 3, 7 and 9 are prime to $1+3i$.

To get a general expression for $\phi(\mu)$ in terms of μ, we may employ any one of the three methods used to obtain the corresponding expression in R.

We shall sketch the proof briefly, following the third method used in R (see Chap. III, § 4).

The completion of this and the two remaining proofs will serve as exercises.

THEOREM 9. *If $\alpha=\beta\gamma$, where β and γ are any integers of $k(i)$, there are in a complete residue system, mod α, exactly $n(\gamma)$ numbers that are divisible by β.*

Let
$$\gamma_1, \gamma_2, \cdots, \gamma_{n(\gamma)} \qquad 1)$$
be a complete system of incongruent numbers, mod γ. The numbers
$$\beta\gamma_1, \beta\gamma_2, \cdots, \beta\gamma_{n(\gamma)} \qquad 2)$$
are incongruent, mod α, for if
$$\beta\gamma_h \equiv \beta\gamma_i, \text{ mod } \alpha,$$
then
$$\gamma_h \equiv \gamma_i, \text{ mod } \gamma.$$
which is impossible.

Moreover, every integer $\beta\delta$, divisible by β is congruent to some one of the numbers 2), mod α; for δ is congruent to some one, say γ_i, of the numbers 1), mod γ, and from
$$\delta \equiv \gamma_i, \text{ mod } \gamma,$$
it follows that
$$\beta\delta \equiv \beta\gamma_i, \text{ mod } \alpha.$$
Since, also, every integer congruent, mod α, to one of the numbers 2) is divisible by β (see § 11 and Chap. III, § 1, ix), and the numbers 2) are $n(\gamma)$ in number, there are in every complete residue system, mod α, exactly $n(\gamma)$ numbers that are divisible by β.

THEOREM 10. *If π be any prime of $k(i)$,*
$$\phi(\pi^m) = n[\pi^m]\left(1 - \frac{1}{n[\pi]}\right).$$

From the last theorem we see that among the $n[\pi^m]$ numbers of a complete residue system, mod π^m, there are exactly $n[\pi^{m-1}]$ that are divisible by π, and hence $n[\pi^m]-n[\pi^{m-1}]$ that are prime to π^m; that is
$$\phi(\pi^m)=n[\pi^m]\left(1-\frac{1}{n[\pi]}\right).$$

To derive the general expression for $\phi(\mu)$ we have now to prove the theorem for $k(i)$ corresponding to Th. 4, Chap. III.

THEOREM 11. *If $\mu_1, \mu_2, \cdots, \mu_s$ be integers of $k(i)$ prime each to each*
$$\phi(\mu_1\mu_2\cdots\mu_s)=\phi(\mu_1)\phi(\mu_2)\cdots\phi(\mu_s).$$

Ex. We have
$$-3+11i=(1+3i)(3+2i),$$
where $1+3i$ and $3+2i$ are prime to each other.

Hence $\phi(-3+11i)=\phi(1+3i)\phi(3+2i)=4\cdot 12=48.$

The proof of this theorem depends directly upon the following theorem which can be proved exactly as in R (Chap. III, § 14):

THEOREM 12. *If*
$$\mu=\mu_1\mu_2\cdots\mu_s$$
where $\mu_1, \mu_2, \cdots, \mu_s$ are integers of $k(i)$ prime each to each, and if $\alpha_1, \alpha_2, \cdots, \alpha_s$ be any integers of $k(i)$, there exist integers, ω, such that
$$\omega\equiv\alpha_1, \bmod \mu_1,\quad \omega\equiv\alpha_2, \bmod \mu_2, \cdots, \omega\equiv\alpha_s, \bmod \mu_s,$$
and all these integers are congruent each to each, mod μ. Moreover
$$\omega\equiv\alpha_1\beta_1+\alpha_2\beta_2+\cdots+\alpha_s\beta_s, \bmod \mu,$$
where
$$\beta_i\equiv 1, \bmod \mu_i, \text{ and } \beta_i\equiv 0, \bmod \mu_1\cdots\mu_{i-1}\mu_{i+1}\cdots\mu_s,\ i=1,2,\cdots,s.$$

We can now obtain easily the general expression for $\phi(\mu)$, μ being any integer of $k(i)$.

THEOREM 13. *If μ be any integer of $k(i)$ and $\pi_1, \pi_2, \cdots, \pi_s$ the different prime factors of μ, then*
$$\phi(\mu)=n[\mu]\left(1-\frac{1}{n[\pi_1]}\right)\left(1-\frac{1}{n[\pi_2]}\right)\cdots\left(1-\frac{1}{n[\pi_s]}\right).$$

Let
$$\mu=\pi_1^{e_1}\pi_2^{e_2}\cdots\pi_s^{e_s}.$$

By Th. 11 we have

$$\phi(\mu) = \phi(\pi_1^{e_1})\phi(\pi_2^{e_2}) \cdots \phi(\pi_s^{e_s}),$$

from which by Th. 10 it follows that

$$\phi(\mu) = n[\pi_1^{e_1}]\left(1 - \frac{1}{n[\pi_1]}\right) n[\pi_2^{e_2}]\left(1 - \frac{1}{n[\pi_2]}\right) \cdots n[\pi_s^{e_s}]\left(1 - \frac{1}{n[\pi_s]}\right)$$

and hence that

$$\phi(\mu) = n[\mu]\left(1 - \frac{1}{n[\pi_1]}\right)\left(1 - \frac{1}{n[\pi_2]}\right)\cdots\left(1 - \frac{1}{n[\pi_s]}\right).$$

Ex. We have

$$-201 - 43i = (1+i)(2+i)^2(3+2i)^2,$$

and hence $\phi(-201-43i)$

$$= n(-201-43i)\left(1 - \frac{1}{n[1+i]}\right)\left(1 - \frac{1}{n[2+i]}\right)\left(1 - \frac{1}{n[3+2i]}\right)$$

$$= 42250 \cdot \tfrac{1}{2} \cdot \tfrac{4}{5} \cdot \tfrac{12}{13},$$

$$= 15600.$$

THEOREM 14. *If $\delta_1, \delta_2, \cdots, \delta_r$ be the different divisors of μ, then*

$$\sum_{1,r}^{n} \phi(\delta_n) = n[\mu].$$

For proof see corresponding theorem in R (Chap. III, Th. 6).

Ex. We have $-3 + 11i = (1+i)(2+i)(3+2i)$.

The different divisors of $-3+11i$ are 1, $1+i$, $2+i$, $3+2i$, $1+3i$, $1+5i$, $4+7i$, and $-3+11i$, and for these the corresponding values of ϕ are 1, 1, 4, 12, 4, 12, 48, 48, whose sum is seen to be 130, $= n[-3+11i]$.

§ 13. Residue Systems Formed by Multiplying the Numbers of a Given System by an Integer Prime to the Modulus.

THEOREM 15. *If $\mu_1, \mu_2, \cdots, \mu_{n[\mu]}$ be a complete residue system, mod μ, and α any integer prime to μ, then $\alpha\mu_1, \alpha\mu_2, \cdots, \alpha\mu_{n[\mu]}$ is also a complete residue system, mod μ.*

The integers $\alpha\mu_1, \alpha\mu_2, \cdots, \alpha\mu_{n[\mu]}$ are incongruent each to each, mod μ, for from

$$\alpha\mu_i \equiv \alpha\mu_j, \text{ mod } \mu,$$

it would follow that, since α is prime to μ,

$$\mu_i \equiv \mu_j, \text{ mod } \mu,$$

which is contrary to the hypothesis that $\mu_1, \mu_2, \cdots, \mu_{n[\mu]}$ form a complete residue system, mod μ. The integers $\alpha\mu_1, \alpha\mu_2, \cdots, \alpha\mu_{n[\mu]}$ are, moreover, $n[\mu]$ in number. They form, therefore, a complete residue system, mod μ.

Cor. *If $\rho_1, \rho_2, \cdots, \rho_{\phi(\mu)}$ be a reduced residue system, mod μ, and α be prime to μ, then $\alpha\rho_1, \alpha\rho_2, \cdots, \alpha\rho_{\phi(\mu)}$ is also a reduced residue system, mod μ*; for $\alpha\rho_1, \alpha\rho_2, \cdots, \alpha\rho_{\phi(\mu)}$ are incongruent each to each, mod μ, prime to μ and $\phi(\mu)$ in number.

§14. The Analogue for $k(i)$ of Fermat's Theorem.

A theorem analogous to the generalized Fermat's theorem for rational integers can be proved for the integers of $k(i)$; that is,

THEOREM 16. *If μ be any integer of $k(i)$ and α any integer prime to μ, then*

$$\alpha^{\phi(\mu)} \equiv 1, \text{ mod } \mu.$$

Let $\alpha_1, \alpha_2, \cdots, \alpha_{\phi(\mu)}$ be a reduced residue system, mod μ; then

$$\alpha\alpha_1, \alpha\alpha_2, \cdots, \alpha\alpha_{\phi(\mu)}$$

is also such a system (Th. 15, Cor.).

Since $$\alpha\alpha_1, \alpha\alpha_2, \cdots, \alpha\alpha_{\phi(\mu)}$$

and $$\alpha_1, \alpha_2, \cdots, \alpha_{\phi(\mu)}$$

are both systems of this kind, each integer in the one system must be congruent, mod μ, to one and only one integer in the other system, though perhaps in a different order; that is,

$$\left.\begin{array}{ll} \alpha\alpha_1 & \equiv \alpha_{k_1} \\ \alpha\alpha_2 & \equiv \alpha_{k_2} \\ \cdot & \cdot \\ \cdot & \cdot \\ \cdot & \cdot \\ \alpha\alpha_{\phi(\mu)} & \equiv \alpha_{k_{\phi(\mu)}} \end{array}\right\}, \text{ mod } \mu.$$

Hence

$$\alpha^{\phi(\mu)}\alpha_1\alpha_2 \cdots \alpha_{\phi(\mu)} \equiv \alpha_{k_1}\alpha_{k_2} \cdots \alpha_{k_{\phi(\mu)}}, \text{ mod } \mu,$$

and since $$\alpha_1\alpha_2 \cdots \alpha_{\phi(\mu)} = \alpha_{k_1}\alpha_{k_2} \cdots \alpha_{k_{\phi(\mu)}},$$

and is prime to μ, we have

$$\alpha^{\phi(\mu)} \equiv 1, \bmod \mu.$$

Cor. 1. *If π be a prime and α any integer not divisible by π, then*

$$\alpha^{n[\pi]-1} \equiv 1, \bmod \pi.$$

This is the analogue of Fermat's Theorem.

Cor. 2. *If π be a prime and α any integer of $k(i)$, then*

$$\alpha^{n[\pi]} \equiv \alpha, \bmod \pi.$$

Ex. 1. Let $\pi = 1 + 2i$, and $\alpha = 1 + i$;

then $(1+i)^{\phi(1+2i)} \equiv 1, \bmod 1+2i,$

or $(1+i)^4 = -4 \equiv 1, \bmod 1+2i.$

Ex. 2. Let $\mu = 1 + 3i$ and $\alpha = 3$;

then $3^{\phi(1+3i)} \equiv 1, \bmod 1+3i,$

or $81 \equiv 1, \bmod 1+3i.$

Ex. 3. If α and μ be any two integers of $k(i)$ and $\alpha = \alpha_1\delta$, $\mu = \mu_1\delta$, where δ is the greatest common divisor of α and μ, show that the necessary and sufficient condition for

$$\alpha^{\phi(\mu)+1} \equiv \alpha, \bmod \mu,$$

is that μ_1 be prime to δ.

§ 15. Congruences of Condition.

The remarks at the beginning of § 9, Chap. III, apply equally to congruences in $k(i)$, and the theory of congruences of condition in $k(i)$ can be developed in exactly the same manner as in R.

In $k(i)$ the coefficients of the polynomials are any integers of $k(i)$.

With this change we can show that a polynomial in a single variable x can be resolved in one and but one way into prime factors with respect to a modulus which is a prime of $k(i)$, and upon this theorem build a theory for congruences in one unknown just as in R.

The theories of power residues, binomial congruences and indices may be developed similarly for the integers of $k(i)$.

§ 16. Two Problems.

We shall now discuss briefly two problems which are of interest in the theory of numbers, the first being especially famous. They can be solved without making use of numbers other than those of R, but their solution is greatly assisted by the introduction of the realm $k(i)$.

Problem 1. To represent a rational prime as the sum of two squares.[1]—Let p be a rational prime and suppose the desired representation possible. Then

$$p = a^2 + b^2,$$

and hence

$$p = (a + bi)(a - bi);$$

that is, the representation is possible when and only when p is the product of two conjugate primes of $k(i)$. Hence

i. *No prime of the form $4n + 3$ can be represented as the sum of two squares,* since a prime of this form is a prime in $k(i)$.

ii. *The number 2 and every prime of the form $4n + 1$ can be represented as the sum of two squares.*

Moreover, this representation is unique, for if we have two different representations

$$p = a^2 + b^2 \text{ and } p = a_1^2 + b_1^2,$$

then

$$p = (a + bi)(a - bi) \text{ and } p = (a_1 + b_1 i)(a_1 - b_1 i);$$

that is, p would be factorable in two different ways into prime factors in $k(i)$, which is impossible. Hence 2 and every prime of the form $4n + 1$ can be represented in one and only one way as the sum of two squares, but no prime of the form $4n + 3$ can be so represented.

Problem 2. To represent any positive rational integer, m, as the sum of two squares.

Let

$$m = p_1 p_2 \cdots p_r \cdot q_1^{t_1} q_2^{t_2} \cdots q_s^{t_s},$$

where $p_1, p_2, \cdots, p_r$ are rational primes of the form $4n + 1$ or 2,

[1] Fermat: Works, Vol. I, p. 294.
For solution of this problem without the aid of $k(i)$ see Dirichlet-Dedekind: § 68; also Mathews: § 91.

two or more of which may be alike, and $q_1, q_2, \cdots, q_s$ rational primes of the form $4n+3$, that are all different from one another. If the representation be possible,

$$m = a^2 + b^2;$$

and hence
$$m = (a+bi)(a-bi).$$

The representation is therefore possible when and only when we can factor m into two conjugate factors in $k(i)$. The necessary and sufficient condition for this is that all the t's be even, in which case we have, if

$$p_1 = \pi_1\pi_1', \; p_2 = \pi_2\pi_2', \cdots, p_r = \pi_r\pi_r',$$

$$m = (\pi_1\pi_2 \cdots \pi_r q_1^{t_1/2} q_2^{t_2/2} \cdots q_s^{t_s/2}) \times (\pi_1'\pi_2' \cdots \pi_r' q_1^{t_1/2} q_2^{t_2/2} \cdots q_s^{t_s/2}). \qquad 1)$$

Hence if a positive rational integer, m, contain a prime factor of the form $4n+3$ an odd number of times, m cannot be represented as the sum of two squares. In all other cases the representation is possible.

Moreover, supposing the factorization 1) to be possible, it can be effected in general in several different ways, as for example,

$$m = (\pi_1'\pi_2 \cdots \pi_r q_1^{t_1/2} q_2^{t_2/2} \cdots q_s^{t_s/2}) \times (\pi_1\pi_2' \cdots \pi_r' q_1^{t_1/2} q_2^{t_2/2} \cdots q_s^{t_s/2}),$$

and since each of these factorizations yields a different representation of m as the sum of two squares, the problem can be solved in exactly as many different ways.

If $m = 2^n p_1^{e_1} p_2^{e_2} \cdots p_r^{e_r} q_1^{t_1} q_2^{t_2} \cdots q_s^{t_s}$, where the p's are primes of the form $4n+1$, all different, the q's primes of the form $4n+3$, and the t's all even, then, if N be the number of different ways in which m can be represented as the sum of two squares, we have $N = \frac{1}{2}(e_1+1)(e_2+1)\cdots(e_r+1)$ or $\frac{1}{2}(e_1+1)(e_2+1)\cdots(e_r+1)+\frac{1}{2}$ according as some or none of the e's are uneven. (See Gauss: Disq. Arith., V, 182.)

Ex.
$$\begin{aligned} 65 = 13 \cdot 5 &= (1+2i)(1-2i)(2+3i)(2-3i), \\ &= [(1+2i)(2+3i)][(1-2i)(2-3i)], \\ &= (-4+7i)(-4-7i) = 4^2+7^2, \end{aligned}$$

or
$$\begin{aligned} &= [(1+2i)(2-3i)][(1-2i)(2+3i)], \\ &= (8+i)(8-i) = 8^2+1^2. \end{aligned}$$

Thus 65 can be expressed in two ways as the sum of two squares.

§ 17. Primary Integers of $k(i)$.

When an integer, α, plays the role of divisor it is unnecessary to distinguish between its associates. This is, however, not the case when α is combined with other numbers by the operations of addition or subtraction. For example, when α is the modulus of a congruence we may consider α to be any one of its associates, but when α is a coefficient some particular one of its associates must be designated. This distinction between the associates of α is the same as that made in the rational realm between a and $-a$.

There, for example, the quadratic reciprocity law is given for *positive* primes, since although we have always

$$\left(\frac{q}{p}\right)=\left(\frac{q}{-p}\right),$$

we do not have in general

$$\left(\frac{q}{p}\right)=\left(\frac{-q}{p}\right).$$

An integer so singled out from its associates according to some prescribed rule is called a primary integer.

This rule of selection should evidently be such that the product of any two primary integers is primary; that is, if α and β be the integers selected as primary from $\alpha, -\alpha, i\alpha, -i\alpha$ and $\beta, -\beta, i\beta, -i\beta$, respectively, then $\alpha\beta$ should be the integer that according to the same rule should be selected as primary from $\alpha\beta, -\alpha\beta, i\alpha\beta, -i\alpha\beta$.

Gauss gives two rules of selection, both of which obey the principle just enunciated. The first rule is based entirely upon this principle, the second partially. Gauss makes use of the second rule and this one will now be described.

The rule will be given here without employing the above mentioned principle, and will then be shown to obey it.

We first divide the integers of $k(i)$ into two classes according as their norms are odd or even, those of the first class being called odd integers, those of the second class even integers.[1]

[1] Bachmann: Die Lehre von der Kreisteilung, p. 152.

If $n[a+bi], = a^2+b^2$, be odd, it is evident that either a or b is odd, the other even.

If $n[a+bi]$ be even, a and b are both odd or both even.

Every prime of $k(i)$ except $1+i$ is evidently an odd integer. Since $1+i$ and $1-i$ are associates, it is evident that $n[\alpha]$ divisible by 2 is not only a necessary but a sufficient condition that α shall be divisible by $1+i$.

We see, therefore, that *a necessary and sufficient condition for an integer of $k(i)$ to be even is that it shall be divisible by $1+i$.*

The selection of one of the four associates of an integer is now made as follows. Considering first only the odd integers of $k(i)$, we have the following rule:

That number $x+yi$ of the four associated odd integers

$$a+bi, \quad -a-bi, \quad -b+ai, \quad b-ai \tag{1}$$

is singled out as primary in which we have simultaneously either

$$\left.\begin{array}{ll} & x\equiv 1;\ y\equiv 0 \\ \textit{or} & x\equiv -1;\ y\equiv 2 \end{array}\right\},\ \text{mod } 4, \tag{2}$$

where x denotes the real part and y the coefficient of i.

That one and only one such integer exists in the group 1) is shown as follows. Since $a+bi$ is an odd integer, a and b can neither be both odd nor both even. Suppose a even, b odd. Then one of the integers, b or $-b$, is of the form $4n+1$, the other of the form $4n-1$.

If now $$a\equiv 0, \text{ mod } 4,$$

that one of two integers, $b-ai, -b+ai$, will be primary in which the real part has the form $4n+1$.

If $$a\equiv 2, \text{ mod } 4,$$

that one of the integers, $b-ai, -b+ai$, will be primary in which the real part has the form $4n-1$.

It is evident in both these cases that none of the remaining associates satisfy the conditions.

Similarly we see that when a is odd and b even, one and only one of the four associates 1) satisfies 2).

If a be a rational integer, that one of the integers, $a, -a$, is primary which has the form $4n+1$. The negative rational primes prime in $k(i)$ are thus seen to be primary. Two conjugate odd integers are evidently either both primary or both non-primary. It can be easily shown that the above rule of selection is equivalent to the following:

That one of four associated odd integers is primary which is congruent to 1, mod $2+2i$. 3)

Ex. Of the four associated odd integers

$$9+12i, \quad -9-12i, \quad 12-9i, \quad -12+9i,$$

$9+12i$ satisfies the conditions 2); for we have

$$9 \equiv 1 \text{ and } 12 \equiv 0, \bmod 4.$$

Hence $9+12i$ is primary.

We also see that $\qquad 9+12i \equiv 1, \bmod 2+2i.$

It is easily seen that $9+12i$ is the only one of its associates which satisfies the conditions 2) or their equivalent 3).

Since every prime of $k(i)$ except $1+i$ is an odd integer, we can now distinguish between the associates of every prime except $1+i$. In the case of $1+i$ we may take any one of its associates, say $1+i$, as the primary one. The primary primes of $k(i)$ whose norms are less than 50 are

$$1+i, \ -1+2i, \ -1-2i, \ -3, \ 3+2i, \ 3-2i, \ 1+4i, \ 1-4i,$$
$$-5+2i, \ -5-2i, \ -1+6i, \ -1-6i, \ 5+4i, \ 5-4i, \ -7.$$

Remembering that a necessary as well as sufficient condition for an integer, μ, to be even is that it shall be divisible by $1+i$, we can distinguish between the associates of μ by taking that one as primary which when written in the form $(1+i)^h\nu$ has the factor ν, which is an odd integer, primary. We shall now show that the product of two odd primary integers is a primary integer.

Let $\alpha, =a+bi$, and $\beta, =c+di$, be any two odd primary integers. Then one of the following cases must occur.

$$\begin{array}{cccc} \text{i.} & \text{ii.} & \text{iii.} & \text{iv.} \\ a\equiv 1 & a\equiv 1 & a\equiv -1 & a\equiv -1 \\ b\equiv 0 & b\equiv 0 & b\equiv 2 & b\equiv 2 \\ c\equiv 1 & c\equiv -1 & c\equiv 1 & c\equiv -1 \\ d\equiv 0 & d\equiv 2 & d\equiv 0 & d\equiv 2 \end{array} \left.\vphantom{\begin{array}{c}1\\1\\1\\1\\1\end{array}}\right\}, \bmod 4,$$

and $$\alpha\beta = (ac - bd) + (ad + bc)i = e + fi,$$

gives one of the following corresponding cases:

$$\begin{array}{cccc} \text{i.} & \text{ii.} & \text{iii.} & \text{iv.} \\ e \equiv 1 & e \equiv -1 & e \equiv -1 & e \equiv 1 \\ f \equiv 0 & f \equiv 2 & f \equiv 2 & f \equiv 0 \end{array} \Bigg\}, \bmod 4.$$

Hence $\alpha\beta$ is always an odd primary integer, if α and β be odd primary integers. This may be shown more simply by means of the condition 3).

From this it follows at once that the product of any two primary integers is primary. We may now express the unique factorization law for the integers of $k(i)$ as follows:

A primary integer can be resolved in one and only one way into a product of primary prime factors.

The term primary integer is generally taken to mean what is here called an odd primary integer.

§ 18. Quadratic Residues and the Quadratic Reciprocity Law in $k(i)$.[1]

If α and μ be any integers of $k(i)$ prime to each other, we say, as in R, that α is a quadratic residue or non-residue of μ according as the congruence

$$x^2 \equiv \alpha, \bmod \mu,$$

has or has not roots.

Ex. 1. The congruence

$$x^2 \equiv 1 + i, \bmod 1 - 2i,$$

has the roots ± 2; for

$$(\pm 2)^2 \equiv 1 + i, \bmod 1 - 2i,$$

since $$4 - (1 + i) = 3 - i = (1 + i)(1 - 2i).$$

Hence $1 + i$ is a quadratic residue of $1 - 2i$.

Ex. 2. On the other hand the congruence

$$x^2 \equiv 3, \bmod 1 - 2i,$$

has no roots, for substituting the integers ± 1, ± 2, of a reduced residue system, mod $1 - 2i$, we have

$$\left.\begin{array}{l} 1 \not\equiv 3 \\ 4 \not\equiv 3 \end{array}\right\}, \bmod 1 - 2i.$$

[1] See Gauss: Theoria Residuorum Biquadraticorum, §§ 56–60; Works. Vol. 2, pp. 126–130.

Hence 3 is a quadratic non-residue of $1-2i$.

The theory of quadratic residues can be developed for $k(i)$ along lines so nearly identical with those for the same subject in the rational realm that only the briefest outline will be given here.

We have, as before, two questions to answer: first, *what integers are, and what are not, quadratic residues of a given modulus;* second, *of what moduli is a given integer a quadratic residue and of what moduli is it a non-residue?*

The first question can be easily answered. The second is much more difficult. We shall confine ourselves in what follows to the case where the modulus is a prime π. We observe first that every odd integer of $k(i)$, that is, every integer prime to $1+i$, is congruent to 1, mod $1+i$, and hence is a quadratic residue of $1+i$.

For π, an odd prime, we have the following theorem, the proof of which is like that of the corresponding theorem for rational integers (Chap. IV, Th. 1).

THEOREM 17. *The necessary and sufficient condition that α shall be a quadratic residue of π is that*

$$\alpha^{\frac{n[\pi]-1}{2}} \equiv 1, \text{ mod } \pi.$$

Ex. 3. Let $\pi = 1-2i$, $\alpha = 1+i$. We have

$$(1+i)^{\frac{n[\pi]-1}{2}} = (1+i)^2 = 2i \equiv 1, \text{ mod } 1-2i.$$

Hence $1+i$ is a quadratic residue of $1-2i$.

Ex. 4. Let $\pi = 1-2i$, $\alpha = 3$. We have

$$3^{\frac{n[\pi]-1}{2}} = 3^2 = 9 \not\equiv 1, \text{ mod } 1-2i.$$

Hence 3 is a quadratic non-residue of $1-2i$. These results are confirmed by Ex.'s 1 and 2 above.

Cor. *The integer α is a quadratic residue or non-residue of π according as we have*

$$\alpha^{\frac{n[\pi]-1}{2}} \equiv 1 \text{ or } -1, \text{ mod } \pi.[1]$$

Let now, as in the rational realm, the symbol (α/π) have the

[1] See Chap. IV. Th. 1. Cor. 1.

value 1 or -1 according as α is a quadratic residue or non-residue of π, we have

$$\left(\frac{\alpha}{\pi}\right) \equiv \alpha^{\frac{n[\pi]-1}{2}}, \text{ mod } \pi.$$

The symbol (α/π) obeys the following laws

i. If $\alpha \equiv \beta$, mod π,

then
$$\left(\frac{\alpha}{\pi}\right) = \left(\frac{\beta}{\pi}\right).$$

ii.
$$\left(\frac{\alpha_1\alpha_2}{\pi}\right) = \left(\frac{\alpha_1}{\pi}\right)\left(\frac{\alpha_2}{\pi}\right).$$

iii. Since
$$\left(\frac{-1}{\pi}\right) = \left(\frac{i}{\pi}\right)^2 = 1,$$

we have
$$\left(\frac{-\alpha}{\pi}\right) = \left(\frac{-1}{\pi}\right)\left(\frac{\alpha}{\pi}\right) = \left(\frac{\alpha}{\pi}\right).$$

iv. Since
$$\left(\frac{\alpha}{\pi}\right) = \left(\frac{-\alpha}{\pi}\right), \text{ and } \left(\frac{\alpha}{\pi}\right) = \left(\frac{\alpha}{-\pi}\right),$$

it follows that
$$\left(\frac{\alpha}{\pi}\right) = \left(\frac{-\alpha}{\pi}\right) = \left(\frac{\alpha}{-\pi}\right) = \left(\frac{-\alpha}{-\pi}\right).$$

v. Since $\gamma^2 \equiv \alpha$, mod π,

implies $\gamma'^2 \equiv \alpha'$, mod π',

we have
$$\left(\frac{\alpha}{\pi}\right) = \left(\frac{\alpha'}{\pi'}\right).$$

Every integer α can be written in the form

$$\alpha = i^r(1+i)^s\rho_1\rho_2\cdots\rho_n,$$

where $r = 0, 1, 2$ or 3, $s = 0$ or a positive integer, and $\rho_1, \rho_2, \cdots, \rho_n$ are odd primary primes. We have then

$$\left(\frac{\alpha}{\pi}\right) = \left(\frac{i}{\pi}\right)^r\left(\frac{1+i}{\pi}\right)^s\left(\frac{\rho_1}{\pi}\right)\left(\frac{\rho_2}{\pi}\right)\cdots\left(\frac{\rho_n}{\pi}\right),$$

and the determination of the value of (α/π) is seen to be resolved into the determination of the values of

$$\left(\frac{i}{\pi}\right), \left(\frac{1+i}{\pi}\right) \text{ and } \left(\frac{\rho}{\pi}\right),$$

where ρ is an odd primary prime.

The close similarity between this resolution of our original problem into simpler ones and the corresponding case in the rational realm should be noticed.

THEOREM 18. *The unit i is a quadratic residue or non-residue of a prime π according as $n[\pi]$ is of the form $8m+1$ or $8m+5$.*

If π be a prime of the first degree, $n[\pi]$ is a positive rational prime of the form $4k+1$, and hence either of the form $8m+1$ or $8m+5$.

If π be a prime of the second degree, $n[\pi]$ is the square of a rational prime of the form $4k+3$, and hence of the form $8m+1$.

We have from Th. 17

$$\left(\frac{i}{\pi}\right) \equiv i^{\frac{n[\pi]-1}{2}}, \text{ mod } \pi,$$

and hence

$$\left(\frac{i}{\pi}\right) \equiv (-1)^{\frac{n[\pi]-1}{4}}, \text{ mod } \pi,$$

or since

$$(-1)^{\frac{n[\pi]-1}{4}} = 1 \text{ or } -1$$

$$\left(\frac{i}{\pi}\right) = (-1)^{\frac{n[\pi]-1}{4}}$$

But $(n[\pi]-1)/4$ is even or odd according as $n[\pi]$ is of the form $8m+1$ or $8m+5$.

Hence $(i/\pi) = 1$ or -1 according as $n[\pi]$ is of the form $8m+1$ or $8m+5$. We observe that i is a quadratic residue of all primes of the second degree. The solution of the same question for $1+i$ is obtained by Gauss inductively as follows:[1]

We find by means of Th. 17 that $1+i$ is a quadratic residue of the following primary primes $-1+2i$, $3-2i$, $-5-2i$, $-1-6i$, $5+4i$, $5-4i$, -7, $7+2i$, $-5+6i$, etc., and a quadratic non-residue of $-1-2i$, -3, $3+2i$, $1+4i$, $1-4i$, $-5+2i$, $-1+6i$, $7-2i$, $-5-6i$, $-3+8i$, $-3-8i$, $5+8i$, $5-8i$, $9+4i$, $9-4i$, etc.

[1] Th. Res. Biquad., Com. Sec., § 58; Works, Vol. II, p. 128.

Examining these series of primes we see that those in the first class are all such that

$$a+b\equiv 1, \text{ mod } 8,$$

and those in the second class such that

$$a+b\equiv -3, \text{ mod } 8.$$

Hence it seems probable that $1+i$ is a quadratic residue or non-residue of an odd primary prime, $a+bi$, according as we have

$$a+b\equiv 1 \text{ or } -3, \text{ mod } 8,$$

one of which cases must always occur (see definition of primary integer).

Since the quadratic character of an integer is the same with respect to all associates of π, and in particular

$$\left(\frac{1+i}{a+bi}\right)=\left(\frac{1+i}{-a-bi}\right),$$

we see that, if the above induction be correct, $1+i$ is a quadratic residue or non-residue of $-a-bi$ according as

$$-a-b\equiv -1 \text{ or } 3, \text{ mod } 8,$$

$a+bi$ being an odd primary prime.

Assuming the correctness of the above inductive reasoning, we have the following theorem:

THEOREM 19. *If $a+bi$ be a prime such that a is odd and b even, $1+i$ is a quadratic residue or non-residue of $a+bi$, according as* $a+b\equiv \pm 1$ *or* ± 3, mod *8*.

This theorem may be proved by treating it as a special case of a more general theorem (Th. 22), which we shall consider in the next section.[1] To determine the value of $\left(\frac{1-i}{a+bi}\right)$ we have only to remember that

$$\left(\frac{1-i}{a+bi}\right)=\left(\frac{1+i}{a-bi}\right) \text{ (see v above)},$$

[1] For an independent proof see Dirichlet, Crelle, Vol. XXX, p. 312.

and hence since

$$\left(\frac{1+i}{a-bi}\right) = 1, \text{ when } a+(-b) \equiv \pm 1, \text{ mod } 8,$$

and

$$= -1, \text{ when } a+(-b) \equiv \pm 3, \text{ mod } 8,$$

we have

$$\left(\frac{1-i}{a+bi}\right) = 1, \text{ when } a-b \equiv \pm 1, \text{ mod } 8,$$

$$= -1, \text{ when } a-b \equiv \pm 3, \text{ mod } 8.$$

Ex. 1. Deduce the above criterion for the value of $\left(\frac{1-i}{a+bi}\right)$ from the fact that $\left(\frac{1-i}{a+bi}\right) = \left(\frac{i}{a+bi}\right)\left(\frac{1+i}{a+bi}\right)$.

Ex. 2. Under what condition is

$$\left(\frac{1+i}{a+bi}\right) = \left(\frac{1-i}{a+bi}\right).$$

Gauss proceeds next to the consideration of the question: *Of what odd primary prime moduli is a given odd primary prime a quadratic residue and of what a non-residue?* The analysis employed in the discussion of this question so beautifully exemplifies what can be accomplished in the theory of numbers by induction, this constituting, as Gauss says,[1] "the peculiar charm" of this branch of mathematics, that we shall give it in full.

The following is a free translation of §§ 59, 60, Commentatio Secunda, Theoria Residuorum Biquadraticorum.

"Passing to the odd prime numbers, we find the number $-1+2i$ to be a quadratic residue of the moduli $3+2i$, $1-4i$, $-5+2i$, $-1-6i$, $7-2i$, $-3+8i$, $5+8i$, $5-8i$, $9+4i$, etc., but a non-residue of the moduli $-1-2i$, -3, $3-2i$, $1+4i$, $-1+6i$, $5+4i$, $5-4i$, -7, $7+2i$, $-5+6i$, $-5-6i$, $-3-8i$, $9-4i$, etc.

Reducing the moduli of the first class to their residues of least absolute value with respect to the modulus $-1+2i$, we find these to be -1 and 1 only; for instance, $3+2i \equiv -1$, $1-4i \equiv -1$, $-5+2i \equiv 1$, $-5-2i \equiv -1$, etc.

[1] Gauss: Works, Vol. II, pp. 152 and 157.

On the other hand, all moduli of the second class are found to be congruent to either i or $-i$ with respect to the modulus $-1+2i$.[1]

But the numbers 1 and -1 are themselves quadratic residues of the modulus $-1+2i$, while i and $-i$ are non-residues of the same modulus; wherefore, so far as induction may be trusted, we obtain the theorem: *The number $-1+2i$ is a quadratic residue or non-residue of the prime number $a+bi$ according as $a+bi$ is a quadratic residue or non-residue of $-1+2i$ itself, if $a+bi$ be the primary one of its four associates, or more exactly if merely a be odd and b even.*

Moreover, from this theorem follow immediately similar theorems for the numbers $1-2i$, $-1-2i$, $1+2i$.

Since $$\left(\frac{1-2i}{a+bi}\right)=\left(\frac{-1}{a+bi}\right)\left(\frac{-1+2i}{a+bi}\right)=\left(\frac{-1+2i}{a+bi}\right),$$

and $$\left(\frac{-1+2i}{a+bi}\right)=\left(\frac{a+bi}{-1+2i}\right),$$

we have $$\left(\frac{1-2i}{a+bi}\right)=\left(\frac{a+bi}{1-2i}\right).$$

Also $$\left(\frac{-1-2i}{a+bi}\right)=\left(\frac{-1+2i}{a-bi}\right)=\left(\frac{a-bi}{-1+2i}\right)=\left(\frac{a+bi}{-1-2i}\right)$$

and then as above $$\left(\frac{1+2i}{a+bi}\right)=\left(\frac{a+bi}{1+2i}\right).$$

Instituting a like inductive enquiry concerning the numbers -3 or 3, we find that both are quadratic residues of the moduli $3+2i$, $3-2i$, $-1+6i$, $-1-6i$, $-5+6i$, $-5-6i$, $-3+8i$, $-3-8i$, $9+4i$, $9-4i$, etc., but non-residues of $-1+2i$, $-1-2i$, $1+4i$, $1-4i$, $-5+2i$, $-5-2i$, $5+4i$, $5-4i$, $7+2i$, $7-2i$, $5+8i$, $5-8i$, etc.

The former are congruent with respect to the modulus 3 to some one of the four numbers $1, -1, i, -i$; the latter, however, to some one of the four numbers $1+i$, $1-i$, $-1+i$, $-1-i$.[2]

[1] It will be observed that $1, -1, i, -i$ constitute a reduced residue system, mod $-1+2i$.

[2] The numbers $1, -1, i, -i, 1+i, 1-i, -1+i, -1-i$ constitute a reduced residue system, mod 3.

The numbers $1, -1, i, -i$ are themselves quadratic residues of 3, while $1+i, 1-i, -1+i, -1-i$ are non-residues.

Induction teaches, therefore, that the prime number $a+bi$, supposing a odd, b even, has the same relation to the number -3 as -3 has to $a+bi$, in so far as the one is a quadratic residue or quadratic non-residue of the other, and like relations hold between 3 and $a+bi$.

Applying a like inductive process to other prime numbers, we find in every case this most elegant law of reciprocity confirmed, and in the arithmetic of the complex numbers we are led to this fundamental theorem concerning quadratic residues:

THEOREM 20.[1] *If a_1+b_1i and a_2+b_2i be two prime numbers such that a_1 and a_2 are both odd, b_1 and b_2 both even, then each will be a quadratic residue or each will be a quadratic non-residue of the other.*

But notwithstanding the extreme simplicity of the theorem its demonstration presents great difficulties, which, however, shall not delay us here, since the theorem itself is merely a special case of a more general theorem, which exhausts, as it were, the whole theory of biquadratic residues." We shall conclude this brief résumé of the theory of quadratic residues in $k(i)$ with the solution of three examples.

EX. 1. To determine the quadratic character of $5-4i$ with respect to the modulus $11+6i$.

We have by the above theorem

$$\left(\frac{5-4i}{11+6i}\right)=\left(\frac{11+6i}{5-4i}\right)=\left(\frac{6+10i}{5-4i}\right)$$

[1] Since $\left(\frac{\alpha}{\pi}\right)=\left(\frac{-\alpha}{\pi}\right)=\left(\frac{\alpha}{-\pi}\right)=\left(\frac{-\alpha}{-\pi}\right)$ it is not necessary to limit α and π to odd primary integers, but only to odd primary integers or those with their signs changed; that is, integers of the form $a+bi$, where a is odd and b even.

Expressed symbolically the theorem is

$$\left(\frac{a_1+b_1i}{a_2+b_2i}\right)=\left(\frac{a_2+b_2i}{a_1+b_1i}\right)$$

Dirichlet gives a simple proof independent of the theory of biquadratic residues; Crelle: Vol. IX, p. 379; also H. J. S. Smith: Works, Vol. I, p. 76.

But $$6+10i=(1+i)^3(1-4i).$$

Hence $$\left(\frac{5-4i}{11+6i}\right)=\left(\frac{1+i}{5-4i}\right)^3\left(\frac{1-4i}{5-4i}\right)$$
$$=\left(\frac{1+i}{5-4i}\right)\left(\frac{1-4i}{5-4i}\right)$$

But $\left(\frac{1+i}{5-4i}\right)=1$, since $5+(-4)\equiv 1$, mod 8, (Th. 19), and by Th. 20

$$\left(\frac{1-4i}{5-4i}\right)=\left(\frac{5-4i}{1-4i}\right)=\left(\frac{4}{1-4i}\right)=\left(\frac{2}{1-4i}\right)^2=1.$$

Hence $$\left(\frac{5-4i}{11+6i}\right)=1,$$

and the congruence $$x^2\equiv 5-4i, \text{ mod } 11+6i,$$

has roots.

Ex. 2. To determine the prime moduli of which $1+2i$ is a quadratic residue, and those of which it is a non-residue. Let $a+bi$ be a primary prime and hence a odd, and b even.

Then

$$\left(\frac{1+2i}{a+bi}\right)=\left(\frac{a+bi}{1+2i}\right)=\left(\frac{1}{1+2i}\right),\ \left(\frac{i}{1+2i}\right),\ \left(\frac{-1}{1+2i}\right) \text{ or } \left(\frac{-i}{1+2i}\right),$$

according as $a+bi\equiv 1,\ i,\ -1$, or $-i$, mod $1+2i$.

But

$$\left(\frac{1}{1+2i}\right)=1,\ \left(\frac{i}{1+2i}\right)=-1.\ \left(\frac{-1}{1+2i}\right)=1, \text{ and } \left(\frac{-i}{1+2i}\right)=-1,$$

Hence $1+2i$ is a quadratic residue of $a+bi$ when

$$a+bi\equiv 1 \text{ or } -1, \text{ mod } 1+2i$$

and a quadratic non-residue when

$$a+bi\equiv i \text{ or } -i, \text{ mod } 1+2i.$$

Therefore $1+2i$ is a quadratic residue of all primary primes included in the forms $$\mu(1+2i)\pm 1, \qquad 1)$$

and a quadratic non-residue of all primary primes included in the forms

$$\mu(1+2i)\pm i. \qquad 2)$$

Ex. 3. To determine the prime moduli of which $3+6i$ is a quadratic residue, and those of which it is a non-residue.

Let $a+bi$ be a primary prime.

We have $$\left(\frac{3+6i}{a+bi}\right)=\left(\frac{3}{a+bi}\right)\left(\frac{1+2i}{a+bi}\right).$$

We find as in the last example that $\left(\frac{3}{a+bi}\right)=1$, when $a+bi$ is a primary prime contained in one of the forms

$$3\mu \pm 1,\ 3\mu \pm i, \qquad 3)$$

and $\left(\frac{3}{a+bi}\right) = -1$, when $a+bi$ is a primary prime contained in one of the forms

$$3\mu \pm (1+i),\ 3\mu \pm (1-i). \qquad 4)$$

Combining these with the results obtained in the last example, we see that $3+6i$ is a quadratic residue of all primary primes contained simultaneously in the forms 1) and 3), or simultaneously in the forms 2) and 4), and their associates. On the other hand $3+6i$ is a quadratic non-residue of all primary primes contained simultaneously in the forms 1) and 4), or simultaneously in the forms 2) and 3). These conditions may in each case be combined into a single one by Th. 12.

§ 19. Biquadratic Residues.

It is impossible to leave the realm $k(i)$ without a few words as to the history of the first treatment of these numbers from the point of view of the theory of numbers, marking as it did a distinct epoch in the development of this branch of mathematics.

On the fifth of April, 1825, Gauss laid before the Royal Society of Göttingen a paper[1] upon the subject of biquadratic residues, a brief report[2] of which is given in the "Göttingische Gelehrte Anzeigen" for April 11, 1825.

He remarks in this report that: "The development of the *general* theory which requires *a most peculiar extension of the field of the higher arithmetic*[3] is reserved for future continuation, only those investigations being taken up in this first paper which can be completely carried through without this extension," giving thereby a foretaste of a step which was to revolutionize the theory of numbers; a step, however, the results of which he did not publish until six years later.

In this first paper Gauss defines a biquadratic residue as fol-

[1] Theoria Residuorum Biquadraticorum: Commentatio Prima. Works, Vol. 2, p. 65.

[2] *Ibid.*, p. 165.

[3] Italics are the author's. See also H. J. S. Smith: Report on the Theory of Numbers, Arts. 24–36; Works, Vol. I, pp. 70–86, and Bachmann: Die Lehre von der Kreisteilung, Vorlesung 12th. The reader is especially advised to consult Gauss' reports on his two papers and H. J. S. Smith's résumé.

lows: "An integer a is called a biquadratic residue of the integer p when there exist numbers of the form $x^4 - a$ which are divisible by p, and a biquadratic non-residue of p when no number of this form is divisible by p," or we may say, as in Chap. III, § 34, that an integer, a, is a biquadratic residue or non-residue of an integer, p, according as the congruence

$$x^4 - a \equiv 0, \bmod p,$$

has or has not roots.

Limiting the investigation now to the case in which p is a positive prime of the form $4n+1$ and a not divisible by p, all other cases being as he says reducible to this one, he separates all integers, a, not divisible by p, into four classes, according as

$$a^{\frac{1}{4}(p-1)} \equiv 1, f, -1, \text{or} -f, \bmod p,$$

where f is a root of the congruence

$$f^2 + 1 \equiv 0, \bmod p.$$

Every integer of a reduced residue system, mod p, satisfies the congruence

$$x^{p-1} - 1 \equiv 0, \bmod p, \tag{1}$$

which may be written

$$(x^{\frac{1}{4}(p-1)} - 1)(x^{\frac{1}{4}(p-1)} - f)(x^{\frac{1}{4}(p-1)} + 1)(x^{\frac{1}{4}(p-1)} + f) \equiv 0, \bmod p, \tag{2}$$

where $f, -f$ are the roots of the congruence

$$x^2 + 1 \equiv 0, \bmod p.$$

Since the congruence 1) has exactly $p-1$ roots, each of the four congruences into which 2) can be resolved has exactly $\frac{1}{4}(p-1)$ roots and the integers of a reduced residue system, mod p, are seen to fall into four classes, each containing $\frac{1}{4}(p-1)$ integers, according as they satisfy the first, second, third or fourth of these congruences.

The first class comprises those integers for which the congruence 1) is solvable; that is, the biquadratic residues of p (Chap. III, Th. 31); the third comprises those integers which are quadratic but not biquadratic residues of p; the second and fourth classes are made up of the quadratic non-residues of p.

We see, therefore, that, as Gauss remarks, all biquadratic residues of p are also quadratic residues of p and all quadratic non-residues of p are also biquadratic non-residues of p; but that not all quadratic residues of p are biquadratic residues of p. Gauss now divides the investigation, as in the case of quadratic residues, into two parts according as p or a is supposed given; that is, according as we are to find what integers are biquadratic residues of a given prime modulus and what non-residues, or of what prime moduli a given integer is a biquadratic residue, and of what a non-residue.

The first of these is elementary in comparison with the second and easily solved. Of the second part he treats three special cases, $a = -1$, $a = \pm 2$, but does nothing with the general case. These three special cases, however, he fully discusses, remarking upon the exceeding difficulty of the cases $a = \pm 2$.

In this connection H. J. S. Smith says:[1] "The result arrived at in the case of 2 is that, if p be resolved into the sum of an even and an uneven square (a resolution which is always possible in one and only one way), so that $p = a^2 + b^2$ (where we may suppose a and b taken with such signs that $a \equiv 1$, mod 4, $b \equiv af$, mod p), 2 belongs to the first, second, third, or fourth class according as $\frac{1}{2}b$ is of the form $4n$, $4n+1$, $4n+2$ or $4n+3$.

"The equation $p = a^2 + b^2$ shows that $p = (a + bi)(a - bi)$, or that p, being the product of two conjugate imaginary factors, is in a certain sense not a prime number. Gauss was thus led to introduce *as modulus* instead of p one of its imaginary factors; an innovation which necessitated the construction of an arithmetical theory of complex imaginary numbers of the form $a + bi$."

In a paper[2] communicated to the Royal Society of Göttingen, April 15, 1831, a report[3] of which is given in the "Göttingische Anzeigen" for April 23, 1831, Gauss continues his investigations in this subject, limiting himself still to the case where p is a positive rational prime of the form $4n + 1$, a an integer not divisible by p.

[1] Works, Vol. I, p. 71.

[2] Th. Res. Biq., Com. Sec., Works, Vol. II. § 93.

[3] *Ibid.*, p. 169.

He obtains by *induction,* but does not prove, theorems concerning the moduli of which certain special values of a ($\pm 3, 5, -7, -11, 13, 17, -19, -23$) are biquadratic residues, and those of which they are non-residues, but says in the above mentioned report: "Although all these special theorems can be discovered so easily by induction it appears nevertheless extremely difficult to find a general law for these forms, even if much that is common makes itself evident, and it is still more difficult to find proofs for these theorems. The methods used for the numbers 2 and -2 in the first paper can not be applied here, and if other similar methods such as that used in dealing with the first and third classes, could serve to solve the problem, they prove themselves, however, entirely unsuitable as foundations for complete proofs. One soon recognizes, therefore, that it is only by entirely new paths that one can penetrate into this rich domain of the higher arithmetic. The author has already pointed out in the first paper that for this purpose a peculiar extension of the field of the higher arithmetic is indispensable, without, however, explaining more fully wherein this consisted; the design of the present paper is to make known the nature of this extension. It is simply that a true basis for the theory of the biquadratic residues is to be found only by making the field of the higher arithmetic, which usually covers only the real whole numbers, include also the imaginary ones, the latter being given full equality of citizenship with the former. As soon as one has perceived the bearing of this principle, the theory appears in an entirely new light, and its results become surprisingly simple."

This widening of the field of the higher arithmetic consists, then, in considering our integers to be all those numbers of the form $a+bi$, in which a and b are rational integers. The definitions of divisibility, prime number, etc., and the principal theorems relating to rational integers having been shown to have their analogues for the integers of this extended system, our realm $k(i)$, as has been proved in the preceding pages, Gauss then develops briefly the theory of quadratic residues for the integers of this new system. Passing to the subject of biquadratic residues, he separates all integers not divisible by a given modulus into four classes, as follows:

"If the modulus be a complex prime number, $a+bi$, where a is always assumed odd, b even, and k a complex number not divisible by $a+bi$, then, for the sake of brevity p being written for a^2+b^2, we have in all cases

$$k^{\frac{1}{4}(p-1)} \equiv 1, i, -1, -i, \bmod a+bi,$$

and thereby all numbers not divisible by $a+bi$ are separated into four classes, to which in the above order the biquadratic characters 0, 1, 2, 3 are ascribed." That is, the biquadratic character of an integer, k, with respect to a prime modulus, $a+bi$, is the exponent of the lowest power of i to which $k^{\frac{1}{4}(p-1)}$ is congruent, mod $a+bi$, where $p=a^2+b^2$.

"It will be observed that, when $a+bi$ is a prime of the first degree, the fourfold classification of the real residues of $a+bi$ which we thus obtain is identical with that obtained for p, $=n[a+bi]$, in the real theory; for the numbers f and $-f$, being the roots of the congruence

$$x^2+1\equiv 0, \bmod p,$$

satisfy the same congruence for either of the complex factors, $a+bi$, $a-bi$, of p, and are therefore congruent respectively to $+i$ and $-i$, for one of these factors, and to $-i$ and $+i$ for the other.[1]

"Evidently the character 0 belongs to the biquadratic residues, the remaining ones, 1, 2, 3, to the biquadratic non-residues, to the character 2 corresponding quadratic residues, to the characters 1 and 3 on the other hand quadratic non-residues.

"One recognizes at once that it is only necessary to determine this character for such values of k as are themselves complex primes, and here induction leads immediately to most simple results. If, first of all, we put $k=1+i$, it is seen that the character of this number is always congruent to

$$\tfrac{1}{8}(-a^2+2ab-3b^2+1), \bmod 4$$

[1] See H. J. S. Smith: Works, p. 197.

and similar expressions are found for the cases $k = 1 - i, -1 + i, -1 - i$.

"If, on the other hand, k be such a prime number $c + di$, that c is odd and d even, we can obtain by induction a reciprocity law quite analogous to the fundamental theorem for quadratic residues; this theorem can be expressed most simply in the following manner:

"*If $c + d - 1$ as well as $a + b - 1$ be divisible by 4 (to which case all others can be easily reduced), and the character of the number $c + di$ with respect to the modulus $a + bi$ be denoted by l_1, that on the other hand of $a + bi$ with respect to the modulus $c + di$ by l_2, then $l_1 = l_2$ when one (or both) of the numbers d and b is divisible by 4; on the other hand $l_1 = l_2 \pm 2$, when neither of the numbers d, b is divisible by 4.*

"These theorems contain in truth all the essentials of the theory of the biquadratic residues; easy as it is to discover them by induction, it is most difficult to prove them rigorously, especially the second, the fundamental theorem of the biquadratic residues. On account of the great length of the present paper the author finds himself obliged to postpone to a third paper[1] the presentation of a proof of the latter theorem, which has been in his possession for twenty years. On the other hand, the present paper contains the complete proof of the first theorem relating to the number $1 + i$, upon which are dependent the theorems relating to $1 - i, -1 + i, -1 - i$. This proof will give some idea of the complexity of the subject."

The above will be made plainer to the reader by the following brief résumé. The integer α is said to be a biquadratic residue

[1] Gauss never published his proof of this theorem, but soon after the theorem was published Jacobi succeeded in proving it, and communicated this proof to his pupils in his lectures at Königsberg in the winter of 1836–37. He did not, however, publish his proof, and the first published proofs are by Eisenstein, who gave in all five. See Crelle, Vol. XXVIII, p. 53, p. 223, and Vol. XXX, p. 185; also H. J. S. Smith: Works, Vol. I, p. 78, and Bachmann: Die Lehre von der Kreisteilung, p. 168.

or non-residue of a prime, π, a being prime to π, according as the congruence

$$x^4 \equiv a, \bmod \pi,$$

is or is not solvable.

From Th. 16 we have

$$a^{n[\pi]-1} \equiv 1, \bmod \pi, \qquad 3)$$

and since, excluding the case $\pi = 1 + i$,[1] $n[\pi] - 1$ is always divisible by 4, we may write 3) in the form

$$\left(a^{\frac{n[\pi]-1}{4}} - 1\right)\left(a^{\frac{n[\pi]-1}{4}} - i\right)\left(a^{\frac{n[\pi]-1}{4}} + 1\right)\left(a^{\frac{n[\pi]-1}{4}} + i\right) \equiv 0, \bmod \pi,$$

each of the congruences

$$\left.\begin{aligned} a^{\frac{n[\pi]-1}{4}} &\equiv 1 \\ a^{\frac{n[\pi]-1}{4}} &\equiv i \\ a^{\frac{n[\pi]-1}{4}} &\equiv -1 \\ a^{\frac{n[\pi]-1}{4}} &\equiv -i \end{aligned}\right\}, \bmod \pi,$$

which may be written in the common form

$$a^{\frac{n[\pi]-1}{4}} \equiv i^r, \bmod \pi, \ r = 0, 1, 2, 3,$$

is seen to have exactly $(n[\pi] - 1)/4$ incongruent roots, and the integers of a reduced residue system, mod π, fall into four classes according as they satisfy the first, second, third or fourth of these congruences.

The integers of the first class are the biquadratic residues of π, for

$$a^{\frac{n[\pi]-1}{4}} \equiv 1, \bmod \pi,$$

is the necessary and sufficient condition that a shall be a biquadratic residue of π.

The integers of the first and third classes are together the quadratic residues of π, for they are the roots of the congruence

$$a^{\frac{n[\pi]-1}{2}} \equiv 1, \bmod \pi.$$

[1] It is easily seen that every integer not divisible by $1 + i$ is a biquadratic residue of $1 + i$.

The integers of the second and fourth classes are together the quadratic non-residues of π, for they are the roots of the congruence

$$\alpha^{\frac{n[\pi]-1}{2}} \equiv -1, \text{ mod } \pi.$$

The exponent of the power of i for which the congruence

$$\alpha^{\frac{n[\pi]-1}{4}} \equiv i^r, \text{ mod } \pi, \ r=0, 1, 2, 3$$

is satisfied is called the biquadratic character of α with respect to π and this power of i is denoted by the symbol $(\alpha/\pi)_4$, so that we have always

$$\left(\frac{\alpha}{\pi}\right)_4 \equiv \alpha^{\frac{n[\pi]-1}{4}}, \text{ mod } \pi.$$

The symbol $(\alpha/\pi)_4$, which is due to H. J. S. Smith, seems preferable to $((\alpha/\pi))$, which was adopted by Jacobi, as by a change of subscript it will serve for the theory of residues of other degrees.

If now (α/π) have the meaning previously assigned, we see easily that

$$\left(\frac{\alpha}{\pi}\right) = \left(\frac{\alpha}{\pi}\right)_4^2.$$

If we understand by the quadratic character of α, mod π, instead of 1 or -1, the exponent of the lowest power of -1 to which α is congruent, mod π, the notation for quadratic residues will be brought into accordance with that given above for biquadratic residues.

The symbol $(\alpha/\pi)_4$ obeys the following laws:

From $\alpha_1 \equiv \alpha_2$, mod π, it follows that

$$\left(\frac{\alpha_1}{\pi}\right)_4 = \left(\frac{\alpha_2}{\pi}\right)_4.$$

If α_1 and α_2 be two integers, which may be equal, not divisible by π, then from

$$\left(\frac{\alpha_1}{\pi}\right)_4 \equiv \alpha_1^{\frac{n[\pi]-1}{4}}, \text{ mod } \pi,$$

and

$$\left(\frac{\alpha_2}{\pi}\right)_4 \equiv \alpha_2^{\frac{n[\pi]-1}{4}}, \text{ mod } \pi,$$

it follows that

$$\left(\frac{\alpha_1}{\pi}\right)_4 \left(\frac{\alpha_2}{\pi}\right)_4 \equiv (\alpha_1\alpha_2)^{\frac{n[\pi]-1}{4}}, \text{ mod } \pi,$$

and hence $$\left(\frac{\alpha_1\alpha_2}{\pi}\right)_4=\left(\frac{\alpha_1}{\pi}\right)_4\left(\frac{\alpha_2}{\pi}\right)_4.$$

Since every integer α can be written in the form

$$\alpha = i^r(1+i)^s\rho_1\rho_2\cdots\rho_n,$$

where $r=0, 1, 2, 3$; $s=0$, or a positive integer; and $\rho_1, \rho_2, \cdots, \rho_n$ are odd primary primes, we have

$$\left(\frac{\alpha}{\pi}\right)_4=\left(\frac{i}{\pi}\right)_4^r\left(\frac{1+i}{\pi}\right)_4^s\left(\frac{\rho_1}{\pi}\right)_4\left(\frac{\rho_2}{\pi}\right)_4\cdots\left(\frac{\rho_n}{\pi}\right)_4,$$

and the determination of the value of $\left(\frac{\alpha}{\pi}\right)_4$ is seen to be resolved into the determination of the values of $\left(\frac{i}{\pi}\right)_4$, $\left(\frac{1+i}{\pi}\right)_4$ and $\left(\frac{\rho}{\pi}\right)_4$ where ρ is an odd primary prime.

The following theorem gives a simple criterion for determining the value of $(i/\pi)_4$:

THEOREM 21. *If $\pi = a+bi$ be an odd primary prime, then i has the biquadratic character 0, 1, 2 or 3 with respect to the modulus π, according as we have $a\equiv 1, 7, 5$ or 3, mod 8; that is,*

$$\left(\frac{i}{a+bi}\right)=i^{3\frac{a-1}{2}}.$$

Since $a+bi$ is an odd primary prime, we have either

$$a=4k+1;\ b=4k,$$

or

$$a=4k+3;\ b=4k+2,$$

and hence

$$\left(\frac{i}{a+bi}\right)=i^{\frac{a^2+b^2-1}{4}}=i^{2k},\ \text{when}\ a=4k+1,$$

$$=i^{2k+3},\ \text{when}\ a=4k+3.$$

But $2k\equiv 0$ or 2, mod 4, according as k is even or odd; that is, according as $a=4k+1\equiv 1$ or 5, mod 8;

and $2k+3\equiv 3$ or 1, mod 4, according as k is even or odd; that is, according as

$$a = 4k + 3 \equiv 3 \text{ or } 7, \text{ mod } 8.$$

Hence $$\left(\frac{i}{a+bi}\right)_4 = 1, i, -1 \text{ or } -i.$$

according as $$a \equiv 1, 7, 5, \text{ or } 3, \text{ mod } 8.$$

The following table gives the biquadratic character of i with respect to each odd primary prime whose norm is less than 50.

Biq. Char.	Odd Primary Primes.
0	$1+4i,\ 1-4i,\ -7.$
1	$-1+2i,\ -1-2i,\ -1+6i,\ -1-6i.$
2	$-3,\ 5+4i,\ 5-4i.$
3	$3+2i,\ 3-2i,\ -5+2i,\ -5-2i.$

The following theorem gives the biquadratic character of $1+i$ with respect to an odd primary prime modulus.

THEOREM 22. *If $a+bi$ be any odd primary prime*

$$\left(\frac{1+i}{a+bi}\right)_4 = i^{\frac{a-b-b^2-1}{4}}.$$

For the proof of this theorem see Gauss: Works, Vol. II, p. 135; Eisenstein: Crelle, Vols. 28 and 30; Bachmann: Die Lehre von der Kreisteilung, p. 181.

The following table gives the biquadratic character of $1+i$ with respect to each odd primary prime whose norm is less than 50.

Biq. Char.	Odd Primary Primes.
0	$3-2i,\ 5+4i,\ -1-6i.$
1	$1-4i,\ -5+2i,\ -1+6i.$
2	$-1+2i,\ -5-2i,\ 5-4i,\ -7.$
3	$-1-2i,\ -3,\ 3+2i,\ 1+4i.$

This theorem is easily seen to be the equivalent of Gauss' (p. 209), for although the modulus is here restricted to an odd primary prime, $a+bi$, while in Gauss' it can be either $\pm(a+bi)$, where $a+bi$ is an odd primary prime, this makes no difference, since

$$\left(\frac{1+i}{a+bi}\right)_4=\left(\frac{1+i}{-a-bi}\right)_4.$$

We have only to show therefore that

$$\tfrac{1}{8}(-a^2+2ab-3b^2+1)\equiv\tfrac{1}{4}(a-b-b^2-1), \bmod 4, \qquad 4)$$

where $\qquad a\equiv 1, b\equiv 0$, or $a\equiv -1, b\equiv 2$, mod 4.

Putting

$$a=4a_1+1, b=4b_1, \text{ or } a=4a_1-1, b=4b_1+2$$

in 4), we obtain in both cases

$$(b_1-a_1)(2a_1+2b_1+1)\equiv a_1-b_1, \bmod 4;$$

that is $\qquad (a_1+b_1+1)(a_1-b_1)\equiv 0, \bmod 2,$

is a necessary and sufficient condition that 4) shall hold, and this condition is easily seen to be satisfied by all values of a_1 and b_1.

The value of $(\alpha/\pi)_4$ is determined by means of the reciprocity law given by Gauss, which can be expressed most simply as follows:

THEOREM 23. *The biquadratic characters of two odd primary primes of $k(i)$ with respect to each other are the same or opposite according as one of the primes is $\equiv 1$, mod 4, or both are $\equiv 3+2i$, mod 4.*

This can be expressed symbolically as follows:

$$\left(\frac{\pi}{\rho}\right)_4=(-1)^{\frac{n[\pi]-1}{4}\cdot\frac{n[\rho]-1}{4}}\left(\frac{\rho}{\pi}\right)_4.$$

in which π and ρ are any two odd primary primes of $k(i)$.

Since $\qquad \left(\frac{\pi}{\rho}\right)=\left(\frac{\pi}{\rho}\right)_4^2,$

we have from the last theorem

$$\left(\frac{\pi}{\rho}\right)=\left(\frac{\rho}{\pi}\right),$$

and from this can easily deduce the quadratic reciprocity law as given in Th. 20.

The biquadratic character 0 is opposite to 2, and 1 to 3, this corresponding to $l_1 = l_2 \pm 2$ in Gauss' theorem (p. 210). His condition, that $a+b-1$ and $c+d-1$ shall both be divisible by 4, is evidently satisfied when the primes are primary. Furthermore, it is easily seen from the definition (p. 194) that every odd primary prime is $\equiv 1$ or $3+2i$, mod 4; and this is equivalent to Gauss' condition that b (or d) be divisible or not divisible by 4.

Ex. 1. To determine the value of

$$\left(\frac{1+3i}{5+4i}\right)_4.$$

Resolving $1+3i$ into its primary prime factors, we have

$$\left(\frac{1+3i}{5+4i}\right)_4 = \left(\frac{i}{5+4i}\right)_4^3 \left(\frac{1+i}{5+4i}\right)_4 \left(\frac{-1+2i}{5+4i}\right)_4.$$

By Th. 21
$$\left(\frac{i}{5+4i}\right)_4 = i^{3(5-1)/2} = i^2,$$

and by Th. 22
$$\left(\frac{1+i}{5+4i}\right) = i^0.$$

Since $-1+2i$ and $5+4i$ are odd primary primes we have by Th. 23

$$\left(\frac{-1+2i}{5+4i}\right)_4 = (-1)^{\frac{5-1}{4}\cdot\frac{41-1}{4}} \left(\frac{5+4i}{-1+2i}\right)_4 = \left(\frac{5+4i}{-1+2i}\right)_4,$$

and since
$$5+4i-(1-3i)(-1+2i) = -i;^1$$

that is,
$$5+4i \equiv -i, \bmod -1+2i,$$

we have
$$\left(\frac{5+4i}{-1+2i}\right)_4 = \left(\frac{-i}{-1+2i}\right)_4 = \left(\frac{i}{-1+2i}\right)_4^3 = i^3.$$

Combining these results, we have

$$\left(\frac{1+3i}{5+4i}\right)_4 = i^2 \cdot i^0 \cdot i^3 = i^5 = i;$$

that is, $1+3i$ is a biquadratic non-residue of $5+4i$, or in other words the congruence
$$x^4 \equiv 1+3i, \bmod 5+4i$$
has no roots.

We see also that $1+3i$ is a quadratic non-residue of $5+4i$.

Ex. 2. To classify the odd primary primes of $k(i)$ according to the biquadratic character of $-1+2i$ with respect to each of them.

Let π be any odd primary prime of $k(i)$.

[1] We select $1-3i$ as μ is chosen in Th. A.

We have two cases to consider according as $\pi \equiv 1$ or $3+2i$, mod 4.

i. $\pi \equiv 1$, mod 4.

Then

$$\left(\frac{-1+2i}{\pi}\right)_4 = \left(\frac{\pi}{-1+2i}\right)_4 = \left(\frac{1}{-1+2i}\right)_4, \left(\frac{i}{-1+2i}\right)_4, \left(\frac{-1}{-1+2i}\right)_4$$

$$\text{or} \left(\frac{-i}{-1+2i}\right)_4,$$

according as $\pi \equiv 1$, i, -1 or $-i$, mod $-1+2i$, $1, i, -1, -i$ being a reduced residue system, mod $-1+2i$.

But

$$\left(\frac{1}{-1+2i}\right)_4 = 1, \left(\frac{i}{-1+2i}\right)_4 = i, \left(\frac{-1}{-1+2i}\right) = i^2 \text{ and } \left(\frac{-i}{-1+2i}\right)_4 = i^3.$$

Hence with respect to an odd primary prime, π, $\equiv 1$, mod 4, $-1+2i$ has the biquadratic character 0, 1, 2 or 3, according as we have $\pi \equiv 1, i, -1$, or $-i$, mod $-1+2i$.

ii. $\pi \equiv 3+2i$, mod 4.

Since we have both π and $-1+2i \equiv 3+2i$, mod 4, it follows that

$$\left(\frac{-1+2i}{\pi}\right)_4 = -\left(\frac{\pi}{-1+2i}\right)_4.$$

Hence with respect to an odd primary prime, π, $\equiv 3+2i$, mod 4, $-1+2i$ has the biquadratic character 0, 1, 2 or 3, according as we have $\pi \equiv -1, -i, 1$ or i, mod $-1+2i$.

Combining these conditions we see that $-1+2i$ has with respect to an odd primary prime, π, the biquadratic character

0 where $\pi = \mu(-4+8i)+1$	or	$\mu(-4+8i)+3+2i$,
1 where $\pi = \mu(-4+8i)+1+4i$	or	$\mu(-4+8i)+3-2i$,
2 where $\pi = \mu(-4+8i)+1-4i$	or	$\mu(-4+8i)+3+6i$,
3 where $\pi = \mu(-4+8i)-3$	or	$\mu(-4+8i)+7+2i$,

μ being any integer of $k(i)$.

Ex. 3. Determine whether the congruence

$$x^4 \equiv 9+7i, \text{ mod } 5+4i,$$

has roots.

Ex. 4. Class the odd primary primes of $k(i)$ according to the biquadratic character of $3+i$ with respect to each of them.

CHAPTER VI.

THE REALM $k(\sqrt{-3})$.

§ 1. Numbers of $k(\sqrt{-3})$.

The number $\sqrt{-3}$ is defined by the equation

$$x^2+3=0, \qquad 1)$$

which it satisfies. We can show exactly as in $k(i)$ that all numbers of $k(\sqrt{-3})$ have the form $a+b\sqrt{-3}$, where a and b are rational numbers. The other root, $-\sqrt{-3}$, of 1) defines the realm $k(-\sqrt{-3})$ conjugate to $k(\sqrt{-3})$. These two realms are, however, evidently identical. The number α', $=a-b\sqrt{-3}$, obtained by putting $-\sqrt{-3}$ for $\sqrt{-3}$ in any number α, $=a+b\sqrt{-3}$, of $k(\sqrt{-3})$, is the conjugate of α; for example, $2+\sqrt{-3}$ and $2-\sqrt{-3}$ are conjugate numbers.

A rational number considered as a number of $k(\sqrt{-3})$ is evidently its own conjugate. The product of any number, α, of $k(\sqrt{-3})$ by its conjugate is called its norm, and is denoted by $n[\alpha]$; that is,

$$n[a+b\sqrt{-3}]=(a+b\sqrt{-3})(a-b\sqrt{-3})=a^2+3b^2$$

We see that the norms of all numbers of $k(\sqrt{-3})$ are positive rational numbers. We can prove exactly as in $k(i)$ that *the norm of a product is equal to the product of the norms of its factors;* that is,

$$n[\alpha\beta]=n[\alpha]n[\beta],$$

where α and β are any numbers of $k\sqrt{-3}$.

We observe, just as in $k(i)$, that every number α, $=a+b\sqrt{-3}$, of $k(\sqrt{-3})$ satisfies a rational equation of the second degree, that being the degree of the realm, and that this equation has for its remaining root the conjugate of α.

The numbers of $k(\sqrt{-3})$ fall then, as in $k(i)$, into two classes, *imprimitive* and *primitive,* according as the above equation is *reducible* or *irreducible;* that is, according as $b = $ or $\neq 0$. The imprimitive numbers are therefore the rational numbers, and the primitive numbers all the other numbers of the realm.

It is evident that any primitive number of $k(\sqrt{-3})$ can be taken to define the realm.

This realm as well as the following ones will not be discussed as fully as $k(i)$. Our desire is merely to bring out those points of difference from $k(i)$ which necessitate some change in our conceptions, and to show that after these changes have been made and the unique factorization theorem proved for the integers of the realm, we can get as in $k(i)$ a series of theorems analogous to those for rational integers.

§ 2. Integers of $k(\sqrt{-3})$.

To determine what numbers of $k(\sqrt{-3})$, in addition to the rational integers, are algebraic integers, we observe that as in $k(i)$ the necessary and sufficient conditions that any number, α, $= a + b\sqrt{-3}$, of $k(\sqrt{-3})$ shall be an integer are

$$\alpha + \alpha' = \text{a rational integer},$$

and

$$\alpha\alpha' = \text{a rational integer}.$$

If we write α in the form

$$\frac{a_1 + b_1\sqrt{-3}}{c_1},$$

where $a = a_1/c_1$, and $b = b_1/c_1$, a_1, b_1, c_1 being integers with no common factor, these conditions become

$$\frac{a_1 + b_1\sqrt{-3}}{c_1} + \frac{a_1 - b_1\sqrt{-3}}{c_1} = \frac{2a_1}{c_1} = \text{a rational integer}, \quad 1)$$

$$\left(\frac{a_1 + b_1\sqrt{-3}}{c_1}\right)\left(\frac{a_1 - b_1\sqrt{-3}}{c_1}\right) = \frac{a_1^2 + 3b_1^2}{c_1^2} = \text{a rational integer}. \quad 2)$$

One at least of the three following cases must occur:

i. $c_1 \neq 2$ or 1; ii. $c_1 = 2$; iii. $c_1 = 1$.

i. The impossibility of i is proved as in $k(i)$.

ii. If $c_1 = 2$, $2a_1/c_1$ can be an integer, and yet a_1 not contain the factor 2, $a_1^2 + 3b_1^2$ being divisible by 2^2 when a_1 and b_1 are both odd.

Hence $c_1 = 2$, in which case a_1 and b_1 must both be odd; or $c_1 = 1$. Hence every integer of $k(\sqrt{-3})$ has the form $\frac{1}{2}(a + b\sqrt{-3})$, where a and b are either both odd or both even, and all numbers of this form are integers.

§ 3. **Basis of $k(\sqrt{-3})$.**[1]

A basis of $k(\sqrt{-3})$ is defined as in $k(i)$. It will be observed that the integer $\sqrt{-3}$ defining $k(\sqrt{-3})$ does not constitute with 1 a basis of the realm as i and 1 did in $k(i)$; that is, there are integers of the realm that can not be represented in the form $x + y\sqrt{-3}$, where x and y are rational integers. We shall see, however, that two integers of $k(\sqrt{-3})$ can be found, which form a basis of the realm. For example, 1, $\frac{1}{2}(-1 + \sqrt{-3})$ is a basis of $k(\sqrt{-3})$; for let $\frac{1}{2}(-1 + \sqrt{-3})$, which is seen to be an integer, be represented by ρ, and $\frac{1}{2}(a + b\sqrt{-3})$ be any integer of $k(\sqrt{-3})$. We shall show that $\frac{1}{2}(a + b\sqrt{-3})$ can be put in the form $x + y\rho$, where x and y are rational integers.

Put $$\frac{a + b\sqrt{-3}}{2} = x + y\rho = \frac{2x - y}{2} + \frac{y}{2}\sqrt{-3},$$

which gives $$2x - y = a, \quad y = b,$$

whence $$x = \tfrac{1}{2}(a + b), \quad y = b,$$

and therefore $$\frac{a + b\sqrt{-3}}{2} = \frac{a + b}{2} + b\rho,$$

where $\frac{1}{2}(a + b)$ is a rational integer, since a and b are either both even or both odd. Every integer of $k(\sqrt{-3})$ can be represented therefore in the form $x + y\rho$, where x and y are rational integers; that is, 1, ρ is a basis of $k(\sqrt{-3})$. Moreover, every number of the form $x + y\rho$ can be put in the form $\frac{1}{2}(a + b\sqrt{-3})$, where a and b are both odd or both even, and hence is an integer of $k(\sqrt{-3})$. For, supposing x and y known, and a and b unknown, we see from the above analysis that a and b will be either both odd or both even, according as y is odd or even. The sum, difference and product of any two integers of $k(\sqrt{-3})$ is an integer of $k(\sqrt{-3})$, for

[1] See Chap. V, § 3.

$$(x+y\rho) \pm (x_1+y_1\rho) = x \pm x_1 + (y \pm y_1)\rho,$$

and

$$(x+y\rho)(x_1+y_1\rho) = xx_1 + (xy_1+x_1y)\rho + yy_1\rho^2$$
$$= xx_1 - yy_1 + (xy_1 + x_1y - yy_1)\rho,$$

since

$$\rho^2+\rho+1=0.$$

§ 4. Conjugate and Norm of an Integer of $k(\sqrt{-3})$.

The conjugate of ρ is $\rho' = \frac{1}{2}(-1-\sqrt{-3}) = \rho^2$. Since $\rho+\rho' = \rho+\rho^2 = -1$, and $\rho\rho' = \rho^3 = 1$, ρ satisfies the equation

$$x^2+x+1=0;$$

that is, ρ and ρ^2 are the imaginary cube roots of unity; therefore $k(\sqrt{-3})$ is called the realm of the cube roots of unity. If α, $=a+b\rho$, be any integer of $k(\sqrt{-3})$, its conjugate is α', $=a+b\rho^2$. The conjugate of $a+b\rho^2$ is evidently $a+b\rho^4$, $=a+b\rho$.

Hence

$$n[\alpha] = (a+b\rho)(a+b\rho^2)$$
$$= a^2 + ab(\rho+\rho^2) + b^2\rho^3$$
$$= a^2 - ab + b^2,$$

which is seen to be a positive integer.

For example

$$n[3+2\rho] = 9-6+4=7.$$

§ 5. Discriminant of $k(\sqrt{-3})$.[1]

The discriminant of $k(\sqrt{-3})$ is the squared determinant

$$\begin{vmatrix} 1 & \rho \\ 1 & \rho^2 \end{vmatrix}^2$$

formed from a pair of basis numbers and their conjugates.

Denoting it by d, we have

$$d = -3$$

§ 6. Divisibility of Integers of $k(\sqrt{-3})$.

We define the divisibility of integers of $k(\sqrt{-3})$ exactly as we defined that of the integers of R and $k(i)$, and all that followed from this definition in R and $k(i)$ holds for $k(\sqrt{-3})$.

[1] See Chap. V, §§ 3, 4; the same remarks hold here.

Ex. 1. We see that $4+5\rho$ is divisible by $3+2\rho$, since

$$\begin{aligned} 4+5\rho &= (3+2\rho)(2+\rho) \\ &= 6+7\rho+2\rho^2 \\ &= 4+5\rho, \end{aligned}$$

since $\rho^2 = -1-\rho$.

Ex. 2. On the other hand, $5+2\rho$ is not divisible by $3+\rho$, since there exists no integer of $k(\sqrt{-3})$ which when multiplied by $3+\rho$ gives $5+2\rho$; for let

$$\begin{aligned} 5+2\rho &= (3+\rho)(x+y\rho) \\ &= 3x+(x+3y)\rho+y\rho^2 \qquad\qquad 1) \\ &= 3x-y+(x+2y)\rho; \end{aligned}$$

thus x and y must satisfy the equations

$$3x-y=5,\ x+2y=2,$$

which give $x=12/7$, $y=1/7$; that is, 1) does not hold for integral values of x and y, and hence $5+2\rho$ is not divisible by $3+\rho$.

THEOREM 1. *If α be divisible by β, then $n[\alpha]$ is divisible by $n[\beta]$.*

For from $\alpha=\beta\gamma$ follows $n[\alpha]=n[\beta]n[\gamma]$; that is, $n[\alpha]$ is divisible by $n[\beta]$. As was seen in $k(i)$, the converse of this theorem is not in general true.

A common divisor of two or more integers is defined as in R and $k(i)$.

§ 7. Units of $k(\sqrt{-3})$. Associated Integers.

The units of $k(\sqrt{-3})$ are defined, as in the case of the last two realms, as *those integers of $k(\sqrt{-3})$ that divide every integer of the realm.* They therefore divide 1, and since every divisor of 1 is evidently a unit, the units may also be defined either as *those integers of $k(\sqrt{-3})$ whose reciprocals are also integers of $k(\sqrt{-3})$*, or, since if ϵ be a unit, $n[\epsilon]$ must divide 1, as *those integers of $k(\sqrt{-3})$ whose norms are 1.*

To determine the units of $k(\sqrt{-3})$ we let $\epsilon, =x+y\rho$, be one of them, and put

$$n[\epsilon]=x^2-xy+y^2=(x-\tfrac{1}{2}y)^2+\tfrac{3}{4}y^2=1,$$

from which we see that y can have only the values 0, 1 and -1.

$y = 0$ gives $x^2 = 1$, $x = 1$ or -1, and hence $\epsilon = 1$ or -1;

$y = 1$ gives $x^2 - x + 1 = 1$, $x = 0$ or 1, and hence $\epsilon = \rho$, or $1 + \rho = -\rho^2$;

$y = -1$ gives $x^2 + x + 1 = 1$, $x = 0$ or -1, and hence $\epsilon = -\rho$, or $-1 - \rho = \rho^2$.

Hence ϵ can have any one of the six values $\pm 1, \pm\rho, \pm\rho^2$, which are therefore the units of $k(\sqrt{-3})$.

As $k(\sqrt{-3})$ contains the primitive sixth roots, $\frac{1}{2}(1+\sqrt{-3})$ and $\frac{1}{2}(1-\sqrt{-3})$, of 1, and hence the cube roots of 1, it might more properly be called the "realm of the sixth roots of unity." Taking 1, ω, $=\frac{1}{2}(1+\sqrt{-3})$, as a basis, we would have as the six units of the realm $1, \omega, \omega^2, \omega^3 = -1, \omega^4, \omega^5$, the six sixth roots of unity.

The nomenclature used above is, however, the usual one, and hence has been adopted here.

If two integers, α and β, have no common divisor except the units, they are said to be *prime to each other*, or, excluding the units, *to have no common divisor*.

The six integers, $\alpha, -\alpha, \rho\alpha, -\rho\alpha, \rho^2\alpha, -\rho^2\alpha$, obtained by multiplying any integer, α, of $k(\sqrt{-3})$ by the six units in turn, are called *associated integers;* for example, the six integers, $1 - 6\rho$, $-1 + 6\rho$, $6 + 7\rho$, $-6 - 7\rho$, $-7 - \rho$ and $7 + \rho$ are associated. Any integer which is divisible by α is also divisible by $-\alpha$, $\rho\alpha$, $-\rho\alpha$, $\rho^2\alpha$ and $-\rho^2\alpha$. Hence in all questions of divisibility, associated integers are considered as identical; that is, two factors, one of which can be changed into the other by multiplication by a unit, are looked upon as the same.

§ 8. Prime Numbers of $k(\sqrt{-3})$.

The definitions are identical with those in $k(i)$.

We can determine whether any integer of $k(\sqrt{-3})$ is prime or composite by the method employed for the same problem in $k(i)$, the process depending upon Th. 1.

Ex. 1. To determine whether 2 is a prime or composite number of $k(\sqrt{-3})$.

Put
$$2 = (a + b\rho)(c + d\rho);$$
then
$$4 = (a^2 - ab + b^2)(c^2 - cd + d^2),$$

whence we have either

$$a^2-ab+b^2=2,\ c^2-cd+d^2=2, \qquad 1)$$

or

$$a^2-ab+b^2=1,\ c^2-cd+d^2=4. \qquad 2)$$

It is easily seen that 1) is impossible; for, if

$$a^2-ab+b^2=\left(a-\frac{b}{2}\right)^2+\frac{3b^2}{4}=2,$$

then

$$|b|\leqq 1 \quad \text{and similarly} \quad |a|\leqq 1. \qquad 3)$$

It is evident that no pair of values of a and b, which fulfil the condition 3), can satisfy 1). Hence 1) is impossible, and 2) is the only admissible case; that is, $a+b\rho$ is a unit. Therefore 2 is a prime number in $k(\sqrt{-3})$.

Ex. 2. To determine whether 3 is a prime or composite number of $k(\sqrt{-3})$.

Put

$$3=(a+b\rho)(c+d\rho);$$

then

$$9=(a^2-ab+b^2)(c^2-cd+d^2).$$

whence we have either

$$a^2-ab+b^2=3,\ c^2-cd+d^2=3, \qquad 4)$$

or

$$a^2-ab+b^2=1,\ c^2-cd+d^2=9. \qquad 5)$$

Now, if $a^2-ab+b^2=1$, $a+b\rho$ is a unit and hence 5) is not an actual factorization.

If

$$a^2-ab+b^2=\left(a-\frac{b}{2}\right)^2+\frac{3b^2}{4}=3.$$

then

$$|b|\leqq 2, \quad \text{and} \quad |a|\leqq 2. \qquad 6)$$

The possible values of b which satisfy 6) are $0, \pm 1, \pm 2$. Considering them in turn we see that

$b=0$, gives $a^2=3$, which is impossible,

$b=1$, gives $a^2-a+1=3$, and hence $a=-1$ or 2,

$b=-1$, gives $a^2+a+1=3$, and hence $a=1$ or -2,

$b=2$, gives $a^2-2a+4=3$, and hence $a=1$,

$b=-2$, gives $a^2+2a+4=3$, and hence $a=-1$,

whence $a+b\rho=\pm(1-\rho)$, $\pm(2+\rho)$ or $\pm(1+2\rho)$.

Similarly $c+d\rho=\pm(1-\rho)$, $\pm(2+\rho)$ or $\pm(1+2\rho)$,

and we have

$$3=(1-\rho)(2+\rho)=(-1+\rho)(-2-\rho)=(1+2\rho)(-1-2\rho),$$

the proper combinations of factors being selected by trial. All these factorizations are, however, considered as identical, since the factors in each resolution are associated with the corresponding factors in the other resolutions. All these factors can easily be proved to be primes of $k(\sqrt{-3})$, whence we see that 3 can be resolved into the product of two prime factors in $k(\sqrt{-3})$, and that this resolution is unique. Moreover, all these factors are associates of $1-\rho$, and we have

$$3=-\rho^2(1-\rho)^2.$$

We could have seen directly from the equation defining the realm that

$$3=-(\sqrt{-3})^2.$$

Ex. 3. If we endeavor to resolve $-46+37\rho$ into two factors neither of which is a unit, we find that it can be done in seven essentially different ways, the factors in each product not being associated with the factors in any one of the other products.

$$-46+37\rho=(4+5\rho)(11+18\rho) \quad 7)$$
$$=(-5+6\rho)(8+\rho) \quad 8)$$
$$=(7+2\rho)(-4+9\rho) \quad 9)$$
$$=(1-\rho)(-43-3\rho) \quad 10)$$
$$=(1+3\rho)(29+25\rho) \quad 11)$$
$$=(4+3\rho)(5+22\rho) \quad 12)$$
$$=(5+3\rho)(1+17\rho) \quad 13)$$

We find, however, that none of these factors except $1-\rho$, $1+3\rho$, $4+3\rho$, and $5+3\rho$ are prime numbers, and that we can resolve those which are not prime into prime factors in the following manner:

$$4+5\rho=(1-\rho)(1+3\rho), \qquad 11+18\rho=(4+3\rho)(5+3\rho);$$
$$-5+6\rho=(1+3\rho)(4+3\rho), \qquad 8+\rho=(1-\rho)(5+3\rho);$$
$$7+2\rho=(1-\rho)(4+3\rho), \qquad -4+9\rho=(1+3\rho)(5+3\rho);$$
$$-43-3\rho=(1+3\rho)(4+3\rho)(5+3\rho),$$
$$29+25\rho=(1-\rho)(4+3\rho)(5+3\rho);$$
$$5+22\rho=(1-\rho)(1+3\rho)(5+3\rho),$$
$$1+17\rho=(1-\rho)(1+3\rho)(4+3\rho).$$

When these products are substituted in 7), 8), 9), 10), 11), 12), and 13) we obtain in each case

$$46+37\rho=(1-\rho)(1+3\rho)(4+3\rho)(5+3\rho);$$

that is, when $-46+37\rho$ is represented as a product of factors all of which are prime, the representation is unique. Having made these notions concerning the integers of $k(\sqrt{-3})$ clear, we proceed to what will always be our first goal in the discussion of any realm; that is, to prove that every integer of $k(\sqrt{-3})$ can be expressed in one and only one way as a product of prime numbers.

§ 9. Unique Factorization Theorem for $k(\sqrt{-3})$.

THEOREM A. *If α be any integer of $k(\sqrt{-3})$, and β any integer of $k(\sqrt{-3})$ different from 0, there exists an integer μ of $k(\sqrt{-3})$ such that*

$$n[\alpha-\mu\beta] < n[\beta].$$[1]

Let
$$\alpha/\beta = a + b\rho,$$
where $a = r + r_1$, $b = s + s_1$, r and s being the rational integers nearest to a and b respectively, and hence

$$|r_1| \leqq \tfrac{1}{2},\ |s_1| \leqq \tfrac{1}{2}.$$

We shall show that μ, $= r + s\rho$, will fulfil the required conditions. Since

$$\alpha/\beta - \mu = r_1 + s_1\rho,$$

$$n[\alpha/\beta - \mu] = r_1^2 - r_1 s_1 + s_1^2 \leqq \tfrac{3}{4},$$

whence
$$n[\alpha/\beta - \mu] < 1,$$
or multiplying by $n[\beta]$,

$$n[\alpha - \mu\beta] < n[\beta].$$

The proofs of the two remaining theorems which lead to the Unique Factorization Theorem and the proof of that theorem itself are now word for word identical with those in $k(i)$; we shall therefore merely state these theorems:

THEOREM B. *If α and β be any two integers of $k(\sqrt{-3})$ prime to each other, there exist two integers, ξ and η, of $k(\sqrt{-3})$ such that*

$$\alpha\xi + \beta\eta = 1.$$

THEOREM C. *If the product of two integers, α and β, of $k(\sqrt{-3})$ be divisible by a prime number, π, at least one of the integers is divisible by π.*

This theorem has, of course, the same corollaries as the corresponding one in $k(i)$.

THEOREM 2. *Every integer of $k(\sqrt{-3})$ can be represented in one and only one way as the product of prime numbers.*

[1] See note in $k(i)$ which applies equally here.

§ 10. Classification of the Prime Numbers of $k(\sqrt{-3})$.

By a train of reasoning identical with that employed in $k(i)$, it becomes evident that every prime, π, of $k(\sqrt{-3})$ is a divisor of one and only one rational prime. In order therefore to determine all primes of $k(\sqrt{-3})$, it is only necessary to find the divisors of all rational primes considered as integers of $k(\sqrt{-3})$.

Let $\pi, = a + b\rho$, be any prime of $k(\sqrt{-3})$ and p the positive rational prime of which π is a divisor.

Then $$p = \pi\alpha, \tag{1}$$

and hence $$p^2 = n[\pi]n[\alpha].$$

We have then two cases

$$\text{i.}\quad \begin{cases} n[\pi] = p, \\ n[\alpha] = p, \end{cases} \qquad \text{ii.}\quad \begin{cases} n[\pi] = p^2, \\ n[\alpha] = 1\,. \end{cases}$$

i. From $n[\pi] = \pi\pi' = p$ and 1), it follows that $\alpha = \pi'$. From $n[\pi] = p$ we have $a^2 - ab + b^2 = p$, and hence since every positive rational prime, except 3, is of the form $3n + 1$ or $3n - 1$, we must have, excluding the case $p = 3$, when $p = n[\pi]$,

$$a^2 - ab + b^2 \equiv 1, \text{ mod } 3,$$

or

$$a^2 - ab + b^2 \equiv -1, \text{ mod } 3.$$

The first of these congruences has the solutions

$$\left.\begin{matrix} a \equiv 0; & a \equiv \pm 1; & a \equiv 1; & a \equiv -1 \\ b \equiv \pm 1; & b \equiv 0; & b \equiv 1; & b \equiv -1 \end{matrix}\right\}, \text{ mod } 3,$$

while the second has no solutions.

Hence when a positive rational prime other than 3 is the product of two conjugate primes of $k(\sqrt{-3})$, it has the form $3n + 1$.

The case $p = 3$ is easily disposed of, for the equation

$$p = a^2 - ab + b^2 = 3$$

is satisfied by $a = 1$, $b = -1$, which give

$$3 = (1 - \rho)(1 - \rho^2);$$

hence 3 is the product of two conjugate primes of $k(\sqrt{-3})$.

These factors of 3 are, however, associated, for

$$1 - \rho^2 = -\rho^2(1 - \rho),$$

whence $\quad 3 = -\rho^2(1-\rho)^2$, or $3 = -(\sqrt{-3})^2$;

that is, *3, which is the only rational prime divisor of the discriminant of* $k(\sqrt{-3})$, *is associated with the square of a prime of* $k(\sqrt{-3})$.

ii. From $n[\alpha] = 1$ it follows that α is a unit. Hence p is associated with the prime π; that is, p is a prime in $k(\sqrt{-3})$. When p is of the form $3n-1$, this case always occurs, for we have seen that in order to be factorable in $k(\sqrt{-3})$, a rational prime must either be 3 or of the form $3n+1$.

We shall now show that every rational prime, p, of the form $3n+1$ can be resolved into the product of two conjugate primes of $k(\sqrt{-3})$.

The congruence

$$x^2 \equiv -3, \text{ mod p}, \quad p = 3n+1,$$

has roots; for

$$(-3/p) = (-1/p)(3/p),$$

and if $p = 4k+1$,

$$(-1/p) = 1, \text{ and } (3/p) = (p/3),$$

while, if $p = 4k+3$,

$$(-1/p) = -1, \text{ and } (3/p) = -(p/3),$$

and in both cases therefore

$$(-3/p) = (p/3) = (1/3) = 1.$$

Let a be a root; then

$$a^2 + 3 \equiv 0, \text{ mod } p;$$

that is, $\quad (a+\sqrt{-3})(a-\sqrt{-3}) \equiv 0, \text{ mod } p.$

Since $a+\sqrt{-3}$ and $a-\sqrt{-3}$ are integers of $k(\sqrt{-3})$, p must, if a prime in $k(\sqrt{-3})$, divide one of them; we must have, therefore, either

$$a+\sqrt{-3} = p\,\frac{u+v\sqrt{-3}}{2} \qquad 2)$$

when u and v are either both odd or both even, or

$$a-\sqrt{-3} = p\,\frac{u_1+v_1\sqrt{-3}}{2} \qquad 3)$$

where u_1 and v_1 are either both odd or both even. But 2) and 3) are, however, impossible, since $\frac{1}{2}pv = \pm 1$ implies that v is even, and hence that p is a divisor of 1, which is impossible.

Hence p is not a prime in $k(\sqrt{-3})$, and, since the only way in which a rational prime is factorable in $k(\sqrt{-3})$ is into two conjugate primes, p is factorable in this manner. The primes of $k(\sqrt{-3})$ may therefore be classified according to the rational primes of which they are factors as follows:

1) *All positive rational primes of the form $3n+1$ are factorable in $k(\sqrt{-3})$ into two conjugate primes, called primes of the first degree.*

2) *All positive rational primes of the form $3n-1$ are primes in $k(\sqrt{-3})$, called primes of the second degree.*

3) *The number 3 is associated with the square of a prime of the first degree.*

It can be easily proved as in the case of 2 in $k(i)$, that 3 is the only rational prime which is associated with the square of a prime of the first degree in $k(\sqrt{-3})$. We observe that in $k(\sqrt{-3})$ as well as in $k(i)$ the only rational primes which are associated with the squares of primes of the first degree are those which divide the discriminant of the realm.

§ 11. Factorization of a Rational Prime in $k(\sqrt{-3})$ determined by the value of (d/p).

As in $k(i)$, we can express the above results in a very convenient manner by means of the discriminant, d, of $k(\sqrt{-3})$.

We have seen that, when $p = 3n+1$, $(-3/p) = 1$; that is, $(d/p) = 1$.

When $p = 3$, d is divisible by p, which is expressed symbolically by $(d/p) = 0$.

Hence we can classify the rational primes according to their factorability in $k(\sqrt{-3})$ as follows:

When $\left(\dfrac{d}{p}\right) = 1, \quad p = \pi\pi';$

that is, p is the product of two conjugate primes of the first degree.

When $\left(\dfrac{d}{p}\right) = -1, \quad p = p;$

that is, p is a prime of the second degree.

When $$\left(\frac{d}{p}\right)=0, \quad p=\epsilon\pi^2;$$

that is, p is associated with the square of a prime of the first degree.

The primes of $k(\sqrt{-3})$ whose norms are less than 100 are 2, $1-\rho$, 5, $1+3\rho$, $4+3\rho$, $5+3\rho$, $5+6\rho$, $7+3\rho$, $7+6\rho$, $5+9\rho$, $7+9\rho$, $1+9\rho$, $10+3\rho$, $11+3\rho$.

§ 12. **Cubic Residues.**

If a and m be rational integers and a be prime to m, a is said to be a cubic residue or non-residue of m according as the congruence

$$x^3 \equiv a, \text{ mod } m,$$

has or has not roots.

As in the development of the theory of biquadratic residues, we saw that our field of operation must be not simply the rational integers but the integers of the realm $k(i)$, of which the rational integers are a part, so in the theory of cubic residues we must take as our field of operation the integers of $k(\sqrt{-3})$; that is, we must consider the congruence

$$x^3 \equiv \alpha, \text{ mod } \mu,$$

where α and μ are integers of $k(\sqrt{-3})$ and α prime to μ.

Lack of space forbids even a brief discussion of this subject here but the reader should consult Bachmann: Die Lehre von der Kreistheilung, 14[te] Vorlesung; Jacobi: Works, Vol. 6, p. 223, and Eisenstein: Crelle, Vols. 27 and 28.

CHAPTER VII.

THE REALM $k(\sqrt{2})$.

§ 1. Numbers of $k(\sqrt{2})$.

The number $\sqrt{2}$ is defined by the equation

$$x^2 - 2 = 0,$$

which it satisfies. All numbers of $k(\sqrt{2})$ have the form $a + b\sqrt{2}$, where a and b are rational numbers.

The other root, $-\sqrt{2}$, of $x^2 - 2 = 0$ defines the realm $k(-\sqrt{2})$, conjugate to $k(\sqrt{2})$. The two realms are, however, as in both the previous cases, identical.

The conjugate of α, $= a + b\sqrt{2}$, is α', $= a - b\sqrt{2}$. The product $\alpha\alpha'$ is called as before the norm of α and is denoted by $n[\alpha]$.

In $n[\alpha] = (a + b\sqrt{2})(a - b\sqrt{2}) = a^2 - 2b^2$ we notice the first of a series of important differences between this realm and $k(i)$ and $k(\sqrt{-3})$. The norm of a number of $k(\sqrt{2})$ is not, as heretofore, necessarily a *positive* rational number. It may be either a positive or negative rational number. This will easily be seen to be true of all quadratic realms defined by *real* numbers, while the norms of numbers of quadratic realms defined by imaginary numbers are always positive. Realms of the first kind, as $k(\sqrt{2})$, are called *real realms;* those of the second kind, as $k(i)$ and $k(\sqrt{-3})$, *imaginary realms.*

We have evidently $n[\alpha\beta] = n[\alpha]n[\beta]$, where α and β are any numbers of $k(\sqrt{2})$.

§ 2. Integers of $k(\sqrt{2})$.

Writing all numbers of $k(\sqrt{2})$ in the form

$$\alpha = \frac{a_1 + b_1\sqrt{2}}{c_1},$$

where a_1, b_1, c_1 are rational integers, having no common factor, we can show exactly as in $k(i)$ that a necessary and sufficient condition for α to be an integer is $c_1 = 1$.

Therefore all integers of $k(\sqrt{2})$ have the form $a + b\sqrt{2}$, where a and b are rational integers, and all numbers of this form are integers; that is, $1, \sqrt{2}$ is a basis of $k(\sqrt{2})$.

§ 3. **Discriminant of $k(\sqrt{2})$.**

The discriminant of $k(\sqrt{2})$ is the squared determinant

$$\begin{vmatrix} 1 & \sqrt{2} \\ 1 & -\sqrt{2} \end{vmatrix}^2$$

formed from a pair of basis numbers and their conjugates. Denoting it by d, we have

$$d = 8.$$

§ 4. **Divisibility of Integers of $k(\sqrt{2})$.**

The definition is identical with that given in R, $k(i)$ and $k(\sqrt{-3})$. For example, since

$$14 + 9\sqrt{2} = (2 + \sqrt{2})(5 + 2\sqrt{2})$$

$14 + 9\sqrt{2}$ is divisible by $2 + 2\sqrt{2}$ and $5 + 2\sqrt{2}$.

On the other hand, since no integral values of x and y exist for which the equation

$$5 + 2\sqrt{2} = (1 + 2\sqrt{2})(x + y\sqrt{2})$$

is satisfied, $5 + \sqrt{2}$ is not divisible by $1 + 2\sqrt{2}$.

§ 5. **Units of $k(\sqrt{2})$. Associated Integers.**

The units of $k(\sqrt{2})$, being those integers of $k(\sqrt{2})$ which divide every integer of the realm, divide 1, and since all divisors of 1 are evidently units, they can be defined either as *those integers of $k(\sqrt{2})$ whose norms are either 1 or -1*, or as *those integers of $k(\sqrt{2})$ whose reciprocals are also integers.*

Let $\epsilon, = x + y\sqrt{2}$, be a unit of $k(\sqrt{2})$; we have then either

$$n[\epsilon] = 1, \text{ or } n[\epsilon] = -1;$$

that is i. $x^2 - 2y^2 = 1$, or ii. $x^2 - 2y^2 = -1$.[1]

[1] The reader will recognize i and ii as special cases of Pell's Equation

$$x^2 - Dy^2 = \pm 1,$$

a discussion of which will be found Chap. XIII, § 5. Here we shall treat the question from a different point of view.

We can easily obtain many solutions of both i and ii, as, for example:

$$\text{i.} \quad \begin{cases} x = \pm\ 1, & y = \quad 0, & \epsilon = \pm 1, \\ x = \pm\ 3, & y = \pm\ 2, & \epsilon = \pm 3 \pm 2\sqrt{2}, \\ x = \pm 17, & y = \pm 12, & \epsilon = \pm 17 \pm 12\sqrt{2}, \end{cases}$$

$$\text{ii.} \quad \begin{cases} x = \pm\ 1, & y = \pm\ 1, & \epsilon = \pm 1 \pm \sqrt{2}, \\ x = \pm\ 7, & y = \pm\ 5, & \epsilon = \pm 7 \pm 5\sqrt{2}, \\ x = \pm 41, & y = \pm 29, & \epsilon = \pm 41 \pm 29\sqrt{2}. \end{cases}$$

We shall now show that $k(\sqrt{2})$ has indeed an infinite number of units, each of which can, however, be represented as a power of the unit $1 + \sqrt{2}$, multiplied by $+1$ or -1. This unit $1 + \sqrt{2}$ is called the *fundamental unit*.

THEOREM 1. *All units of $k(\sqrt{2})$ have the form $\pm(1 + \sqrt{2})^n$, where n is a positive or negative rational integer or 0, and all numbers of this form are units of $k(\sqrt{2})$.*

Let $\epsilon = 1 + \sqrt{2}$. We see that every positive power of ϵ is a unit; for

$$n[\epsilon^n] = (n[\epsilon])^n = (-1)^n = 1 \text{ or } -1.$$

Hence ϵ^n is a unit.

Moreover, since $$\epsilon^n\epsilon^{-n} = 1,$$

ϵ^{-n} is a unit also; that is, all negative powers of ϵ are units, Furthermore two different positive powers of ϵ give always different units; for, since $\epsilon, = 1 + \sqrt{2}$, is greater than 1, the positive powers of ϵ are all greater than 1 and continually increase. Hence no two are equal.

Also, since $$\epsilon^{-n} = 1/\epsilon^n,$$

it is evident that ϵ^{-1} is less than 1 and hence that the negative powers of ϵ are all less than 1 and continually decrease. Therefore no two negative powers are equal, and no negative power is equal to any positive power. *Hence every power of ϵ is a unit of $k(\sqrt{2})$, and two different powers give always different units.*

Therefore $k(\sqrt{2})$ possesses the remarkable property of having an infinite number of units. We shall now show that the powers of ϵ multiplied by ± 1 are all the units of $k(\sqrt{2})$; that is, if η be any unit of $k(\sqrt{2})$, it will be of the form

$$\eta = \pm \epsilon^n,$$

where n is positive, negative or 0.

Let $a + b\sqrt{2}$ be any unit of $k(\sqrt{2})$. Then $a - b\sqrt{2}$, $-a + b\sqrt{2}$ and $-a - b\sqrt{2}$ will also be units of $k(\sqrt{2})$. Denote that one of these four units which has both terms positive by η_1 (b may be 0), the remaining three will be $-\eta_1$, η_1' and $-\eta_1'$. We shall show that

$$\eta_1 = \epsilon^n,$$

where n is positive or 0.

Since $$\eta_1 \gtreqless 1,$$
it follows that $$\eta_1 = \epsilon^n,$$
or $$\epsilon^n < \eta_1 < \epsilon^{n+1} \qquad 1)$$
where n is a positive integer or 0. We shall show that the latter case can never arise. Dividing 1) by ϵ^n, we have

$$1 < \eta_1/\epsilon^n < \epsilon,$$

where η_1/ϵ^n is a unit, since the quotient of two units is a unit.

Let $$\eta_1/\epsilon^n = x + y\sqrt{2}.$$
We have $$(x + y\sqrt{2})(x - y\sqrt{2}) = \pm 1,$$
and hence, since $x + y\sqrt{2} > 1$, it follows that

$$|x - y\sqrt{2}| < 1;$$

that is $$-1 < x - y\sqrt{2} < 1.$$

This combined with

$$1 < x + y\sqrt{2} < 1 + \sqrt{2} \qquad 2)$$

gives $$0 < 2x < 2 + \sqrt{2},$$
and hence, x being a rational integer,

$$x = 1.$$

But, if $x = 1$, it is evident that no rational integral value of y will satisfy 2), for positive values of y give

$$1 + y\sqrt{2} \gtreqless 1 + \sqrt{2},$$

and $y = 0$, or a negative integer makes

$$1 + y\sqrt{2} < 1.$$

Hence 1) is impossible, and we have

$$\eta_1 = \epsilon^n,$$

and therefore $$-\eta_1 = -\epsilon^n;$$

and since $$\eta_1\eta_1' = \pm 1,$$

$$\eta_1' = \pm 1/\epsilon^n = \pm \epsilon^{-n}, \text{ and } -\eta_1' = \mp \epsilon^{-n}.$$

Therefore, if η be any one of the four units $\eta_1, -\eta_1, \eta_1', -\eta_1'$, that is any unit of $k(\sqrt{2})$, we have

$$\eta = \pm \epsilon^n,$$

where n is positive, negative or 0.

We can express all units of $k(i)$ in the form i^n, but obtain only the four different ones $1, i, -1, -i$, since $i^4 = 1$.

Likewise we can express all units of $k(\sqrt{-3})$ in the form $\pm \rho^n$, but obtain only the six different ones $1, -1, \rho, -\rho, \rho^2, -\rho^2$, since $\rho^3 = 1$.

Any two integers which differ only by a unit factor are said to be *associated,* and in all questions of divisibility are considered as identical. Thus, if α be a factor of μ, and n any positive or negative rational integer, the infinitely many integers $\pm \epsilon^n\alpha$, that are associated with α, are also factors of μ. All these factors, however, are considered as the same. With this understanding, we shall find that the fact that $k(\sqrt{2})$ has an infinite number of units in no way interferes with our adopting definitions for prime and composite numbers of $k(\sqrt{2})$ identical with those used in the previous realms and proving the unique factorization theorem for the integers of $k(\sqrt{2})$.

§ 6. Prime Numbers of $k(\sqrt{2})$.

The definitions are identical with those in the preceding realms and we can determine whether an integer is prime or composite by the methods employed in those realms.

Ex. 1. To determine whether $13 + 12\sqrt{2}$ is prime or composite.

Put $$13 + 12\sqrt{2} = (a + b\sqrt{2})(c + d\sqrt{2});$$

then $$-119 = (a^2 - 2b^2)(c^2 - 2d^2).$$

There are only four distinct cases to be considered:

$$\text{i.}\quad \begin{cases} a^2-2b^2=17, \\ c^2-2d^2=-7. \end{cases} \qquad \text{ii.}\quad \begin{cases} a^2-2b^2=-17, \\ c^2-2d^2=7. \end{cases}$$

$$\text{iii and iv.}\quad \begin{cases} a^2-2b^2=\pm 119, \\ c^2-2d^2=\pm 1. \end{cases}$$

Both iii and iv give $c+d\sqrt{2}$ a unit and therefore need not be considered. As solutions of i we have

$$a=\pm 5,\quad b=\pm 2,\quad c=\pm 1,\quad d=\pm 2,$$

which give

$$13+12\sqrt{2}=(5+2\sqrt{2})(1+2\sqrt{2})=(-5-2\sqrt{2})(-1-2\sqrt{2}),$$

the proper factors being selected by trial.

Since neither of the integers $5+\sqrt{2}$, $1+2\sqrt{2}$ is a unit, $13+12\sqrt{2}$ is a composite number.

Other solutions of i are

$$a=\pm 7,\quad b=\pm 4,\quad c=\pm 11,\quad d=\pm 8,$$

which give

$$13+12\sqrt{2}=(7-4\sqrt{2})(11+8\sqrt{2})=(-7+4\sqrt{2})(-11-8\sqrt{2}).$$

As solutions of ii we have

$$a=\pm 1,\quad b=\pm 3,\quad c=\pm 5,\quad d=\pm 3,$$

which give

$$13+12\sqrt{2}=(-1+3\sqrt{2})(5+3\sqrt{2})=(1-3\sqrt{2})(-5-3\sqrt{2}).$$

We see, however, that all these factorizations can be derived from any particular one by multiplying the factors by suitable units, and hence are not different; that is,

$$7-4\sqrt{2}=\epsilon^{-2}(5+2\sqrt{2}),\qquad 11+8\sqrt{2}=\epsilon^{2}(1+2\sqrt{2}),$$
$$-1+3\sqrt{2}=\epsilon^{-1}(5+2\sqrt{2}),\qquad 5+3\sqrt{2}=\epsilon\,(1+2\sqrt{2}),$$

where $\epsilon=1+\sqrt{2}$, and we have in general

$$13+12\sqrt{2}=[\pm\epsilon^{n}(5+2\sqrt{2})][\pm\epsilon^{-n}(1+2\sqrt{2})].$$

Ex. 2. Prove that $1+2\sqrt{2}$ is a prime.

§ 7. Unique Factorization Theorem for $k(\sqrt{2})$.

THEOREM A. *If α be any integer of $k(\sqrt{2})$, and β any integer of $k(\sqrt{2})$ different from 0, there exists an integer μ of $k(\sqrt{2})$ such that*

$$|n[\alpha-\mu\beta]|<|n[\beta]|\text{[1]}$$

Let
$$\alpha/\beta=a+b\sqrt{2},$$

[1] See note to corresponding theorem in $k(i)$ which applies equally her

where $a = r + r_1$, $b = s + s_1$, r and s being the rational integers nearest to a and b respectively, and hence

$$|r_1| \leqq \tfrac{1}{2}, \quad |s_1| \leqq \tfrac{1}{2}.$$

We shall show that $\mu, = r + s\sqrt{2}$, will fulfil the required conditions. Since

$$\alpha/\beta - \mu = r_1 + s_1\sqrt{2},$$

$$|n[\alpha/\beta - \mu]| = |r_1^2 - 2s_1^2| \leqq \tfrac{1}{4},$$

whence

$$|n[\alpha/\beta - \mu]| < 1,$$

or, multiplying by $|n[\beta]|$,

$$|n[\alpha - \mu\beta]| < |n[\beta]|.$$

The proofs of the two theorems which lead to the unique factorization theorem and that of the unique factorization theorem itself are identical with those in $k(i)$ and $k(\sqrt{-3})$ with the exception that the absolute value of the norm is substituted for the norm of an integer. This is evidently necessary whenever we make a comparison between two integers of $k(\sqrt{2})$ similar to that made between rational integers when we say that one is greater in absolute value than the other. It is also necessary when we express the result of an enumeration as a function of an integer of $k(\sqrt{2})$. In $k(i)$ and $k(\sqrt{-3})$ the norms of all numbers were positive and hence were their own absolute values.

The result of an enumeration being always a positive integer, the conception of the positive integer being indeed arrived at by considering it as representing the result of an enumeration, to express such a result as a function of an algebraic integer, α, we must have some function of α which is always a positive integer. Such a function is $|n[\alpha]|$.

THEOREM B. *If α and β be any two integers of $k(\sqrt{2})$ prime to each other, there exist two integers, ξ and η, of $k(\sqrt{2})$ such that*

$$\alpha\xi + \beta\eta = 1.$$

THEOREM C. *If the product of two integers, α and β, of $k(\sqrt{2})$ be divisible by a prime number, π, at least one of the integers is divisible by π.*

THEOREM 2. *Every integer of $k(\sqrt{2})$ can be represented in one and only one way as the product of prime numbers.*

§ 8. Classification of the Prime Numbers of $k(\sqrt{2})$.

By a train of reasoning identical with that employed in the preceding realms, it becomes evident that every prime, π, of $k(\sqrt{2})$ is a divisor of one and only one rational prime. In order therefore to obtain all primes of $k(\sqrt{2})$ it is only necessary to resolve all positive rational primes considered as integers of $k(\sqrt{2})$ into their prime factors in that realm.

Let $\pi, = a + b\sqrt{2}$, be any prime of $k(\sqrt{2})$ and p the positive rational prime of which π is a divisor.

Then
$$p = \pi\alpha, \tag{1}$$
and hence
$$p^2 = n[\pi]n[\alpha].$$

We have then two cases

$$\text{i.}\ \begin{cases} n[\pi] = p, \\ n[\alpha] = p. \end{cases} \qquad \text{ii.}\ \begin{cases} n[\pi] = p^2, \\ n[\alpha] = 1. \end{cases}$$

i. From $n[\pi] = \pi\pi' = p$ and 1) it follows that $\alpha = \pi'$.

Since every positive rational prime, except 2, is of one of the forms $8n \pm 1$, $8n \pm 3$, we must have (excluding the case $p = 2$), when
$$p = n[\pi],$$
$$a^2 - 2b^2 \equiv 1, \text{ mod } 8, \tag{2}$$
or
$$a^2 - 2b^2 \equiv -1, \text{ mod } 8, \tag{3}$$
or
$$a^2 - 2b^2 \equiv 3, \text{ mod } 8, \tag{4}$$
or
$$a^2 - 2b^2 \equiv -3, \text{ mod } 8. \tag{5}$$

The first of these congruences has the solutions

$$\left.\begin{matrix} a \equiv \pm 1, & \pm 1, & \pm 3, & \pm 3 \\ b \equiv \pm 2, & 0, & \pm 2, & 0 \end{matrix}\right\}, \text{ mod } 8.$$

The second has the solutions

$$\left.\begin{matrix} a \equiv \pm 1, & \pm 1, & \pm 3, & \pm 3 \\ b \equiv \pm 1, & \pm 3, & \pm 1, & \pm 3 \end{matrix}\right\}, \text{ mod } 8.$$

The last two have no solutions, for they give
$$a^2 \equiv 2b^2 \pm 3, \text{ mod } 8,$$
and hence require that $2b^2 \pm 3$ shall be a quadratic residue of 8. But the only quadratic residues of 8 are 1 and 4, whence it follows

that a necessary condition that 4) or 5) shall have a solution is

$$1 \equiv 2b^2 \pm 3, \text{ mod } 8, \text{ or } 4 \equiv 2b^2 \pm 3, \text{ mod } 8.$$

All four of these congruences are easily seen to have no solutions, and 4) and 5) therefore have no solutions.

Hence when a positive rational prime other than 2 is the product of two conjugate primes of $k(\sqrt{2})$, it has the form $8n \pm 1$.

The case $p = 2$ must next be considered.

The equation $$a^2 - 2b^2 = 2$$
is satisfied by $$a = \pm 2, \quad b = \pm 1.$$
Hence $2 = (2 + \sqrt{2})(2 - \sqrt{2}) = (1 + \sqrt{2})(-1 + \sqrt{2})(\sqrt{2})^2$; that is, *2, which is the only rational prime divisor of the discriminant of $k(\sqrt{2})$ is associated with the square of a prime of $k(\sqrt{2})$.*

ii. Since $n[\alpha] = 1$, α is a unit. Hence p is associated with the prime, π; that is, p is a prime in $k(\sqrt{2})$. When p is of the form $8n \pm 3$ this case always occurs, for we have seen that to be factorable in $k(\sqrt{2})$ a rational prime must either be 2 or of the form $8n \pm 1$.

We shall now show that every rational prime, p, of the form $8n \pm 1$ can be resolved into the product of two conjugate primes of $k(\sqrt{2})$.

The congruence $x^2 \equiv 2$, mod p, $p = 8n \pm 1$, has roots, for $(2/p) = 1$ when $p = 8n \pm 1$.

Let a be a root; then
$$a^2 \equiv 2, \text{ mod } p;$$
that is $$(a + \sqrt{2})(a - \sqrt{2}) \equiv 0, \text{ mod } p.$$

Since $a + \sqrt{2}$ and $a - \sqrt{2}$ are integers of $k(\sqrt{2})$, p, if a prime of $k(\sqrt{2})$, must divide either $a + \sqrt{2}$, or $a - \sqrt{2}$. This is, however, impossible, for from
$$a \pm \sqrt{2} = p(c + d\sqrt{2}),$$
where $c + d\sqrt{2}$ is an integer of $k(\sqrt{2})$, it would follow that
$$pd = \pm 1,$$
which is impossible, since p and d are both rational integers and $p > 1$. Hence p is not a prime in $k(\sqrt{2})$, and since the only way

in which a rational prime can be factored in $k(\sqrt{2})$ is into two conjugate prime factors, p is factorable in this manner.

The primes of $k(\sqrt{2})$ may therefore be classified according to the rational primes of which they are factors as follows:

1) *All positive rational primes of the form $8n \pm 1$ are factorable in $k(\sqrt{2})$ into two conjugate primes, called primes of the first degree.*

2) *All positive rational primes of the form $8n \pm 3$ are primes in $k(\sqrt{2})$, called primes of the second degree.*

3) *The number 2 is associated with the square of a prime of the first degree in $k(\sqrt{2})$.*

It can be shown, as in the cases of 2 in $k(i)$ and 3 in $k(\sqrt{-3})$, that 2 is the only rational prime that is associated with the square of a prime of the first degree. We observe that 2 is the only rational prime divisor of the discriminant.

§ 10. Factorization of a Rational Prime in $k(\sqrt{2})$ determined by the value of (d/p).

As in $k(i)$ and $k(\sqrt{-3})$, the above results can be expressed in tabular form by means of the discriminant of $k(\sqrt{2})$. The formation of such a table will be left to the reader.

§ 11. Congruences in $k(\sqrt{2})$.

The unique factorization theorem having been proved for the integers of $k(\sqrt{2})$, a series of theorems analogous to those deduced in the case of the preceding realms can be shown to hold for the integers of $k(\sqrt{2})$.

Having defined the congruence of two integers of $k(\sqrt{2})$ with respect to a modulus precisely as we defined that of two rational integers, we should find that there are, with respect to a given modulus μ, $|n[\mu]|$ classes of incongruent numbers, and can then deduce for the integers of $k(\sqrt{2})$ Fermat's theorem and other theorems relating to congruences.

§ 12. The Diophantine Equations

$x^2 - 2y^2 = \pm 1$, $x^2 - 2y^2 = \pm p$, and $x^2 - 2y^2 = \pm m$.[1]

It is required to find the rational integral values of x and y

[1] See Chap. XIII, § 5.

for which these equations are satisfied. Since the first member of each of the equations is the norm of $x+y\sqrt{2}$, the problem reduces, in the light of what we have learned about the integers of $k(\sqrt{2})$, to that of finding an integer of $k(\sqrt{2})$ whose norm is the quantity constituting the second member of the equation.

If $a+b\sqrt{2}$ be such an integer, then

$$x=\pm a, \quad y=\pm b,$$

evidently satisfy the equation under consideration. We see also that, if any one of these equations has a single solution, it has an infinite number of solutions, for if $x=a$, $y=b$ be a solution of the given equation, and

$$(a+b\sqrt{2})\epsilon^{2n}=a_1+b_1\sqrt{2},$$

where $\epsilon=1+\sqrt{2}$, and n is any positive or negative integer or 0, then since

$$n[a_1+b_1\sqrt{2}]=n[(a+b\sqrt{2})\epsilon^{2n}]=n[a+b\sqrt{2}],$$

$x=a_1$, $y=b_1$ is also a solution of the given equation. Moreover, since no two powers of ϵ are equal, the solutions obtained by giving n any two different values are different. Hence the solutions are infinite in number. We shall consider now each of the equations in detail.

$$\text{i. } x^2-2y^2=1, \quad \text{ii. } x^2-2y^2=-1.$$

The necessary and sufficient condition that an integer of $k(\sqrt{2})$ shall have the norm ± 1 is that it shall be a unit. All units having the norm 1 are included in the form $\pm(1+\sqrt{2})^{2n}$, and all having the norm -1 in the form $\pm(1+\sqrt{2})^{2n+1}$, n being a positive or negative integer or 0. Negative values of n repeat solutions given by positive values, since $(1+\sqrt{2})^{-n}$ is the conjugate of $(1+\sqrt{2})^n$ or its negative. Hence, if

$$\pm(1+\sqrt{2})^{2n}=a+b\sqrt{2},$$
$$x=\pm a, \quad y=\pm b,$$

satisfy i, and if

$$\pm(1+\sqrt{2})^{2n+1}=a_1+b_1\sqrt{2},$$
$$x=\pm a_1, \quad y=\pm b_1,$$

satisfy ii, and these are all the solutions of i and ii.

For example:

$$\pm(1+\sqrt{2})^2=\pm(3+2\sqrt{2}) \text{ gives } (\pm 3)^2-2(\pm 2)^2=1;$$

that is $x=\pm 3$; $y=\pm 2$ are solutions of i;

while

$$\pm(1+\sqrt{2})^3=\pm(7+5\sqrt{2}) \text{ gives } (\pm 7)^2-2(\pm 5)^2=-1;$$

that is $x=\pm 7$; $y=\pm 5$ are solutions of ii.

$$\text{iii. } x^2-2y^2=p, \quad \text{iv. } x^2-2y^2=-p,$$

where p is a positive rational prime. The necessary and sufficient condition that $\pm p$ should be the norm of an integer of $k(\sqrt{2})$ is $p\equiv\pm 1$, mod 8, or $p=2$. Hence iii and iv are solvable when and only when

$$p\equiv\pm 1, \text{ mod } 8, \text{ or } p=2.$$

Let $p\equiv\pm 1$, mod 8.

If $x=a$, $y=b$ be any solution of iii, all integers of the form

$$(a\pm b\sqrt{2})\epsilon^{2n}=a_1+b_1\sqrt{2}$$

give solutions of iii, $x=\pm a_1$, $y=\pm b_1$; for

$$n[(a\pm b\sqrt{2})\epsilon^{2n}]=n[a\pm b\sqrt{2}](-1)^{2n}=p,$$

and all integers of the form

$$(a\pm b\sqrt{2})\epsilon^{2n+1}=a_2+b_2\sqrt{2}$$

give solutions of iv, $x=\pm a_2$, $y=\pm b_2$; for

$$n[(a\pm b\sqrt{2})\epsilon^{2n+1}]=n[a\pm b\sqrt{2}](-1)^{2n+1}=-p.$$

These are easily seen to be all of the solutions of iii and iv.

Ex. 1. To find all rational integral solutions of the equations

$$x^2-2y^2=7, \quad x^2-2y^2=-7.$$

A solution of the first equation is

$$x=3, \quad y=1.$$

Hence $(3\pm\sqrt{2})(1+\sqrt{2})^{2n}$ gives all solutions of the first equation and $(3\pm\sqrt{2})(1+\sqrt{2})^{2n+1}$ all solutions of the second.

Thus for example

$$(3+\sqrt{2})(1+\sqrt{2})^2=13+9\sqrt{2} \quad \text{gives} \quad (\pm 13)^2-2(\pm 9)^2=7,$$

$$(3-\sqrt{2})(1+\sqrt{2})^2=5+3\sqrt{2} \quad \text{gives} \quad (\pm 5)^2-2(\pm 3)^2=7,$$

$$(3+\sqrt{2})(1+\sqrt{2})=5+4\sqrt{2} \quad \text{gives} \quad (\pm 5)^2-2(\pm 4)^2=-7,$$

$$(3-\sqrt{2})(1+\sqrt{2})=1+2\sqrt{2} \quad \text{gives} \quad (\pm 1)^2-2(\pm 2)^2=-7.$$

$$\text{v. } x^2-2y^2=m, \quad \text{vi. } x^2-2y^2=-m,$$

where m is a positive rational integer. Since m must be the norm of an integer of $k(\sqrt{2})$, and hence must be factorable into two conjugate integers of $k(\sqrt{2})$, the necessary and sufficient condition that v and vi shall have solutions is that every rational prime factor, q, of m such that $q \equiv \pm 3$, mod 8, shall occur to an even power.

If then $$m = p_1 p_2 \cdots p_r q_1^{2t_1} q_2^{2t_2} \cdots q_s^{2t_s},$$
where $$p_1, p_2, \cdots, p_r \equiv \pm 1, \text{ mod } 8, \text{ or } = 2,$$
and $$q_1, q_2, \cdots, q_s \equiv \pm 3, \text{ mod } 8,$$
we have
$$m = (\pi_1 \pi_2 \cdots \pi_r q_1^{t_1} q_2^{t_2} \cdots q_s^{t_s})(\pi_1' \pi_2' \cdots \pi_r' q_1^{t_1} q_2^{t_2} \cdots q_s^{t_s}), \quad 1)$$
$$= (a + b\sqrt{2})(a - b\sqrt{2}) = a^2 - 2b^2,$$
and $x = \pm a$, $y = \pm b$ are solutions of v. If we interchange any π in one factor of 1) with its conjugate, we shall obtain a different factorization of m unless $n[\pi] = 2$, in which case the factorization is not different, since the factors of 2 are identical.

Suppose this interchange of π_i and π_i', $n[\pi] \neq 2$, to have been made, giving
$$m = (a_1 + b_1\sqrt{2})(a_1 - b_1\sqrt{2}) = a_1^2 - 2b_1^2.$$
Then $x = \pm a_1$, $y = \pm b_1$ are new solutions of v. Suppose that by these interchanges of one or more π's with their conjugates we obtain all possible different factorizations of m. Then by multiplying a factor of each of these factorizations by the *even* powers of ϵ in turn we obtain from each factorization an infinite number of solutions of v, and by multiplication by the *odd* powers of ϵ in turn we obtain from each factorization an infinite number of solutions of vi, and these are all the solutions of v and vi. That is, if $$a_1 + b_1\sqrt{2},\ a_2 + b_2\sqrt{2}, \cdots, a_t + b_t\sqrt{2}$$
be each a factor of a different one of the t factorizations of m, all solutions of v are given by
$$(a_i \pm b_i\sqrt{2})\epsilon^{2n} = c_{i_n} + d_{i_n}\sqrt{2},$$
whence $$x = \pm c_{i_n}, \quad y = \pm d_{i_n},$$
and all solutions of vi are given by
$$(a_i \pm b_i\sqrt{2})\epsilon^{2n+1} = e_i + f_{i_n}\sqrt{2},$$

whence $$x = \pm e_{i_n}, \quad y = \pm f_{i_n},$$
where $$i = 1, 2, \cdots, t, \text{ and } n = 0, 1, \cdots.$$

Ex. 2. To find all rational integral solutions of the equations

$$x^2 - 2y^2 = 119 \quad \text{and} \quad x^2 - 2y^2 = -119.$$

We have

$$\begin{aligned} 119 = 7 \cdot 17 &= (3+\sqrt{2})(3-\sqrt{2})(5+2\sqrt{2})(5-2\sqrt{2}) \\ &= [(3+\sqrt{2})(5+2\sqrt{2})][(3-\sqrt{2})(5-2\sqrt{2})] \\ &= (19+11\sqrt{2})(19-11\sqrt{2}), \\ \text{or} \quad &= [(3+\sqrt{2})(5-2\sqrt{2})][(3-\sqrt{2})(5+2\sqrt{2})] \\ &= (11-\sqrt{2})(11+\sqrt{2}). \end{aligned}$$

Whence we see that $(19 \pm 11\sqrt{2})\epsilon^{2n}$ and $(11 \pm \sqrt{2})\epsilon^{2n}$ give all the solutions of the first equation, and $(19 \pm 11\sqrt{2})\epsilon^{2n+1}$ and $(11 \pm \sqrt{2})\epsilon^{2n+1}$ give all the solutions of the second.

Thus, for example:

$$(19+11\sqrt{2})(1+\sqrt{2}) = 41+30\sqrt{2} \text{ gives } (\pm 41)^2 - 2(\pm 30)^2 = -119,$$
$$(19-11\sqrt{2})(1+\sqrt{2}) = -3+8\sqrt{2} \text{ gives } (\pm 3)^2 - 2(\pm 8)^2 = -119,$$
$$(11+\sqrt{2})(1+\sqrt{2}) = 13+12\sqrt{2} \text{ gives } (\pm 11)^2 - 2(\pm 12)^2 = -119,$$
$$(11-\sqrt{2})(1+\sqrt{2}) = 9+10\sqrt{2} \text{ gives } (\pm 9)^2 - 2(\pm 10)^2 = -119.$$

CHAPTER VIII.

The Realm $k(\sqrt{-5})$.

§ 1. Numbers of $k(\sqrt{-5})$.[1]

The number $\sqrt{-5}$ is defined by the equation

$$x^2+5=0,$$

that it satisfies. All numbers of $k(\sqrt{-5})$ have the form $a+b\sqrt{-5}$, where a and b are rational numbers.

The conjugate of α, $=a+b\sqrt{-5}$, is α', $=a-b\sqrt{-5}$; also

$$n[\alpha]=a^2+5b^2,$$

and
$$n[\alpha\beta]=n[\alpha]n[\beta]$$

§ 2. Integers of $k(\sqrt{-5})$.

Writing all numbers of $k(\sqrt{-5})$ in the form

$$\alpha=\frac{a_1+b_1\sqrt{-5}}{c_1},$$

where a_1, b_1, c_1 are rational integers, having no common factor, we can show exactly as in $k(i)$ that a necessary and sufficient condition for α to be an integer is $c_1=1$.

Therefore all integers of $k(\sqrt{-5})$ have the form $a+b\sqrt{-5}$ where a and b are rational integers, and all numbers of this form are integers; that is, $1, \sqrt{-5}$ is a basis of $k(\sqrt{-5})$.

§ 3. Discriminant of $k(\sqrt{-5})$.

The discriminant of $k(\sqrt{-5})$ is

$$\begin{vmatrix} 1, & \sqrt{-5} \\ 1, & -\sqrt{-5} \end{vmatrix}^2 = -20.$$

§ 4. Divisibility of Integers of $k(\sqrt{-5})$.

The definition is identical with that adopted heretofore.

[1] Throughout this chapter see corresponding sections in $k(i)$.

Ex. 1. We see that $1+5\sqrt{-5}$ is divisible by $2+\sqrt{-5}$, since

$$1+5\sqrt{-5}=(2+\sqrt{-5})(3+\sqrt{-5}).$$

Ex. 2. We see that $5+2\sqrt{-5}$ is not divisible by $4+\sqrt{-5}$, since

$$5+2\sqrt{-5}=(4+\sqrt{-5})(x+y\sqrt{-5})$$

holds for no integral values of x and y.

§ 5. Units of $k(\sqrt{-5})$. Associated Integers.

The units of $k(\sqrt{-5})$ are defined as were those of the preceding realms, and as the norm of a number of $k(\sqrt{-5})$ is always positive, the necessary and sufficient condition that $\epsilon, =x+y\sqrt{-5}$, shall be a unit is

$$n[\epsilon]=x^2+5y^2=1,$$

which gives $\qquad y=0, \quad x=\pm 1.$

Hence 1 and -1 are the units of $k(\sqrt{-5})$.

The definition of associated integers and the conventions regarding them are identical with those heretofore adopted; that is, the integers α and $-\alpha$, obtained by multiplying any integer α by the units 1 and -1, are said to be associated, and in all questions of divisibility are considered identical.

§ 6. Prime Numbers of $k(\sqrt{-5})$.

The definitions are identical with those in the preceding realms.

Ex. 1. To determine whether 2 is a prime or composite number in $k(\sqrt{-5})$.

Put $\qquad 2=(x+y\sqrt{-5})(u+v\sqrt{-5});$

then $\qquad 4=(x^2+5y^2)(u^2+5v^2),$

and hence

$$\text{i. } \begin{cases} x^2+5y^2=2 \\ u^2+5v^2=2 \end{cases} \quad \text{or ii. } \begin{cases} x^2+5y^2=4 \\ u^2+5v^2=1 \end{cases}$$

Evidently i is impossible since x and y must be rational integers.

From ii it follows that $u+v\sqrt{-5}$ is a unit. Hence 2 is a prime in $k(\sqrt{-5})$.

Ex. 2. To determine whether $1+\sqrt{-5}$ is a prime or composite number of $k(\sqrt{-5})$.

Put $\qquad 1+\sqrt{-5}=(x+y\sqrt{-5})(u+v\sqrt{-5});$

then $\qquad 6=(x^2+5y^2)(u^2+5v^2),$

and hence

$$\text{i.}\quad \begin{cases} x^2+5y^2=3 \\ u^2+5v^2=2 \end{cases} \quad \text{or ii} \quad \begin{cases} x^2+5y^2=6 \\ u^2+5v^2=1 \end{cases}$$

from which it is evident as above that $1+\sqrt{-5}$ is a prime in $k(\sqrt{-5})$.

We observe that we have in $1+\sqrt{-5}$ the first instance of a prime number whose norm is *not a power of a rational prime.*

We shall see later that a necessary and sufficient condition for the norms of all complex primes of any given quadratic realm to be rational primes is that the unique factorization theorem shall hold for the integers of the realm.

From these two examples it is easily seen that 3 and $1-\sqrt{-5}$ are also primes in $k(\sqrt{-5})$.

§ 7. Failure of the Unique Factorization Theorem in $k(\sqrt{-5})$. Introduction of the Ideal.

We shall now attempt to establish the unique factorization theorem for the integers of $k(\sqrt{-5})$ and begin as in the foregoing realms by endeavoring to prove the following theorem:

THEOREM A. *If α be any integer of $k(\sqrt{-5})$, and β any integer of $k(\sqrt{-5})$ different from 0, there exists an integer μ of $k(\sqrt{-5})$ such that*

$$n[\alpha-\mu\beta]<n[\beta].$$

Let
$$\alpha/\beta=a+b\sqrt{-5},$$
where
$$a=r+r_1,\quad b=s+s_1,$$
r and s being the rational integers nearest to a and b, respectively, and hence

$$|r_1|\leqq\tfrac{1}{2},\quad |s_1|\leqq\tfrac{1}{2}.$$

Let
$$\mu=r+s\sqrt{-5};$$
then
$$\alpha/\beta-\mu=r_1+s_1\sqrt{-5},$$
whence
$$n[\alpha/\beta-\mu]=r_1^2+5s_1^2\leqq 6/4$$
that is, when μ is determined as above, we may have in $k(\sqrt{-5})$

$$n[\alpha/\beta-\mu]>1 \text{ instead of } <1$$

as has been the case in the three previous realms. Hence the integer μ chosen as above will not necessarily satisfy the requirements of the theorem. The method which has hitherto served us for the proof of this theorem therefore fails.

That this theorem actually does fail for some integers of $k(\sqrt{-5})$ is evident from the following example.

Let
$$\alpha = 3 \text{ and } \beta = 1 + \sqrt{-5},$$
then
$$\frac{\alpha}{\beta} = \frac{3}{1+\sqrt{-5}} = \frac{3-3\sqrt{-5}}{6} = \tfrac{1}{2} - \tfrac{1}{2}\sqrt{-5}.$$

We are to find an integer $\mu =, x + y\sqrt{-5}$, such that
$$n[\alpha/\beta - \mu] = (\tfrac{1}{2} - x)^2 + 5(-\tfrac{1}{2} - y)^2 < 1,$$
but this is impossible, for it is evident that for all rational integral values of y, including 0, the term $5(-\frac{1}{2}-y)^2$ is itself > 1. The method of proof adopted for Theorem A is seen to be dependent upon the general form of the norm of a number $r_1 + s_1\omega$, where $1, \omega$ is a basis of the realm. We have thus in $k(i)$, $k(\sqrt{-3})$, $k(\sqrt{2})$ and $k(\sqrt{-5})$ respectively
$$|n[r_1 + s_1\omega]| = |r_1^2 + s_1^2|,\ |r_1^2 - r_1s_1 + s_1^2|,\ |r_1^2 - 2s_1^2|, \text{ and } |r_1^2 + 5s_1^2|,$$
and the method is successful if
$$|r_1| \leqq \tfrac{1}{2}, \quad |s_1| \leqq \tfrac{1}{2}$$
be a sufficient condition for
$$|n[r_1 + s_1\omega]| < 1,$$
which is seen to be the case in $k(i)$, $k(\sqrt{-3})$ and $k(\sqrt{2})$ but not in $k(\sqrt{-5})$.

We can easily determine all quadratic realms in which this method of proof holds; that is, those in which this way of selecting μ is always successful.

Let $k(\sqrt{m})$ be any quadratic realm,[1] $\sqrt{m}$ being a root of the equation $x^2 - m = 0$, where m is a positive or negative rational integer containing no squared factor.

When $m \equiv 2$ or 3, mod 4, $k(\sqrt{m})$ has as a basis $1, \sqrt{m}$, and when $m \equiv 1$, mod 4, $k(\sqrt{m})$ has as a basis $1, (-1+\sqrt{m})/2$ (see chap. X, § 6).

In the first case, it is easily seen that
$$\alpha/\beta - \mu = r_1 + s_1\sqrt{m},$$

[1] See Chap. X, § 1.

and in the second,

$$\alpha/\beta - \mu = r_1 + s_1(-1 + \sqrt{m})/2,$$

which give respectively

$$n[r_1 + s_1\sqrt{m}] = r_1^2 - ms_1^2,$$

and $$n\left[r_1 + s_1\frac{-1+\sqrt{m}}{2}\right] = r_1^2 - r_1s_1 - \frac{m-1}{4}s_1^2$$

Considering first the case $m \equiv 2$ or 3, mod 4, we see that

$$|r_1| \leqq \tfrac{1}{2}, \quad |s_1| \leqq \tfrac{1}{2} \qquad 1)$$

is a sufficient condition that

$$|r_1^2 - ms_1^2| < 1 \qquad 2)$$

when $m = -1$, 2, -2 or 3; but when $|m| > 3$, then 1) is evidently not a sufficient condition for 2). Considering now $m \equiv 1$, mod 4, we see that 1) is a sufficient condition that

$$|r_1^2 - r_1s_1 - \frac{m-1}{4}s_1^2| < 1$$

when and only when $m = -3$, 5 or 13.

Hence Th. A and consequently the unique factorization theorem holds in the realms $k(i)$, $k(\sqrt{-2})$, $k(\sqrt{2})$, $k(\sqrt{3})$, $k(\sqrt{-3})$, $k(\sqrt{5})$, $k(\sqrt{13})$. To these can be added $k(\sqrt{-7})$, for when $m = -7$, which is $\equiv 1$, mod 4, if to 1) we add the condition that, when simultaneously

$$|r_1| = \tfrac{1}{2} \text{ and } |s_1| = \tfrac{1}{2},$$

then the signs of r_1 and s_1 are to be chosen alike, we see that in all cases

$$|r_1^2 - r_1s_1 + 2s_1^2| < 1.$$

Hence the theorem holds for $k(\sqrt{-7})$.

A further slight modification in the method of selecting μ will enable us to show that the theorem holds for $k(\sqrt{-11})$.

It is easily seen that, if

$$|r_1| < 1/\sqrt{5}, \quad |s_1| < 1/\sqrt{5},$$

then $$|r_1^2 - r_1s_1 + 3s_1^2| < 1. \qquad 3)$$

Moreover, if either $|r_1|$ or $|s_1|$ or both $= \tfrac{1}{2}$, then we can choose the signs of r_1 and s_1 so that they are alike, and hence 3) holds.

There remains the case

$$1/\sqrt{5} \leqq |r_1| < 1/2, \quad 1/\sqrt{5} \leqq |s_1| < 1/2$$

i. If r_1 and s_1 have like signs 3) evidently holds.

ii. If r_1 and s_1 have opposite signs, for r_1 we can put r_2, $= r_1 + 1$ or $r_1 - 1$, according as r_1 is negative or positive, having then

$$|r_2| \leqq \frac{\sqrt{5} - 1}{\sqrt{5}}$$

and r_2 of the same sign as s_1, in which case

$$r_2^2 - r_2 s_1 + 3 s_1^2 < 1.$$

Hence Th. A holds for $k(\sqrt{-11})$.[1]

It can be easily seen that the original method of selection, even when modified as above, will give a suitable value of μ in no imaginary quadratic realms other than those enumerated above, and it is furthermore evident that these are the only imaginary quadratic realms in which the theorem holds.

It will be observed, as has been said in $k(i)$, that Th. A is equivalent to saying that in a given realm we can find for any integer β a complete residue system such that the norms of all the integers composing it are less in absolute value than $n[\beta]$. This point of view is illustrated graphically in Chap. V, § 8. It must be carefully noticed, however, that although Th. A is a *sufficient* condition for the validity of the unique factorization theorem, it is not a *necessary* condition, as will be shown later. The proof of the theorem:

THEOREM B. *If α and β be any two integers of $k(\sqrt{-5})$, prime to each other, there exist two integers, ξ and η, of $k(\sqrt{-5})$ such that*

$$\alpha\xi + \beta\eta = 1;$$

has been heretofore based upon Theorem A, which has been seen not to hold for $k(\sqrt{-5})$. This, however, would not, of course, justify the assumption that Th. B does not hold for $k(\sqrt{-5})$; Th. A being a sufficient, but, as we shall see later, not a necessary, condition for the validity of Th. B. Nevertheless, the following

[1] The cases $|r_1| < 1/\sqrt{5}$, $1/\sqrt{5} \leqq |s_1| < 1/2$ and $1/\sqrt{5} \leqq |r_1| < 1/2$, $|s_1| < 1/\sqrt{5}$, must be considered. The inequality can be shown to hold in these cases by the method used in the preceding cases.

simple example will show that Th. B does not hold in general for the integers of $k(\sqrt{-5})$.

Let $$\alpha=3,\quad \beta=1+\sqrt{-5}.$$

We have already seen (§6) that 3 and $1+\sqrt{-5}$ are prime numbers; moreover, they are not associates. Therefore they are prime to each other. We shall show that it is impossible to select two integers, $\xi, =x+y\sqrt{-5}$, and $\eta. =u+v\sqrt{-5}$, such that

$$\alpha\xi+\beta\eta=1 \qquad 4)$$

If $$3(x+y\sqrt{-5})+(1+\sqrt{-5})(u+v\sqrt{-5})=1,$$

then $$3x+u-5v=1,$$
$$3y+u+v=0,$$

and hence $$3x-3y-6v=1,$$

which is impossible since the first member only is divisible by 3. Therefore ξ and η can not be found so as to satisfy 4) and the theorem does not in general hold for the integers of $k(\sqrt{-5})$.

We shall see later (p. 316) that the theorem:

Theorem C. *If the product of two integers, α and β of $k(\sqrt{-5})$ be divisible by a prime number, π, at least one of the integers is divisible by π*, which is a necessary as well as sufficient condition for the unique factorization theorem, requires Th. B as a necessary condition for its validity. The following example will suffice to show that Th. C and the unique factorization theorem do not hold for the integers of $k(\sqrt{-5})$. We have

$$6=2\cdot3=(1+\sqrt{-5})(1-\sqrt{-5}),$$

and we have shown (§6) that 2, 3, $1+\sqrt{-5}$ and $1-\sqrt{-5}$ are prime numbers in $k(\sqrt{-5})$. Moreover, the factors of one product are not associated with the factors of the other. *Therefore 6 is represented in two ways as the product of prime factors.*

That this is not merely a peculiarity of 6 is seen from

$$21=3\cdot7=(1+2\sqrt{-5})(1-2\sqrt{-5}),$$
$$9=3^2=(2+\sqrt{-5})(2-\sqrt{-5}),$$

and $$49=7^2=(2+3\sqrt{-5})(2-3\sqrt{-5}),$$

the factors in the above products being easily proved to be primes of $k(\sqrt{-5})$.

Moreover, that this failure of the unique factorization law does not occur in $k(\sqrt{-5})$ alone may be shown by an examination of the realms $k(\sqrt{-23})$ and $k(\sqrt{-89})$, in which we have respectively

$$27 = 3^3 = (2+\sqrt{-23})(2-\sqrt{-23}),$$

and
$$125 = 5^3 = (6+\sqrt{-89})(6-\sqrt{-89}),$$

$3, 2+\sqrt{-23}$ and $2-\sqrt{-23}$ being prime numbers of $k(\sqrt{-23})$, and 5, $6+\sqrt{-89}$ and $6-\sqrt{-89}$ being prime numbers of $k(\sqrt{-89})$.

It can now be made clear why we could not define the greatest common divisor of two integers, α and β,

i. As the common divisor, δ, of greatest norm.

ii. As the common divisor, δ, such that α/δ and β/δ are prime to each other.

If $\alpha = (1-\sqrt{-5})^2 = -4-2\sqrt{-5}$, and $\beta = (1+\sqrt{-5})(1-\sqrt{-5}) = 6$ then the common divisors of α and β other than the units are 2 and $1-\sqrt{-5}$. Of these $1-\sqrt{-5}$ has the greater norm, 6, but $1-\sqrt{-5}$ is not divisible by 2. Hence δ so determined has not the important property of being divisible by every common divisor of the two integers.

Considering the definition ii we see that there are *two* values of δ, 2 and $1-\sqrt{-5}$, which satisfy it, for $\alpha/2$ and $\beta/2$ are prime to each other, and $\dfrac{\alpha}{1-\sqrt{-5}}$ and $\dfrac{\beta}{1-\sqrt{-5}}$ have the same property. Hence the definition ii, in addition to not determining δ so that it is divisible by every common divisor of α and β, does not even determine it uniquely. It is interesting to see, however, that, if we can find in any realm a common divisor, δ, of two integers α and β, such that every common divisor of α and β divides δ, then δ will satisfy both the requirements i and ii; for, considering i, if δ_1 be a common divisor of α and β it divides δ; that is,

$$\delta = \delta_1\mu,$$

whence
$$n[\delta] = n[\delta_1]\cdot n[\mu],$$

and therefore either
$$|n[\delta_1]| < |n[\delta]|$$

or
$$|n[\delta_1]| = |n[\delta]|.$$

In the latter case

$$n[\mu] = \pm 1,$$

and hence μ is a unit; that is δ and δ_1 are associated. Hence δ satisfies i.

Considering ii, we have

$$\alpha = \delta\alpha_1 \quad\text{and}\quad \beta = \delta\beta_1.$$

Now if α_1 and β_1 be not prime but have a common divisor, δ_1, then δ would not be divisible by every common divisor of α and β, for it would not be divisible by $\delta\delta_1$.

We now ask whether it would be possible to deduce for the integers of $k(\sqrt{-5})$, without the use of the unique factorization theorem, the series of theorems which have flowed from it for the integers of R, $k(i)$, $k(\sqrt{-3})$ and $k(\sqrt{2})$.

It is easily seen that in general these theorems do not hold in $k(\sqrt{-5})$. For example, the analogue for $k(\sqrt{-5})$ of Fermat's theorem would be:

If π be any prime of $k(\sqrt{-5})$ and α any integer not divisible by π, then

$$\alpha^{n[\pi]-1}-1\equiv 0, \text{ mod } \pi,$$

and indeed, if

$$\pi=2 \text{ and } \alpha=1+2\sqrt{-5},$$

2 being a prime and $1+2\sqrt{-5}$ evidently not divisible by 2, we have

$$(1+2\sqrt{-5})^{n[2]-1}-1=(1+2\sqrt{-5})^3-1$$
$$=-60-34\sqrt{-5}\equiv 0, \text{ mod } 2;$$

that is, the theorem holds in this case.

But if
$$\pi=2 \text{ and } \alpha=1+\sqrt{-5},$$

we see that, although 2 and $1+\sqrt{-5}$ satisfy the requirements 2 a prime and $1+\sqrt{-5}$ not divisible by 2,

$$(1+\sqrt{-5})^{n[2]-1}-1=(1+\sqrt{-5})^3-1$$
$$=-15-2\sqrt{-5}\not\equiv 0, \text{ mod } 2.$$

The cause of this peculiar difference in the behavior of $1+2\sqrt{-5}$ and $1+\sqrt{-5}$ towards 2 in this relation will be made clear later (p. 379). Our next thought is can we by the introduction of a new conception of numbers reëstablish the unique factorization law for the integers of $k(\sqrt{-5})$ when the factorization is expressed in terms of these new numbers. The introduction of the so-called *ideal*[1] numbers accomplishes this, primes of $k(\sqrt{-5})$ being in this widened number domain no longer in general looked upon as primes, but as being factorable

[1] The term ideal number is used here in a general sense and is not to be taken to refer particularly to the *ideal numbers* of Kümmer.

in terms of these ideal numbers. When this factorization has been performed we shall find that every integer of $k(\sqrt{-5})$ can be represented in one and only one way as the product of prime ideal numbers.

The following considerations will make clearer their nature, and the ideas which have led to their conception. Let us consider the narrowed number domain composed of all positive rational integers congruent to 1, mod 5; that is,

$$1, 6, 11, 16, 21, 26, 31, 36, 41, 46, \text{etc.} \qquad 5)$$

Our definitions of divisibility and prime number being the same as before, we see that, when our operations are confined to numbers of this domain, the unique factorization law does not in general hold; for example,

$$336 = 6\cdot 56 = 16\cdot 21,$$
$$1806 = 21\cdot 86 = 6\cdot 301,$$
$$1296 = 6^4 = 16\cdot 81,$$

and 6, 16, 21, 56, 81, 86 and 301 are easily seen by multiplication of the numbers 5) to be prime in this domain. The cause of this failure of the unique factorization law is at once seen to lie in the absence of the remaining positive integers. As we suppose these integers to be unknown to us and in fact to have no real existence, we ask by what train of reasoning are we led from the requirements of the task to be accomplished, that is, the reëstablishment of the unique factorization law, to the introduction of these missing integers, or rather the introduction of symbols which have their properties so far as the task in hand is concerned.

Consider $336 = 6\cdot 56 = 16\cdot 21.$

Since 6 is not contained in either 16 or 21, although the product $16\cdot 21$ is divisible by 6, we suppose 6 to be the product of two factors one of which is contained in 16, the other in 21, and denote these factors by (6, 16) and (6, 21), respectively. The factor (6, 16) plays the same rôle with respect to 6 and 16 in all questions of divisibility in which these new numbers are used that the greatest common divisor of two integers plays with respect to these integers when only the original numbers of the domain are involved. We can therefore in this sense consider (6, 16) as the greatest common divisor of 6 and 16. Likewise we consider (6, 21) as the greatest common divisor of 6 and 21, and we write

$$6=(6, 16)(6, 21),$$

denoting by this equation that 6 and the product (6, 16)(6, 21) in all questions of divisibility play the same rôle; that is, every integer that is divisible by 6 is divisible by (6, 16)(6, 21), and conversely. This convention is evidently justified by the fact that in reality (6, 16) is 2 and (6, 21) is 3. Similarly we have

$$56=(56, 16)(56, 21),$$
$$16=(16, 6)(16, 56),$$
$$21=(21, 6)(21, 56),$$

and hence

$$336=6.56=(6, 16)(6, 21)(56, 16)(56, 21)$$
$$=16.21=(16, 6)(16, 56)(21, 6)(21, 56),$$

and the factorization is seen to be the same, the change of order of the numbers in the parenthesis having no effect on the symbol; that is, (6, 16) = (16, 6), etc.

We have now seen that the failure of the unique factorization law in a certain number domain can be remedied by the introduction of a new kind of number each of which is defined by a pair of integers of the domain and may be looked upon as the greatest common divisor of these integers. These numbers might be called the *ideal numbers* of the domain, and although the fact that the numbers of this domain do not form a realm prevents our expanding their conception and definition to the extent that we shall now develop those of the ideal numbers of $k(\sqrt{-5})$, still we shall find that the same conception will enable us to reëstablish the unique factorization law in this realm. We shall not, however, conceive of these new numbers, which we are about to introduce into $k(\sqrt{-5})$, simply as being each the greatest common divisor of a pair of integers of $k(\sqrt{-5})$ and as defined by these integers, but as being each the greatest common divisor of an infinite system of integers of $k(\sqrt{-5})$ and as defined by any finite number of these integers such that all other integers of the system are linear combinations of these with coefficients which are any integers of the realm. These numbers we shall call the ideal numbers, or briefly the *ideals* of $k(\sqrt{-5})$. To make this clearer, consider the equation

$$2 \cdot 3 = (1+\sqrt{-5})(1-\sqrt{-5}).$$

Since 2 divides neither $1+\sqrt{-5}$ nor $1-\sqrt{-5}$, although it divides their product, we must, to reëstablish the unique factorization law, consider 2 as the product of two ideal factors, $\mathfrak{a}$ and $\mathfrak{b}$,[1] which divide $1+\sqrt{-5}$ and $1-\sqrt{-5}$ respectively, the quotients being supposed, of course, to be ideal numbers also. We can denote $\mathfrak{a}$ and $\mathfrak{b}$ by the symbols $(2, 1+\sqrt{-5})$ and $(2, 1-\sqrt{-5})$ respectively. If now $\mathfrak{a}$ be considered to bear the relation of greatest common divisor to 2 and $1+\sqrt{-5}$, it will bear this relation to the entire system of integers, which are linear combinations of 2 and $1+\sqrt{-5}$; that is, those of the form $2\alpha+(1+\sqrt{-5})\beta$, where α and β are any integers of the realm. Conversely, if $\mathfrak{a}$ be considered to bear this relation to the entire system, it will bear it to 2 and $1+\sqrt{-5}$. We consider then $\mathfrak{a}$ to be determined not by 2 and $1+\sqrt{-5}$ alone but by this entire system of integers, and by a natural transition say now that $\mathfrak{a}$ *is* this system of integers.

We write therefore

$$\mathfrak{a}=(2, 1+\sqrt{-5}),$$

understanding by this symbol the entire system of integers which are linear combinations of 2 and $1+\sqrt{-5}$, with coefficients which are any integers of the realm. In order to define $\mathfrak{a}$, it is therefore sufficient to give *any* set of integers such that all linear combinations, with coefficients as above, exactly constitute the above system. Hence we can introduce into the symbol defining $\mathfrak{a}$ any integer that is a linear combination of those already there, and can omit any integer that is a linear combination of those remaining; thus:

[1] Ideals will be denoted by German letters.

$$\begin{aligned}\mathfrak{a} &= (2,\ 1+\sqrt{-5}) \\ &= (2,\ 1+\sqrt{-5},\ 2+2\sqrt{-5},\ 3+3\sqrt{-5}) \\ &= (2,\ 2+2\sqrt{-5},\ 3+3\sqrt{-5}).\end{aligned}$$

The object of the preceding discussion, that has been by no means rigorous, has been first to show the necessity for the introduction of ideal numbers, and second to acquaint the reader in some degree with the ideas which have led to their conception and which induce us to adopt the definition which we shall now give. The justification of this definition will be found in the fact that, after we have defined what is meant by the equality of two ideals and what is meant by their product, we shall see that, when the integers of $k(\sqrt{-5})$ are resolved into their *ideal factors,* the unique factorization law will be once more found to hold. Moreover, we shall see that the behavior of an ideal towards the integers of the system constituting it is such as to warrant our original conception of an ideal as the greatest common divisor of this system.

§ 8. Definition of an Ideal of $k(\sqrt{-5})$.

An ideal of $k(\sqrt{-5})$ is an infinite system of integers composed of all linear combinations of any finite number of integers, $\alpha_1, \alpha_2, \cdots, \alpha_n$, the coefficients being any integers of the realm.[1]

The integers $\alpha_1, \alpha_2, \cdots. \alpha_n$ are said to define the ideal and the integers of the infinite system of integers constituting the ideal are called the *numbers* of the ideal. If an ideal $\mathfrak{a}$ be defined bv the integers $\alpha_1, \alpha_2, \cdots, \alpha_n$ we write

$$\mathfrak{a} = (\alpha_1, \alpha_2, \cdots, \alpha_n),$$

understanding thereby the infinite system of integers of the form

$$\xi_1\alpha_1 + \xi_2\alpha_2 + \cdots + \xi_n\alpha_n, \qquad 1)$$

where $\xi_1, \xi_2, \cdots, \xi_n$ are any integers of the realm. We shall call $(\alpha_1, \alpha_2, \cdots, \alpha_n)$ the *symbol* of the ideal of $\mathfrak{a}$.

[1] The general definition of an ideal of any quadratic realm (Chap. XI, § 1) seems at first sight broader than this definition, but as it is shown that all the numbers of any ideal are linear combinations of a finite number of them, the definitions are equivalent.

If γ be one of the integers included in 1); that is, if

$$\gamma = \lambda_1\alpha_1 + \lambda_2\alpha_2 + \cdots + \lambda_n\alpha_n,$$

where $\lambda_1, \lambda_2, \cdots, \lambda_n$ are integers of the realm, we have

$$\mathfrak{a} = (\alpha_1, \alpha_2, \cdots, \alpha_n) = (\alpha_1, \alpha_2, \cdots, \alpha_n, \gamma), \qquad 2)$$

for the infinite system of integers of the form

$$\eta_1\alpha_1 + \eta_2\alpha_2 + \cdots + \eta_n\alpha_n + \eta_{n+1}\gamma, \qquad 3)$$

where $\eta_1, \eta_2, \cdots, \eta_{n+1}$ are any integers of the realm, is the same as the system 1), since putting the value of γ in 3), we have

$$(\eta_1 + \eta_{n+1}\lambda_1)\alpha_1 + (\eta_2 + \eta_{n+1}\lambda_2)\alpha_2 + \cdots + (\eta_n + \eta_{n+1}\lambda_n)\alpha_n,$$

a system that evidently coincides with 1). It is evident then from 2) that we may, without changing an ideal, introduce into its symbol any integer which is a linear combination of those already there, the coefficients being integers of the realm, and may omit from the symbol any integer which is a linear combination of those remaining.

§ 9. Equality of Ideals.

Two ideals, $\mathfrak{a} = (\alpha_1, \alpha_2, \cdots, \alpha_m)$ and $\mathfrak{b} = (\beta_1, \beta_2, \cdots, \beta_p)$, are equal when the two infinite systems of integers that constitute these ideals are the same. The necessary and sufficient condition for this is that every number, $\alpha_1, \alpha_2, \cdots, \alpha_m$, defining $\mathfrak{a}$ shall be linear in the numbers,[1] $\beta_1, \beta_2, \cdots, \beta_n$, defining $\mathfrak{b}$, and that every β shall be linear in the α's; that is, it is necessary and sufficient that we shall be able to introduce the numbers $\alpha_1, \alpha_2, \cdots, \alpha_n$ into the symbol of $\mathfrak{b}$, and the numbers $\beta_1, \beta_2, \cdots, \beta_n$ into the symbol of $\mathfrak{a}$; in other words, *we must be able to reduce the symbol of either one of the ideals to that of the other.*

Ex. 1. To prove that the two ideals $\mathfrak{a} = (2, 1 + \sqrt{-5})$, and $\mathfrak{b} = (2, 1 - \sqrt{-5})$, are equal. We have

$$(2, 1 + \sqrt{-5}) = (2, 1 + \sqrt{-5}, 1 - \sqrt{-5}),$$

since

$$1 - \sqrt{-5} = 2(-\sqrt{-5}) + (1 + \sqrt{-5});$$

and

$$(2, 1 + \sqrt{-5}, 1 - \sqrt{-5}) = (2, 1 - \sqrt{-5});$$

since

$$1 + \sqrt{-5} = (\sqrt{-5})2 + (1 - \sqrt{-5}).$$

[1] When we say that α_i is linear in $\beta_1, \beta_2, \cdots, \beta_n$ we shall understand that $\alpha_i = \xi_1\beta_1 + \xi_2\beta_2 + \cdots + \xi_n\beta_n$, where $\xi_1, \xi_2, \cdots, \xi_n$ are integers of the realm.

Having reduced the symbol of $\mathfrak{a}$ to that of $\mathfrak{b}$, the two ideals are seen to be the same.

Ex. 2. To prove that the two ideals $\mathfrak{a}=(3, 1+\sqrt{-5})$, and $\mathfrak{b}=(3, 1-\sqrt{-5})$, are unequal.

If we can show that any number, as $1+\sqrt{-5}$, of $\mathfrak{a}$ is not a number of $\mathfrak{b}$, the two ideals will evidently be unequal. If $1+\sqrt{-5}$ be a number of $\mathfrak{b}$, then two integers, $x+y\sqrt{-5}$, $u+v\sqrt{-5}$, of $k(\sqrt{-5})$ must exist such that

$$1+\sqrt{-5}=(x+y\sqrt{-5})3+(u+v\sqrt{-5})(1-\sqrt{-5}),$$

and hence

$$1=3x+u+5v,$$

$$1=3y+v-u,$$

whence by addition

$$2=3x+3y+6v,$$

an equation between rational integers that is impossible, since 3 is a divisor of the right hand member but not of the left hand member.

Hence the required integers do not exist, and $1+\sqrt{-5}$ is therefore not a number of the ideal $\mathfrak{b}$. The ideals are therefore unequal.

Ex. 3. To prove that the two ideals $\mathfrak{a}=(2, 1+\sqrt{-5})$, and $\mathfrak{b}=(4, 2+2\sqrt{-5})$, are unequal.

Although, as is easily seen, the numbers defining the second ideal may be introduced into the symbol of the first ideal, we cannot introduce the number 2 of the first ideal into the symbol of the second; that is, we cannot find two integers, $x+y\sqrt{-5}$, $u+v\sqrt{-5}$, such that

$$2=(x+y\sqrt{-5})4+(u+v\sqrt{-5})(2+2\sqrt{-5}),$$

for from this equation it would follow that

$$2=4x+2u-10v,$$

$$0=4y+2u+2v,$$

whence by subtraction

$$2=4x-4y-12v,$$

an equation in rational integers that is impossible, since 4 is a divisor of the second member but not of the first member. The two ideals are therefore unequal.

Ex. 4. Show that

$$(2, 1+\sqrt{-5}) \neq (3, 1+\sqrt{-5}).$$

Ex. 5. Show that

$$(29, 32-27\sqrt{-5})=(3+2\sqrt{-5}).$$

Ex. 6. Show that

$$(49, 21-7\sqrt{-5}, 21+7\sqrt{-5}, 14)=(7).$$

Ex. 7. Show that

$$(3-\sqrt{-5}, 1+2\sqrt{-5})=(7, 3-\sqrt{-5}).$$

§ 10. Principal and Non-Principal Ideals.

If among the numbers of an ideal, $\mathfrak{a}$, there exist a number, α, such that all numbers of the ideal are multiples of α, then $\mathfrak{a}$ is said to be a *principal ideal,* and we have

$$\mathfrak{a} = (\alpha).$$

If such a number does not exist, $\mathfrak{a}$ is said to be a *non-principal ideal.* The necessary and sufficient condition for $\mathfrak{a}$ to be a principal ideal is evidently that we shall be able to introduce into the symbol of $\mathfrak{a}$ a number α such that all the numbers defining $\mathfrak{a}$ are multiples of α. If such a number cannot be introduced, $\mathfrak{a}$ is a non-principal ideal. Let us consider a few ideals with a view to determining whether they are principal or non-principal ideals.

i. (7), $(2+\sqrt{-5})$, $(6, 8, 2+6\sqrt{-5})$, $(3, 3\sqrt{-5})$, $(3, \sqrt{-5})$, $(5, \sqrt{-5})$.

ii. $(2, 1+\sqrt{-5})$, $(3, 1+\sqrt{-5})$, $(3, 1-\sqrt{-5})$.

Considering those of the set i, (7) and $(2+\sqrt{-5})$ are seen at once from the definition to be principal ideals; also

$$(6, 8, 2+6\sqrt{-5}) = (6, 8, 2+6\sqrt{-5}, 2) = (2),$$

$$(3, 3\sqrt{-5}) = (3),$$

$$(3, \sqrt{-5}) = (3, \sqrt{-5}, -5) = (3, \sqrt{-5}, -5, 1) = (1),$$

$$(5, \sqrt{-5}) = (\sqrt{-5}).$$

Hence all ideals of the first set are principal ideals.

Consider now the ideals of the set ii. If $(2, 1+\sqrt{-5})$ be a principal ideal, then there must exist a number, α, of the ideal such that 2 and $1+\sqrt{-5}$ are both multiples of α.

The numbers 2 and $1+\sqrt{-5}$, being primes in $k(\sqrt{-5})$ and not associated, have as their only common divisors ± 1. Hence α must be 1 or -1.

Since, if 1 be a number of the ideal, -1 is also one of its numbers and vice versa, it is sufficient to see whether we can find two integers $x+y\sqrt{-5}$ and $u+v\sqrt{-5}$, such that

$$1 = 2(x+y\sqrt{-5}) + (1+\sqrt{-5})(u+v\sqrt{-5}). \qquad 1)$$

We have from 1)

$$1 = 2x + u - 5v,$$

$$0 = 2y + v + u,$$

which give by subtraction

$$1 = 2x - 2y - 6v,$$

an equation in rational integers that is impossible, since the second number only is divisible by 2. Hence 1 is not a number of the ideal $(2, 1 + \sqrt{-5})$, and this ideal is therefore a non-principal ideal.

Ex. 1. Show in like manner that $(3, 1 + \sqrt{-5})$ and $(3, 1 - \sqrt{-5})$ are non-principal ideals.

Ex. 2. Show that $(7, 1 + 2\sqrt{-5})$ and $(7, 1 - 2\sqrt{-5})$ are non-principal ideals.

Ex. 3. Show that $(21, 9 + 3\sqrt{-5}, -2 + 4\sqrt{-5})$ is a principal ideal.

Had we introduced the conception of the ideal in the realms $k(i)$, $k(\sqrt{-3})$ and $k(\sqrt{2})$, we should have seen that in all these realms every ideal is a principal ideal, for if $\mathfrak{a}, = (\alpha_1, \alpha_2, \cdots, \alpha_n)$, be an ideal, defined as above, of any one of these realms, then, since the unique factorization law holds in all these realms, we could in every case find integers $\xi_1, \xi_2, \cdots, \xi_n$ such that

$$\xi_1\alpha_1 + \xi_2\alpha_2 + \cdots + \xi_n\alpha_n = \delta,$$

where δ is the greatest common divisor of $\alpha_1, \alpha_2, \cdots, \alpha_n$. Hence we have

$$\mathfrak{a} = (\alpha_1, \alpha_2, \cdots, \alpha_n, \delta) = (\delta),$$

a principal ideal.

On the other hand, we have seen (Th. B) that it is not always possible in $k(\sqrt{-5})$ to find the integers $\xi_1, \xi_2, \cdots, \xi_n$; hence the fact that not all ideals of $k(\sqrt{-5})$ are principal ideals.

§ 11. Multiplication of Ideals.

By the product of two ideals

$$\mathfrak{a}, = (\alpha_1, \alpha_2, \cdots, \alpha_m), \text{ and } \mathfrak{b}, = (\beta_1, \beta_2, \cdots, \beta_n),$$

we understand the ideal defined by all possible products of a number defining $\mathfrak{a}$ *by a number defining* $\mathfrak{b}$*; that is,*

$$\mathfrak{ab} = (\alpha_1\beta_1, \alpha_1\beta_2, \cdots, \alpha_1\beta_n, \cdots, \alpha_m\beta_1, \cdots, \alpha_m\beta_n).$$

In other words, the product of $\mathfrak{a}$ and $\mathfrak{b}$ is the ideal whose numbers are all possible products of a number of $\mathfrak{a}$ by a number of $\mathfrak{b}$, together with all linear combinations of these products. It is evident from the above definition that the commutative and associated laws hold in the multiplication of ideals; that is, $\mathfrak{ab}=\mathfrak{ba}$ and $\mathfrak{ab}\cdot\mathfrak{c}=\mathfrak{a}\cdot\mathfrak{bc}$.

Ex. 1.

$$(3, 1+\sqrt{-5})(3, 1-\sqrt{-5}) = (9, 3-3\sqrt{-5}, 3+3\sqrt{-5}, 6).$$
$$= (9, 3-3\sqrt{-5}, 3+3\sqrt{-5}, 6, 3),$$
$$= (3).$$

Ex. 2. $(2, 1+\sqrt{-5})^2 = (2, 1+\sqrt{-5})(2, 1+\sqrt{-5}),$
$$= (4, 2+2\sqrt{-5}, -4+2\sqrt{-5}),$$
$$= (4, 2+2\sqrt{-5}, -4+2\sqrt{-5}, 2),$$

since $2+2\sqrt{-5}-(-4+2\sqrt{-5})-4=2$. Hence, since all numbers in the symbol are multiples of 2, which is a number of the symbol,

$$(2, 1+\sqrt{-5})^2 = (2).$$

Ex. 3.

$$(2, 1+\sqrt{-5})(3, 1+\sqrt{-5})=(6, 2+2\sqrt{-5}, 3+3\sqrt{-5}, -4+2\sqrt{-5})$$
$$=(6, 2+2\sqrt{-5}, 3+3\sqrt{-5}, 1+\sqrt{-5}),$$

since $$2+2\sqrt{-5}-6=-4+2\sqrt{-5}$$

and $$3+3\sqrt{-5}-(2+2\sqrt{-5})=1+\sqrt{-5},$$

whence, since all numbers in the symbol are multiples of $1+\sqrt{-5}$,

$$(2, 1+\sqrt{-5})(3, 1+\sqrt{-5}) = (1+\sqrt{-5}).$$

Ex. 4.

$$(2, 1+\sqrt{-5})(3, 1-\sqrt{-5}) = (6, 2-2\sqrt{-5}, 3+3\sqrt{-5}, 6)$$
$$= (6, 2-2\sqrt{-5}, 3+3\sqrt{-5}, 1-\sqrt{-5}),$$

since $$6-(2-2\sqrt{-5})-(3+3\sqrt{-5}) = 1-\sqrt{-5},$$

whence, since

$$3+3\sqrt{-5}=6-(2-2\sqrt{-5})-(1-\sqrt{-5}),$$
$$(2, 1+\sqrt{-5})(3, 1-\sqrt{-5}) = (6, 2-2\sqrt{-5}, 1-\sqrt{-5})$$
$$= (1-\sqrt{-5}),$$

since all the numbers in the symbol are multiples of $1-\sqrt{-5}$.

Ex. 5. Show that

a) $(3, 1+2\sqrt{-5})(3, 1-2\sqrt{-5}) = (3),$

b) $(7, 1+2\sqrt{-5})(7, 1-2\sqrt{-5}) = (7),$

c) $(3, 1+2\sqrt{-5})(7, 1+2\sqrt{-5}) = (1+2\sqrt{-5}),$

d) $(3, 1-2\sqrt{-5})(7, 1-2\sqrt{-5}) = (1-2\sqrt{-5}).$

§ 12. **Divisibility of Ideals.**

An ideal, $\mathfrak{a}$, is said to be divisible by an ideal, $\mathfrak{b}$, when there exists an ideal, $\mathfrak{c}$, such that

$$\mathfrak{a}=\mathfrak{b}\mathfrak{c};$$

$\mathfrak{b}$ and $\mathfrak{c}$ are then said to be *divisors* or *factors* of $\mathfrak{a}$.

§ 13. **The Unit Ideal.**

Every ideal $\mathfrak{a}$, $=(\alpha_1, \alpha_2, \cdots, \alpha_m)$, of $k(\sqrt{-5})$ is divisible by the ideal (1), for

$$\mathfrak{a}(1)=(\alpha_1, \alpha_2, \cdots, \alpha_n)(1)=(\alpha_1, \alpha_2, \cdots, \alpha_n)=\mathfrak{a}.$$

That (1) is the only ideal of $k(\sqrt{-5})$ possessing this property can be easily shown.

Suppose that there is another ideal $\mathfrak{d}=(\delta_1, \delta_2, \cdots, \delta_n)$, which is a divisor of every ideal of $k(\sqrt{-5})$. Since it divides the ideal (1), we must have

$$(1)=\mathfrak{d}\mathfrak{m},$$

where

$$\mathfrak{m}=(\mu_1, \mu_2, \cdots, \mu_m).$$

Then

$$(1)=(\delta_1, \delta_2, \cdots, \delta_n)(\mu_1, \mu_2, \cdots, \mu_m),$$

$$=(\delta_1\mu_1, \cdots, \delta_1\mu_m, \cdots, \delta_n\mu_1, \cdots, \delta_n\mu_m),$$

and hence

$$1=\xi_1\delta_1\mu_1+\xi_2\delta_1\mu_2+\cdots+\xi_{mn}\delta_n\mu_m \qquad 1)$$

$$=\lambda_1\delta_1+\lambda_2\delta_2+\cdots+\lambda_n\delta_n,$$

where $\xi_1, \xi_2, \cdots, \xi_{mn}$ and hence $\lambda_1, \lambda_2, \cdots, \lambda_n$ are integers of $k(\sqrt{-5})$. Therefore 1 is a number of $\mathfrak{d}$ and

$$\mathfrak{d}=(\delta_1, \delta_2, \cdots, \delta_n, 1)=(1).$$

The ideal (1) is therefore the only ideal which divides every ideal of $k(\sqrt{-5})$. Hence it is called the *unit ideal* of $k(\sqrt{-5})$. It is evidently the whole system of integers of $k(\sqrt{-5})$. It should be noticed that from 1) it follows also that 1 is a number of $\mathfrak{m}$, and in general we may show by this method that, *if an ideal $\mathfrak{a}$ be divisible by an ideal $\mathfrak{b}$ then all numbers of $\mathfrak{a}$ are numbers of $\mathfrak{b}$.*

§ 14. **Prime Ideals.**

An ideal different from (1) and divisible only by itself and (1) is called a prime ideal. An ideal with divisors other than itself and (1) is called a composite ideal.

We shall show that $(2, 1+\sqrt{-5})$ is a prime ideal. If this be not the case, two ideals, $\mathfrak{a}$ and $\mathfrak{b}$, neither of which is (1), must exist such that

$$(2, 1+\sqrt{-5})=\mathfrak{a}\mathfrak{b}.$$

Let $\mathfrak{a}=(\alpha_1, \alpha_2, \cdots, \alpha_m)$, $\mathfrak{b}=(\beta_1, \beta_2, \cdots, \beta_n)$.

Then we should have

$$(2, 1+\sqrt{-5})=(\alpha_1, \alpha_2, \cdots, \alpha_m)(\beta_1, \beta_2, \cdots, \beta_n).$$

It may be shown now by the method employed in the last paragraph that 2 and $1+\sqrt{-5}$ are numbers of each of the ideals $\mathfrak{a}$ and $\mathfrak{b}$, and hence

$$(2, 1+\sqrt{-5})=(\alpha_1, \cdots, \alpha_m, 2, 1+\sqrt{-5})(\beta_1, \cdots, \beta_n, 2, 1+\sqrt{-5}).$$

Let α_i, $=a+b\sqrt{-5}$, be any one of the integers $\alpha_1, \alpha_2, \cdots, \alpha_m$; then

$$\alpha_i=b(1+\sqrt{-5})+a-b.$$

But $a-b$ is a rational integer, and hence is of the form $2c$ or $2c+1$, where c is a rational integer. We have therefore either

$$\alpha_i=b(1+\sqrt{-5})+2c, \qquad 1)$$

or

$$\alpha_i=b(1+\sqrt{-5})+2c+1. \qquad 2)$$

If 1) be the case, α_i may be omitted from the symbol $\mathfrak{a}$. If 2) be the case, we have

$$\alpha_i-b(1+\sqrt{-5})-2c=1,$$

and 1 may therefore be introduced into the symbol of $\mathfrak{a}$; all other numbers could then be omitted and we should have

$$\mathfrak{a}=(1).$$

Proceeding in this manner with each of the numbers α_1, α_2, $\cdots, \alpha_m$, we see that one of the two following cases must occur, either all of the numbers $\alpha_1, \alpha_2, \cdots, \alpha_m$ are linear combinations of 2 and $1+\sqrt{-5}$, and hence may be omitted from the symool of $\mathfrak{a}$, in which case we have

$$\mathfrak{a}=(2, 1+\sqrt{-5}),$$

or some number of $\mathfrak{a}$ is not a linear combination of 2 and $1+\sqrt{-5}$, in which case 1 may be introduced into the symbol of $\mathfrak{a}$ and we have

$$\mathfrak{a}=(1).$$

The same is evidently true for $\mathfrak{b}$. We have therefore as the only possible factorizations of $(2, 1+\sqrt{-5})$

$$(2, 1+\sqrt{-5}) = (1)(1) = (1), \qquad 3)$$

or
$$= (2, 1+\sqrt{-5})(2, 1+\sqrt{-5}), \qquad 4)$$

or
$$= (2, 1+\sqrt{-5})(1),$$

or
$$= (1)(2, 1+\sqrt{-5}).$$

It has already been proved that

$$(2, 1+\sqrt{-5}) \neq (1),$$

hence 3) is impossible.

Likewise it may easily be shown that 4) is impossible, for we have seen (§ 11) that

$$(2, 1+\sqrt{-5})^2 = (2),$$

while, since $1+\sqrt{-5}$ is not a multiple of 2,

$$(2, 1+\sqrt{-5}) \neq (2).$$

Hence 4) is impossible.

The only divisors of $(2, 1+\sqrt{-5})$ are therefore the ideal itself and (1). Hence $(2, 1+\sqrt{-5})$ is a prime ideal.

It may be shown similarly that $(3, 1+\sqrt{-5})$ and $(3, 1-\sqrt{-5})$ are prime ideals. The proof in these cases is suggested as an exercise.

Ex. Prove that every ideal of the form $(p, 1+q\sqrt{-5})$, where p and q are rational primes different from each other, is a prime ideal.

§ 15. Restoration of the Unique Factorization Law in Terms of Ideal Factors.

We shall now show that although the factorization of 6 into its *prime number* factors in $k(\sqrt{-5})$ is not unique, nevertheless, when we resolve the principal ideal (6) into its *prime ideal* factors this factorization is unique.[1] There are evidently two different factorizations of (6) into *principal* ideal factors; that is,

$$(6) = (2)(3) = (1+\sqrt{-5})(1-\sqrt{-5}). \qquad 1)$$

[1] We speak of the factorization of an integer a into its ideal factors, meaning thereby always the factorization of the principal ideal (a) defined by a.

These factors are, however, not *prime* ideals, for we have shown (§ 11) that

$$(2) = (2, 1+\sqrt{-5})^2,$$
$$(3) = (3, 1+\sqrt{-5})(3, 1-\sqrt{-5}),$$
$$(1+\sqrt{-5}) = (2, 1+\sqrt{-5})(3, 1+\sqrt{-5}),$$

and
$$(1-\sqrt{-5}) = (2, 1+\sqrt{-5})(3, 1-\sqrt{-5}).$$

We have shown also (§ 14) that these factors of (2), (3), $(1+\sqrt{-5})$ and $(1-\sqrt{-5})$ are all *prime* ideals.

Substituting in 1) we have

$$(6) = (2)(3) = (2, 1+\sqrt{-5})^2(3, 1+\sqrt{-5})(3, 1-\sqrt{-5}),$$

and

$$\begin{aligned}(6) &= (1+\sqrt{-5})(1-\sqrt{-5})\\ &= (2, 1+\sqrt{-5})(3, 1+\sqrt{-5})(2, 1-\sqrt{-5})(3, 1-\sqrt{-5})\\ &= (2, 1+\sqrt{-5})^2(3, 1+\sqrt{-5})(3, 1-\sqrt{-5}).\end{aligned}$$

Hence (6) can be factored in one and but one way into prime ideal factors.

Ex. Show that the factorizations of 9, 14, 21, and 49 into prime number factors are not unique but that the factorizations of (9), (14), (21), and (49) into prime ideal factors are unique.

We have now shown that the introduction of the conception of the ideal in $k(\sqrt{-5})$ has accomplished, at least in the particular example given, what we desired; that is, the restoration of the unique factorization law.

Instead of showing that the unique factorization law holds in general in $k(\sqrt{-5})$ when the factorization is expressed in terms of prime ideal factors, and then investigating the properties of the integers and ideals of this realm, we shall proceed at once to the discussion of the general quadratic realm defined by the root of any irreducible quadratic equation. Among these realms are included, of course, the special realms $k(i)$, $k(\sqrt{-3})$, $k(\sqrt{2})$ and $k(\sqrt{-5})$. We shall see that when the factorization in any quadratic realm whatever is expressed in terms of prime ideal factors it is unique, and we shall be able to deduce general theorems for the integers and ideals of any realm similar to those found for the integers of realms in which the unique factorization law held in the ordinary sense. We shall find, moreover, that the introduction of the ideal will lead us to the discovery of new and deeper properties of these realms.

The introduction of ideal factors is due to Kummer, but the form used in the text and known as ideals is due to Dedekind. For an account of Kummer's researches see his papers, Crelle, Vol. XXXV, pp. 319 and 327, especially the former, in which he announces his introduction of the ideal number; in the latter paper he expands the theory. A brief account of Kummer's conception is given in the eleventh supplement to Dedekind's edition of Dirichlet lectures, pp. 545–550; see also Bachmann, Allgemeine Arithmetik der Zahlenkörper, pp. 150–160, for a very interesting discussion of Kummer's ideal numbers and other methods of reinstating the unique factorization law in the general algebraic number realm.

CHAPTER IX.

General Theorems Concerning Algebraic Numbers.

§ 1. Polynomials in a Single Variable.[1]

Before beginning the study of the general quadratic realm we shall give a few theorems which are necessary for our future investigations.

First of all, we shall prove a theorem concerning the divisibility of polynomials in a single variable. By a polynomial in a single variable, x, is meant, as has been said, an expression of the form

$$a_0x^n + a_1x^{n-1} + \cdots + a_n,$$

where n is a positive rational integer and the a's are quantities not containing x. The sum, difference and product of two polynomials in x are evidently polynomials in x.

In what follows we shall in all cases assume the a's to be rational numbers.

A polynomial, $f(x)$, is said to be divisible by another polynomial, $f_1(x)$, when a third polynomial, $f_2(x)$, exists such that

$$f(x) = f_1(x)f_2(x).$$

It is evident that all polynomials of the 0th degree, that is, the rational numbers, divide every polynomial in x.

If $f_1(x)$ and $f_2(x)$ have no common divisors other than constants, they are said to be prime to each other, or to have no common divisor.

Theorem 1. *If $f_1(x)$ and $f_2(x)$ be two polynomials in x without a common divisor, there exist two polynomials in x, $\phi_1(x)$ and $\phi_2(x)$, such that*

$$\phi_1(x)f_1(x) + \phi_2(x)f_2(x) = 1.$$

[1] Weber: Algebra, Vol. I., §§ 1 to 6.

Let $f_1(x)$ and $f_2(x)$ be of degrees m and n, respectively, and

$$m \gtreqless n.$$

By division we may put f_1 in the form

$$f_1 = q_1 f_2 + f_3, \qquad 1)$$

where q_1, the quotient, and f_3, the remainder, are polynomials in x, and f_3 is of lower degree than f_2.

Likewise we may put f_2 in the form

$$f_2 = q_2 f_3 + f_4, \qquad 2)$$

where f_3 and f_4 are polynomials in x, and f_4 of lower degree than f_3.

Continuing this process, which is none other than that of finding the greatest common divisor of $f_1(x)$ and $f_2(x)$, we have

$$f_3 = q_3 f_4 + f_5, \qquad 3)$$

$$f_4 = q_4 f_5 + f_6,$$

and arrive finally at a point where the remainder is a constant, f_k, different from 0, since f_1 and f_2 are prime to each other. We have then

$$f_{k-2} = q_{k-2} f_{k-1} + f_k.$$

Putting now the value of f_3 from 1) in 2) we have

$$f_4 = (1 + q_1 q_2) f_2 - q_2 f_1;$$

that is

$$f_4 = r_1 f_1 + r_2 f_2,$$

where r_1 and r_2 are polynomials in x. Putting the expressions for f_3 and f_4 in terms of f_1 and f_2 in 3), we obtain

$$f_5 = s_1 f_1 + s_2 f_2,$$

where s_1, s_2 are polynomials in x. Continuing this process, we obtain finally

$$f_k = w_1 f_1 + w_2 f_2,$$

where w_1, w_2 are polynomials in x. As has been said, f_k is a constant different from 0. Putting therefore

$$w_1 = f_k \phi_1(x), \quad w_2 = f_k \phi_2(x),$$

we have

$$f_k\phi_1(x)f_1(x)+f_k\phi_2(x)f_2(x)=f_k,$$

and hence

$$\phi_1(x)f_1(x)+\phi_2(x)f_2(x)=1,$$

where $\phi_1(x)$ and $\phi_2(x)$ are polynomials in x.

We may generalize the above theorem as follows:

THEOREM 2. *If $f_1(x)$ and $f_2(x)$ be two polynomials in x without a common divisor and $g(x)$ any polynomial in x, there exist two polynomials in x, $\Phi_1(x)$ and $\Phi_2(x)$, such that $\Phi_2(x)$ is of lower degree than $f_1(x)$ and*

$$\Phi_1(x)f_1(x)+\Phi_2(x)f_2(x)=g(x).$$

By Th. 1 there exist two polynomials in x, $\phi_1(x)$, $\phi_2(x)$, such that

$$\phi_1(x)f_1(x)+\phi_2(x)f_2(x)=1. \qquad 4)$$

Multiplying 4) by $g(x)$ we have

$$g(x)\phi_1(x)f_1(x)+g(x)\phi_2(x)f_2(x)=g(x). \qquad 5)$$

Putting $g(x)\phi_2(x)$ in the form

$$g(x)\phi_2(x)=q(x)f_1(x)+r(x),$$

where $q(x)$ and $r(x)$ are polynomials in x and $r(x)$ is of lower degree than $f_1(x)$, and substituting in 5), we have

$$[g(x)\phi_1(x)+q(x)f_2(x)]f_1(x)+r(x)f_2(x)=g(x);$$

that is

$$\Phi_1(x)f_1(x)+\Phi_2(x)f_2(x)=g(x),$$

where $\Phi_1(x)$ and $\Phi_2(x)$ are polynomials in x, and $\Phi_2(x)$ is of lower degree than $f_1(x)$.

A polynomial, $f(x)$, is said to be irreducible in the realm $k(\alpha)$ when it cannot be resolved into integral factors whose coefficients are numbers of $k(\alpha)$. When $f(x)$ has rational coefficients and is said simply to be irreducible, no realm being specified, the rational realm is understood; that is, $f(x)$ is not resolvable into integral factors having rational coefficients.

THEOREM 3. *An irreducible polynomial, $f(x)$, can have no factor in common with another polynomial, $F(x)$, unless $F(x)$ be divisible by $f(x)$.*

The coefficients of the greatest common divisor of the two polynomials $F(x)$ and $f(x)$ are derived from the coefficients of these two polynomials by rational operations and are therefore rational numbers, since the coefficients of $F(x)$ and $f(x)$ are rational numbers.

But $f(x)$ is divisible by no polynomial in x with rational coefficients except itself and the rational numbers. Hence either $F(x)$ and $f(x)$ have no common factor or $F(x)$ is divisible by $f(x)$.

COR. 1. *If $f(x)$ be irreducible and $F(x)$ vanish for one root of the equation $f(x)=0$, it vanishes for all roots of $f(x)=0$.* For, if $F(x)$ vanish for a root of $f(x)=0$, $F(x)$ and $f(x)$ must have a common factor. But this can only be $f(x)$.

COR. 2. *If $f(x)$ be irreducible and $F(x)$ be a function of lower degree than $f(x)$ that vanishes for one root of $f(x)=0$, then $F(x)$ must vanish identically; that is, all coefficients of $F(x)$ are 0.*

§ 2. Numbers of a Realm.

Let us consider the realm $k(\alpha)$ of the nth degree, α being a root of the irreducible rational equation

$$f(x)=x^n+a_1x^{n-1}+\cdots+a_n=0, \qquad 1)$$

whose remaining roots we denote by $\alpha', \alpha'', \cdots, \alpha^{(n-1)}$.

Any number θ of $k(\alpha)$, being produced from α by repeated performance of the operations of addition, subtraction, multiplication and division, is a rational function of α with rational coefficients and hence can be expressed in the form

$$\theta=\frac{\chi(\alpha)}{\psi(\alpha)},$$

where $\chi(\alpha)$ and $\psi(\alpha)$ are rational integral functions of α with rational coefficients. The realm $k(\alpha)$ is composed therefore of all rational functions of α with rational coefficients, the denominator never being 0.

We shall now show that every number of the realm can be expressed as a rational integral function of α with rational coefficients.

The degrees of $\chi(\alpha)$ and $\psi(\alpha)$ can be made lower than the nth by virtue of the relation

$$\alpha^n + a_1\alpha^{n-1} + \cdots + a_n = 0.$$

Since $\psi(\alpha)$ is different from 0 and of degree lower than the nth, $\psi(x)$ is not divisible by $f(x)$, and hence, since $f(x)$ is irreducible, $\psi(x)$ is prime to $f(x)$ (Th. 3). We can therefore by Th. 2 find two polynomials in x, $\Phi_1(x)$, $\Phi_2(x)$, with rational coefficients and $\Phi_2(x)$ of lower degree than the nth, such that

$$\Phi_1(x)f(x) + \Phi_2(x)\psi(x) = \chi(x). \qquad 2)$$

Putting α for x in 2) we have

$$\Phi_2(\alpha)\psi(\alpha) = \chi(\alpha),$$

and hence

$$\frac{\chi(\alpha)}{\psi(\alpha)} = \Phi_2(\alpha);$$

that is, $$\theta = b_0 + b_1\alpha + b_2\alpha^2 + \cdots + b_{n-1}\alpha^{n-1},$$

where $b_0, b_1, \cdots, b_{n-1}$ are rational numbers. This representation of θ is unique, for, if we had also

$$\theta = c_0 + c_1\alpha + c_2\alpha^2 + \cdots + c_{n-1}\alpha^{n-1},$$

then it would follow that

$$b_0 - c_0 + (b_1 - c_1)\alpha + \cdots + (b_{n-1} - c_{n-1})\alpha^{n-1} = 0;$$

that is, a polynomial in x of degree lower than the nth would vanish for $x = \alpha$, but this by Th. 3, Cor. 2 is impossible unless all the coefficients of the polynomial are 0. Hence

$$b_0 = c_0, \cdots, b_{n-1} = c_{n-1},$$

and the two representations are identical.

The numbers of the realm are seen therefore to be coextensive with the totality of rational integral functions of α with rational coefficients and of degree not higher than the $(n-1)$th.

We shall next prove the following simple theorem:

THEOREM 4. *Every number θ of $k(\alpha)$ satisfies a rational equation, whose degree is the same as that of the realm, and whose remaining roots are the conjugates of θ.*

Form the equation

$$\begin{aligned}\Phi(t) &= (t-\theta)(t-\theta')\cdots(t-\theta^{(n-1)}) \\ &= t^n + d_1 t^{n-1} + \cdots + d_n = 0, \qquad 3)\end{aligned}$$

where $\theta', \theta'', \cdots, \theta^{(n-1)}$ are the conjugates of θ.

The coefficients, $d_1, d_2, \cdots, d_n$, of 3) are symmetric functions of the roots of 1) and hence rational functions of the coefficients of 1). Hence $d_1, d_2, \cdots, d_n$ are rational numbers. Therefore θ satisfies a rational equation of the nth degree, whose remaining roots are the conjugates of θ. Every number of the realm is therefore evidently an algebraic number.

We turn now to the reducibility of $\Phi(t)$, and shall prove the following theorem:

THEOREM 5. *The function $\Phi(t)$ is either irreducible or is a power of an irreducible function. The n conjugates of a number of $k(\alpha)$ are either all different or else fall into n_2 systems, each containing n_1 numbers all alike. In the first case, $\Phi(t)$ is irreducible, in the second, $\Phi(t)$ is the n_1th power of an irreducible function of the n_2th degree.*

If $\Phi(t)$ be reducible it must be a product of irreducible factors, each of which vanishes for one or more of the quantities

$$\theta, \theta', \cdots, \theta^{(n-1)}.$$

Let

$$\Phi(t) = \phi_1(t)\phi_2(t)\cdots\phi_{n_1}(t),$$

where $\phi_1(t), \phi_2(t), \cdots, \phi_{n_1}(t)$ are irreducible and let $\phi_1(t)$ vanish for $t=\theta$; that is,

$$\phi_1(\theta)=0.$$

We have seen that

$$\theta = g(\alpha),$$

where α is the number defining the realm and $g(\alpha)$ a rational integral function of α with rational coefficients. Then

$$\phi_1[g(\alpha)]=0.$$

The equations

$$\phi_1[g(x)] = 0 \text{ and } f(x) = 0$$

have therefore a root in common, and, since $f(x)$ is irreducible, $\phi_1[g(x)]$ must vanish for all roots of $f(x)=0$; that is,

$$\phi_1[g(\alpha')] = 0, \phi_1[g(\alpha'')] = 0, \cdots, \phi_1[g(\alpha^{(n-1)})].$$

But $\quad \theta' = g(\alpha'), \theta'' = g(\alpha''), \cdots, \theta^{(n-1)} = g(\alpha^{(n-1)}).$

Hence

$$\phi_1(\theta) = 0, \phi_1(\theta') = 0, \cdots, \phi_1(\theta^{(n-1)}) = 0;$$

that is, $\phi_1(t)$ vanishes for all of the n conjugate numbers $\theta, \theta', \cdots, \theta^{(n-1)}$.

If these numbers be all different, $\phi_1(t)$ is of the nth degree and hence identical with $\Phi(t)$.

If, however, there be among them only n_2 which are different from each other, say

$$\theta, \theta', \cdots, \theta^{(n_2-1)},$$

then $\quad \phi_1(t) = (t-\theta)(t-\theta') \cdots (t-\theta^{(n_2-1)}).$

Since, moreover, every irreducible factor of $\Phi(t)$ vanishes for one of the quantities $\theta, \theta', \cdots, \theta^{n-1}$, and hence for all of them (Th. 3, Cor. 2), every one of these irreducible factors of $\Phi(t)$ is identical with $\phi_1(t)$; that is $\phi_2(t), \phi_3(t), \cdots, \phi_n(t)$ are all identical with $\phi_1(t)$.

Therefore $\Phi(t)$ is in this case a power of $\phi_1(t)$; that is,

$$\Phi(t) = [\phi_1(t)]^{n_1}, \text{ where } n_1 n_2 = n.$$

We have seen (Chap. I, § 1) that every algebraic number satisfies a single irreducible rational equation.

We see now from the above that the degree of this equation is a divisor of the degree of the realm of which θ is a number. According as the degree of this equation is the same as or lower than that of the realm, θ is said to be a *primitive* or *imprimitive* number of the realm.

Thus θ is a primitive number of $k(\alpha)$ when it is different from all of its conjugates and an imprimitive number when this is not the case.

THEOREM 6. *Any primitive number θ of $k(\alpha)$ may be taken to define the realm; that is,*

$$k(\theta)=k(\alpha).$$

Let θ be any primitive number of $k(\alpha)$ and $\theta', \theta'', \cdots, \theta^{(n-1)}$ its conjugates, and let ω be any number of $k(\alpha)$ and $\omega', \omega'', \cdots, \omega^{(n-1)}$ its conjugates. We shall show that ω can be expressed as a rational function of θ with rational coefficients, and hence that $k(\theta)=k(\alpha)$.

We have

$$\Phi(t)=(t-\theta)(t-\theta')\cdots(t-\theta^{(n-1)}).$$

Then

$$\Phi(t)\left(\frac{\omega}{t-\theta}+\frac{\omega'}{t-\theta'}+\cdots+\frac{\omega^{(n-1)}}{t-\theta^{(n-1)}}\right)=\Psi(t). \qquad 4)$$

where $\Psi(t)$ is a polynomial in t of the $(n-1)$th degree, whose coefficients are rational numbers, for they are symmetric functions of the roots of the irreducible rational equation satisfied by α, and hence rational functions of its coefficients. Putting θ for t in 4) we have

$$\omega(\theta-\theta')(\theta-\theta'')\cdots(\theta-\theta^{(n-1)})=\Psi(\theta),$$

or, putting as usual

$$d/dt\cdot\Phi(t)=\Phi'(t)=(t-\theta')(t-\theta'')\cdots(t-\theta^{(n-1)})+\text{terms}$$

containing the factor $t-\theta$, we have

$$\omega=\frac{\Psi(\theta)}{\Phi'(\theta)},$$

where $\Phi'(\theta)$ is a polynomial in t with rational coefficients, and is different from 0, since θ is different from all its conjugates. Every number of $k(\alpha)$ can therefore be expressed as a rational function of θ with rational coefficients. Hence all numbers of $k(\alpha)$ are numbers of $k(\theta)$, and therefore

$$k(\alpha)=k(\theta).$$

THEOREM 7. *If* $f(x)=x^n+a_1x^{n-1}+\cdots+a_n=0 \qquad 5)$
be an irreducible rational equation, and θ, one of its roots, be an

algebraic integer, the remaining roots, $\theta', \theta'', \cdots, \theta^{(n-1)}$, *are also algebraic integers.*

This theorem follows directly from Th. 4, Chap. II. It may also be proved as follows.

Since θ is an integer, it must satisfy an equation

$$F(x) = x^m + b_1 x^{n-1} + \cdots + b_n = 0, \qquad 6)$$

whose coefficients are rational integers. But if $F(x)$ vanish for one root of the irreducible equation 5), it vanishes for all roots of 5). Hence $\theta', \theta'', \cdots, \theta^{(m-1)}$ satisfy 6) and are integers.

THEOREM 8. *The sum, difference, product and quotient, the denominator of the latter not being zero, of two algebraic numbers are algebraic numbers.*

Let α and β be two algebraic numbers, which satisfy respectively the two irreducible rational equations

$$x^m + a_1 x^{m-1} + \cdots + a_m = 0, \qquad 7)$$

$$x^n + b_1 x^{n-1} + \cdots + b_n = 0. \qquad 8)$$

The necessary and sufficient condition that $\alpha + \beta$ shall be an algebraic number is that it shall satisfy a rational equation.

Form the equation

$$[x - (\alpha + \beta)] \cdots [(x - (\alpha^{(i)} + \beta^{(j)})] \cdots [x - (\alpha^{(m-1)} + \beta^{(n-1)})]$$
$$= x^{mn} + c_1 x^{mn-1} + \cdots + c_{mn} = 0, \qquad 9)$$

whose roots are the mn numbers

$$\alpha + \beta, \begin{cases} \alpha = \alpha, \alpha', \cdots, \alpha^{(m-1)}, \\ \beta = \beta, \beta', \cdots, \beta^{(n-1)}. \end{cases}$$

The coefficients $c_1, c_2, \cdots, c_{mn}$ of 9) are symmetric functions of the roots of 7) and 8), and hence rational functions of the coefficients of 7) and 8).

But the coefficients of 7) and 8) are rational numbers.

Hence the coefficients of 9) are rational numbers, and $\alpha + \beta$ is therefore an algebraic number. The proofs for $\alpha - \beta$, $\alpha\beta$ and α/β are of the same character.

COR. 1. *Every rational function of any number of algebraic numbers with rational coefficients is an algebraic number.*

COR. 2. *The sum, difference and product of two algebraic integers are algebraic integers; for in this case the c's being not only rational but integral functions of the a's and b's, and the a's and b's being now integers, the c's are themselves rational integers.*

COR. 3. *Every rational integral function of any number of algebraic integers with rational integral coefficients is an algebraic integer.*

We obtain a still more general theorem when we notice that, if we allow the coefficients $b_1, b_2, \cdots, b_n$ of the equation

$$x^n + b_1 x^{n-1} + \cdots + b_n = 0 \qquad 10)$$

to be any algebraic numbers instead of restricting them to rational numbers, the roots of 10) will nevertheless be *algebraic* numbers.

THEOREM 9. *If ω be a root of the equation*

$$F(x) = x^n + \alpha_1 x^{n-1} + \cdots + \alpha_n = 0,$$

where $\alpha_1, \alpha_2, \cdots, \alpha_n$ are any algebraic numbers, it is itself an algebraic number.

Let $\alpha_1, \alpha_2, \cdots, \alpha_n$ satisfy rational equations of degree $m_1, m_2, \cdots, m_n$, respectively, and let the remaining roots of these equations be

$$\begin{array}{l} \alpha_1', \alpha_1'', \cdots, \alpha_1^{(m_1-1)}, \\ \alpha_2', \alpha_2'', \cdots, \alpha_2^{(m_2-1)}, \\ \vdots \quad \vdots \qquad \vdots \\ \alpha_n', \alpha_n'', \cdots, \alpha_n^{(m_n-1)}. \end{array}$$

Let $m = m_1 m_2 \cdots m_n$ and form by putting for α_i $\alpha_i, \alpha_i', \cdots, \alpha_i^{(m_i-1)}$ $(i = 1, 2, \cdots, n)$ the m polynomials in x

$$\begin{array}{ll} F(x) & = x^n + \alpha_1 x^{n-1} + \cdots + \alpha_n, \\ F_1(x) & = x^n + \alpha_1' x^{n-1} + \cdots + \alpha_n, \\ F_2(x) & = x^n + \alpha_1'' x^{n-1} + \cdots + \alpha_n, \\ — & — \quad — \quad — \quad — \\ — & — \quad — \quad — \quad — \\ F_{m-1}(x) & = x^n + \alpha_1^{(m_1-1)} x^{n-1} + \cdots + \alpha_n^{(m_n-1)}. \end{array}$$

Form the product

$$FF_1F_2 \cdots F_{m-1} = f(x).$$

The coefficients of $f(x)$ will be symmetric functions of the roots of the rational equations satisfied by $\alpha_1, \alpha_2, \cdots, \alpha_n$, and hence rational functions of their coefficients. They are therefore rational numbers and ω, being a root of the rational equation

$$f(x)=0,$$

is an algebraic number.

Ex. 1. Let ω be a root of the equation

$$F(x)=x^2+\sqrt{2}x+\sqrt{3}=0. \qquad 11)$$

We see that $\sqrt{2}$ and $\sqrt{3}$ are roots respectively of the rational equations

$$x^2-2=0 \quad \text{and} \quad x^2-3=0,$$

whose remaining roots are $-\sqrt{2}$ and $-\sqrt{3}$. We have

$$F_1(x)=x^2+\sqrt{2}x-\sqrt{3},$$
$$F_2(x)=x^2-\sqrt{2}x+\sqrt{3},$$
$$F_3(x)=x^2-\sqrt{2}x-\sqrt{3},$$

and $$f(x)=F\,F_1F_2F_3=x^8-4x^6-2x^4-12x^2+9=0 \qquad 12)$$

Hence, ω being a root of 12), is an algebraic number. It is moreover an integer, since the coefficients of 11) are integers (see Cor. 1 below).

Cor. 1. *If ω be a root of the equation*

$$F(x)=x^n+\alpha_1x^{n-1}+\cdots+\alpha_n=0,$$

where $\alpha_1, \alpha_2, \cdots, \alpha_n$ are algebraic integers, it is itself an algebraic integer; for the coefficients of $f(x)$ formed as above are not only rational but integral functions of the coefficients of the rational equations satisfied by the α's and these are now rational integers. Hence the coefficients of $f(x)$ are rational integers, and ω is an integer.

Theorem 10. *Every algebraic number can by multiplication by a suitable rational integer be made an algebraic integer.*

Let the algebraic number, α, be a root of the rational equation

$$x^n+a_1x^{n-1}+a_2x^{n-2}+\cdots+a_n=0,$$

and let a_0 be the least common denominator of the a's. Then

$$\alpha^n+\frac{b_1}{a_0}\cdot\alpha^{n-1}+\frac{b_2}{a_0}\cdot\alpha^{n-2}+\cdots+\frac{b_n}{a_0}=0, \qquad 13)$$

where the b's are rational integers.

Multiplying 13) by a_0^n, we have

$$(a_0\alpha)^n + b_1(a_0\alpha)^{n-1} + a_0b_2(a_0\alpha)^{n-2} + \cdots + a_0^{n-1}b_n = 0;$$

that is, $a_0\alpha$ is a root of the equation

$$y^n + b_1y^{n-1} + a_0b_2y^{n-2} + \cdots + a_0^{n-1}b_n = 0,$$

whose coefficients are rational integers, and is therefore an algebraic integer.

Ex. Let α be a root of

$$x^3 + \tfrac{1}{2}x^2 + \tfrac{4}{3}x + \tfrac{5}{4} = 0,$$

that is, of

$$x^3 + \tfrac{6}{12}x^2 + \tfrac{16}{12}x + \tfrac{15}{12} = 0. \qquad 14)$$

Multiplying 14) by 12^3, we have

$$(12x)^3 + 6(12x)^2 + 192(12x) + 2160 = 0.$$

Thus 12α is a root of the equation

$$y^3 + 6y^2 + 192y + 2160 = 0,$$

and hence an integer.

This is seen to be simply the transformation of 13) into an equation whose roots are a times those of 1), a being selected so as to make the coefficients of the new equation integers.

CHAPTER X.

The General Quadratic Realm.

§ 1. Number Defining the Realm.

By the general quadratic realm we understand the realm defined by a root of the general irreducible quadratic equation of the form

$$ax^2+bx+c=0, \qquad 1)$$

where a, b and c are rational integers.

If α be a root of 1), this realm is denoted by $k(\alpha)$. If α' be the other root of 1), the realm $k(\alpha')$ is the conjugate realm of $k(\alpha)$ (Chap. I, § 4).

Solving 1), we have

$$\alpha=\frac{-b+\sqrt{b^2-4ac}}{2a}, \quad \alpha'=\frac{-b-\sqrt{b^2-4ac}}{2a}.$$

Put

$$b^2-4ac=l^2m,$$

where m contains no square factor; then

$$\sqrt{b^2-4ac}=l\sqrt{m},$$

and

$$k(\alpha)=k(\sqrt{m});$$

for

$$\alpha=\frac{-b+l\sqrt{m}}{2a}$$

is evidently a number of $k(\sqrt{m})$ and

$$\sqrt{m}=\frac{2a\alpha+b}{l}$$

is a number of $k(\alpha)$.

Hence $k(\alpha)=k(\sqrt{m})$.[1]

Hence, to consider all quadratic realms, it is sufficient to consider all realms defined by a root of an equation of the form

$$x^2-m=0, \qquad 2)$$

[1] See Chap. IX, Th. 6.

where m is any rational integer containing no squared factor. We shall understand in what follows by $\sqrt{m}$ the positive real or imaginary root of 2), and shall assume that m contains no square factor.

The conjugate realms $k(\alpha)$ and $k(\alpha')$ are identical, since α is evidently a number of $k(\alpha')$ and α' a number of $k(\alpha)$.

The general quadratic realm is the simplest example of what is known as a *Galois realm;* that is, one which is identical with all its conjugate realms.

§ 2. **Numbers of the Realm. Conjugate and Norm of a Number. Primitive and Imprimitive Numbers.**

Let α be a root of the irreducible quadratic equation

$$x^2 + px + q = 0.$$

Every number, ω, of $k(\alpha)$ is a rational function of α with rational coefficients, and hence has the form

$$\omega = \frac{a + b\alpha}{c + d\alpha},$$

where a, b, c and d are rational numbers.

The number $$\omega' = \frac{a + b\alpha'}{c + d\alpha'}$$

obtained from ω by the substitution of α' for α is the conjugate of ω (Chap. I, § 4). The numbers of $k(\alpha)$ that are rational are seen to be their own conjugates. We shall show now that every number, ω, of $k(\alpha)$ can be put in the form

$$\omega = e + f\alpha,$$

where e and f are rational numbers.[1]

First, let α be $\sqrt{m}$. Then we have

$$\omega = \frac{a + b\sqrt{m}}{c + d\sqrt{m}}. \qquad 1)$$

[1] See Chapter IX, § 2, for general theorem of which this is a special case. Simplified proofs are given here of this and several following theorems.

Multiplying the numerator and denominator of 1) by $c-d\sqrt{m}$, we obtain

$$\omega=\frac{ac-bdm}{c^2-d^2m}+\frac{bc-ad}{c^2-d^2m}\sqrt{m}.$$

All numbers of $k(\sqrt{m})$ can therefore be put in the form $e+f\sqrt{m}$, where e and f are rational numbers.

If $\omega, =a+b\sqrt{m}$, be any number of $k(\sqrt{m})$ it satisfies the quadratic equation

$$x^2-2ax+a^2-mb^2=0, \qquad 2)$$

whose other root is $\omega', =a-b\sqrt{m}$, the conjugate of ω. Hence every number ω of $k(\sqrt{m})$ satisfies a rational equation of the second degree (Chap. IX, Th. 4). We say that α is a *primitive* or *imprimitive* number of $k(\sqrt{m})$ according as the equation 2) is irreducible or reducible.

The necessary and sufficient condition for 2) to be irreducible is evidently $b\neq 0$. In other words, α is a primitive number if it be different from its conjugate (Chap. IX, Th. 5).

If $b=0$, and hence $\omega=\omega'=a$, then ω satisfies the rational equation of the first degree

$$x-a=0.$$

The primitive numbers of a realm are thus seen to be those defined by equations of the *same degree as that of the realm* (Chap. IX, Th. 5). The imprimitive numbers of a quadratic realm are evidently the rational numbers.

If ω be a primitive number of a realm of the nth degree and the identity

$$a_0+a_1\omega+\cdots+a_{n-1}\omega^{n-1}=b_0+b_1\omega+\cdots+b_{n-1}\omega^{n-1} \qquad 3)$$

exist where the a's and b's are rational numbers, then the coefficients of the same powers of ω in the two members of 3) must be equal; that is,

$$a_0=b_0,\quad a_1=b_1,\quad \cdots,\quad a_{n-1}=b_{n-1};$$

for otherwise ω would satisfy an equation of degree lower than the nth, which is contrary to the assumption that ω is a primitive number of the realm.

We have shown (Chap. IX, Th. 6) that any algebraic number realm can be defined by any one of its primitive numbers. This can be proved for the special case of quadratic realms very simply as follows:

Let α be a primitive number and ω any number of $k(\sqrt{m})$. We have seen above that α and ω can be put in the forms

$$\alpha = a + b\sqrt{m}, \tag{4}$$

$$\omega = c + d\sqrt{m}, \tag{5}$$

where a, b, c and d are rational numbers.

From 4) we have $$\sqrt{m} = \frac{\alpha - a}{b},$$

and from 5) $$\omega = \frac{bc - ad}{b} + \frac{d}{b}\alpha.$$

Hence every number ω of $k(\sqrt{m})$ can be written in the form

$$\omega = e + f\alpha,$$

where e and f are rational numbers and α a primitive number of $k(\sqrt{m})$. Hence

$$k(\sqrt{m}) = k(\alpha),$$

and we have proved not only that every quadratic realm may be defined by any one of its primitive numbers, α, but that every number, ω, of the realm $k(\alpha)$ may be put in the form

$$\omega = e + f\alpha,$$

where e and f are rational numbers (Chap. IX, § 2).

We may evidently choose as the primitive number defining the realm an integer. In what follows we shall suppose this to have been done. The product of a number, ω, of $k(\alpha)$ by its conjugate ω' is its norm[1] and is denoted by $n[\omega]$; that is,

$$n[\omega] = \omega\omega'.$$

Since $n[\omega]$ is a symmetric function of the roots of the rational equation satisfied by α, it is a rational function of the coefficients of this equation, and hence a rational number. In particular when the realm is defined by $\sqrt{m}$, we have

$$n[\omega] = (a + b\sqrt{m})(a - b\sqrt{m}) = a^2 - b^2m.$$

[1] Hilbert: Bericht, § 3.

§ 3. Discriminant of a Number.[1]

The square of the difference of a number α and its conjugate is called the discriminant of the number and is denoted by $d[\alpha]$; that is,

$$d[\alpha] = (\alpha - \alpha')^2 = \begin{vmatrix} 1 & \alpha \\ 1 & \alpha' \end{vmatrix}^2$$

It is evidently a rational number and the discriminant of the quadratic equation

$$x^2 + a_1 x + a_2 = 0,$$

whose roots are α and α'.

If α be a primitive number of the realm its discriminant is different from 0, and conversely, if $d[\alpha]$ be different from 0, α is a primitive number.

§ 4. Basis of a Quadratic Realm.

THEOREM 1. *There exist in every quadratic realm two integers, ω_1, ω_2, such that every integer, ω, of the realm can be expressed in the form*

$$\omega = a_1\omega_1 + a_2\omega_2,$$

where a_1, a_2 are rational integers.[2]

Suppose the realm to be defined by an integer, α, a supposition in no way limiting the generality of the proof, and let ω be any integer of $k(\alpha)$. By the preceding paragraph ω can be put in the form

$$\omega = r_1 + r_2\alpha, \tag{1}$$

where r_1 and r_2 are rational numbers. We have

$$\omega' = r_1 + r_2\alpha'. \tag{2}$$

Solving 1) and 2) for r_1 and r_2 by means of determinants, we have

[1] Hilbert: Bericht, § 3.

[2] Hilbert: Bericht, Satz 5. This proof could have been somewhat simplified had greater use been made of the fact that the realm under consideration was quadratic, but it seemed desirable to give the proof in a form at once extendable to realms of any degree.

$$r_1 = \frac{\begin{vmatrix} \omega & \alpha \\ \omega' & \alpha' \end{vmatrix}}{\begin{vmatrix} 1 & \alpha \\ 1 & \alpha' \end{vmatrix}} = \frac{\begin{vmatrix} \omega & \alpha \\ \omega' & \alpha' \end{vmatrix} \cdot \begin{vmatrix} 1 & \alpha \\ 1 & \alpha' \end{vmatrix}}{\begin{vmatrix} 1 & \alpha \\ 1 & \alpha' \end{vmatrix}^2} = \frac{A_1}{d[\alpha]},$$

$$r_2 = \frac{\begin{vmatrix} 1 & \omega \\ 1 & \omega' \end{vmatrix}}{\begin{vmatrix} 1 & \alpha \\ 1 & \alpha' \end{vmatrix}} = \frac{\begin{vmatrix} 1 & \omega \\ 1 & \omega' \end{vmatrix} \cdot \begin{vmatrix} 1 & \alpha \\ 1 & \alpha' \end{vmatrix}}{\begin{vmatrix} 1 & \alpha \\ 1 & \alpha' \end{vmatrix}^2} = \frac{A_2}{d[\alpha]},$$

where A_1 and A_2 are rational integral functions of the integers ω, ω', α and α' with integral coefficients and hence integers (Chap. IX, Th. 8, Cor. 3).

Moreover, $d[\alpha]$ is a rational number and hence $A_1, = r_1 d[\alpha]$, and $A_2, = r_2 d[\alpha]$, are rational numbers. Therefore, A_1 and A_2 are rational integers. Hence every integer, ω, of $k[\alpha]$ can be put in the form

$$\omega = \frac{A_1 + A_2\alpha}{d[\alpha]}, \tag{3}$$

where A_1 and A_2 are rational integers and $d[\alpha]$ is the discriminant of α.

Suppose, now, all integers of the realm to be written in the form 3) and consider those in which A_2 is not equal to 0. Among these there will be some in which A_2 will be smaller in absolute value than in any of the remaining ones.

Let
$$\omega_2 = \frac{A_1' + A_2'\alpha}{d[\alpha]}$$

be one of these. Then A_2' will be the greatest common divisor of the values of A_2 in all integers of the realm; for if this be not the case, let

$$\omega_3 = \frac{A_1'' + A_2''\alpha}{d[\alpha]}$$

be any integer such that A_2'' is not divisible by A_2', and let A be the greatest common divisor of A_2' and A_2''. Then we can find two rational integers a and b such that

$$aA_2' + bA_2'' = A,$$

and hence

$$\gamma = a\omega_2 + b\omega_3 = \frac{aA_1' + bA_1'' + (aA_2' + bA_2'')\alpha}{d[\alpha]}$$

$$= \frac{aA_1' + bA_1'' + A\alpha}{d[\alpha]},$$

is an integer in which the coefficient of α is less in absolute value than A_2', which is contrary to the supposition that there is no value of A_2 less in absolute value than A_2'. Hence

$$A_2 = a_2 A_2',$$

where a_2 is a rational integer.

Denoting $\omega - a_2\omega_2$ by ω^*, we have

$$\omega^* = \omega - a_2\omega_2 = \frac{A_1 + A_2\alpha - a_2A_1' - a_2A_2'\alpha}{d[\alpha]} = \frac{A_1 - a_2A_1'}{d[\alpha]}.$$

Consider now those integers of the realm in which $A_2 = 0$, but $A_1 \neq 0$.[1]

There will be one or more among them in which A_1 is less in absolute value than in any of the remaining ones.

Let $$\omega_1 = A_1'''/d[\alpha]$$

be one of them. We see as above that A_1''' is the greatest common divisor of the values of A_1 in all the integers in which

$$A_2 = 0, \quad A_1' \neq 0,\text{[2]}$$

and hence $$\omega^* = \omega - a_2\omega_2 = a_1\omega_1,$$

or $$\omega = a_1\omega_1 + a_2\omega_2. \qquad 4)$$

There exist, therefore, in every quadratic realm two integers, ω_1, ω_2, such that every integer, ω, of the realm can be expressed in the form 4), when a_1, a_2 are rational integers.

[1] The remainder could be worded much more simply, if the fact that $(A_1 - a_2A_1')/d[\alpha]$ is a rational integer be made use of, but the above form seems better as it is in line with the general theorem.

[2] The integers, in which $A_2 = 0$ and $A_1 \neq 0$, are evidently the rational integers, 0 excluded. Also $A_1''' = d[\alpha]$, and $\omega_1 = 1$. We have $A_1 - a_2A_1' = a_1A_1'''$, where a_1 is a rational integer.

Every pair of integers, ω_1, ω_2, possessing this property is called a basis of $k(\alpha)$.

COR 1. *If ω_1, ω_2 be a basis of $k(\alpha)$, then ω_1', ω_2' is a basis of the conjugate realm $k(\alpha')$.*

THEOREM 2. *If ω_1, ω_2 be a basis of $k(\sqrt{m})$, the necessary and sufficient condition that*

$$\omega_1^* = a_1\omega_1 + a_2\omega_2,$$

$$\omega_2^* = b_1\omega_1 + b_2\omega_2,$$

where a_1, a_2, b_1, b_2 are rational integers, shall be also a basis of $k(\sqrt{m})$ is

$$\begin{vmatrix} a_1 & a_2 \\ b_1 & b_2 \end{vmatrix} = \pm 1.$$ [1]

For the proof of this theorem see the corresponding one in $k(i)$ (Chap. V, Th. 2).

§ 5. Discriminant of the Realm.

If ω_1, ω_2 be a basis of $k(\sqrt{m})$, the square of the determinant formed by these integers and their conjugates is called the discriminant of the realm and is denoted by d; that is,

$$d = \begin{vmatrix} \omega_1 & \omega_2 \\ \omega_1' & \omega_2' \end{vmatrix}^2.$$ [2]

We see that d is a rational integer, for it is an integral symmetric function of the roots, $\sqrt{m}$, $-\sqrt{m}$, of the equation

$$x^2 - m = 0,$$

and hence a rational integral function of the coefficients of this equation, which are rational integers.

That the value of d is independent of the basis chosen may be shown as in $k(i)$.

The discriminant of every integer of the realm is divisible by the discriminant of the realm; for, if

$$\alpha = a_1\omega_1 + a_2\omega_2,$$

[1] Hilbert: Bericht, p. 181.

[2] Hilbert: Bericht, p. 194.

be any integer of $k(\sqrt{m})$, and

$$1 = b_1\omega_1 + b_2\omega_2,$$

then

$$d[\alpha] = \begin{vmatrix} 1 & \alpha \\ 1 & \alpha' \end{vmatrix}^2 = \begin{vmatrix} b_1\omega_1 + b_2\omega_2 & a_1\omega_1 + a_2\omega_2 \\ b_1\omega_1' + b_2\omega_2' & a_1\omega_1' + a_2\omega_2' \end{vmatrix}^2$$

$$= \begin{vmatrix} b_1 & b_2 \\ a_1 & a_2 \end{vmatrix}^2 \begin{vmatrix} \omega_1 & \omega_2 \\ \omega_1' & \omega_2' \end{vmatrix}^2$$

$$= A^2 d.$$

If
$$d[\alpha] = d,$$
then

$$\begin{vmatrix} b_1 & b_2 \\ a_1 & a_2 \end{vmatrix} = \pm 1,$$

and 1, α, is a basis of the realm.

We see, moreover, that when $d[\alpha]$ is not divisible by the square of a rational intege·, we have

$$d[\alpha] = d,$$

and hence 1, α, is a basis.[1]

The converse of this theorem is, however, not true; that is $d[\alpha]$ may be divisible by the square of a rational integer and still 1, α, be a basis.

[1] The definition and deductions of this paragraph are immediately extendable to the general algebraic realm of the nth degree. The last fact mentioned is of especial importance as it may be shown by the method used in the text that, if θ be a root of

$$x^n + a_1 x^{n-1} + \cdots + a_n = 0,$$

where $a_1, \cdots, a_n$ are rational integers, and $d[\theta]$ be not divisible by the square of a rational integer, then $1, \theta, \ldots, \theta^{n-1}$ is a basis of $k(\theta)$. The great value of this fact is that although we may by the method of § 4 prove the existence of a basis in a realm of the nth degree, we have, however, general methods of determining a basis only in the cases of $n = 2$ or 3. The case $n = 2$ will be discussed in the next paragraph; that for $n = 3$ will be found in Woronoj: The Algebraic Integers which are Functions of a Root of an Equation of the Third Degree, this being a translation of the Russian title. A short account of this method will be found in: Tafel der Klassenanzahlen für Kubische Zahlkörper, by the author.

Thus in $k(i)$, $d[i]$, $=-4$, is divisible by 2^2, but 1, i is a basis of $k(i)$.

§ 6. Determination of a Basis of $k(\sqrt{m})$.

We have seen that every number of $k(\sqrt{m})$ can be written in the form

$$\alpha = r_1 + r_2\sqrt{m},$$

where r_1 and r_2 are rational numbers.

Let $$r_1 = a/c, \text{ and } r_2 = b/c,$$

where c is the least common multiple of the denominators of r_1 and r_2, r_1 and r_2 being in their lowest terms.

Then $$\alpha = \frac{a + b\sqrt{m}}{c}, \tag{1}$$

where a, b and c are rational integers having no common factor. The necessary and sufficient condition that α shall be an integer of $k(\sqrt{m})$ is that it satisfy an equation of the form

$$x^2 + px + q = 0, \tag{2}$$

where p and q are rational integers, the other root of 2) being the conjugate of α; that is,

$$\alpha' = \frac{a - b\sqrt{m}}{c}.$$

Hence we have as the necessary and sufficient conditions that α shall be an integer of $k(\sqrt{m})$

$$\alpha + \alpha' = \frac{2a}{c} = \text{a rational integer}, \tag{3}$$

$$\alpha\alpha' = \frac{a^2 - mb^2}{c^2} = \text{a rational integer}. \tag{4}$$

Remembering that a, b and c have no common factor, and m no square factor, we shall show that c can have a value different from 1 only when $m \equiv 1$, mod 4, and then can take only the value 1 or 2.

i. Let $c = pc_1$, p being a prime different from 2. Then from 3) it follows that
$$a \equiv 0, \text{ mod } p,$$
and from 4) that
$$a^2 - mb^2 \equiv 0, \text{ mod } p^2,$$
and hence
$$mb^2 \equiv 0, \text{ mod } p^2. \qquad 5)$$

But 5) is impossible since m can not contain the squared factor p^2, and if b were divisible by p then a, b and c would have a common factor p. Hence c can contain no prime factor different from 2.

ii. Let $c = 2^e$. We can prove exactly as in i that e can not be greater than 1.

Let $e = 1$; that is, $c = 2$. Then from 4) it follows that
$$a^2 - mb^2 \equiv 0, \text{ mod } 4, \qquad 6)$$

From 6) we see that a can not be even, for this would require
$$a^2 \equiv 0, \text{ mod } 4,$$
and hence
$$mb^2 \equiv 0, \text{ mod } 4,$$
from which it would follow that either m contains the squared factor 2^2, or a, b and c have the common factor 2.

Hence
$$a = 2a_1 + 1.$$
Likewise
$$b = 2b_1 + 1;$$
for b even gives
$$b^2 \equiv 0, \text{ mod } 4,$$
and hence from 4)
$$a^2 \equiv 0, \text{ mod } 4,$$
which we have seen to be impossible. We see therefore that, if $c = 2$, a and b must both be odd in order that α may be an integer; that is,
$$a = 2a_1 + 1 \text{ and } b = 2b_1 + 1.$$

We must now determine the form that m must have in order that $a^2 - mb^2$ may be divisible by 4; that is, that c may be 2. From $a = 2a_1 + 1$ and $b = 2b_1 + 1$ it follows that
$$a^2 \equiv 1, \text{ mod } 4,$$
and
$$b^2 \equiv 1, \text{ mod } 4,$$

and hence from $a^2 - mb^2 \equiv 0$, mod 4, it follows that

$$1 - m \equiv 0, \text{ mod } 4. \tag{7}$$

Therefore a and b odd and $m \equiv 1$, mod 4, are the necessary and sufficient conditions that $a^2 - mb^2$ may be divisible by 4. We can have therefore $c = 2$ when and only when these conditions are satisfied. Hence, when $m \equiv 1$, mod 4, every integer, α, of $k(\sqrt{m})$ has the form

$$\alpha = \frac{a + b\sqrt{m}}{2},$$

where a and b are both odd or both even, and every number of this form is an integer of $k(\sqrt{m})$.

When $m \equiv 2$ or 3, mod 4, the condition 7) not being satisfied, c can not equal 2, and every integer of $k(\sqrt{m})$ has the form

$$\alpha = a + b\sqrt{m},$$

where a and b are rational integers. Every number of this form is evidently an integer of $k(\sqrt{m})$. The cases $m \equiv 1$, 2 or 3, mod 4, include all possible forms of m, $m \equiv 0$, mod 4, being excluded, since m would then contain a squared factor. These three cases are illustrated respectively by the realms $k(\sqrt{-3})$, $k(\sqrt{2})$ and $k(\sqrt{-1})$.

We shall now show that, if ω represent $\sqrt{m}$, $\sqrt{m}$ or $(1 + \sqrt{m})/2$, according as $m \equiv 3$, 2 or 1, mod 4, then all integers of $k(\sqrt{m})$ can be expressed in the form

$$\alpha = u + v\omega,$$

where u and v are rational integers. This is at once evident when $m \equiv 3$ or 2, mod 4.

To show it when $m \equiv 1$, mod 4, we observe first that

$$\omega = \frac{1 + \sqrt{m}}{2}$$

is then an integer, for it is of the form $(a + b\sqrt{m})/2$, where a and b are both odd.

Then, if
$$\alpha = \frac{a + b\sqrt{m}}{2},$$

be any integer of $k(\sqrt{m})$ $(m \equiv 1, \bmod 4)$, we have, since

$$\sqrt{m} = 2\omega - 1,$$

$$\alpha = \frac{a + b(2\omega - 1)}{2} = \frac{a - b}{2} + b\omega;$$

that is
$$\alpha = u + v\omega,$$

where $u = (a - b)/2$, $v = b$ are rational integers; for a and b are rational integers, and $(a - b)/2$ is an integer, since a and b are both odd or both even.

Examples.

1. Give a basis of each of the following realms: $k(\sqrt{5})$, $k(\sqrt{6})$, $k(\sqrt{-10})$, $k(\sqrt{-13})$, $k(\sqrt{15})$ and $k(\sqrt{-21})$.

2. Tell whether each of the following pairs of numbers is a basis of the realm to which it belongs, $2 + 3\sqrt{6}$, $1 + \sqrt{6}$; $1 + \sqrt{6}$, $7 + 6\sqrt{6}$; $\frac{1}{2}(3 + 7\sqrt{5})$, $\frac{1}{2}(-1 - 3\sqrt{5})$.

CHAPTER XI.

THE IDEALS OF A QUADRATIC REALM.

§ 1. Definition. Numbers of an Ideal.

An ideal of a number realm is a system of integers, $\alpha_1, \alpha_2, \alpha_3, \cdots$, *of the realm infinite in number and such that every linear combination,* $\lambda_1\alpha_1 + \lambda_2\alpha_2 + \lambda_3\alpha_3 + \cdots$, *of them, where* $\lambda_1, \lambda_2, \lambda_3, \cdots$ *are any integers of the realm, is an integer of the system.*[1]

The integers of the infinite system which constitutes the ideal are called the *numbers of the ideal.*

§ 2. Basis of an Ideal. Canonical Basis. Principal and Non-Principal Ideals.

THEOREM 1. *There exist in every ideal* $\mathfrak{a}$ *of a quadratic realm two numbers,* ι_1, ι_2, *such that every number of the ideal can be expressed in the form*

$$\iota = l_1\iota_1 + l_2\iota_2,$$

where l_1 *and* l_2 *are rational integers.*

Suppose all numbers of $\mathfrak{a}$ to be written in the form

$$\iota = a_1\omega_1 + a_2\omega_2,$$

where ω_1, ω_2 is a basis of the realm, and consider those for which

$$a_2 \neq 0.$$

Among them must be some in which a_2 is smaller in absolute value than in any of the remaining ones.

Let $\iota_2, = b\omega_1 + c\omega_2$, be one of these; then c will be the greatest common divisor of the values of a_2 in all the numbers of $\mathfrak{a}$ (see Chap. X, Th. 1).

We have $$a_2 = l_2 c,$$

[1] The definition given in $k(\sqrt{-5})$ will be seen later to coincide with this. See also Hilbert: Bericht, p. 182.

where l_2 is a rational integer, and hence

$$\iota - l_2\iota_2 = (a_1 - l_2 b)\omega_1.$$

Consider now those numbers of $\mathfrak{a}$ in which $a_2 = 0$, but $a_1 \neq 0$. Just as before we can show that there exists among them certainly one, $\iota_1 = a\omega_1$, such that a is the greatest common divisor of the values of a_1 in all the numbers of the ideal for which

$$a_2 = 0, \quad a_1 \neq 0.$$

Hence $$a_1 - l_2 b = l_1 a,$$

where l_1 is a rational integer, and

we have $$\iota - l_2\iota_2 = l_1\iota_1;$$

that is $$\iota = l_1\iota_1 + l_2\iota_2,$$

hence ι_1, ι_2 are the desired numbers.

Any pair of numbers of $\mathfrak{a}$ such as ι_1, ι_2, having the property required by the theorem, is called a basis of the ideal $\mathfrak{a}$. The necessary and sufficient condition that any other pair of numbers of $\mathfrak{a}$

$$\iota_1^* = a_1\iota_1 + a_2\iota_2,$$
$$\iota_2^* = b_1\iota_1 + b_2\iota_2,$$

shall be a basis of $\mathfrak{a}$ is that

$$\begin{vmatrix} a_1 & a_2 \\ b_1 & b_2 \end{vmatrix} = \pm 1.$$ [1]

This condition can be satisfied by an infinite number of sets of rational integers, a_1, a_2, b_1, b_2, and hence each ideal has an infinite number of bases. We shall call the particular basis $a\omega_1$, $b\omega_1 + c\omega_2$ defined as above a *canonical basis*. Taking $1, \omega$ as a basis of the realm, we have as a basis of $\mathfrak{a}$ a, $b + c\omega$, an especially convenient form, in which a is evidently the rational integer smallest in absolute value occurring in $\mathfrak{a}$.

COR. 1. *If* $a_1\omega_1 + a_2\omega_2$, $b_1\omega_1 + b_2\omega_2$ *and* $c_1\omega_1 + c_2\omega_2$, $d_1\omega_1 + d_2\omega_2$ *be bases of the same ideal, then*

$$\left\| \begin{matrix} a_1 & a_2 \\ b_1 & b_2 \end{matrix} \right\| = \left\| \begin{matrix} c_1 & c_2 \\ d_1 & d_2 \end{matrix} \right\|$$

[1] See Chap. V, Th. 2.

COR. 2. *If* $a_1\omega_1 + a_2\omega_2$, $b_1\omega_1 + b_2\omega_2$ *be a basis of an ideal*, $\mathfrak{a}$, *and* $c_1\omega_1 + c_2\omega_2$, $d_1\omega_1 + d_2\omega_2$ *be any two numbers of* $\mathfrak{a}$, *and*

$$\left\|\begin{matrix} c_1 & c_2 \\ d_1 & d_2 \end{matrix}\right\| = \left\|\begin{matrix} a_1 & a_2 \\ b_1 & b_2 \end{matrix}\right\|$$

then $c_1\omega_1 + c_2\omega_2$, $d_1\omega_1 + d_2\omega_2$ *is also a basis of* $\mathfrak{a}$.

Th. 1 shows at once that all ideals of a quadratic realm would be obtained, if we paired the integers of the realm in all possible ways and took each pair α, β, as defining an ideal (α, β); for among these pairs would be certainly a basis of every ideal of the realm. In this pairing, however, each ideal would be repeated an infinite number of times. The definition given of an ideal (§ 1) holds for realms of any degree, as does a theorem similar to Th. 1: namely, in every ideal of a realm of the nth degree there exist n integers, $\iota_1, \iota_2, \cdots, \iota_n$, such that every number of the ideal can be expressed in the form $l_1\iota_1 + l_2\iota_2 + \cdots + l_n\iota_n$, where $l_1, l_2, \cdots, l_n$ are rational integers. See Hilbert: Bericht, Satz 6.

If $\alpha_1, \alpha_2, \cdots, \alpha_r$ be r numbers of $\mathfrak{a}$ such that every number of $\mathfrak{a}$ can be represented in the form

$$\lambda_1\alpha_1 + \lambda_2\alpha_2 + \cdots + \lambda_r\alpha_r, \qquad 1)$$

where $\lambda_1, \lambda_2, \cdots, \lambda_r$ are integers of the realm, we can define $\mathfrak{a}$ by the symbol $(\alpha_1, \alpha_2, \cdots, \alpha_r)$; that is, we write

$$\mathfrak{a} = (\alpha_1, \alpha_2, \cdots, \alpha_r),$$

understanding thereby the infinite system of integers of the form 1), the λ's taking all possible values. We shall call $\alpha_1, \alpha_2, \cdots, \alpha_r$ the numbers *defining* the ideal $\mathfrak{a}$.

The numbers of $\mathfrak{a}$ are all those of the form 1). We may introduce into the symbol any integer which is a linear combination of those already there without changing the ideal defined by it. Thus, if

$$\alpha_s = \lambda_1\alpha_1 + \lambda_2\alpha_2 + \cdots + \lambda_r\alpha_r,$$

we have $\mathfrak{a} = (\alpha_1, \alpha_2, \cdots, \alpha_r) = (\alpha_1, \alpha_2, \cdots, \alpha_r, \alpha_s)$;

for the system of integers

$$\lambda_1\alpha_1 + \lambda_2\alpha_2 + \cdots + \lambda_r\alpha_r$$

is coextensive with the system

$$\lambda_1\alpha_1 + \lambda_2\alpha_2 + \cdots + \lambda_r\alpha_r + \lambda_s\alpha_s,$$

the λ's taking all possible values.

Likewise, if any integer in the symbol be a combination of the remaining ones therein, it may be omitted from the symbol.

Thus, if $$\alpha_1 = \lambda_2\alpha_2 + \lambda_3\alpha_3 + \cdots + \lambda_r\alpha_r,$$

we can write

$$\mathfrak{a} = (\alpha_1, \alpha_2, \cdots, \alpha_r) = (\alpha_2, \cdots, \alpha_r).$$

We speak for the sake of brevity of $(\alpha_1, \alpha_2, \cdots, \alpha_r)$ as the ideal $\mathfrak{a}$, and instead of saying that we introduce a number, α_s, into the symbol of $\mathfrak{a}$ or omit it from the symbol, say that we introduce α_s into the ideal $\mathfrak{a}$ or omit it from the ideal, although α_s is and remains a number of $\mathfrak{a}$. It will be convenient also, if ι_1, ι_2 be a basis of $\mathfrak{a}$, to speak of (ι_1, ι_2) as a basis representation of $\mathfrak{a}$. The determination of the question whether an integer α belongs to a given ideal $\mathfrak{a}$ will be greatly simplified by some properties of ideals which will be developed later. It can, however, be easily decided now, if we have a basis of the given ideal, for if $\alpha = a_1 + a_2\omega$[1], be any integer of the realm and $b_1 + b_2\omega$, $c_1 + c_2\omega$ be a basis of $\mathfrak{a}$, the necessary and sufficient condition that α shall be a number of $\mathfrak{a}$ is evidently that two rational integers l_1, l_2 exist, which satisfy the equation

$$l_1(b_1 + b_2\omega) + l_2(c_1 + c_2\omega) = a_1 + a_2\omega. \qquad 2)$$

Equating the coefficients of the powers of ω in the two members of 2), we obtain the equations

$$\begin{aligned} b_1 l_1 + c_1 l_2 &= a_1, \\ b_2 l_1 + c_2 l_2 &= a_2, \end{aligned} \qquad 3)$$

which determine l_1, l_2.

If the values of l_1, l_2 found from 3) be integral, α is a number of $\mathfrak{a}$, otherwise not. If we have not found a basis of $\mathfrak{a}$, we can generally determine whether α is a number of $\mathfrak{a}$ by means of the fundamental condition that α is or is not a number of $\mathfrak{a}$ according as α is or is not a linear combination of the numbers defining $\mathfrak{a}$ with coefficients which are integers of the realm. For an example of this method see p. 259.

[1] Unless the contrary be stated, 1, ω is taken as a basis of the realm.

An ideal which consists of all and only those numbers of the form $\lambda\alpha$, where α is a particular integer and λ any integer of the realm, is called a *principal* ideal and is denoted by (α). An ideal not having this property is called a *non-principal* ideal. For examples of principal and non-principal ideals see Chap. VIII, § 10. It should be observed that although all numbers of a principal ideal, (α), are multiples of the single integer α, when as multiplier we take any integer of the realm, nevertheless, just as in the case of a non-principal ideal, a basis of (α) consists of two integers, $\alpha\omega_1$, $\alpha\omega_2$, where ω_1, ω_2 is a basis of the realm, for every number of (α) has the form

$$(a_1\omega_1 + a_2\omega_2)\alpha = a_1\alpha\omega_1 + a_2\alpha\omega_2,$$

where a_1, a_2 are rational integers.

For example: a basis of $(1+\sqrt{-5})$ is $1+\sqrt{-5}$, $(1+\sqrt{-5})\sqrt{-5}$; that is, $1+\sqrt{-5}$, $-5+\sqrt{-5}$.

If the difference of two integers α and β be a number of the ideal $\mathfrak{a}$, this fact is expressed symbolically by writing

$$\alpha \equiv \beta, \text{ mod } \mathfrak{a}, \qquad 4)$$

and we say that α is congruent to β with respect to the modulus $\mathfrak{a}$.

The fact that $\alpha - \beta$ is not a number of $\mathfrak{a}$ is expressed symbolically by writing

$$\alpha \not\equiv \beta, \text{ mod } \mathfrak{a}, \qquad 5)$$

and α is said to be incongruent to β with respect to the modulus $\mathfrak{a}$. Every number, α, of the ideal $\mathfrak{a}$ is congruent to 0 with respect to the modulus $\mathfrak{a}$, or in symbols

$$\alpha \equiv 0, \text{ mod } \mathfrak{a}. \qquad 6)$$

No meaning other than the symbolic expression of the facts mentioned must be attached for the present to 4), 5) and 6). Thus we write

$$3-2\sqrt{-5} \equiv 1+2\sqrt{-5}, \text{ mod } (7,\ 3+\sqrt{-5}),$$

since $\quad 3-2\sqrt{-5}-(1+2\sqrt{-5}) = 2-4\sqrt{-5}$

is a number of $(7,\ 3+\sqrt{-5})$, and we write

$$1+5\sqrt{-5} \not\equiv 2-3\sqrt{-5}, \text{ mod } (1+2\sqrt{-5}),$$

since $\quad 1+5\sqrt{-5}-(2-3\sqrt{-5})=-1+8\sqrt{-5}$
is not a number of $(1+2\sqrt{-5})$.

Although the actual determination of a basis of any given ideal of a quadratic realm must be postponed until the properties of ideals have been more fully investigated, we can, however, now determine whether any two given numbers of an ideal $\mathfrak{a}$ are a basis of $\mathfrak{a}$.

The necessary and sufficient condition for α_1, α_2 to be a basis of the ideal $\mathfrak{a}, =(\alpha_1, \alpha_2, \cdots, \alpha_r)$, is evidently, since every number of $\mathfrak{a}$ has the form $\lambda_1\alpha_1+\lambda_2\alpha_2+\cdots+\lambda_r\alpha_r$, that for every possible choice of the λ's we shall be able to find two rational integers, l_1, l_2, such that

$$\lambda_1\alpha_1+\lambda_2\alpha_2+\cdots+\lambda_r\alpha_r=l_1\alpha_1+l_2\alpha_2. \qquad 7)$$

Let ω_1, ω_2 be a basis of the realm, and

$$\left.\begin{array}{l}\alpha_i=a_i\omega_1+b_i\omega_2\\ \lambda_i=c_i\omega_1+d_i\omega_2\end{array}\right\} i=1, 2, \cdots, r.$$

We have on equating the coefficients of the number defining the realm in the two members of 7) two equations between rational integers, whose satisfaction by suitably chosen rational integral values of l_1, l_2 for all possible choices of the c's and d's is the necessary and sufficient condition that α_1, α_2 shall be a basis of $\mathfrak{a}$.

Ex. 1. That $3, 1+\sqrt{-5}$ is a basis of $(3, 1+\sqrt{-5})$ may be easily shown by the above method. Every number of $(3, 1+\sqrt{-5})$ has the form

$$(c_1+d_1\sqrt{-5})3+(c_2+d_2\sqrt{-5})(1+\sqrt{-5}), \qquad 8)$$

where c_1, d_1, c_2, d_2 are rational integers.

If $3, 1+\sqrt{-5}$ be a basis of $(3, 1+\sqrt{-5})$, then every number of the form 8) must be expressible in the form $l_1 3+l_2(1+\sqrt{-5})$, where l_1, l_2, are rational integers, and hence for every possible choice of c_1, d_1, c_2, d_2, we must be able to find rational integral values of l_1, l_2, which satisfy the equation

$$(c_1+d_1\sqrt{-5})3+(c_2+d_2\sqrt{-5})(1+\sqrt{-5})=l_1 3+l_2(1+\sqrt{-5}),$$

or

$$3c_1+c_2-5d_2+(3d_1+c_2+d_2)\sqrt{-5}=3l_1+l_2+l_2\sqrt{-5}. \qquad 9)$$

Equating the coefficients of the different powers of $\sqrt{-5}$, we have

$$3c_1 + c_2 - 5d_2 = 3l_1 + l_2 \qquad 10)$$

$$3d_1 + c_2 + d_2 = l_2, \qquad 11)$$

as the two equations whose satisfaction by rational integral values of l_1, l_2 for every possible choice of c_1, d_1, c_2, d_2 is the necessary and sufficient condition that $3, 1+\sqrt{-5}$ shall be a basis of $(3, 1+\sqrt{-5})$. Subtracting 11) from 10), we obtain

$$\begin{aligned} 3c_1 - 3d_1 - 6d_2 &= 3l_1, \\ 3d_1 + c_2 + d_2 &= l_2, \end{aligned} \qquad 12)$$

a system equivalent to 10), 11), and which evidently fulfils the required conditions.

Hence $3, 1+\sqrt{-5}$ is a basis of $(3, 1+\sqrt{-5})$. In this particular case, we might have arrived at the result by simply observing that $1+\sqrt{-5}$ must be the required basis number $b+c\sqrt{-5}$, since c has in $1+\sqrt{-5}$ the smallest possible value; that is, 1.

Moreover 3 must be the basis number a, for if $(3, 1+\sqrt{-5})$ contain a rational integer smaller in absolute value than 3, it would contain 1 and we should have

$$(3, 1+\sqrt{-5}) = (1),$$

that is easily shown to be impossible, the equation

$$(c_1 + c_2\sqrt{-5})3 + (d_1 + d_2\sqrt{-5})(1+\sqrt{-5}) = 1$$

not being satisfied by rational integral values of c_1, c_2, d_1, d_2. Therefore $3, 1+\sqrt{-5}$ is a canonical basis of $(3, 1+\sqrt{-5})$.

Having shown that $3, 1+\sqrt{-5}$ is a basis of $(3, 1+\sqrt{-5})$, we know that the necessary and sufficient condition for any two numbers, ι_1, ι_2, to be a basis of $(3, 1+\sqrt{-5})$ is that

$$\begin{aligned} \iota_1 &= a_1 3 + a_2(1+\sqrt{-5}), \\ \iota_2 &= b_1 3 + b_2(1+\sqrt{-5}), \end{aligned} \qquad 13)$$

where a_1, a_2, b_1, b_2 are rational integers satisfying the condition

$$\begin{vmatrix} a_1 & a_2 \\ b_1 & b_2 \end{vmatrix} = \pm 1.$$

This condition is evidently satisfied by an infinite number of sets of values of a_1, a_2, b_1, b_2, from which we obtain by 13) an infinite number of different bases of $(3, 1+\sqrt{-5})$. Thus since

$$\begin{vmatrix} 3 & 1 \\ 11 & 4 \end{vmatrix} = 1,$$

we see that

$$\begin{aligned} 3 \cdot 3 + 1 \cdot (1+\sqrt{-5}) &= 10 + \sqrt{-5} \\ 11 \cdot 3 + 4(1+\sqrt{-5}) &= 37 + 4\sqrt{-5} \end{aligned}$$

is a basis of $(3, 1+\sqrt{-5})$.

On the other hand

$$5-\sqrt{-5}=2\cdot 3-1(1+\sqrt{-5}),$$
$$11-4\sqrt{-5}=5\cdot 3-4(1+\sqrt{-5}),$$

is not a basis of $(3, 1+\sqrt{-5})$, since

$$\begin{vmatrix} 2 & -1 \\ 5 & -4 \end{vmatrix} = -3 \neq \pm 1.$$

By means of the condition given in Th. 1, Cor. 1, it may be shown even more easily that $5-\sqrt{-5}$, $11-4\sqrt{-5}$ is not a basis of $(3, 1+\sqrt{-5})$; for 1, $\sqrt{-5}$ being a basis of the realm, we have

$$3=3\cdot 1+0\cdot\sqrt{-5},\qquad 5-\sqrt{-5}=5\cdot 1+-1\cdot\sqrt{-5},$$
$$1+\sqrt{-5}=1\cdot 1+1\cdot\sqrt{-5},\quad 11-4\sqrt{-5}=11\cdot 1+-4\cdot\sqrt{-5},$$

$$\left\|\begin{matrix} 3 & 0 \\ 1 & 1 \end{matrix}\right\| \neq \left\|\begin{matrix} 5 & -1 \\ 11 & -4 \end{matrix}\right\|.$$

Ex. 2. We can show in like manner that $\dfrac{-3+\sqrt{-3}}{2}$, $\dfrac{3+5\sqrt{-3}}{2}$ is not a basis of the ideal $(-2+\omega, -1+5\omega)$ of the realm $k(\sqrt{-3})$, 1, $\dfrac{1+\sqrt{-3}}{2}$ being taken as a basis of the realm.

Proceeding as in Ex. 1 we see that the necessary and sufficient condition for $-2+\omega$, $-1+5\omega$ to be a basis of the given ideal is that the equation

$$\begin{aligned}(c_1+d_1\omega)(-2+\omega)+(c_2+d_2\omega)(-1+5\omega)\\ =l_1(-2+\omega)+l_2(-1+5\omega)\end{aligned} \tag{14}$$

shall be satisfied by rational integral values of l_1, l_2 for every possible choice of c_1, d_1, c_2, d_2.

Performing the multiplications indicated in 14), putting $\omega^2=-1+\omega$, and equating coefficients of like powers of ω in the two members, we have the equations

$$-2c_1-c_2-d_1-5d_2=-2l_1-l_2$$
$$c_1+5c_2-d_1+4d_2=l_1+5l_2$$

which give

$$-9c_1-6d_1-21d_2=-9l_1$$
$$9c_2-3d_1+3d_2=9l_2\ .$$

These equations evidently do not give integral values for l_1, l_2 for every possible choice of c_1, d_1, c_2, d_2; for example, for $c_1=d_1=c_2=0, d_2=1$. Hence $-2+\omega$, $-1+5\omega$ is not a basis of $(-2+\omega, -1+5\omega)$. We have chosen an ideal of the realm $k(\sqrt{-3})$, in which the unique factorization law holds in the ordinary sense, to emphasize the fact that with the introduction of ideals all quadratic realms are to be treated alike, and that all theorems to be deduced hereafter will be equally valid whether the unique factorization law holds in the ordinary sense or not.

Ex. 3. Show both by the above method and by the nature of a canonical basis that $7,\ 3+\sqrt{-5}$ is a basis of the ideal $(7,\ 3+\sqrt{-5})$; also that $3+\sqrt{-5},\ 5+4\sqrt{-5}$ is a basis of the same ideal. In $k(\sqrt{-23})$ show that $3,\ \frac{1+\sqrt{-23}}{2}$ is a basis of the ideal $\left(3,\ \frac{1+\sqrt{-23}}{2}\right)$; also that $4+\sqrt{-23},\ \frac{9+3\sqrt{-23}}{2}$ is a basis of the same ideal.

In $k(\sqrt{6})$ show that $10+3\sqrt{6},\ 6+2\sqrt{6}$ is a basis of the ideal $(10+3\sqrt{6},\ 6+2\sqrt{6})$.

Ex. 4. Show that $7+7\sqrt{-5},\ -5+3\sqrt{-5}$ is not a basis of the ideal $(7+7\sqrt{-5},\ -5+3\sqrt{-5})$.

Ex. 5. Show that $\left(3,\ \frac{1+\sqrt{13}}{2}\right)$ is a principal ideal of $k(\sqrt{13})$. Show that the two ideals $\left(2,\ \frac{1+\sqrt{-15}}{2}\right)$ and $\left(3,\ \frac{3+\sqrt{-15}}{2}\right)$ are both non-principal ideals of $k(\sqrt{-15})$, but that their product is a principal ideal. Show that $(2,\ 1+\sqrt{-13})$ is a non-principal ideal of $k(\sqrt{-13})$.

§ 3. Conjugate of an Ideal.

If $\mathfrak{a}$ be any ideal, the ideal, whose numbers are the conjugates of the numbers of $\mathfrak{a}$, is called the conjugate of $\mathfrak{a}$ and is denoted by $\mathfrak{a}'$.[1] It is easily seen that, if $\mathfrak{a}=(\alpha_1,\ \alpha_2,\ \cdots,\ \alpha_n)$ be any ideal, then $\mathfrak{a}'=(\alpha_1',\ \alpha_2',\ \cdots,\ \alpha_n')$ is the conjugate of $\mathfrak{a}$; for, if

$$\lambda_1\alpha_1+\lambda_2\alpha_2+\cdots+\lambda_n\alpha_n$$

be any number of $\mathfrak{a}$, its conjugate

$$\lambda_1'\alpha_1'+\lambda_2'\alpha_2'+\cdots+\lambda_n'\alpha_n'$$

is a number of $\mathfrak{a}'$, and vice versa.

Moreover, if $a_1\omega_1+a_2\omega_2,\ b_1\omega_1+b_2\omega_2$ be a basis of $\mathfrak{a}$, where $\omega_1,\ \omega_2$ is a basis of the realm, then $a_1\omega_1'+a_2\omega_2',\ b_1\omega_1'+b_2\omega_2'$ is a basis of $\mathfrak{a}'$. The truth of the last statement is readily seen when we remember that, if $a_1\omega_1+a_2\omega_2,\ b_1\omega_1+b_2\omega_2$ be a basis of $\mathfrak{a}$, then every number, α, of $\mathfrak{a}$ can be expressed in the form

$$\alpha=a(a_1\omega_1+a_2\omega_2)+b(b_1\omega_1+b_2\omega_2),$$

where a and b are rational integers.

The corresponding number, α', of $\mathfrak{a}'$, being expressible in the form

$$\alpha'=a(a_1\omega_1'+a_2\omega_2')+b(b_1\omega_1'+b_2\omega_2'),$$

it is evident that $a_1\omega_1'+a_2\omega_2',\ b_1\omega_1'+b_2\omega_2'$ is a basis of $\mathfrak{a}'$.

[1] Hilbert: Bericht, p. 191.

For example, the conjugate of $(2+3\sqrt{-5}, 7+2\sqrt{-5}, 17)$ is $(2-3\sqrt{-5}, 7-2\sqrt{-5}, 17)$; also since $3, 1+\sqrt{-5}$ is a basis of $(3, 1+\sqrt{-5})$, $3, 1-\sqrt{-5}$ is a basis of $(3, 1-\sqrt{-5})$.

§ 4. Equality of Ideals.

Two ideals, $\mathfrak{a}, = (\alpha_1, \alpha_2, \cdots, \alpha_r)$, and $\mathfrak{b}, = (\beta_1, \beta_2, \cdots, \beta_s)$, are said to be equal, and we write $\mathfrak{a} = \mathfrak{b}$, when every number of $\mathfrak{a}$ is a number of $\mathfrak{b}$ and every number of $\mathfrak{b}$ is a number of $\mathfrak{a}$.

The necessary and sufficient condition for the equality of $\mathfrak{a}$ and $\mathfrak{b}$ is that every number, α_i, defining $\mathfrak{a}$ shall be expressible in the form

$$\alpha_i = \lambda_1\beta_1 + \lambda_2\beta_2 + \cdots + \lambda_s\beta_s,$$

and that every number, β_j, defining $\mathfrak{b}$ shall be expressible in the form

$$\beta_j = \mu_1\alpha_1 + \mu_2\alpha_2 + \cdots + \mu_r\alpha_r.$$

The practical test of equality is to see whether the symbol defining either one of the ideals can be reduced to that defining the other by the introduction and omission of numbers under the laws given in the preceding paragraph.[1]

Ex. 1. Show that $(6+2\sqrt{-5}, 56+7\sqrt{-5}) = (15+5\sqrt{-5}, 7)$.
Ex. 2. Show that

$$\left(\frac{1+\sqrt{13}}{2}, 5+8\sqrt{13}, 5+2\sqrt{13}\right) = (5+14\sqrt{13}, 6\sqrt{13}).$$

Ex. 3. Show that $(7, 1+\sqrt{-13}) \neq (7, 1-\sqrt{-13})$.

§ 5. Multiplication of Ideals.

By the product $\mathfrak{ab}$ of the two ideals

$$\mathfrak{a} = (\alpha_1, \alpha_2, \cdots, \alpha_r) \text{ and } \mathfrak{b} = (\beta_1, \beta_2, \cdots, \beta_s)$$

is understood the ideal, whose numbers consist of all possible products of a number of $\mathfrak{a}$ by a number of $\mathfrak{b}$, together with all linear combinations of such products with coefficients which are any integers of the realm.[2]

We have therefore

$$\mathfrak{ab} = (\alpha_1\beta_1, \cdots, \alpha_1\beta_s, \cdots, \alpha_r\beta_1, \cdots, \alpha_r\beta_s),$$

[1] See Chap. VIII, § 9.
[2] Hilbert: Bericht, p. 183; also see Chap. VIII, § 11.

where the numbers defining $\mathfrak{ab}$ are all possible products of the numbers defining $\mathfrak{a}$ by those defining $\mathfrak{b}$.

If $$\mathfrak{a} = (\alpha) \text{ and } \mathfrak{b} = (\beta_1, \beta_2, \cdots, \beta_s),$$

then $$\mathfrak{ab} = (\alpha\beta_1, \alpha\beta_2, \cdots, \alpha\beta_s).$$

If $$\mathfrak{a} = (\alpha) \text{ and } \mathfrak{b} = (\beta),$$

then $$\mathfrak{ab} = (\alpha\beta),$$

and we see that the product of two principal ideals is a principal ideal.

It is evident from the definition that

$$\mathfrak{ab} = \mathfrak{ba},$$

and that $$\mathfrak{ab} \cdot \mathfrak{c} = \mathfrak{a} \cdot \mathfrak{bc};$$

that is, that the commutative and associative laws of multiplication hold for ideals.

Ex. Show that

$$(2, \sqrt{-26})(3, 1-\sqrt{-26})(5, 2+\sqrt{-26}) = (2+\sqrt{-26}).$$

§ 6. Divisibility of Ideals. The Unit Ideal. Prime Ideals.

An ideal, $\mathfrak{a}$, is said to be divisible by an ideal, $\mathfrak{b}$, when there exists an ideal, $\mathfrak{c}$, such that

$$\mathfrak{a} = \mathfrak{bc}.$$

We say that $\mathfrak{b}$ and $\mathfrak{c}$ are *divisors* of $\mathfrak{a}$, and that $\mathfrak{a}$ is a *multiple* of $\mathfrak{b}$ and $\mathfrak{c}$. We have as a direct consequence of the above definition:

If each of a series of ideals $\mathfrak{a}_1, \mathfrak{a}_2, \mathfrak{a}_3, \cdots$, be a multiple of the next following one, then each is a multiple of all that follow.

If two or more ideals, $\mathfrak{a}, \mathfrak{b}, \mathfrak{c}, \cdots$, be each divisible by an ideal $\mathfrak{j}$, $\mathfrak{j}$ is said to be a *common divisor* or *common factor* of $\mathfrak{a}, \mathfrak{b}, \mathfrak{c}, \cdots$.

THEOREM 2. *If the ideal $\mathfrak{a}$ be divisible by the ideal $\mathfrak{b}$, then all numbers of $\mathfrak{a}$ belong to $\mathfrak{b}$.*

For suppose that

$$\mathfrak{a} = \mathfrak{bc},$$

where

$$\mathfrak{a} = (\alpha_1, \alpha_2, \cdots, \alpha_r),\ \mathfrak{b} = (\beta_1, \beta_2, \cdots, \beta_s),\ \mathfrak{c} = (\gamma_1, \gamma_2, \cdots, \gamma_t);$$

then $$\mathfrak{a} = (\beta_1\gamma_1, \cdots, \beta_1\gamma_t, \cdots, \beta_s\gamma_1, \cdots, \beta_s\gamma_t).$$

The numbers, $\beta_1\gamma_1, \cdots, \beta_s\gamma_t$, defining $\mathfrak{a}$ are seen to be numbers of $\mathfrak{b}$. Hence all numbers of $\mathfrak{a}$ are numbers of $\mathfrak{b}$.

Therefore

$$\mathfrak{b} = (\beta_1, \beta_2, \cdots, \beta_s, \alpha_1, \alpha_2, \cdots, \alpha_r),$$

and $$\mathfrak{c} = (\gamma_1, \gamma_2, \cdots, \gamma_t, \alpha_1, \alpha_2, \cdots, \alpha_r).$$

COR. *If two ideals be such that each is a divisor of the other, they are identical.*

The converse of Theorem 2 is also true; that is, *if all numbers of* $\mathfrak{a}$ *be numbers of* $\mathfrak{b}$, $\mathfrak{a}$ *is divisible by* $\mathfrak{b}$, but its proof must be deferred until some necessary theorems have been demonstrated.

Every ideal is divisible by the ideal (1), which consists of all integers of the realm. Therefore (1) is called the *unit ideal.*

The only ideal having this property is evidently (1), for every divisor of (1) contains all integers of the realm and is (1). We observe that $(\eta) = (1)$, where η is any unit of the realm.

Since $(1)\mathfrak{a} = \mathfrak{a}$, there is, in the case of ideals, no distinction to be made corresponding to that made between associated integers. *An ideal, not the unit ideal and divisible only by itself and the unit ideal, is called a prime ideal.*

In $k(\sqrt{-5})$, $(2, 1+\sqrt{-5})$, $(3, 1+\sqrt{-5})$, $(3, 1-\sqrt{-5})$ were shown to be prime ideals (see p. 264).

Two ideals are said to be prime to each other when they have no common divisor except (1). *Two integers* α *and* β *of the realm are said to be prime to each other when the principal ideals* (α) *and* (β) *are prime to each other.*

For the sake of brevity we shall often say that an integer α is divisible by an ideal $\mathfrak{a}$, instead of saying that the principal ideal (α) is divisible by $\mathfrak{a}$. The latter meaning is, of course, always to be understood. Similar expressions, such as "α prime to $\mathfrak{a}$," "the greatest common divisor of α and $\mathfrak{a}$," etc., are to be taken in the same sense.

By means of the definition of divisibility and the fact that every ideal has a basis, we can prove the following important theorem:

THEOREM 3. *An ideal* $\mathfrak{j}$ *is divisible by only a finite number of different ideals.*[1]

Let
$$\mathfrak{a} = (a\omega_1 + b\omega_2,\ c\omega_1 + d\omega_2)$$
be a divisor of $\mathfrak{j}$, where $a\omega_1 + b\omega_2$, $c\omega_1 + d\omega_2$ is a basis of $\mathfrak{a}$, ω_1, ω_2 being a basis of the realm.

Let β be any number of $\mathfrak{j}$. Then, since
$$n[\beta] = \beta\beta' \equiv 0, \text{ mod } \mathfrak{j},$$
and $\mathfrak{a}$ is a divisor of $\mathfrak{j}$, we see that by Th. 2
$$n[\beta] \equiv 0, \text{ mod } \mathfrak{a};$$
that is, the rational integer $n[\beta]$ belongs to every divisor of $\mathfrak{j}$. Denote now $n[\beta]$ by n and let a_1, b_1, c_1, d_1 be the smallest positive remainders of a, b, c, d with respect to n. Then
$$\begin{aligned}\mathfrak{a} &= (a\omega_1 + b\omega_2,\ c\omega_1 + d\omega_2,\ n)\\ &= (a_1\omega_1 + b_1\omega_2,\ c_1\omega_1 + d_1\omega_2,\ n) \qquad 1)\end{aligned}$$

Suppose every divisor of $\mathfrak{j}$ to be expressed in the form 1). Since a_1, b_1, c_1, d_1 can each take only the finite number of values $0, 1, 2, \cdots, |n| - 1$, it is evident that the number of different divisors of $\mathfrak{j}$ is finite.

§ 7. Unique Factorization Theorem for Ideals.

We shall now proceed to prove the theorem whose truth is the *raison d'être* of the ideal; that is, *that every ideal can be represented in one and only one way as a product of prime ideals.*

This theorem will enable us to develop for the ideals of the general quadratic realm a series of theorems similar to those already given for the integers of certain realms in which the ordinary unique factorization theorem held.

The proof of the unique factorization theorem for the ideals

[1] Hilbert: Bericht, Hülfsatz 1.

of the general quadratic realm will be very like that for the integers of R, $k(\sqrt{-1})$, $k(\sqrt{-3})$ and $k(\sqrt{2})$. It depends directly upon the theorem that, *if the product of two ideals be divisible by a prime ideal, at least one of the factors must be divisible by this prime ideal.* The latter theorem is a consequence of a series of three theorems which have no analogues in those relating to integers. It depends, in the first place, directly upon the theorem referred to on p. 304, that, *if all the numbers of an ideal belong to another ideal, the first ideal is divisible by the second.* This depends, in turn, upon the theorem, that, *if the products* $\mathfrak{ab}$, $\mathfrak{ac}$ *of two ideals,* $\mathfrak{b}$ *and* $\mathfrak{c}$, *by a third ideal* $\mathfrak{a}$ *be equal, then* $\mathfrak{b}=\mathfrak{c}$, and this upon the theorem, that *for every ideal there exists another ideal such that the product of the two is a principal ideal.*

This last theorem is the starting point of the proof of the unique factorization theorem and needs for its demonstration a theorem which we shall proceed to give.

THEOREM 4. *If the coefficients,* α_1, α_2, β_1, β_2 *of the two rational integral functions of* x,

$$\phi(x)=\alpha_1 x+\alpha_2 \text{ and } \psi(x)=\beta_1 x+\beta_2,$$

be integers of $k(\sqrt{m})$ *and* ω, *an integer of* $k(\sqrt{m})$, *divide each of the coefficients,* $\gamma_1, \gamma_2, \gamma_3$, *of the product of the two functions,*

$$F(x)=\phi(x)\cdot\psi(x)=\alpha_1\beta_1x^2+(\alpha_1\beta_2+\alpha_2\beta_1)x+\alpha_2\beta_2$$
$$=\gamma_1x^2+\gamma_2x+\gamma_3,$$

then each of the numbers $\alpha_1\beta_1$, $\alpha_1\beta_2$, $\alpha_2\beta_1$, $\alpha_2\beta_2$ *is divisible by* ω.[1]

Suppose α_1 and $\beta_1 \neq 0$. Then $\gamma_1 \neq 0$. We have

$$F(x)=\alpha_1\beta_1\left(x+\frac{\alpha_2\beta_1}{\alpha_1\beta_1}\right)\left(x+\frac{\alpha_1\beta_2}{\alpha_1\beta_1}\right)=\gamma_1\left(x+\frac{\alpha_2\beta_1}{\gamma_1}\right)\left(x+\frac{\alpha_1\beta_2}{\gamma_1}\right).$$

Hence $-\alpha_2\beta_1/\gamma_1$ and $-\alpha_1\beta_2/\gamma_1$ are the roots of

$$x^2+\frac{\gamma_2}{\gamma_1}x+\frac{\gamma_3}{\gamma_1}=0.$$

[1] Hurwitz: Nachr. der K. Ges. der Wiss. zu Göttingen, 1895; also Hilbert: Bericht, Hülfsatz 2.

Let ξ represent either $\alpha_2\beta_1$ or $\alpha_1\beta_2$; we have

$$\left(-\frac{\xi}{\gamma_1}\right)^2+\frac{\gamma_2}{\gamma_1}\left(-\frac{\xi}{\gamma_1}\right)+\frac{\gamma_3}{\gamma_1}=0;$$

and, multiplying this equation by γ_1^2,

$$\xi^2-\gamma_2\xi+\gamma_1\gamma_3=0.$$

Since γ_2 and $\gamma_1\gamma_3$ are divisible by ω and ω^2 respectively, the coefficients of the equation

$$\left(\frac{\xi}{\omega}\right)^2-\frac{\gamma_2}{\omega}\left(\frac{\xi}{\omega}\right)+\frac{\gamma_1\gamma_3}{\omega^2}=0,$$

that ξ/ω satisfies, are integers. Hence ξ/ω is an integer (Chap. IX, Th. 9, Cor. 1); that is, $\alpha_1\beta_2$ and $\alpha_2\beta_1$ are divisible by ω.

THEOREM 5. *For every ideal* $\mathfrak{a}$ *of a quadratic realm there exists an ideal* $\mathfrak{b}$ *of the realm such that the product* $\mathfrak{ab}$ *is a principal ideal.*[1]

Let $\mathfrak{a}=(\alpha_1, \alpha_2)$ where α_1, α_2 is a basis[2] of $\mathfrak{a}$. We shall show that the conjugate of $\mathfrak{a}$, that is, the ideal $\mathfrak{b}, =(\alpha_1', \alpha_2')$, where α_1', α_2' are the conjugates of α_1, α_2, has the desired property.[3]

Let $\qquad \phi(x)=\alpha_1x+\alpha_2$ and $\psi(x)=\alpha_1'x+\alpha_2'$.

Form the product

$$\begin{aligned}\phi(x)\psi(x)&=\alpha_1\alpha_1'x^2+(\alpha_1\alpha_2'+\alpha_1'\alpha_2)x+\alpha_2\alpha_2'\\&=\gamma_1x^2+\gamma_2x+\gamma_3.\end{aligned}$$

Let θ be a number defining the realm and let the irreducible rational equation of which θ is a root be

$$x^2+a_1x+a_2=0. \qquad 1)$$

Since $\gamma_1, \gamma_2, \gamma_3$ are symmetric functions of the roots of 1), they

[1] Hilbert: Bericht, Satz 8.

[2] The simplification effected by the use of the basis representation of an ideal is that, in a quadratic realm, the basis consists of two numbers and hence Th. 4 need be proved only for functions of the first degree.

[3] In the realm of the nth degree the ideal that will have the desired property is the product of the conjugates of $\mathfrak{a}$. This ideal is, however, not the only ideal having the desired property (Chap. XIV, § 1).

are rational functions of its coefficients 1, a_1, a_2. Hence $\gamma_1, \gamma_2, \gamma_3$ are rational numbers. But $\gamma_1, \gamma_2, \gamma_3$ are also integers, since $\alpha_1, \alpha_1', \alpha_2, \alpha_2'$ are integers (Chap. IX, Th. 8, Cor. 2). Hence $\gamma_1, \gamma_2, \gamma_3$ are rational integers.

Let a be the greatest common divisor of $\gamma_1, \gamma_2, \gamma_3$. Then

$$\mathfrak{ab} = (\alpha_1\alpha_1', \alpha_1\alpha_2', \alpha_1'\alpha_2, \alpha_2\alpha_2')$$

is equal to the principal ideal (a); for by Chap. II, Th. B, we can find three rational integers, t_1, t_2, t_3, such that

$$\begin{aligned} a &= t_1\gamma_1 + t_2\gamma_2 + t_3\gamma_3 \\ &= t_1\alpha_1\alpha_1' + t_2(\alpha_1\alpha_2' + \alpha_1'\alpha_2) + t_3\alpha_2\alpha_2' \end{aligned}$$

Hence a is a number of $\mathfrak{ab}$ and we have

$$\mathfrak{ab} = (\alpha_1\alpha_1', \alpha_1\alpha_2', \alpha_1'\alpha_2, \alpha_2\alpha_2', a).$$

But by Th. 4 each of the numbers $\alpha_1\alpha_1', \alpha_1\alpha_2', \alpha_1'\alpha_2, \alpha_2\alpha_2'$ is a multiple of a. Hence we can omit them from the symbol and have

$$\mathfrak{ab} = (a).$$

Therefore $\mathfrak{b}$ is the required ideal.

It will be observed that we have proved that the product of an ideal of a quadratic realm by its conjugate is a *rational* principal ideal. This will be of use later.

THEOREM 6. *If* $\mathfrak{a}$, $\mathfrak{b}$ *and* $\mathfrak{c}$ *be ideals and* $\mathfrak{ac} = \mathfrak{bc}$, *then* $\mathfrak{a} = \mathfrak{b}$.[1]

Let

$$\mathfrak{a} = (\alpha_1, \alpha_2, \cdots, \alpha_r),\ \mathfrak{b} = (\beta_1, \beta_2, \cdots, \beta_s),\ \mathfrak{c} = (\gamma_1, \gamma_2, \cdots, \gamma_t),$$

and let $\mathfrak{m}, = (\mu_1, \mu_2, \cdots, \mu_n)$, be an ideal such that

$$\mathfrak{cm} = (\gamma_1\mu_1, \cdots, \gamma_t\mu_n) = (\alpha),$$

a principal ideal.

Then $$\mathfrak{acm} = \mathfrak{bcm},$$

or $$\mathfrak{a}(\alpha) = \mathfrak{b}(\alpha),$$

or $$(\alpha_1\alpha, \alpha_2\alpha, \cdots, \alpha_r\alpha) = (\beta_1\alpha, \beta_2\alpha, \cdots, \beta_s\alpha).$$

Since these two ideals are equal, every number of the one must

[1] Hilbert: Bericht, Satz 9.

be a linear combination of the numbers defining the other, with coefficients which are integers of the realm.

Hence, if $\alpha_i\alpha$ be any number of the first and $\beta_j\alpha$ any number of the second, we have

$$\alpha_i\alpha = \xi_1\beta_1\alpha + \xi_2\beta_2\alpha + \cdots + \xi_s\beta_s\alpha,$$

and $$\beta_j\alpha = \eta_1\alpha_1\alpha + \eta_2\alpha_2\alpha + \cdots + \eta_r\alpha_r\alpha,$$

where the ξ's and η's are integers of the realm. Hence

$$\alpha_i = \xi_1\beta_1 + \xi_2\beta_2 + \cdots + \xi_s\beta_s,$$

$$\beta_j = \eta_1\alpha_1 + \eta_2\alpha_2 + \cdots + \eta_r\alpha_r.$$

Hence every number of $\mathfrak{a}$ is a number of $\mathfrak{b}$, and every number of $\mathfrak{b}$ is a number of $\mathfrak{a}$, and consequently

$$\mathfrak{a} = \mathfrak{b}.$$

THEOREM 7. *If all numbers of an ideal $\mathfrak{c}$ belong to an ideal $\mathfrak{a}$, $\mathfrak{c}$ is divisible by $\mathfrak{a}$.*[1]

Let $\mathfrak{c} = (\gamma_1, \cdots, \gamma_t)$ and $\mathfrak{a} = (\alpha_1, \cdots, \alpha_r, \gamma_1, \cdots, \gamma_t)$; and let $\mathfrak{m}, = (\mu_1, \cdots, \mu_n)$, be an ideal such that

$$\mathfrak{am} = (\alpha_1\mu_1, \cdots, \alpha_r\mu_n, \gamma_1\mu_1, \cdots, \gamma_t\mu_n) = (\alpha),$$

a principal ideal.

Then all numbers of $\mathfrak{am}$, and hence $\gamma_1\mu_1, \cdots, \gamma_1\mu_n, \cdots, \gamma_t\mu_1, \cdots, \gamma_t\mu_n$, must be divisible by α. Hence all numbers of

$$\mathfrak{mc} = (\gamma_1\mu_1, \cdots, \gamma_1\mu_n, \cdots, \gamma_t\mu_n)$$

are divisible by α; that is,

$$\mathfrak{mc} = (\nu_1\alpha, \cdots, \nu_{nt}\alpha) = (\alpha)(\nu_1, \cdots, \nu_{nt}) = (\alpha)\mathfrak{b}. \qquad 2)$$

Multiplying both members of 2) by $\mathfrak{a}$, we have

$$\mathfrak{amc} = (\alpha)\mathfrak{ab},$$

or $$\mathfrak{c} = \mathfrak{ab}.$$

Hence $\mathfrak{c}$ is divisible by $\mathfrak{a}$.

[1] Hilbert: Bericht, Satz 10.

This theorem justifies our use of the notation

$$\alpha \equiv 0, \text{ mod } \mathfrak{a},$$

to denote that (α) is a multiple of $\mathfrak{a}$. For, if α be a number of $\mathfrak{a}$, then from the above theorem it follows that (α) is divisible by $\mathfrak{a}$.

From Th. 2 we saw that a necessary condition for an ideal $\mathfrak{a}$ to be divisible by an ideal $\mathfrak{b}$ is that all numbers of $\mathfrak{a}$ shall belong to $\mathfrak{b}$; from Th. 7 we see that this condition is also sufficient. Hence every common divisor, $\mathfrak{d}$, of two ideals

$$\mathfrak{a} = (\alpha_1, \cdots, \alpha_r), \quad \mathfrak{b} = (\beta_1, \cdots, \beta_s)$$

must contain all numbers of both $\mathfrak{a}$ and $\mathfrak{b}$; that is,

$$\mathfrak{d} = (\alpha_1, \cdots, \alpha_r, \beta_1, \cdots, \beta_s, \delta_1, \cdots, \delta_t),$$

where $\delta_1, \cdots, \delta_t$ are any integers of the realm, and every ideal of this form is a common divisor of $\mathfrak{a}$ and $\mathfrak{b}$.

Among the common divisors of $\mathfrak{a}$ and $\mathfrak{b}$ is one, $\mathfrak{g}$, to which belong no numbers other than the numbers of $\mathfrak{a}$ and $\mathfrak{b}$, together with the linear combinations of these numbers; that is,

$$\mathfrak{g} = (\alpha_1, \alpha_2, \cdots, \alpha_r, \beta_1, \beta_2, \cdots, \beta_s).$$

This ideal $\mathfrak{g}$ is divisible by every common divisor, $\mathfrak{d}$, of $\mathfrak{a}$ and $\mathfrak{b}$, for $\mathfrak{d}$ must contain all numbers of $\mathfrak{a}$ and $\mathfrak{b}$, and hence all the numbers of $\mathfrak{g}$, and therefore is a divisor of $\mathfrak{g}$.

As in the case of rational integers, $\mathfrak{g}$ is called the *greatest common divisor* of $\mathfrak{a}$ and $\mathfrak{b}$.

That $\mathfrak{g}$ is the only ideal having this property is evident; for did a second, $\mathfrak{h}$, exist, then $\mathfrak{g}$ must be divisible by $\mathfrak{h}$ and $\mathfrak{h}$ by $\mathfrak{g}$, and hence $\mathfrak{g}$ and $\mathfrak{h}$ be identical (Th. 2, Cor.).

Likewise the necessary and sufficient condition that an ideal, $\mathfrak{m}$, shall be a common multiple of $\mathfrak{a}$ and $\mathfrak{b}$ is that all numbers of $\mathfrak{m}$ shall be common to both $\mathfrak{a}$ and $\mathfrak{b}$.

Among the common multiples of $\mathfrak{a}$ and $\mathfrak{b}$ is one to which belong all numbers common to both $\mathfrak{a}$ and $\mathfrak{b}$, together with the linear combinations of these numbers.

This ideal, $\mathfrak{l}$, is evidently a divisor of every common multiple of $\mathfrak{a}$ and $\mathfrak{b}$. That $\mathfrak{l}$, moreover, is the only ideal having this property may be shown as in the case of $\mathfrak{g}$.

As in the case of rational integers, $\mathfrak{l}$ is called the *least common multiple* of $\mathfrak{a}$ and $\mathfrak{b}$.

We shall denote the greatest common divisor of $\mathfrak{a}$ and $\mathfrak{b}$ by the symbol $\mathfrak{a}+\mathfrak{b}$, and the least common multiple of $\mathfrak{a}$ and $\mathfrak{b}$ by the symbol $\mathfrak{a}-\mathfrak{b}$. No idea of addition or subtraction is to be conveyed by these symbols.

From Theorems 2 and 7 we have the important result that an ideal $\mathfrak{a}, = (\alpha_1, \alpha_2, \cdots, \alpha_r)$, is the greatest common divisor of the numbers defining it considered as principal ideals; that is, $\mathfrak{a}$ is the greatest common divisor of $(\alpha_1), (\alpha_2), \cdots, (\alpha_r)$.

The fact that we can at once write the greatest common divisor of any number of ideals by placing in a single symbol all the numbers defining the ideals is of use in numerical work with ideals. Thus, if we can show that the greatest common divisor of two ideals so written is (1), we know that the ideals are prime to each other.

Ex. The greatest common divisor of $(3+\sqrt{-5})$ and $(8+\sqrt{-5})$ is $(3+\sqrt{-5}, 8+\sqrt{-5})$, and we have

$$(3+\sqrt{-5}, 8+\sqrt{-5}) = (3+\sqrt{-5}, 8+\sqrt{-5}, 5, 14)$$
$$= (3+\sqrt{-5}, 8+\sqrt{-5}), 5, 14, 1) = (1)$$

Hence $(3+\sqrt{-5})$ and $(8+\sqrt{-5})$ are prime to each other.

The ideas of the greatest common divisor and least common multiple of two ideals may be at once extended to any number of ideals.

Thus, if $\mathfrak{a}_1, \mathfrak{a}_2, \cdots, \mathfrak{a}_m$ be any number of ideals of a realm, there is among the common divisors of $\mathfrak{a}_1, \mathfrak{a}_2, \cdots, \mathfrak{a}_m$ one, $\mathfrak{g}$, to which belong no numbers other than the numbers of $\mathfrak{a}_1, \mathfrak{a}_2, \cdots, \mathfrak{a}_m$, together with the linear combinations of these numbers; that is,

if $\quad \mathfrak{a}_1 = (\alpha_1, \cdots, \alpha_r),\ \mathfrak{a}_2 = (\beta_1, \cdots, \beta_s), \cdots,\ \mathfrak{a}_m = (\mu_1, \cdots, \mu_t),$

then $\quad \mathfrak{g} = (\alpha_1, \cdots, \alpha_r, \beta_1, \cdots, \beta_s, \cdots, \mu_1, \cdots, \mu_t).$

That $\mathfrak{g}$ is divisible by every common divisor of $\mathfrak{a}_1, \mathfrak{a}_2, \cdots, \mathfrak{a}_m$ and is the only ideal having this property is seen as in the case of two ideals. We call $\mathfrak{g}$ the greatest common divisor of $\mathfrak{a}_1, \mathfrak{a}_2, \cdots, \mathfrak{a}_m$.

Likewise the ideal, $\mathfrak{l}$, to which belong all numbers common to $\mathfrak{a}_1, \mathfrak{a}_2, \cdots, \mathfrak{a}_m$, together with their linear combinations and no others, is evidently the only common multiple of $\mathfrak{a}_1, \mathfrak{a}_2, \cdots, \mathfrak{a}_m$ that is a divisor of every common multiple of $\mathfrak{a}_1, \mathfrak{a}_2, \cdots, \mathfrak{a}_m$. It is therefore called the least common multiple of $\mathfrak{a}_1, \mathfrak{a}_2, \cdots, \mathfrak{a}_m$.

We write symbolically

$$\mathfrak{g} = \mathfrak{a}_1 + \mathfrak{a}_2 + \cdots + \mathfrak{a}_m,$$

and

$$\mathfrak{l} = \mathfrak{a}_1 - \mathfrak{a}_2 - \cdots - \mathfrak{a}_m.$$

We have as an immediate consequence of Th. 7 and the definition of the least common multiple of two or more ideals the following:

COR. *If an ideal* $\mathfrak{a}$ *be divisible by each of the ideals* $\mathfrak{b}_1, \mathfrak{b}_2, \cdots, \mathfrak{b}_r$, *then* $\mathfrak{a}$ *is divisible by the least common multiple of* $\mathfrak{b}_1, \mathfrak{b}_2, \cdots, \mathfrak{b}_r$.

We shall see later that the greatest common divisor, as defined above for ideals, possesses the remaining two properties which distinguished the greatest common divisor of two or more integers in those realms in which the unique factorization law held in the ordinary sense (see p. 318).

We have now a full justification of our introduction in $k(\sqrt{-5})$ of the ideals $(2, 1+\sqrt{-5})$, $(3, 1+\sqrt{-5})$, $(2, 1-\sqrt{-5})$ and $(3, 1-\sqrt{-5})$ as the greatest common divisors respectively of (2) and $(1+\sqrt{-5})$, (3) and $(1+\sqrt{-5})$, (2) and $(1-\sqrt{-5})$, and (3) and $(1-\sqrt{-5})$.

Th. 7 having been proved, the remaining theorems necessary for the proof of the unique factorization theorem and the proof of that theorem itself for ideals are strictly analogous to the corresponding theorems in the realms in which the unique factorization law held in the ordinary sense.

It may seem singular that the divisors of an ideal, $\mathfrak{a}$, are in a way larger systems of numbers than the ideal, $\mathfrak{a}$, itself; that is, they contain not only the numbers of $\mathfrak{a}$ but in addition any other numbers of the realm that we choose to introduce.

When, however, we remember that by Th. 7 an ideal divides every one of its numbers considered as a principal ideal, it is evident that, in general, the more numbers we introduce into the symbol of an ideal, that are not linear combinations of those already there, so much the more do we narrow the ideal by thus placing more restrictions upon it.

For example; the ideal $(14, 3+\sqrt{-14})$ is the greatest common divisor of (14) and $(3+\sqrt{-14})$, and the ideal $(14, 3+\sqrt{-14}, 2)$, that contains all numbers of $(14, 3+\sqrt{-14})$ and other numbers besides, divides not only (14) and $(3+\sqrt{-14})$, and hence is a divisor of $(14, 3+\sqrt{-14})$, but must also divide (2).

It is analogous to the case of rational integers when we observe that 120 is divisible by every common divisor of 120 and 18, and that every common divisor of 120 and 18 is divisible by the common divisors of 120, 18 and 4.

Examples.

1. Find the greatest common divisor of $(8+\sqrt{-14})$ and $(4-\sqrt{-14})$.

2. Find the greatest common divisor of $(26, 10+2\sqrt{-14}, 13\sqrt{-14}, -14+5\sqrt{-14})$ and $(10, 2+2\sqrt{-14}, 5\sqrt{-14}, -14+\sqrt{-14})$.

3. Show that the two ideals $(5, -4+\sqrt{-14})$ and $(13, 5-12\sqrt{-14})$ are prime to each other.

4. Making use of form of canonical basis, show that $(23, 8+\sqrt{-5})$ is a prime ideal.

5. Show that $(p, b+\omega)$ is a prime ideal, p being a rational prime, b any rational integer, and $1, \omega$ a basis of the realm.

6. If p and q be two different rational primes, show that in no realm can (p) and (q) have a common ideal factor different from (1).

7. Show that $(1+\sqrt{-5})$ is the least common multiple of $(3, 1+\sqrt{-5})$ and $(2, 1+\sqrt{-5})$.

8. Find the least common multiple of $(6, 4+\sqrt{-14})$ and $(10, 6+\sqrt{-14})$.

9. Show that, if $\mathfrak{a}$ be divisible by $\mathfrak{a}_1$ and $\mathfrak{b}$ by $\mathfrak{b}_1$, then $\mathfrak{ab}$ is divisible by $\mathfrak{a}_1\mathfrak{b}_1$.

10. Show that, if $\mathfrak{ab}$ be divisible by $\mathfrak{ac}$, then $\mathfrak{b}$ is divisible by $\mathfrak{c}$ and in particular that, if $\mathfrak{a}$ be divisible by $\mathfrak{ab}$, then $\mathfrak{b}=(1)$.

11. Show that, if $\mathfrak{a}$, $\mathfrak{b}$ and $\mathfrak{c}$ be any ideals, then

$$[\mathfrak{a}+\mathfrak{b}]\mathfrak{c}=\mathfrak{ac}+\mathfrak{bc}.$$

12. Show that

$$[\mathfrak{a}+\mathfrak{b}+\mathfrak{c}]\,[\mathfrak{bc}+\mathfrak{ca}+\mathfrak{ab}]=[\mathfrak{b}+\mathfrak{c}][\mathfrak{c}+\mathfrak{a}][\mathfrak{a}+\mathfrak{b}].$$

13. Show that, if $\mathfrak{a}$ be divisible by $\mathfrak{a}_1$, and $\mathfrak{b}$ by $\mathfrak{b}_1$, then $\mathfrak{a}+\mathfrak{b}$ is divisible by $\mathfrak{a}_1+\mathfrak{b}_1$, and also that $\mathfrak{a}-\mathfrak{b}$ is divisible by $\mathfrak{a}_1-\mathfrak{b}_1$.

14. Show that, if $\mathfrak{a}$ and $\mathfrak{b}$ be any two ideals, then $\mathfrak{a}+\mathfrak{b}$ is the system of all numbers of the form $\alpha+\beta$, where α is a number of $\mathfrak{a}$ and β a number of $\mathfrak{b}$.

15. Show that, if $\mathfrak{a}$, $\mathfrak{b}$ and $\mathfrak{c}$ be any three ideals,

$$\mathfrak{a}-[\mathfrak{b}-\mathfrak{c}]=[\mathfrak{a}-\mathfrak{b}]-\mathfrak{c}.$$

16. Show that

$$[\mathfrak{a}+\mathfrak{b}][\mathfrak{a}-\mathfrak{b}]=\mathfrak{ab}.$$

17. Show that, if $\mathfrak{a}$ and $\mathfrak{b}$ be prime to each other, then

$$\mathfrak{a}-\mathfrak{b}=\mathfrak{ab}.$$

THEOREM 8. *If $\mathfrak{a}$ and $\mathfrak{b}$ be any two ideals prime to each other, there exist a number α of $\mathfrak{a}$ and a number β of $\mathfrak{b}$ such that*

$$\alpha+\beta=1.$$[1]

Let $\mathfrak{a}=(\alpha_1,\alpha_2,\cdots,\alpha_r)$ and $\mathfrak{b}=(\beta_1,\beta_2,\cdots,\beta_s)$.

Since $\mathfrak{a}$ and $\mathfrak{b}$ are prime to each other their greatest common divisor is (1); that is,

$$\mathfrak{a}+\mathfrak{b}=(\alpha_1,\alpha_2,\cdots,\alpha_r,\beta_1,\beta_2,\cdots,\beta_s)=(1).$$

But, since 1 is a number of $\mathfrak{a}+\mathfrak{b}$, it must be a linear combination of

$$\alpha_1,\alpha_2,\cdots,\alpha_r,\beta_1,\beta_2,\cdots,\beta_s;$$

that is,

$$\xi_1\alpha_1+\xi_2\alpha_2+\cdots+\xi_r\alpha_r+\eta_1\beta_1+\eta_2\beta_2+\cdots+\eta_s\beta_s=1,$$

where the ξ's and η's are integers of the realm.

But $\xi_1\alpha_1+\xi_2\alpha_2+\cdots+\xi_r\alpha_r=\alpha$, is a number of $\mathfrak{a}$,

and $\eta_1\beta_1+\eta_2\beta_2+\cdots+\eta_s\beta_s=\beta$, is a number of $\mathfrak{b}$,

and we have

$$\alpha+\beta=1.$$

[1] This is the analogue of Th. B. See Hilbert: Bericht, Satz 11.

COR. *If* $\mathfrak{a}_1, \mathfrak{a}_2, \cdots, \mathfrak{a}_m$ *be ideals whose greatest common divisor is* (*1*), *then there exist in* $\mathfrak{a}_1, \mathfrak{a}_2, \cdots, \mathfrak{a}_m$ *numbers* $\alpha_1, \alpha_2, \cdots, \alpha_m$, *respectively, such that*

$$\alpha_1 + \alpha_2 + \cdots + \alpha_m = 1.$$

THEOREM 9. *If the product of two ideals,* $\mathfrak{a}$ *and* $\mathfrak{b}$, *be divisible by a prime ideal* $\mathfrak{p}$, *at least one of the ideals is divisible by* $\mathfrak{p}$.[1]

Assume that $\mathfrak{a}$ is not divisible by $\mathfrak{p}$. Then $\mathfrak{a}$ and $\mathfrak{p}$ are prime to each other and there exists by Th. 8 a number, α, of $\mathfrak{a}$ and a number, π, of $\mathfrak{p}$ such that

$$\alpha + \pi = 1.$$

Let now β be any number of $\mathfrak{b}$, and multiply the last equation by β; then

$$\alpha\beta + \pi\beta = \beta.$$

But $\alpha\beta$ is a number of $\mathfrak{ab}$, and hence by Th. 2 of $\mathfrak{p}$, since $\mathfrak{ab}$ is divisible by $\mathfrak{p}$. Moreover, $\pi\beta$ is a number of $\mathfrak{p}$. Hence β is a number of $\mathfrak{p}$; that is, all numbers of $\mathfrak{b}$ are numbers of $\mathfrak{p}$, and $\mathfrak{b}$ is therefore by Th. 7 divisible by $\mathfrak{p}$.

COR. 1. *If the product of any number of ideals be divisible by a prime ideal,* $\mathfrak{p}$, *at least one of the ideals is divisible by* $\mathfrak{p}$.

COR. 2. *If neither of two ideals be divisible by a prime ideal,* $\mathfrak{p}$, *their product is not divisible by* $\mathfrak{p}$.

COR. 3. *If the product of two ideals,* $\mathfrak{a}$ *and* $\mathfrak{b}$, *be divisible by an ideal,* $\mathfrak{j}$, *and neither* $\mathfrak{a}$ *nor* $\mathfrak{b}$ *be divisible by* $\mathfrak{j}$, *then* $\mathfrak{j}$ *is a composite ideal.*

If all the ideals of a realm be principal ideals, the unique factorization theorem in the usual form holds for the integers of the realm; for, if α and β be any two integers prime to each other in the usual sense, then the ideals (α) and (β) are prime to each other, for all factors of (α) and (β) are principal ideals. Hence the ideal (α, β) must be the unit ideal (1); for (α, β) divides both (α) and (β) and they have no common divisor other than (1).

Since $$(\alpha, \beta) = (1),$$

[1] This is the analogue of Th. C. See Hilbert: Bericht, Satz 11.

there must exist two integers, ξ and η, of the realm such that

$$\alpha\xi+\beta\eta=1.$$

Th. B would therefore hold for the integers of the realm, and we have seen that Th. C, and hence the unique factorization theorem, follow immediately. The converse of this, that, whenever the unique factorization theorem in its usual form holds for the integers of a realm, the ideals of the realm are all principal ideals, is true, but a further development of the theory of ideals is necessary for its proof. If, however, Th. B. hold, then not only does the unique factorization theorem hold, but, if $\mathfrak{a}, = (\alpha_1, \alpha_2, \cdots, \alpha_r)$, be any ideal of the realm and δ be the g. c. d. of $\alpha_1, \alpha_2, \cdots, \alpha_r$, there exist integers $\xi_1, \xi_2, \cdots, \xi_r$, as in $k(i)$ such that

$$\alpha_1\xi_1+\alpha_2\xi_2+\cdots+\alpha_r\xi_r=\delta.$$

Hence we have

$$\mathfrak{a}=(\alpha_1, \alpha_2, \cdots, \alpha_r)=(\alpha_1, \alpha_2, \cdots, \alpha_r, \delta)=(\delta),$$

a principal ideal.

THEOREM 10. *Every ideal can be represented in one and only one way as the product of prime ideals.*[1]

Let $\mathfrak{j}$ be any ideal. If $\mathfrak{j}$ be a prime ideal the theorem is evident. If $\mathfrak{j}$ be not a prime ideal, it has some divisor, $\mathfrak{a}$, different from $\mathfrak{j}$ and from (1). Then

$$\mathfrak{j}=\mathfrak{a}\mathfrak{b}.$$

If $\mathfrak{a}$ be not a prime ideal we have

$$\mathfrak{a}=\mathfrak{a}_1\mathfrak{a}_2,$$

where $\mathfrak{a}_1$ and $\mathfrak{a}_2$ are both different from $\mathfrak{a}$ and (1). Then

$$\mathfrak{j}=\mathfrak{a}_1\mathfrak{a}_2\mathfrak{b}.$$

If any of the ideals $\mathfrak{a}_1$, $\mathfrak{a}_2$, $\mathfrak{b}$ be not prime, we factor them, and, proceeding in this manner, we reach finally a point where the factorization can be carried no further, for an ideal, $\mathfrak{j}$, is divisible by only a finite number of ideals (Th. 3).

The ideal $\mathfrak{j}$ has now been resolved into its prime ideal factors.

[1] Hilbert: Bericht, Satz 7.

Let $$\mathfrak{j}=\mathfrak{p}_1\mathfrak{p}_2\cdots\mathfrak{p}_r,$$

where $\mathfrak{p}_1, \mathfrak{p}_2, \cdots, \mathfrak{p}_r$ are prime ideals, be the representation so obtained. We shall show that this representation is unique. Suppose that $\mathfrak{j}$ could be represented in another way as a product of prime ideals, say

$$\mathfrak{j}=\mathfrak{q}_1\mathfrak{q}_2\cdots\mathfrak{q}_s.$$

Then $$\mathfrak{p}_1\mathfrak{p}_2\cdots\mathfrak{p}_r=\mathfrak{q}_1\mathfrak{q}_2\cdots\mathfrak{q}_s. \qquad 3)$$

Since $\mathfrak{p}_1$ is a divisor of the product $\mathfrak{q}_1\mathfrak{q}_2\cdots\mathfrak{q}_s$, it is a divisor of one of its factors (Th. 9, Cor. 1), say $\mathfrak{q}_1$, from which follows

$$\mathfrak{p}_1=\mathfrak{q}_1.$$

Then it follows from 3) that

$$\mathfrak{p}_2\cdots\mathfrak{p}_r=\mathfrak{q}_2\cdots\mathfrak{q}_s.$$

Proceeding in this manner, we see that for each factor in the product $\mathfrak{p}_1\mathfrak{p}_2\cdots\mathfrak{p}_r$ there is an equal one in the product $\mathfrak{q}_1\mathfrak{q}_2\cdots\mathfrak{q}_s$, and, reversing the process, that for each factor in the product $\mathfrak{q}_1\mathfrak{q}_2\cdots\mathfrak{q}_s$, there is an equal one in the product $\mathfrak{p}_1\mathfrak{p}_2\cdots\mathfrak{p}_r$, and that, if a factor be repeated in one product, it is repeated exactly as often in the other.

The two representations are therefore identical, and the theorem is proved.

COR. *If the product of two ideals, $\mathfrak{a}$, $\mathfrak{b}$, be divisible by an ideal, $\mathfrak{m}$, and $\mathfrak{a}$ be prime to $\mathfrak{m}$, then $\mathfrak{b}$ is divisible by $\mathfrak{m}$.*

If we denote by $\mathfrak{p}_1, \mathfrak{p}_2, \cdots, \mathfrak{p}_r$ the different prime ideals that are factors of $\mathfrak{j}$, and by $e_1, e_2, \cdots, e_r$ the number of times that they are repeated respectively, we have

$$\mathfrak{j}=\mathfrak{p}_1^{e_1}\mathfrak{p}_2^{e_2}\cdots\mathfrak{p}_r^{e_r}.$$

It is convenient sometimes to allow one or more of the exponents to take the value 0, $e_i=0$ indicating that $\mathfrak{j}$ does not contain $\mathfrak{p}_i$ as a factor. It is evident that an ideal $\mathfrak{j}$ is then and only then divisible by an ideal $\mathfrak{d}$ if every prime ideal which divides $\mathfrak{d}$ occurs to at least as high a power as a factor in $\mathfrak{j}$ as it does in $\mathfrak{d}$.

Every divisor of $\mathfrak{j}$ has therefore the form

$$\mathfrak{d}=\mathfrak{p}_1^{m_1}\mathfrak{p}_2^{m_2}\cdots\mathfrak{p}_r^{m_r}, \qquad 4)$$

where $$m_i \leqq e_i; \quad i = 1, 2, \cdots; r,$$

and every ideal of the form 4) is a divisor of $\mathfrak{j}$. If we let m_i run through the $e_i + 1$ values, $0, 1, \cdots, e_i$, and do this for each of the exponents $m_1, m_2, \cdots, m_r$, we obtain

$$(e_1 + 1)(e_2 + 1) \cdots (e_r + 1)$$

different sets of values for these exponents, and each of these sets gives a different divisor of $\mathfrak{j}$. The number of divisors of $\mathfrak{j}$ is therefore $(e_1 + 1)(e_2 + 1) \cdots (e_r + 1)$.

If $$\mathfrak{j} = \mathfrak{p}_1^{m_1} \mathfrak{p}_2^{m_2} \cdots \mathfrak{p}_r^{m_r},$$

and $$\mathfrak{h} = \mathfrak{p}_1^{n_1} \mathfrak{p}_2^{n_2} \cdots \mathfrak{p}_r^{n_r},$$

where $\mathfrak{p}_1, \mathfrak{p}_2, \cdots, \mathfrak{p}_r$ are different prime ideals, be any two ideals, the ideal

$$\mathfrak{g} = \mathfrak{p}_1^{g_1} \mathfrak{p}_2^{g_2} \cdots \mathfrak{p}_r^{g_r},$$

where g_i is the lesser of the two exponents m_i and $n_i (i = 1, 2, \cdots, r)$, is the greatest common divisor of $\mathfrak{j}$ and $\mathfrak{h}$.

The ideal

$$\mathfrak{l} = \mathfrak{p}_1^{l_1} \mathfrak{p}_2^{l_2} \cdots \mathfrak{p}_r^{l_r},$$

where l_i is the greater of the two exponents m_i and $n_i (i = 1, 2, \cdots, r)$ is the least common multiple of $\mathfrak{j}$ and $\mathfrak{h}$.

We see from this representation of the greatest common divisor, $\mathfrak{g}$, of $\mathfrak{j}$ and $\mathfrak{h}$ that, of all common divisors of $\mathfrak{j}$ and $\mathfrak{h}$, $\mathfrak{g}$ has the greatest norm, and that the quotients, $\mathfrak{j}/\mathfrak{g}$ and $\mathfrak{h}/\mathfrak{g}$, are prime to each other (see p. 18).

THEOREM 11 *If $\mathfrak{a}$ and $\mathfrak{m}$ be any two ideals, there exists a number, α, of $\mathfrak{a}$ such that the quotient $(\alpha)/\mathfrak{a}$ is prime to $\mathfrak{m}$.*

For example, if $\mathfrak{a}, = (2, 1 + \sqrt{-5})$, and $\mathfrak{m}, = (3, 1 + \sqrt{-5})$, be the given ideals, then $\alpha = 2$ satisfies the requirements of the theorem, for

$$\frac{(2)}{(2, 1 + \sqrt{-5})} = (2, 1 + \sqrt{-5}),$$

that is easily seen to be prime to $(3, 1+\sqrt{-5})$.

If $\mathfrak{a}, = (2, 1+\sqrt{-5})$, and $\mathfrak{m}, = (1+\sqrt{-5})$, be the given ideals, then $\alpha, = 2+1+\sqrt{-5}, = 3+\sqrt{-5}$, satisfies the requirements of the theorem for

$$\frac{(3+\sqrt{-5})}{(2, 1+\sqrt{-5})} = (7, 3+\sqrt{-5}),$$

that is prime to $(1+\sqrt{-5})$.

For the actual determination of α in general see Chap. XII, § 7.

We proceed now to prove the theorem.

The truth of this theorem for the case where $\mathfrak{m}$ is any prime ideal $\mathfrak{p}$ is at once evident. For, if there did not exist a number, α of $\mathfrak{a}$ such that $(\alpha)/\mathfrak{a}$ is not divisible by $\mathfrak{p}$, then all numbers of $\mathfrak{a}$ would belong to $\mathfrak{a}\mathfrak{p}$ and by Th. 7 $\mathfrak{a}$ would be divisible by $\mathfrak{a}\mathfrak{p}$, which is impossible. To prove the theorem for the general case, let the different prime factors of $\mathfrak{m}$ be $\mathfrak{p}_1, \mathfrak{p}_2, \cdots, \mathfrak{p}_m$, and form the products

$$\mathfrak{a}_1 = \mathfrak{a}\mathfrak{p}_2 \cdots \mathfrak{p}_m, \quad \mathfrak{a}_2 = \mathfrak{a}\mathfrak{p}_1\mathfrak{p}_3 \cdots \mathfrak{p}_m, \cdots, \quad \mathfrak{a}_m = \mathfrak{a}\mathfrak{p}_1 \cdots \mathfrak{p}_{m-1},$$

which consist of $\mathfrak{a}$ multiplied in turn by the combinations of $\mathfrak{p}_1, \mathfrak{p}_2, \cdots, \mathfrak{p}_m$ taken $m-1$ at a time. Let $\alpha_1, \alpha_2, \cdots, \alpha_m$ be numbers of $\mathfrak{a}_1, \mathfrak{a}_2, \cdots, \mathfrak{a}_m$ respectively, such that $(\alpha_1)/\mathfrak{a}_1$, $(\alpha_2)/\mathfrak{a}_2$, $\cdots$, $(\alpha_m)/\mathfrak{a}_m$ are prime respectively to $\mathfrak{p}_1, \mathfrak{p}_2, \cdots, \mathfrak{p}_m$, the existence of such numbers having been proved above since $\mathfrak{p}_1, \mathfrak{p}_2, \cdots, \mathfrak{p}_m$ are prime ideals. Then

$$\alpha = \alpha_1 + \alpha_2 + \cdots + \alpha_m,$$

is the required number; for α is divisible by $\mathfrak{a}$, since $\alpha_1, \alpha_2, \cdots, \alpha_m$ are all divisible by $\mathfrak{a}$, $\mathfrak{a}_i$ being divisible by $\mathfrak{a}$, whence all numbers of $\mathfrak{a}_i$ belong to $\mathfrak{a}$; moreover, α is not divisible by any of the m products

$$\mathfrak{a}\mathfrak{p}_1, \mathfrak{a}\mathfrak{p}_2, \cdots, \mathfrak{a}\mathfrak{p}_m,$$

as, for example, $\mathfrak{a}\mathfrak{p}_1$, since $\alpha_2, \alpha_3, \cdots, \alpha_m$ are all divisible by $\mathfrak{a}\mathfrak{p}_1$, but α_1 is not divisible by $\mathfrak{a}\mathfrak{p}_1$.

It is evident, therefore, that the quotient $(\alpha)/\mathfrak{a}$ is divisible by none of the prime factors $\mathfrak{p}_1, \mathfrak{p}_2, \cdots, \mathfrak{p}_m$ of $\mathfrak{m}$, and hence is prime to $\mathfrak{m}$.

Hence α is the required number.

THEOREM 12. *In every ideal, $\mathfrak{a}$, there exist two numbers, α_1, α_2, such that*

$$\mathfrak{a} = (\alpha_1, \alpha_2);$$

that is, such that $\mathfrak{a}$ is the greatest common divisor of (α_1) and (α_2).

Let α_1 be any number of $\mathfrak{a}$.

By Th. 11 there exists in $\mathfrak{a}$ a number, α_2, such that the quotient $(\alpha_2)/\mathfrak{a}$ is prime to (α_1); or, in other words, such that the greatest common divisor of (α_1) and (α_2) is $\mathfrak{a}$.

But, since $\mathfrak{a}$ is the greatest common divisor of (α_1) and (α_2), it contains all and only numbers of the form

$$\beta_1\alpha_1 + \beta_2\alpha_2,$$

where β_1, β_2 are any integers of the realm. Hence

$$\mathfrak{a} = (\alpha_1, \alpha_2).$$

The truth of this theorem is at once evident for quadratic realms for we have shown (Th. 1) the existence in every ideal, $\mathfrak{a}$, of a quadratic realm of two numbers ι_1, ι_2 such that $\mathfrak{a} = (\iota_1, \iota_2)$. The proof in the above form has been given, however, as it applies to the general realm of the nth degree; see Hilbert: Bericht, Satz 12.

The following theorem is given not only for its own interest but because from it we obtain a new proof of Th. 11 that is not dependent upon the unique factorization theorem. Dedekind makes the unique factorization theorem depend upon Th. 13 (see Dirichlet-Dedekind, § 178, IX).

THEOREM 13. *If the ideal $\mathfrak{a}$ be divisible by none of the ideals $\mathfrak{c}_1, \mathfrak{c}_2, \cdots, \mathfrak{c}_n$, then there is a number, α, of $\mathfrak{a}$ that is contained in none of the ideals $\mathfrak{c}_1, \mathfrak{c}_2, \cdots, \mathfrak{c}_n$.*

If $\mathfrak{a}$ should be a principal ideal, the theorem is evident. Also, if there should be only a single ideal, $\mathfrak{c}$, the theorem holds, for, if all numbers of $\mathfrak{a}$ were divisible by $\mathfrak{c}$, $\mathfrak{a}$ would be divisible by $\mathfrak{c}$, which is contrary to the original hypothesis. We shall now prove that, if the theorem hold for $n < r$ it holds for $n = r$, and hence, since it is true for $n = 1$, it holds in general. To each of the ideals $\mathfrak{c}_1, \mathfrak{c}_2, \cdots, \mathfrak{c}_r$, as $\mathfrak{c}_s$, there corresponds an ideal $\mathfrak{b}_s$ such that

$$\mathfrak{a}\mathfrak{b}_s = \mathfrak{a} - \mathfrak{c}_s,$$

where $\mathfrak{b}_s$ is evidently different from (1).

The ideal $\mathfrak{a}$ is divisible by none of the r products

$$\mathfrak{a}\mathfrak{b}_1, \mathfrak{a}\mathfrak{b}_2, \cdots, \mathfrak{a}\mathfrak{b}_r, \qquad 5)$$

since all of the $\mathfrak{b}$'s are different from (1).

But each one of the $\mathfrak{c}$'s divides one of these products. Hence, if we can prove the existence of a number of $\mathfrak{a}$, which belongs to none of the products 5), this number will be the desired number α, for if α were divisible by $\mathfrak{c}_s$, it, being divisible by $\mathfrak{a}$, would be divisible by the least common multiple of $\mathfrak{a}$ and $\mathfrak{c}_s$; that is, $\mathfrak{a}\mathfrak{b}_s$. We have now two cases to consider according as the ideals $\mathfrak{b}_1, \mathfrak{b}_2, \cdots, \mathfrak{b}_r$ are, or are not, prime each to each. If they be not prime each to each, some pair of them, say $\mathfrak{b}_1, \mathfrak{b}_2$, must have a greatest common divisor, $\mathfrak{b}_1 + \mathfrak{b}_2$, that is different from (1).

Then $\mathfrak{a}$ is not divisible by $\mathfrak{a}(\mathfrak{b}_1 + \mathfrak{b}_2)$, and hence, according to our assumption that the theorem holds for $n < r$, there exists in $\mathfrak{a}$ a number, α, that is divisible by none of the $r - 1$ ideals

$$\mathfrak{a}(\mathfrak{b}_1 + \mathfrak{b}_2), \mathfrak{a}\mathfrak{b}_3, \cdots, \mathfrak{a}\mathfrak{b}_r,$$

and hence also is not divisible by $\mathfrak{a}\mathfrak{b}_1$ and $\mathfrak{a}\mathfrak{b}_2$, since they are divisible by $\mathfrak{a}(\mathfrak{b}_1 + \mathfrak{b}_2)$. Therefore α is not divisible by any of the $\mathfrak{c}$'s. We must consider now the case where the r ideals, $\mathfrak{b}_1, \mathfrak{b}_2, \cdots, \mathfrak{b}_r$ are prime each to each.

Each of these ideals, as $\mathfrak{b}_s$, is prime to the product, $\mathfrak{h}_s$, of all the remaining ones, and, since they are all different from (1), $\mathfrak{h}_s$ is not divisible by $\mathfrak{b}_s$. Hence $\mathfrak{a}\mathfrak{h}_s$ is not divisible by $\mathfrak{a}\mathfrak{b}_s$, and there is therefore a number α_s, in $\mathfrak{a}\mathfrak{h}_s$ that is not divisible by $\mathfrak{a}\mathfrak{b}_s$.

The number $\alpha, = \alpha_1 + \alpha_2 + \cdots + \alpha_r$, where $\alpha_1, \alpha_2, \cdots, \alpha_r$ are numbers of $\mathfrak{a}\mathfrak{h}_1, \mathfrak{a}\mathfrak{h}_2, \cdots, \mathfrak{a}\mathfrak{h}_r$ respectively, is a number of $\mathfrak{a}$, for each of the numbers $\alpha_1, \alpha_2, \cdots, \alpha_r$ is a number of an ideal divisible by $\mathfrak{a}$, and is therefore a number of $\mathfrak{a}$.

Moreover, α is divisible by none of the r products $\mathfrak{a}\mathfrak{b}_1, \mathfrak{a}\mathfrak{b}_2, \cdots, \mathfrak{a}\mathfrak{b}_r$; for, since the ideals $\mathfrak{h}_2, \mathfrak{h}_3, \cdots, \mathfrak{h}_r$ are all divisible by $\mathfrak{b}_1$, all the ideals $\mathfrak{a}\mathfrak{h}_2, \cdots, \mathfrak{a}\mathfrak{h}_r$ are divisible by $\mathfrak{a}\mathfrak{b}_1$, and hence $\alpha_2, \alpha_3, \cdots, \alpha_r$ are numbers of $\mathfrak{a}\mathfrak{b}_1$.

But α_1 is not a number of $\mathfrak{a}\mathfrak{b}_1$, and hence α is not a number of $\mathfrak{a}\mathfrak{b}_1$.

In like manner it may be proved that α is divisible by none of the ideals $\mathfrak{a}\mathfrak{b}_2, \mathfrak{a}\mathfrak{b}_3, \cdots, \mathfrak{a}\mathfrak{b}_r$.

Hence α is the number sought.

Second Proof of Theorem 11.[1]

If $\mathfrak{m} = (1)$, every number of $\mathfrak{a}$ satisfies the requirement of Th. 11.

If $\mathfrak{m} \neq (1)$, let $\mathfrak{c}_1, \mathfrak{c}_2, \cdots, \mathfrak{c}_n$ be all the ideals different from $\mathfrak{a}$ that divide $\mathfrak{a}\mathfrak{m}$ and are divisible by $\mathfrak{a}$.

By Th. 3 these ideals are finite in number and hence there is in $\mathfrak{a}$ a number, α, that is divisible by none of them (Th. 13).

Hence the greatest common divisor, $\mathfrak{a}\mathfrak{m} + (\alpha)$, of $\mathfrak{a}\mathfrak{m}$ and (α) is different from all the $\mathfrak{c}$'s. But $\mathfrak{a}\mathfrak{m} + (\alpha)$ divides $\mathfrak{a}\mathfrak{m}$ and is divisible by $\mathfrak{a}$, and the only ideal different from the $\mathfrak{c}$'s, that has this property, is $\mathfrak{a}$.

Hence
$$\mathfrak{a}\mathfrak{m} + (\alpha) = \mathfrak{a}, \qquad 6)$$
or, what is the same thing, $(\alpha)/\mathfrak{a}$ is prime to $\mathfrak{m}$.

From 6) it follows at once that
$$\mathfrak{a}\mathfrak{m} - (\alpha) = \mathfrak{m}(\alpha).$$

[1] Dirichlet-Dedekind: § 178, X.

CHAPTER XII.

CONGRUENCES WHOSE MODULI ARE IDEALS.[1]

§ 1. Definition. Elementary Theorems.

If the difference of two integers, α and β, be a number of the ideal $\mathfrak{a}$, we have said that α was congruent to β with respect to the modulus $\mathfrak{a}$, and have denoted this fact by writing

$$\alpha \equiv \beta, \bmod \mathfrak{a}. \qquad 1)$$

In particular, if α be a number of $\mathfrak{a}$, we write

$$\alpha \equiv 0, \bmod \mathfrak{a}.$$

The appropriateness of these symbolic expressions is made evident by Chap. XI, Th. 7; for from it we see that the necessary and sufficient condition for $\alpha - \beta$ to be a number of $\mathfrak{a}$ is that it shall be divisible by $\mathfrak{a}$. These expressions are capable of many of the transformations to which ordinary congruences between rational integers can be subjected. The congruence 1) leads to

$$\alpha - \beta \equiv 0, \bmod \mathfrak{a}, \qquad 2)$$

and conversely 2) leads to 1).

The following deductions will be seen to correspond number for number to those given in the case of rational integers (Chap. III, § 1). Their proofs are so simple that they will be left to the reader. For them we fall back upon our original definition of

$$\alpha \equiv \beta, \bmod \mathfrak{a},$$

as meaning that $\alpha - \beta$ is a number of $\mathfrak{a}$, or, what is the same thing, that the principal ideal $(\alpha - \beta)$ is divisible by $\mathfrak{a}$. Observe the similarity between this and the method employed in the case of rational integers, where we made use of our original definition of

$$a \equiv b, \bmod m,$$

[1] Hilbert: Bericht, Cap. III.

as meaning that $a-b$ is divisible by m.

i. *If* $\alpha\equiv\beta$, mod $\mathfrak{a}$,

and $\beta\equiv\gamma$, mod $\mathfrak{a}$,

then $\alpha\equiv\gamma$, mod $\mathfrak{a}$;

for, if $\alpha-\beta$ and $\beta-\gamma$ be numbers of $\mathfrak{a}$, $\alpha-\beta+\beta-\gamma, =\alpha-\gamma$, is a number of $\mathfrak{a}$.

The infinite system of integers of the realm which are congruent to a given integer, and hence each to each, mod $\mathfrak{a}$, are said to form a *number class*, mod $\mathfrak{a}$.

ii. *If* $\alpha\equiv\beta$, mod $\mathfrak{a}$,

and $\gamma\equiv\delta$, mod $\mathfrak{a}$,

then $\alpha\pm\gamma\equiv\beta\pm\delta$, mod $\mathfrak{a}$.

iii. *If* $\alpha\equiv\beta$, mod $\mathfrak{a}$,

then $\mu\alpha\equiv\mu\beta$, mod $\mathfrak{a}$.

iv. *If* $\alpha\equiv\beta$, mod $\mathfrak{a}$,

and $\gamma\equiv\delta$, mod $\mathfrak{a}$,

then $\alpha\gamma\equiv\beta\delta$, mod $\mathfrak{a}$;

and, in particular, if

$\alpha\equiv\beta$, mod $\mathfrak{a}$,

then $\alpha^s\equiv\beta^s$, mod $\mathfrak{a}$.

v. *If* $f(x)=\alpha_0x^n+\alpha_1x^{n-1}+\cdots+\alpha_n$,

be a polynomial in x, whose coefficients are any integers of the realm, and if

$\beta\equiv\gamma$, mod $\mathfrak{a}$,

then $f(\beta)\equiv f(\gamma)$, mod $\mathfrak{a}$.

vi. *If* $\mu\alpha\equiv\mu\beta$, mod $\mathfrak{a}$, 3)

then $\alpha\equiv\beta$, mod $\mathfrak{a}/\mathfrak{d}$,

where $\mathfrak{d}$ is the greatest common divisor of (μ) *and* $\mathfrak{a}$.

For let $(\mu)=\mathfrak{dm}$ and $\mathfrak{a}=\mathfrak{db}$, where $\mathfrak{m}$ and $\mathfrak{b}$ are prime to each other; then, since $\mu[\alpha-\beta]$ is a number of $\mathfrak{a}$, $\mathfrak{dm}(\alpha-\beta)$ is divisible by $\mathfrak{db}$.

Hence $\mathfrak{m}(\alpha-\beta)$ is divisible by $\mathfrak{b}$, and therefore, since $\mathfrak{m}$ is prime to $\mathfrak{b}$, $(\alpha-\beta)$ is divisible by $\mathfrak{b}$ (Chap. XI, Th. 10, Cor.). We have, therefore, since $\mathfrak{b}=\mathfrak{a}/\mathfrak{d}$.

$$\alpha\equiv\beta, \text{ mod } \mathfrak{a}/\mathfrak{d}.$$

In particular, if μ be prime to $\mathfrak{a}$, then

$$\alpha\equiv\beta, \text{ mod } \mathfrak{a}.$$

Hence in this case the congruence 1) may be divided by μ.

This indeed is an immediate consequence of the fact that the greatest common divisor of (μ) and $\mathfrak{a}$ is (1); for then there i a number $\mu\xi$ of (μ) and a number γ of $\mathfrak{a}$ such that

$$\mu\xi+\gamma=1;$$

that is, there exists an integer ξ such that

$$\mu\xi\equiv 1, \text{ mod } \mathfrak{a}. \qquad 4)$$

Multiplying the congruence 3) by ξ, we obtain

$$\alpha\equiv\beta, \text{ mod } \mathfrak{a}.$$

Conversely, if there exists a number ξ, which satisfies the congruence 4), the greatest common divisor of (μ) and $\mathfrak{a}$ is (1); that is, (μ) is prime to $\mathfrak{a}$.

vii. *If*
$$\alpha\equiv\beta, \text{ mod } \mathfrak{a}$$
and $\mathfrak{d}$ *be a divisor of* $\mathfrak{a}$, *then*

$$\alpha\equiv\beta, \text{ mod } \mathfrak{d}.$$

viii. *If* $\alpha\equiv\beta$ *with respect to each of the moduli* $\mathfrak{a}_1, \mathfrak{a}_2, \cdots, \mathfrak{a}_n$, *then*
$$\alpha\equiv\beta, \text{ mod } \mathfrak{l},$$
where $\mathfrak{l}$ *is the least common multiple of* $\mathfrak{a}_1, \mathfrak{a}_2, \cdots, \mathfrak{a}_n$.

ix. *If*
$$\alpha\equiv\beta, \text{ mod } \mathfrak{a},$$
then (α) *and* (β) *have the same greatest common divisor with* $\mathfrak{a}$;

that is, all numbers of the same number class, mod $\mathfrak{a}$, *have the same greatest common divisor with* $\mathfrak{a}$.

Let $\mathfrak{d}$ be the greatest common divisor of (α) and $\mathfrak{a}$. Then, since $\mathfrak{d}$ is a divisor of $\mathfrak{a}$, we have by vii

$$\alpha \equiv \beta, \text{ mod } \mathfrak{d}.$$

But
$$\alpha \equiv 0, \text{ mod } \mathfrak{d},$$

and hence
$$\beta \equiv 0, \text{ mod } \mathfrak{d}.$$

In particular, if any number of a class, mod $\mathfrak{a}$, be prime to $\mathfrak{a}$, then all numbers of this class are prime to $\mathfrak{a}$.

§ 2. The Norm of an Ideal. Classification of the Numbers of an Ideal with respect to Another Ideal.

If we separate the integers of a realm into classes with respect to an ideal, $\mathfrak{a}$, of the realm, putting two integers into the same or different classes according as they are congruent or incongruent to each other with respect to $\mathfrak{a}$, then the number of these classes is called the norm of $\mathfrak{a}$, and is denoted by $n[\mathfrak{a}]$.

This definition of the norm of an ideal is seen to be in accordance with the principal property possessed by the absolute value of the norm of an integer. We shall show later that the original definition of the norm of an integer as the product of an integer by its conjugate has also its analogue in the case of ideals.

A system of numbers formed by selecting one from each of the classes formed as above with respect to an ideal, $\mathfrak{a}$, is called a *complete system of incongruent numbers,* mod $\mathfrak{a}$, or a *complete residue system,* mod $\mathfrak{a}$. There are evidently in such a system exactly $n[\mathfrak{a}]$ numbers.

Instead of separating all the integers of a realm into classes with regard to their congruence with respect to an ideal, we may consider simply the numbers of a single ideal, $\mathfrak{a}$, and put two of these numbers, α_1, α_2, into the same or different classes with respect to an ideal, $\mathfrak{b}$, according as we have

$$\alpha_1 \equiv \alpha_2, \text{ mod } \mathfrak{b}, \text{ or } \alpha_1 \not\equiv \alpha_2, \text{ mod } \mathfrak{b}.$$

We shall denote by the symbol $\{\mathfrak{a}, \mathfrak{b}\}$ the number of such classes into which the numbers of $\mathfrak{a}$ fall with respect to $\mathfrak{b}$.[1]

[1] See Dirichlet-Dedekind: § 171.

Evidently $\{\mathfrak{a}, \mathfrak{b}\}$ is not greater than $n[\mathfrak{b}]$, since $\mathfrak{a}$ does not comprise all integers of the realm k unless $\mathfrak{a} = (1)$, in which case $\{(1), \mathfrak{b}\} = n[\mathfrak{b}]$.

It will be interesting to make use of this classification of the numbers of one ideal with respect to another ideal to prove an important theorem (see p. 336) and we proceed now to prove the following relations:

i. $$\{\mathfrak{a}, \mathfrak{b}\} = \{\mathfrak{a}, \mathfrak{a} - \mathfrak{b}\}.$$

ii. $$\{\mathfrak{a}, \mathfrak{b}\} = \{\mathfrak{a} + \mathfrak{b}, \mathfrak{b}\}.$$

iii. $$\{\mathfrak{a}(\eta), \mathfrak{b}(\eta)\} = \{\mathfrak{a}, \mathfrak{b}\}.$$

iv. $$\{\mathfrak{a}, \mathfrak{c}\} = \{\mathfrak{a}, \mathfrak{b}\}\{\mathfrak{b}, \mathfrak{c}\},$$

where $\mathfrak{a}$ is a divisor of $\mathfrak{b}$, and $\mathfrak{b}$ a divisor of $\mathfrak{c}$.

i. To prove $$\{\mathfrak{a}, \mathfrak{b}\} = \{\mathfrak{a}, \mathfrak{a} - \mathfrak{b}\}.$$

We observe that $\mathfrak{a} - \mathfrak{b}$, the least common multiple of $\mathfrak{a}$ and $\mathfrak{b}$, is composed of all numbers common to both $\mathfrak{a}$ and $\mathfrak{b}$.

Hence, if α_1, α_2 be two numbers of $\mathfrak{a}$ such that

$$\alpha_1 \equiv \alpha_2, \text{ mod } \mathfrak{b},$$

that is, such that $\alpha_1 - \alpha_2$ is a number of $\mathfrak{b}$, then, since $\alpha_1 - \alpha_2$ is also a number of $\mathfrak{a}$, it must be a number of $\mathfrak{a} - \mathfrak{b}$, and therefore

$$\alpha_1 \equiv \alpha_2, \text{ mod } \mathfrak{a} - \mathfrak{b}.$$

Conversely, if

$$\alpha_1 \equiv \alpha_2, \text{ mod } \mathfrak{a} - \mathfrak{b},$$

then $\alpha_1 - \alpha_2$ is a number of $\mathfrak{b}$; that is,

$$\alpha_1 \equiv \alpha_2, \text{ mod } \mathfrak{b}.$$

Hence any two numbers of $\mathfrak{a}$, that are congruent to each other with respect to $\mathfrak{b}$, are congruent to each other with respect to $\mathfrak{a} - \mathfrak{b}$ and vice versa. Therefore we have

$$\{\mathfrak{a}, \mathfrak{b}\} = \{\mathfrak{a}, \mathfrak{a} - \mathfrak{b}\}.$$

ii. To prove $$\{\mathfrak{a}, \mathfrak{b}\} = \{\mathfrak{a} + \mathfrak{b}, \mathfrak{b}\}.$$

Let $$\alpha_1, \alpha_2, \cdots, \alpha_m \; (m = \{\mathfrak{a}, \mathfrak{b}\}) \qquad 1)$$

be a complete system of incongruent numbers of $\mathfrak{a}$ with respect to $\mathfrak{b}$. Then every number of $\mathfrak{a}+\mathfrak{b}$ is congruent to one of these numbers with respect to $\mathfrak{b}$, for all numbers of $\mathfrak{a}+\mathfrak{b}$ can be written in the form $\alpha+\beta$, where α is a number of $\mathfrak{a}$ and β a number of $\mathfrak{b}$. And from

$$\alpha \equiv \alpha_i, \text{ mod } \mathfrak{b},$$

where α_i is one of the numbers 1), we have

$$\alpha+\beta \equiv \alpha_i, \text{ mod } \mathfrak{b},$$

since $$\beta \equiv 0, \text{ mod } \mathfrak{b}.$$

Moreover, since $\mathfrak{a}+\mathfrak{b}$ contains all the numbers of $\mathfrak{a}$, some numbers of $\mathfrak{a}+\mathfrak{b}$ will be congruent to each one of the integers of the system 1), mod $\mathfrak{b}$. Hence

$$\{\mathfrak{a}, \mathfrak{b}\} = \{\mathfrak{a}+\mathfrak{b}, \mathfrak{b}\}.$$

iii. To prove

$$\{\mathfrak{a}(\eta), \mathfrak{b}(\eta)\} = \{\mathfrak{a}, \mathfrak{b}\}.$$

Let $$\alpha_1, \alpha_2, \cdots, \alpha_m \; (m = \{\mathfrak{a}, \mathfrak{b}\})$$

be a complete system of incongruent numbers of $\mathfrak{a}$ with respect to $\mathfrak{b}$, then $$\alpha_1\eta, \alpha_2\eta, \cdots, \alpha_m\eta$$

form a complete system of incongruent numbers of $\mathfrak{a}(\eta)$ with respect to the mod $\mathfrak{b}(\eta)$; for they are all incongruent, mod $\mathfrak{b}(\eta)$, to each other, since, if

$$\alpha_g\eta \equiv \alpha_h\eta, \text{ mod } \mathfrak{b}(\eta),$$

then $$\alpha_g \equiv \alpha_h, \text{ mod } \mathfrak{b},$$

which is impossible. Furthermore, every number of $\mathfrak{a}(\eta)$ is congruent to one of these integers, mod $\mathfrak{b}(\eta)$, for, if $\alpha\eta$ be any number of $\mathfrak{a}(\eta)$, and

$$\alpha \equiv \alpha_i, \text{ mod } \mathfrak{b},$$

then $(\alpha-\alpha_i)\eta$ is a number of $\mathfrak{b}(\eta)$, and hence

$$\alpha\eta \equiv \alpha_i\eta, \text{ mod } \mathfrak{b}(\eta).$$

Hence $$\{\mathfrak{a}(\eta), \mathfrak{b}(\eta)\} = \{\mathfrak{a}, \mathfrak{b}\}.$$

iv. To prove that, if $\mathfrak{a}$ be a divisor of $\mathfrak{b}$ and $\mathfrak{b}$ a divisor of $\mathfrak{c}$, then

$$\{\mathfrak{a}, \mathfrak{c}\} = \{\mathfrak{a}, \mathfrak{b}\}\{\mathfrak{b}, \mathfrak{c}\}.$$

Let
$$\alpha_1, \alpha_2, \cdots, \alpha_m \ (m = \{\mathfrak{a}, \mathfrak{b}\}) \qquad 2)$$

be a complete system of incongruent numbers of $\mathfrak{a}$ with respect to the modulus $\mathfrak{b}$, and let

$$\beta_1, \beta_2, \cdots, \beta_n \ (n = \{\mathfrak{b}, \mathfrak{c}\}) \qquad 3)$$

be a complete system of incongruent numbers of $\mathfrak{b}$, mod $\mathfrak{c}$. We shall show that the mn numbers

$$\alpha_r + \beta_s \begin{cases} r = 1, 2, \cdots, m \\ s = 1, 2, \cdots, n \end{cases} \qquad 4)$$

which are all evidently numbers of $\mathfrak{a}$, form a complete system of incongruent numbers of $\mathfrak{a}$, mod $\mathfrak{c}$.

The numbers 4) are incongruent each to each, mod $\mathfrak{c}$; for, if

$$\alpha_a + \beta_b \equiv \alpha_c + \beta_d, \text{ mod } \mathfrak{c}, \qquad 5)$$

then, since $\mathfrak{b}$ is a divisor of $\mathfrak{c}$,

$$\alpha_a + \beta_b \equiv \alpha_c + \beta_d, \text{ mod } \mathfrak{b},$$

and hence, since β_b and β_d are numbers of $\mathfrak{b}$,

$$\alpha_a \equiv \alpha_c, \text{ mod } \mathfrak{b},$$

which is impossible unless $\alpha_a = \alpha_c$. But, if $\alpha_a = \alpha_c$, then from 5) we have

$$\beta_b \equiv \beta_d, \text{ mod } \mathfrak{c},$$

which is impossible. Hence the numbers 4) are incongruent each to each, mod $\mathfrak{c}$.

Moreover, every number, α, of $\mathfrak{a}$ is congruent to some one of the numbers 4), mod $\mathfrak{c}$; for suppose

$$\alpha \equiv \alpha_i, \text{ mod } \mathfrak{b},$$

where α_i is one of the numbers 2), then $\alpha - \alpha_i$ is a number of $\mathfrak{b}$, and we have

$$\alpha - \alpha_i \equiv \beta_h, \text{ mod } \mathfrak{c},$$

where β_h is one of the numbers 3), and hence

$$\alpha \equiv \alpha_i + \beta_h, \text{ mod } \mathfrak{c},$$

where $\alpha_i + \beta_h$ is one of the numbers 4).

The numbers of a complete system of incongruent numbers of $\mathfrak{a}$, mod $\mathfrak{c}$, are therefore exactly mn in number, and hence

$$\{\mathfrak{a}, \mathfrak{c}\} = \{\mathfrak{a}, \mathfrak{b}\}\{\mathfrak{b}, \mathfrak{c}\}.$$

THEOREM 1. *If $\iota_1, = a_1\omega_1 + a_2\omega_2$, $\iota_2, = b_1\omega_1 + b_2\omega_2$, be a basis of the ideal $\mathfrak{a}$, the absolute value of the determinant of the coefficients a_1, a_2, b_1, b_2 is equal to the norm of $\mathfrak{a}$; that is,*

$$n[\mathfrak{a}] = \left\| \begin{matrix} a_1 & a_2 \\ b_1 & b_2 \end{matrix} \right\|.[1]$$

Let $$\mathfrak{a} = (a\omega_1, b\omega_1 + c\omega_2),$$

where $a\omega_1, b\omega_1 + c\omega_2$ is a canonical basis, a and c being taken positive. Since

$$\left\| \begin{matrix} a_1 & a_2 \\ b_1 & b_2 \end{matrix} \right\| = \left\| \begin{matrix} a & 0 \\ b & c \end{matrix} \right\| = ac \qquad \text{(Chap. XI, § 2)},$$

it is sufficient to show that

$$n[\mathfrak{a}] = ac.$$

In the expression

$$u\omega_1 + v\omega_2 \qquad 6)$$

let u run through the values $0, 1, \cdots, a-1$, and v through the values $0, 1, \cdots, c-1$. We shall show that the ac numbers so formed constitute a complete system of incongruent numbers with respect to $\mathfrak{a}$. They are incongruent each to each with respect to $\mathfrak{a}$; for, if $u_1\omega_1 + v_1\omega_2$ and $u_2\omega_1 + v_2\omega_2$ be any two of them, and

$$u_1\omega_1 + v_1\omega_2 \equiv u_2\omega_1 + v_2\omega_2, \text{ mod } \mathfrak{a},$$

then $$(u_1 - u_2)\omega_1 + (v_1 - v_2)\omega_2 \equiv 0, \text{ mod } \mathfrak{a},$$

and hence, since c is the greatest common divisor of the coefficient of ω_2 in all numbers of $\mathfrak{a}$,

[1] Hilbert: Bericht, Satz 19.

$$v_1 - v_2 \equiv 0, \text{ mod } c.$$

But v_1 and v_2 are both less than c, hence

$$v_1 = v_2.$$

It follows that

$$(u_1 - u_2)\omega_1 \equiv 0, \text{ mod } \mathfrak{a},$$

and hence, since a is the greatest common divisor of the coefficients of ω_1 in all numbers of $\mathfrak{a}$ in which the coefficient of ω_2 is 0,

$$u_1 - u_2 \equiv 0, \text{ mod } a.$$

But u_1 and u_2 are both less than a, hence

$$u_1 = u_2.$$

Thus

$$u_1\omega_1 + v_1\omega_2 = u_2\omega_1 + v_2\omega_2,$$

and the numbers 6) are incongruent each to each with respect to $\mathfrak{a}$. Moreover, every integer of the realm is congruent to one of the numbers 6) with respect to $\mathfrak{a}$. For, let

$$\omega = t_1\omega_1 + t_2\omega_2$$

be any integer of the realm, and let

$$t_2 = mc + r_2,$$

where m and r_2 are rational integers and r_2 satisfies the conditions

$$0 \leqq r_2 < c.$$

Also let

$$t_1 - mb = na + r_1,$$

where n and r_1 are rational integers and r_1 satisfies the conditions

$$0 \leqq r_1 < a.$$

Then

$$t_1\omega_1 + t_2\omega_2 = (mb + na + r_1)\omega_1 + (mc + r_2)\omega_2$$
$$= na\omega_1 + m(b\omega_1 + c\omega_2) + r_1\omega_1 + r_2\omega_2,$$

and hence

$$t_1\omega_1 + t_2\omega_2 \equiv r_1\omega_1 + r_2\omega_2, \text{ mod } \mathfrak{a}.$$

But $r_1\omega_1 + r_2\omega_2$ is one of the numbers 6).

Hence every integer of the realm is congruent to one of these numbers with respect to $\mathfrak{a}$, and therefore, since they are ac in number

$$n[\mathfrak{a}] = ac.$$

Hence
$$n[\mathfrak{a}] = \begin{Vmatrix} a_1 & a_2 \\ b_1 & b_2 \end{Vmatrix}$$

From this theorem we see that the norm of an ideal is always finite.

Ex. Since $7, 3+\sqrt{-5}$ is a basis of the ideal $(7, 3+\sqrt{-5})$,

$$n(7, 3+\sqrt{-5}) = \begin{Vmatrix} 7 & 0 \\ 3 & 1 \end{Vmatrix} = 7.$$

In the case of non-principal ideals, we shall omit [ ] and write merely n before the symbol to denote the norm, as in the example just given.

COR. 1. *Since, if* $a_1\omega_1 + a_2\omega_2, b_1\omega_1 + b_2\omega_2$ *be a basis of* $\mathfrak{a}$, *then* $a_1\omega_1' + a_2\omega_2', b_1\omega_1' + b_2\omega_2'$ *is a basis of* $\mathfrak{a}'$ *(Chap. XI, § 3), we have*

$$n[\mathfrak{a}'] = \begin{Vmatrix} a_1 & a_2 \\ b_1 & b_2 \end{Vmatrix} = n[\mathfrak{a}].$$

COR. 2. *If* (a) *be a principal ideal, where* a *is a rational integer, then*

$$n[(a)] = a^2;$$

for $a\omega_1, a\omega_2$ is a basis of (a), and hence

$$n[(a)] = \begin{Vmatrix} a & 0 \\ 0 & a \end{Vmatrix} = a^2.$$

We can prove by this method that the norm of any principal ideal (α) is equal to the absolute value of the norm of the integer α which defines (α); that is

$$n[(\alpha)] = |n[\alpha]|.$$

But a simpler proof can be found, based upon a theorem to be given later.

COR. 3. *If* $\mathfrak{a}, = (a_1\omega_1 + a_2\omega_2, b_1\omega_1 + b_2\omega_2)$, *be any ideal and*

$$\begin{Vmatrix} a_1 & a_2 \\ b_1 & b_2 \end{Vmatrix} = n[\mathfrak{a}],$$

then $a_1\omega_1 + a_2\omega_2, b_1\omega_1 + b_2\omega_2$ *is a basis of* $\mathfrak{a}$.

THEOREM 2. *If $\mathfrak{a}=\mathfrak{b}\mathfrak{c}$, where $\mathfrak{b}$ and $\mathfrak{c}$ are any ideals, there are exactly $n[\mathfrak{c}]$ numbers of a complete system of incongruent numbers, mod $\mathfrak{a}$, which are divisible by $\mathfrak{b}$.*

Let
$$\gamma_1, \gamma_2, \cdots, \gamma_{n[\mathfrak{c}]} \qquad 7)$$
be a complete system of incongruent numbers, mod $\mathfrak{c}$, and let β be a number of $\mathfrak{b}$ such that $(\beta)/\mathfrak{b}$ is prime to $\mathfrak{c}$ (Chap. XI, Th. 11). The numbers
$$\beta\gamma_1, \beta\gamma_2, \cdots, \beta\gamma_{n[\mathfrak{c}]} \qquad 8)$$
are incongruent each to each, mod $\mathfrak{a}$; for, if
$$\beta\gamma_h \equiv \beta\gamma_i, \text{ mod } \mathfrak{a},$$
then
$$\gamma_h \equiv \gamma_i, \text{ mod } \mathfrak{c} \ (\S\ 1, \text{vi}),$$
which is impossible.

Moreover, every integer, β_1, divisible by $\mathfrak{b}$ is congruent, mod $\mathfrak{a}$, to some integer of the form $\mu\beta$, for since $\mathfrak{b}$ is the greatest common divisor of $\mathfrak{a}, = (\alpha_1, \alpha_2)$, and (β), we have
$$\mathfrak{b} = (\alpha_1, \alpha_2, \beta),$$
whence, since β_1 is a number of $\mathfrak{b}$, it follows that
$$\beta_1 = \xi_1\alpha_1 + \xi_2\alpha_2 + \mu\beta,$$
where ξ_1, ξ_2 and μ are integers of the realm, and hence
$$\beta_1 \equiv \mu\beta, \text{ mod } \mathfrak{a}.$$
But every integer of the form $\mu\beta$ is congruent, mod $\mathfrak{a}$, to some one of the numbers 8); for μ is congruent to some one, say, γ_i, of the numbers 7), mod $\mathfrak{c}$, and from
$$\mu \equiv \gamma_i, \text{ mod } \mathfrak{c},$$
it follows easily that
$$\beta\mu \equiv \beta\gamma_i, \text{ mod } \mathfrak{a}.$$

Since, also, every integer congruent to one of the numbers 8), mod $\mathfrak{a}$, is divisible by $\mathfrak{b}$ (§ 1, ix), and the numbers 8) are $n[\mathfrak{c}]$ in number, there are in every complete system of incongruent numbers, mod $\mathfrak{a}$, exactly $n[\mathfrak{c}], = n[\mathfrak{a}]/n[\mathfrak{b}]$, numbers that are divisible by $\mathfrak{b}$.

THEOREM 3. *The norm of the product of two ideals, $\mathfrak{a}$, $\mathfrak{b}$, is equal to the product of their norms.*[1]

Let α be a number of $\mathfrak{a}$ such that the quotient $(\alpha)/\mathfrak{a}$ is prime to $\mathfrak{b}$ (Chap. XI, Th. 11).

Let $$\alpha_1, \alpha_2, \cdots, \alpha_{n[\mathfrak{a}]} \tag{9}$$

and $$\beta_1, \beta_2, \cdots, \beta_{n[\mathfrak{b}]} \tag{10}$$

be complete systems of incongruent numbers with respect to $\mathfrak{a}$ and $\mathfrak{b}$, respectively. Then the $n[\mathfrak{a}]n[\mathfrak{b}]$ numbers of the form

$$\alpha\eta + \xi \begin{cases} \xi = \alpha_1, \alpha_2, \cdots, \alpha_{n[\mathfrak{a}]} \\ \eta = \beta_1, \beta_2, \cdots, \beta_{n[\mathfrak{b}]} \end{cases} \tag{11}$$

where ξ and η run through the values 9) and 10), respectively, form a complete system of incongruent numbers with respect to $\mathfrak{ab}$, and hence are $n[\mathfrak{ab}]$ in number.

To show this it is necessary and sufficient to show first that no two of the integers 11) are congruent to each other with respect to the modulus $\mathfrak{ab}$, and second that every integer of the realm is congruent to one of them with respect to $\mathfrak{ab}$.

Let $\alpha\beta_i + \alpha_l$ and $\alpha\beta_j + \alpha_m$ be any two of the integers 11).

If $$\alpha\beta_i + \alpha_l \equiv \alpha\beta_j + \alpha_m, \bmod \mathfrak{ab}, \tag{12}$$

then $$\alpha(\beta_i - \beta_j) + \alpha_l - \alpha_m \equiv 0, \bmod \mathfrak{a},$$

and hence, since

$$\alpha(\beta_i - \beta_j) \equiv 0, \bmod \mathfrak{a},$$

we have $$\alpha_l - \alpha_m \equiv 0, \bmod \mathfrak{a},$$

whence $$\alpha_l = \alpha_m.$$

Then from 12) it would follow that

$$\alpha(\beta_i - \beta_j) \equiv 0, \bmod \mathfrak{ab},$$

and hence, since $(\alpha) + \mathfrak{ab}$ is $\mathfrak{a}$,

$$\beta_i - \beta_j \equiv 0, \bmod \mathfrak{b},$$

which is impossible unless

$$\beta_i = \beta_j.$$

[1] Hilbert: Bericht, Satz 18.

Therefore 12) is impossible and the integers 11) are incongruent each to each, mod $\mathfrak{ab}$. Moreover, if ω be any integer of the realm, we have

$$\alpha_s \equiv \omega, \text{ mod } \mathfrak{a}, \qquad 13)$$

where α_s is one of the integers 9).

Now from 13) it follows that $\omega - \alpha_s$ is divisible by $\mathfrak{a}$. But every integer of a complete residue system, mod $\mathfrak{ab}$, that is divisible by $\mathfrak{a}$ is congruent to one of the integers

$$\alpha\beta_1, \alpha\beta_2, \cdots, \alpha\beta_{n[\mathfrak{b}]}, \qquad 14)$$

mod $\mathfrak{ab}$ (Th. 2); that is, the integers 14) are representatives of all and only those incongruent number classes, mod $\mathfrak{ab}$, whose numbers are divisible by $\mathfrak{a}$.

Hence we have

$$\omega - \alpha_s \equiv \alpha\beta_r, \text{ mod } \mathfrak{ab},$$

whence

$$\omega \equiv \alpha\beta_r + \alpha_s, \text{ mod } \mathfrak{ab},$$

where $\alpha\beta_r + \alpha_s$ is one of the numbers 11).

The numbers 11) form therefore a complete system of incongruent numbers, mod $\mathfrak{ab}$, and hence

$$n[\mathfrak{ab}] = n[\mathfrak{a}]n[\mathfrak{b}].$$

A complete system of incongruent numbers, mod $\mathfrak{ab}$, fall into $n[\mathfrak{a}]$ classes each containing $n[\mathfrak{b}]$ numbers, such that the numbers of each class are congruent each to each, mod $\mathfrak{a}$, but the numbers of any class are incongruent to all those of any other class, mod $\mathfrak{a}$. We may arrange these classes as follows:

$$\begin{array}{l}\alpha\beta_1 + \alpha_1, \alpha\beta_2 + \alpha_1, \cdots, \alpha\beta_{n[\mathfrak{b}]} + \alpha_1,\\ \alpha\beta_1 + \alpha_2, \alpha\beta_2 + \alpha_2, \cdots, \alpha\beta_{n[\mathfrak{b}]} + \alpha_2,\\ \cdot\ \cdot\ \cdot\ \cdot\ \cdot\ \cdot\ \cdot\ \cdot\ \cdot\ \cdot\ \cdot\ \cdot\ \cdot\ \cdot\\ \alpha\beta_1 + \alpha_{n[\mathfrak{a}]}, \alpha\beta_2 + \alpha_{n[\mathfrak{a}]}, \cdots, \alpha\beta_{n[\mathfrak{b}]} + \alpha_{n[\mathfrak{a}]},\end{array}$$

where $\alpha, \alpha_1, \alpha_2, \cdots, \alpha_{n[\mathfrak{a}]}, \beta_1, \beta_2, \cdots, \beta_{n[\mathfrak{b}]}$ are as defined above.

It will be seen that the numbers of each row are all and only those of the complete system of incongruent numbers, mod $\mathfrak{ab}$, that are congruent to each other, mod $\mathfrak{a}$.

There are, therefore, exactly $n[\mathfrak{b}]$ numbers of a complete residue system, mod $\mathfrak{ab}$, that are congruent to any given number, mod $\mathfrak{a}$. In particular there are, as we have already seen, exactly $n[\mathfrak{b}]$ numbers of a complete residue system, mod $\mathfrak{ab}$, which are divisible by $\mathfrak{a}$.

It will be interesting to obtain by means of the development of § 2 another proof of the above important theorem.

We begin by proving that

$$\{\mathfrak{a}, \mathfrak{ab}\} = n[\mathfrak{b}].$$

Let α be a number of $\mathfrak{a}$ such that $\mathfrak{ab} + (\alpha) = \mathfrak{a}$; then

$$\mathfrak{ab} - (\alpha) = \mathfrak{b}(\alpha),$$

for the least common multiple of two ideals is equal to their product divided by their greatest common divisor. We have now

$$\begin{aligned}\{(\alpha), \mathfrak{ab}\} &= \{(\alpha) + \mathfrak{ab}, \mathfrak{ab}\} \quad (\S\ 2, \text{ii})\\ &= \{\mathfrak{a}, \mathfrak{ab}\},\end{aligned}$$

and also

$$\begin{aligned}\{(\alpha), \mathfrak{ab}\} &= \{(\alpha), (\alpha) - \mathfrak{ab}\} \quad (\S\ 2, \text{i})\\ &= \{(\alpha), (\alpha)\mathfrak{b}\}\\ &= \{(1), \mathfrak{b}\} \quad (\S\ 2, \text{iii})\\ &= n[\mathfrak{b}].\end{aligned}$$

Hence $$\{\mathfrak{a}, \mathfrak{ab}\} = n[\mathfrak{b}].$$

To prove the theorem, we observe that, since (1) is a divisor of $\mathfrak{a}$, and $\mathfrak{a}$ is a divisor of $\mathfrak{ab}$, we have by § 2, iv

$$\{(1), \mathfrak{ab}\} = \{(1), \mathfrak{a}\}\{\mathfrak{a}, \mathfrak{ab}\}$$

and hence $$n[\mathfrak{ab}] = n[\mathfrak{a}]n[\mathfrak{b}].$$

We have seen (Chap. XI, Th. 5) that the product of an ideal, $\mathfrak{a}$, by its conjugate, $\mathfrak{a}'$, is a rational principal ideal (a). We shall now show that

$$n[\mathfrak{a}] = |a|;$$

or in other words,

THEOREM 4. *If $\mathfrak{a}$ be an ideal of a quadratic realm and $\mathfrak{a}'$ its conjugate, then*

$$\mathfrak{aa}' = (n[\mathfrak{a}]).$$

We have $\mathfrak{aa}' = (a)$ (Chap. XI, Th. 5), where a is a rational integer which may be assumed to be positive.

Hence $$n[\mathfrak{a}]n[\mathfrak{a}'] = n[(a)] = a^2 \text{ (Th. 1. Cor. 2)}.$$

But $$n[\mathfrak{a}'] = n[\mathfrak{a}] \text{ (Th. 1, Cor. 1).}$$

Hence $$n[\mathfrak{a}] = a,$$

and $$\mathfrak{a}\mathfrak{a}' = (n[\mathfrak{a}]).$$

This theorem for the general realm of the nth degree is that $\mathfrak{a}\mathfrak{a}'\mathfrak{a}'' \cdots \mathfrak{a}^{(n-1)} = (n[\mathfrak{a}])$, where $\mathfrak{a}', \mathfrak{a}'', \cdots, \mathfrak{a}^{(n-1)}$ are the conjugates of $\mathfrak{a}$. The proof in the case of the quadratic realm here given is much simplified by having seen (Chap. XI, Th. 5) that in a quadratic realm the multiplication of $\mathfrak{a}$ by $\mathfrak{a}'$ gives a principal ideal. See Hilbert: Bericht, p. 191.

This property of the norm of an ideal might be taken as its definition. It would then be exactly in line with that of the norm of an integer. From Th. 4 it is evident that $n[\mathfrak{a}]$ is divisible by $\mathfrak{a}$, as in the case of integers.

THEOREM 5. *The norm of a principal ideal, (α), is equal to the absolute value of the norm of the integer α defining the ideal; that is,*

$$n[(\alpha)] = |n[\alpha]|.$$[1]

Let (α) be any principal ideal and (α') its conjugate.

Then $$(\alpha)(\alpha') = (n[(\alpha)]) \text{ (Th. 4),}$$

and also $$(\alpha)(\alpha') = (\alpha\alpha').$$

But $$\alpha\alpha' = n[\alpha] = a,$$

a rational integer, since the norm of an algebraic integer is a rational integer, and

$$n[(\alpha)] = b,$$

a positive rational integer.

Hence $$(a) = (b).$$

Since a is therefore divisible by b, and b by a, we have

$$|a| = b,$$

and hence

$$n[(\alpha)] = |n[\alpha]|.$$

[1] Hilbert: Bericht, Satz 20.

THEOREM 6. *The norm of a prime ideal, $\mathfrak{p}$, is a power of the rational prime which $\mathfrak{p}$ divides.*[1]

Let 1, ω be a basis of the realm and $\mathfrak{p}=(a, b+c\omega)$, where $a, b+c\omega$ is a canonical basis of $\mathfrak{p}$. It is evident that a is a prime, for, if $a=a_1a_2$, then since $\mathfrak{p}$ divides a, it must divide either a_1 or a_2, say a_1, then a_1 would be a number of $\mathfrak{p}$, which would be contrary to the hypothesis that $a, b+c\omega$ is a canonical basis of $\mathfrak{p}$, and hence that a is the smallest rational number of $\mathfrak{p}$. Hence a is a prime, p.

We have then

$$(p)=\mathfrak{p}\mathfrak{a},$$

whence
$$n[(p)]=n[\mathfrak{p}]n[\mathfrak{a}],$$

and
$$p^2=n[\mathfrak{p}]n[\mathfrak{a}], \qquad \text{(Th. 1, Cor. 2).}$$

Hence, since $n[\mathfrak{p}]$ and $n[\mathfrak{a}]$ are positive rational integers, we have either

$$n[\mathfrak{p}]=p, \tag{15}$$

or
$$n[\mathfrak{p}]=p^2; \tag{16}$$

we call $\mathfrak{p}$ a prime ideal of the *first* or *second degree* according as 15) or 16) occurs; that is, *the norm of a prime ideal, $\mathfrak{p}$, is a power of the rational prime which $\mathfrak{p}$ divides, and the exponent of this power is called the degree of $\mathfrak{p}$.*

For example:

$$n(3, 1+\sqrt{-5})=3,$$

and hence $(3, 1+\sqrt{-5})$ is a prime ideal of the first degree; on the other hand,

$$n[(2)]=2^2=4,$$

and hence (2) is a prime ideal of the second degree, both $(3, 1+\sqrt{-5})$ and (2) having been shown to be prime ideals.

COR. 1. *In a canonical basis, p, $b+c\omega$, of a prime ideal, $\mathfrak{p}$, the coefficient c is 1 or p, according as $\mathfrak{p}$ is of the first or second degree.*

[1] This theorem holds for realms of any degree, but the method of proof used here is not applicable to those of degree higher than the second. See Hilbert: Bericht, Satz 17.

Ex. 1. If $\mathfrak{a}$ and $\mathfrak{b}$ be two ideals and $\mathfrak{a}$ be prime to $n[\mathfrak{b}]$, then $n[\mathfrak{a}]$ is prime to $n[\mathfrak{b}]$.

Ex. 2. If $\mathfrak{p}_1, \mathfrak{p}_2, \cdots, \mathfrak{p}_n$ be prime ideals of the first degree no two of which are conjugate, and whose norms are $p_1, p_2, \cdots, p_n$, show that the smallest rational integer in the product $\mathfrak{p}_1\mathfrak{p}_2 \cdots \mathfrak{p}_n$ is $p_1 p_2 \cdots p_n$.

Ex. 3. If the ideal $\mathfrak{a}$ does not contain the factor (p), where p is a rational prime, and $n[\mathfrak{a}]$ be divisible by p^n but not by p^{n+1}, then $\mathfrak{a}$ is divisible by $\mathfrak{p}^n$, where $n[\mathfrak{p}]=p$.

§ 3. Determination and Classification of the Prime Ideals of a Quadratic Realm.

The last theorem furnishes us with a method for obtaining and classifying the prime ideals of any quadratic realm, $k(\sqrt{m})$, similar to that employed for the prime numbers of $k(i)$, $k(\sqrt{-3})$ and $k(\sqrt{2})$. We have seen that every prime ideal divides a rational prime; hence, to obtain all prime ideals of $k(\sqrt{m})$ we need only factor all rational primes into their prime ideal factors in $k(\sqrt{m})$. If $\mathfrak{p}$ be a prime ideal and p the rational prime which $\mathfrak{p}$ divides[1] (since $(-p)=(p)$ we may assume p positive), there are, it has been shown, two cases to be distinguished. That is, if

$$(p)=\mathfrak{p}\mathfrak{j},$$

then

$$p^2=n[\mathfrak{p}]n[\mathfrak{j}],$$

and we have either

i. $$n[\mathfrak{p}]=p\ ;\quad n[\mathfrak{j}]=p,$$

or ii. $$n[\mathfrak{p}]=p^2;\quad n[\mathfrak{j}]=1,$$

and hence $$\mathfrak{j}=(1).$$

From i it follows by Th. 4 and the unique factorization theorem that

$$(p)=\mathfrak{p}\mathfrak{p}';\ \text{that is,}\ \mathfrak{j}=\mathfrak{p}';$$

and from ii that

$$(p)=\mathfrak{p}.$$

[1] That only one rational prime can be divisible by a prime ideal $\mathfrak{p}$ is evident from the fact that, if two primes p and q were divisible by $\mathfrak{p}$, then their rational greatest common divisor 1 would be a number of $\mathfrak{p}$, and $\mathfrak{p}$ would be (1).

In i, (p) is factorable into two conjugate prime ideals of the first degree.

In ii, (p) is a prime ideal of the second degree.

We shall now determine the relation which the form of p bears to the occurrence of these cases, and shall see that the factorization of (p) depends upon whether the discriminant of the realm is a quadratic residue, a quadratic non-residue, or a multiple of p.

We shall show first that the necessary and sufficient condition for the factorability of (p) is that d shall be a quadratic residue of p or divisible by p, hence proving incidentally that the condition for the non-factorability of (p) is that d shall be a quadratic non-residue of p.

Suppose that i occurs; that is,

$$(p) = \mathfrak{p}\mathfrak{p}'. \tag{1}$$

Since $n[\mathfrak{p}] = p$, there are p incongruent number classes with respect to $\mathfrak{p}$. We may take as representatives of these classes the numbers $0, 1, \cdots, p-1$; for, since p is the smallest rational number in $\mathfrak{p}$, the differences of no two of these numbers is a number of $\mathfrak{p}$, and they are therefore incongruent to each other with respect to $\mathfrak{p}$.

It is evident that $\sqrt{m}$, which is an integer, is congruent to one of these numbers, say a, with respect to $\mathfrak{p}$; that is,

$$a - \sqrt{m} \equiv 0, \text{ mod } \mathfrak{p},$$

therefore, since $a + \sqrt{m}$ is an integer of $k(\sqrt{m})$,

$$(a - \sqrt{m})(a + \sqrt{m}) = a^2 - m \equiv 0, \text{ mod } \mathfrak{p},$$

and hence, since $a^2 - m$ is a rational number and p the smallest rational number in $\mathfrak{p}$,

$$a^2 - m \equiv 0, \text{ mod } p. \tag{2}$$

Hence that m shall be a quadratic residue of p or divisible by p is a necessary condition for the factorability of (p).

We must now distinguish between the two cases $p \neq 2$ and $p = 2$.

First let $p \neq 2$. It may be shown that in this case

$$a^2 - m \equiv 0, \text{ mod } p,$$

is a sufficient as well as necessary condition for the factorability of (p); for from

$$a^2 - m = (a - \sqrt{m})(a + \sqrt{m}) \equiv 0, \text{ mod } p,$$

it follows (Chap. XI, Th. 9) that, if (p) be unfactorable, either

$$a - \sqrt{m} \equiv 0, \text{ mod } (p),$$

or

$$a + \sqrt{m} \equiv 0, \text{ mod } (p),$$

and hence either

$$\left.\begin{aligned} a - \sqrt{m} &= \frac{x + y\sqrt{m}}{2} p \\ \text{or} \qquad a + \sqrt{m} &= \frac{x + y\sqrt{m}}{2} p \end{aligned}\right\} \qquad 3)$$

where x and y are either both even or both odd, the latter case being possible only when $m \equiv 1$, mod 4.

The equations 3) lead to the impossible equations

$$\mp 1 = yp/2.$$

Hence 3) are impossible, and that m shall be a quadratic residue of p or divisible by p is a sufficient as well as necessary condition for the factorability of (p). Therefore that m shall be a quadratic non-residue of p is a necessary and sufficient condition for the non-factorability of (p).

Now let the symbol (n/q), where q is an odd rational prime and n any rational integer, denote 1, -1, or 0, according as n is a quadratic residue or non-residue of q, or a multiple of q.

We shall now obtain the factors of (p) when $(p) = \mathfrak{p}\mathfrak{p}'$, and shall show that when $(m/p) = 1$ they are different, and when $(m/p) = 0$ they are alike; that is, (p) is then the square of a prime ideal.

When $(m/p)=1$, a is not divisible by p, and we shall show by actual multiplication that

$$(p)=(p,\ a+\sqrt{m})(p,\ a-\sqrt{m}).$$

We have

$$\begin{aligned}(p,\ a+\sqrt{m})(p,\ a-\sqrt{m})&=(p^2,\ pa-p\sqrt{m},\ pa+p\sqrt{m},\ a^2-m)\\ &=(p^2,\ pa-p\sqrt{m},\ 2pa,\ a^2-m)\\ &=(p^2,\ pa-p\sqrt{m},\ 2pa,\ a^2-m,\ p)\\ &=(p),\end{aligned}$$

since p is the greatest common divisor of p^2 and $2pa$ and may therefore be introduced into the symbol.

We shall show now that

$$(p,\ a+\sqrt{m})\neq(p,\ a-\sqrt{m}).$$

If they were the same, both would equal

$$\begin{aligned}(p,\ a+\sqrt{m},\ a-\sqrt{m})&=(p,\ a+\sqrt{m},\ 2a)\\ &=(p,\ a+\sqrt{m},\ 2a,\ 1)\\ &=(1),\end{aligned}$$

since p and $2a$ are two rational numbers prime to each other and 1 may therefore be introduced into the symbol. Hence (p) is the product of two different conjugate prime ideals when m is a quadratic residue of p.

When $(m/p)=0$, a is divisible by p, and we have by similar analysis

$$\begin{aligned}(p)&=(p,\ \sqrt{m})(p,\ -\sqrt{m})\\ &=(p,\ \sqrt{m})^2.\end{aligned}$$

Hence (p) is the square of a prime ideal, when m is divisible by p.

We see that, since the discriminant of the realm, $d,=m$ or $4m$, according as $m\equiv 1$, mod 4, or $\equiv 2$ or 3, mod 4,

$$(d/p)=(m/p).$$

We may express the results so far obtained conveniently as follows:

If p be an odd rational prime, (p) is the product of two different conjugate prime ideals, or is itself a prime ideal, or is the square of a prime ideal, according as

$$(d/p) = 1, \ -1, \text{ or } 0.$$

To obtain basis representations of $\mathfrak{p}$ we make use of Th. 1, Cor. 3, and at once recognize that when $(m/p) = 1$ and $m \equiv 2$ or 3, mod 4,

$$(p, a + \sqrt{m})$$

is the required representation, for

$$\begin{Vmatrix} p & 0 \\ a & 1 \end{Vmatrix} = p = n[\mathfrak{p}].$$

In the case $m \equiv 1$, mod 4, $(p, a + \sqrt{m})$ is not a basis representation of $\mathfrak{p}$, for when we express $a + \sqrt{m}$ as a linear combination of the basis numbers $1, (1 + \sqrt{m})/2$ of the realm, we have

$$\mathfrak{p} = \left(p, a - 1 + 2\left(\frac{1 + \sqrt{m}}{2}\right)\right),$$

that is not a basis representation, since

$$\begin{Vmatrix} p & 0 \\ a - 1 & 2 \end{Vmatrix} = 2p \neq n[\mathfrak{p}].$$

In this case we can, however, get a basis representation of $\mathfrak{p}$ as follows: since p is odd, a can be chosen so as to be not only a root of $a^2 \equiv m$, mod p, but also odd. Supposing this done, we can introduce into the symbol of $\mathfrak{p}$ the number $(a + \sqrt{m})/2$, and then omit $a + \sqrt{m}$, obtaining

$$\begin{aligned} \mathfrak{p} &= \left(p, \frac{a + \sqrt{m}}{2}\right) \\ &= \left(p, \frac{a - 1}{2} + \frac{1 + \sqrt{m}}{2}\right), \end{aligned}$$

which is a basis representation of $\mathfrak{p}$, since

$$\begin{Vmatrix} p & 0 \\ \frac{a - 1}{2} & 1 \end{Vmatrix} = p = n[\mathfrak{p}].$$

We consider now the case $(m/p)=0$.

In the cases $m\equiv 2$ or 3, mod 4, we have as the required basis representation

$$\mathfrak{p}=(p, \sqrt{m})$$

since

$$\begin{Vmatrix} p & 0 \\ 0 & 1 \end{Vmatrix} = p = n[\mathfrak{p}].$$

When $m\equiv 1$, mod 4, we can introduce the number $(p+\sqrt{m})/2$ into the symbol $(p, \sqrt{m})$, since p is odd, and thus have

$$\mathfrak{p}=(p, \sqrt{m})=\left(p, \sqrt{m}, \frac{p+\sqrt{m}}{2}\right)=\left(p, \frac{p-1}{2}+\frac{1+\sqrt{m}}{2}\right)$$

as a basis representation, since

$$\begin{Vmatrix} p & 0 \\ \frac{p-1}{2} & 1 \end{Vmatrix} = p = n[\mathfrak{p}].$$

Let now $p=2$.

We have in all cases $(m/2)=1$ or 0; that is, the necessary condition for the factorability of (2) is always satisfied. As to the sufficiency of this condition we must however distinguish three cases according as $m\equiv 3$, 2 or 1, mod 4. When $m\equiv 3$, mod 4, we have $(m/2)=1$, and from 2), $a=1$.

Putting, therefore, in equations 3) $p=2$ and $a=1$, and remembering that when $m\equiv 3$, mod 4, x and y must both be even, we see that 3) leads to the impossible equation

$$1= x.$$

Hence $(m/2)=1$, in the case $m\equiv 3$, mod 4, is a sufficient condition for the factorability of (2).

We have indeed

$$(2)=(2, 1+\sqrt{m})(2, 1-\sqrt{m})$$

for 2 and $1+\sqrt{m}$ are evidently numbers of $\mathfrak{p}$ and

$$\begin{Vmatrix} 2 & 0 \\ 1 & 1 \end{Vmatrix} = 2 = n[\mathfrak{p}].$$

Hence $(2, 1+\sqrt{m})$ and $(2, 1-\sqrt{m})$ are the factors of (2). But evidently

$$(2, 1+\sqrt{m}) = (2, 1-\sqrt{m}),$$

and hence

$$(2) = (2, 1+\sqrt{m})^2,$$

a result which may be verified by multiplication. Thus when $m \equiv 3$, mod 4, (2) is the square of a prime ideal.

When $m \equiv 2$, mod 4, we have $(m/2) = 0$, and from 2) $a = 0$. Putting, therefore, in 3) $p = 2$ and $a = 0$, and remembering that when $m \equiv 2$, mod 4, x and y must be even, we see that 3) leads to the impossible equations

$$\pm 1 = y.$$

Hence $(m/2) = 0$ is also a sufficient condition for the factorability of (2). We can show just as above that in this case

$$(2) = (2, \sqrt{m})^2.$$

When $m \equiv 1$, mod 4, we have $(m/2) = 1$, and from 2) $a = 1$. Putting $p = 2$ and $a = 1$ in 3) we see, however, that $x = 1$, $y = -1$ satisfy the first of these equations and $x = 1$, $y = 1$ the second, $(1-\sqrt{m})/2$ and $(1+\sqrt{m})/2$ both being integers of $k(\sqrt{m})$, when $m \equiv 1$, mod 4. Hence both $(1-\sqrt{m})$ and $(1+\sqrt{m})$ are divisible by (2) and nothing is known as to whether (2) is prime or not.

To determine when $(2) = \mathfrak{p}\mathfrak{p}'$ we may proceed as follows: If $(2) = \mathfrak{p}\mathfrak{p}'$, then 0, 1 is a complete system of incongruent numbers with respect to $\mathfrak{p}$, and hence $(1+\sqrt{m})/2$ must be congruent to either 0 or 1 with respect to $\mathfrak{p}$; that is, we must have either

$$\frac{1+\sqrt{m}}{2} \equiv 0, \text{ mod } \mathfrak{p},$$

or

$$1 - \frac{1+\sqrt{m}}{2} = \frac{1-\sqrt{m}}{2} \equiv 0, \text{ mod } \mathfrak{p};$$

and hence in any case

$$\left(\frac{1+\sqrt{m}}{2}\right)\left(\frac{1-\sqrt{m}}{2}\right) = \frac{1-m}{4} \equiv 0, \text{ mod } \mathfrak{p}.$$

But $(1-m)/4$ is a rational integer and we must have therefore

$$\frac{1-m}{4} \equiv 0, \bmod 2, \qquad 4)$$

since 2 is the smallest rational number in $\mathfrak{p}$.

From 4) it follows that

$$1-m \equiv 0, \bmod 8;$$

that is, $$m \equiv 1, \bmod 8,$$

is a necessary condition for the factorability of (2) when $m \equiv 1$, mod 4.

We must now distinguish two cases according as $m \equiv 1$ or 5, mod 8. In the latter case (2) is evidently a prime ideal, for 4) is no longer satisfied. We shall proceed to show that when $m \equiv 1$, mod 8, (2) is the product of two different conjugate prime ideals. If (2) be factorable, $\mathfrak{p}$ must contain one of the numbers $(1+\sqrt{m})/2$, $(1-\sqrt{m})/2$, and hence $\mathfrak{p}'$ the other. Moreover, we have

$$\begin{Vmatrix} 2 & 0 \\ 0 & 1 \end{Vmatrix} = 2 = n(\mathfrak{p}).$$

Hence, if (2) be factorable, we have

$$(2) = \left(2, \frac{1+\sqrt{m}}{2}\right)\left(2, \frac{1-\sqrt{m}}{2}\right),$$

and this may be shown to be correct, for by multiplication we get

$$\begin{aligned}\left(2, \frac{1+\sqrt{m}}{2}\right)\left(2, \frac{1-\sqrt{m}}{2}\right) &= \left(4, 1-\sqrt{m}, 1+\sqrt{m}, \frac{1-m}{4}\right) \\ &= \left(4, 1-\sqrt{m}, \frac{1-m}{4}, 2\right) \\ &= (2),\end{aligned}$$

since $(1-m)/4$ and $1-\sqrt{m}$ are divisible by 2, when $m \equiv 1$, mod 8. Moreover,

$$\left(2, \frac{1+\sqrt{m}}{2}\right) + \left(2, \frac{1-\sqrt{m}}{2}\right),$$

for, if they were the same, they would both equal

$$\left(2, \frac{1+\sqrt{m}}{2}, \frac{1-\sqrt{m}}{2}\right)=\left(2, \frac{1+\sqrt{m}}{2}, \frac{1-\sqrt{m}}{2}, 1\right)=(1),$$

which is, of course, impossible. Hence, when $m\equiv 1$, mod 8, (2) is the product of two different conjugate prime ideals.

We may collect the results obtained for (2) as follows:

(2) is the square of a prime ideal when $m\equiv 3$ or 2, mod 4; it is the product of two different conjugate prime ideals, when $m\equiv 1$, mod 8, and it is a prime ideal when $m\equiv 5$, mod 8.

We have evidently as basis representations of the factors of (2) in these cases respectively

$$(2)=(2, 1+\sqrt{m})^2, \qquad (2)=(2, \sqrt{m})^2,$$

$$(2)=\left(2, \frac{1+\sqrt{m}}{2}\right)\left(2, \frac{1-\sqrt{m}}{2}\right),$$

$$(2)=(2, 1+\sqrt{m}).$$

Let now the symbol $(n/2)$ denote 1, —1, or 0 according as n is a quadratic residue or non-residue of 8 or is divisible by 2, and observe that, when $m\equiv 3$ or 2, mod 4, $d=4m$, and hence is always divisible by 2, and that when $m\equiv 1$, mod 4, $d=m$, and hence is a quadratic residue of 8 when and only when $m\equiv 1$, mod 8, and a quadratic non-residue of 8 when and only when $m\equiv 5$, mod 8. We may now combine the results obtained for $p=2$ with those for $p\neq 2$ in the following theorem:

THEOREM 7. *If p be any rational prime, (p) is the product of two different conjugate prime ideals of the first degree, a prime ideal of the second degree, or the square of a prime ideal of the first degree, according as $(d/p)=1, -1$, or 0.*[1]

An ideal $\mathfrak{a}$ of a quadratic realm such that $\mathfrak{a}=\mathfrak{a}'$ and which contains as a factor no ideal (a), where a is a rational integer different from ± 1, is called an ambiguous ideal. The ambiguous prime ideals of a quadratic realm are evidently the prime factors of (d).

The following table gives basis representations of the prime factors of (p) in a convenient form for reference.

[1] See Hilbert: Bericht, Satz 97.

In it a satisfies the congruence $a^2 \equiv m$, mod p, and is, moreover an odd integer in the case when $m \equiv 1$, mod 4.

	$m \equiv 1$, mod 4	$m \equiv 2$ or 3, mod 4
$\left(\frac{d}{p}\right) = 1$	$(p) = \left(p, \frac{a+\sqrt{m}}{2}\right)\left(p, \frac{a-\sqrt{m}}{2}\right)$	$(p) = (p, a+\sqrt{m})(p, a-\sqrt{m})$
$\left(\frac{d}{p}\right) = -1$	$(p) = \left(p, \frac{p+p\sqrt{m}}{2}\right)$	$(p) = (p, p\sqrt{m})$
$\left(\frac{d}{p}\right) = 0$	$(p) = \left(p, \frac{p+\sqrt{m}}{2}\right)^2$	$(p) = (p, a+\sqrt{m})^2$

Ex. 1. $k(\sqrt{-13})$

We have $-13 \equiv 3$, mod 4, whence $1, \sqrt{-13}$ is a basis of $k(\sqrt{-13})$ and $d = -52$.
Since

$$\left(\frac{-52}{2}\right) = 0,$$

and $1^2 \equiv -13$, mod 2, we have $(2) = (2, 1+\sqrt{-13})^2$. Since

$$\left(\frac{-52}{3}\right) = -1,$$

(3) is a prime ideal. Since

$$\left(\frac{-52}{5}\right) = -1,$$

(5) is a prime ideal.

Ex. 2. Find basis representations of the prime ideal factors of all rational primes less than 20 in the realms $k(\sqrt{-7})$, $k(\sqrt{11})$ and $k(\sqrt{30})$.

Ex. 3. If the norm of any ideal be divisible by an odd power of a rational prime, p, then p is factorable into two conjugate prime ideals of the first degree.

§ 4. Resolution of any Given Ideal into its Prime Factors.

We have in the last section given a general method for resolving any principal ideal defined by a rational prime number into its prime ideal factors.

The resolution of any given ideal $\mathfrak{a}$ can be effected by observing that the product of the norms of the prime factors of $\mathfrak{a}$ must equal $n[\mathfrak{a}]$, and hence the only possible prime factors of $\mathfrak{a}$ are the prime ideal factors of the rational primes which divide $n[\mathfrak{a}]$.

We then determine by actual multiplication which of the finite number of prime ideals satisfying this condition are the proper ones.

We shall see that the resolution of any ideal $\mathfrak{a}, = (\alpha_1, \alpha_2, \cdots, \alpha_n)$, can be made to depend upon the resolution of the principal ideals (α_1), (α_2), $\cdots$, (α_n), and shall illustrate by the following example the resolution of a principal ideal into its prime factors.

Let $k(\sqrt{-5})$ be the given realm and $(10+\sqrt{-5})$ be the given ideal; then

$$n[(10+\sqrt{-5})] = 105 = 3\cdot5\cdot7.$$

Hence $(10+\sqrt{-5})$ must be the product of three prime ideals whose norms are respectively 3, 5 and 7. The prime ideals whose norms are 3 are evidently $(3, 1+\sqrt{-5})$ and $(3, 1-\sqrt{-5})$. The only one whose norm is 5 is $(\sqrt{-5})$. Those whose norms are 7 are $(7, 3+\sqrt{-5})$ and $(7, 3-\sqrt{-5})$.

By multiplication we can determine which of the four possible combinations of these ideals is the correct one. We can, however, materially shorten the process by observing that, if $(10+\sqrt{-5})$ be divisible by $(7, 3-\sqrt{-5})$, then $(10+\sqrt{-5})$ is a number of $(7, 3-\sqrt{-5})$; that is,

$$\begin{aligned}(7, 3-\sqrt{-5}) &= (7, 3-\sqrt{-5}, 10+\sqrt{-5}) \\ &= (7, 3-\sqrt{-5}, 10+\sqrt{-5}, 13) \\ &= (7, 3-\sqrt{-5}, 10+\sqrt{-5}, 13, 1) \\ &= (1),\end{aligned}$$

which is impossible.

Hence $(7, 3-\sqrt{-5})$ is not a factor of $(10+\sqrt{-5})$.

Since $7, 3-\sqrt{-5}$ is a basis of $(7, 3-\sqrt{-5})$ we could have determined whether or not $10+\sqrt{-5}$ is a number of $(7, 3-\sqrt{-5})$ by seeing whether or not

$$10+\sqrt{-5} = 7x + (3-\sqrt{-5})y$$

where x and y are rational integers. This equation gives $x = 13/7$, $y = -1$, and it is again proved that $(10+\sqrt{-5})$ is not divisible by $(7, 3-\sqrt{-5})$. In like manner we can show that $(3, 1-\sqrt{-5})$ does not divide $(10+\sqrt{-5})$. Hence

$$(10+\sqrt{-5}) = (3, 1+\sqrt{-5})(\sqrt{-5})(7, 3+\sqrt{-5}).$$

Had we first tested either $(7, 3+\sqrt{-5})$ or $(3, 1+\sqrt{-5})$ we should have found, of course, that $(10+\sqrt{-5})$ was divisible by it.

If $n[(\alpha)]$ be divisible by a higher power, p^r, than the first of a rational prime, p, then either (p) is a prime ideal in which case α is divisible by $p^{r/2}$, this case being possible therefore only when r is even, or (p) is the product of two conjugate prime ideals, $\mathfrak{p}, \mathfrak{p}'$, of the first degree.

In this case (α) may be divisible by both $\mathfrak{p}$ and $\mathfrak{p}'$, and hence α by p, or (α) may be divisible simply by a power of one of the ideals, say $\mathfrak{p}$.

If
$$\alpha = p^e \alpha_1,$$
where α_1 is not divisible by p, then (α_1) cannot be divisible by the product $\mathfrak{p}\mathfrak{p}'$ and hence, if $n[(\alpha_1)]$ be divisible by p^s, then α_1 is divisible by either $\mathfrak{p}^s$ or $\mathfrak{p}'^s$, these cases occurring respectively as (α_1) is divisible by $\mathfrak{p}$ or $\mathfrak{p}'$.

The resolution of any principal ideal into its prime factors can therefore be effected.

Let now $\mathfrak{a} = (\alpha_1, \alpha_2, \cdots, \alpha_n)$ be any ideal. Since $\mathfrak{a}$ is the greatest common divisor of the principal ideals $(\alpha_1), (\alpha_2), \cdots, (\alpha_n)$, we can effect the resolution of $\mathfrak{a}$ into its prime ideal factors by resolving the ideals $(\alpha_1), (\alpha_2), \cdots, (\alpha_n)$ into their prime factors and taking their greatest common divisor; this will be $\mathfrak{a}$.

Ex. 1. Let $(21, 10+\sqrt{-5})$ be the given ideal. We have found above that
$$(10+\sqrt{-5}) = (3, 1+\sqrt{-5})(\sqrt{-5})(7, 3+\sqrt{-5}),$$
and we have evidently
$$(21) = (3, 1+\sqrt{-5})(3, 1-\sqrt{-5})(7, 3+\sqrt{-5})(7, 3-\sqrt{-5}).$$
Hence
$$(21, 10+\sqrt{-5}) = (3, 1+\sqrt{-5})(7, 3+\sqrt{-5})$$
is the resolution of $(21, 10+\sqrt{-5})$ into its prime factors.

Ex. 2. Resolve the ideal (30) into its prime ideal factors in the realms $k(\sqrt{-5})$, $k(\sqrt{-7})$ and $k(\sqrt{30})$.

Ex. 3. Resolve the ideal $(24-\sqrt{26})$ into its prime ideal factors in the realm $k(\sqrt{26})$.

Results should be verified by multiplication.

There are many devices which shorten numerical work with ideals, some of which will be illustrated later in the solution of examples.

§ 5. Determination of the Norm of any Given Ideal.

If an ideal has been resolved into its prime factors, or if we have a basis of the ideal, its norm is easily found.

Let $\mathfrak{a}, = (\alpha_1, \alpha_2, \cdots, \alpha_n)$, be the given ideal, and let

$$\mathfrak{a} = \mathfrak{p}_1 \mathfrak{p}_2 \cdots \mathfrak{p}_r$$

be the resolution of $\mathfrak{a}$ into its prime factors; then

$$n[\mathfrak{a}] = n[\mathfrak{p}_1] n[\mathfrak{p}_2] \cdots n[\mathfrak{p}_r].$$

If we have a basis $a_1\omega_1 + a_2\omega_2$, $b_1\omega_1 + b_2\omega_2$ of $\mathfrak{a}$, we have, of course, at once

$$n[\mathfrak{a}] = \left\| \begin{matrix} a_1 & a_2 \\ b_1 & b_2 \end{matrix} \right\|.$$

THEOREM 8. *The greatest common divisor of the norms of the numbers of* $\mathfrak{a}$ *is* $n[\mathfrak{a}]$.

Let $n[\mathfrak{a}] = a$, and let α be a number of $\mathfrak{a}$ such that $(\alpha)/\mathfrak{a}$ is prime to (a). Then, if α' be the conjugate of α and $\mathfrak{a}'$ the conjugate of $\mathfrak{a}$, we have $(\alpha')/\mathfrak{a}'$ also prime to (a), and hence $(n[\alpha])/(a)$ prime to (a). Therefore a is the greatest common divisor of $n[a]$ and $n[\alpha]$, and hence of the norms of all numbers of $\mathfrak{a}$.[1]

It should be observed that the greatest common divisor of the norms of the numbers *defining* $\mathfrak{a}$ is not necessarily $n[\mathfrak{a}]$, though, of course, $n[\mathfrak{a}]$ is a divisor of it; for example,

$$(1 + \sqrt{-5},\ 1 - \sqrt{-5}) = (2,\ 1 + \sqrt{-5})$$

is an ideal whose norm is 2, but the greatest common divisor of $n[1 + \sqrt{-5}]$ and $n[1 - \sqrt{-5}]$ is 6.

§ 6. Determination of a Basis of any Given Ideal.

Let $\mathfrak{a}, = (\alpha_1, \alpha_2, \cdots, \alpha_n)$, be the given ideal and let $n[\mathfrak{a}]$ be known. If two numbers, $\alpha_i, = a_1\omega_1 + a_2\omega_2$, $\alpha_j, = b_1\omega_1 + b_2\omega_2$, of $\mathfrak{a}$ be known, such that

$$\left\| \begin{matrix} a_1 & a_2 \\ b_1 & b_2 \end{matrix} \right\| = n[\mathfrak{a}],$$

[1] Hilbert: Bericht, Satz 21.

then evidently α_i, α_j constitute a basis of $\mathfrak{a}$. If no numbers satisfying this condition be known, we can determine a canonical basis, a, $b+c\omega$, of $\mathfrak{a}$, where a and c may be assumed positive, as follows:

We observe first that, if a_1, $b_1+c_1\omega$ be a canonical basis of an ideal $\mathfrak{a}$, and e a rational integer, then a_1e, $b_1e+c_1e\omega$ is a canonical basis of the ideal $\mathfrak{a}(e)$. The determination of a basis of $\mathfrak{a}$ can therefore be reduced always to the determination of a canonical basis of an ideal which is the product only of prime ideals of the first degree, no two of which are conjugates.

Having resolved $\mathfrak{a}$ into its prime factors, we collect all pairs of conjugate prime ideals of the first degree and all prime ideals of the second degree. The product of these factors will be the principal ideal (e) where e is a rational integer, and we have

$$\mathfrak{a}=\mathfrak{a}_1(e),$$

where $\mathfrak{a}_1$ is the product of prime ideals of the first degree only, no two of which are conjugates, and whose norms are

$$p_1, p_2, \cdots, p_m.$$

To find a canonical basis a_1, $b_1+c_1\omega$ of $\mathfrak{a}_1$, we observe that a_1, being the smallest rational integer divisible by $\mathfrak{a}_1$, must be $p_1p_2\cdots p_m$, and furthermore that, since

$$a_1c_1=n[\mathfrak{a}_1]=p_1p_2\cdots p_m,$$

$$c_1=1.$$

Hence $p_1p_2\cdots p_m$, $b_1+\omega$ is a canonical basis of $\mathfrak{a}_1$, where b_1 is to be determined. Since $n[b_1+\omega]$ is a rational integer and a number of $\mathfrak{a}_1$ we have

$$n[b_1+\omega]\equiv 0, \text{ mod } p_1p_2\cdots p_m; \qquad 1)$$

that is, when $\omega=\sqrt{m}$, $b_1^2-m\equiv 0$, mod $p_1p_2\cdots p_m$, 2)

and when

$$\omega=\frac{1+\sqrt{m}}{2}, \quad \frac{(2b_1+1)^2-m}{4}\equiv 0, \quad \text{mod } p_1p_2\cdots p_m. \qquad 3)$$

It will be easily seen that 2) and 3) have solutions which fall into pairs, $b_1, -b_1$ and $2b_1+1, -2b_1-1$, and that each pair of solutions of 2) gives the numbers

$$b_1+\sqrt{m}, \quad -b_1+\sqrt{m},$$

and each pair of solutions of 3) the numbers

$$\frac{2b_1+1+\sqrt{m}}{2}, \quad \frac{-2b_1-1+\sqrt{m}}{2}.$$

One of the numbers so obtained must belong to $\mathfrak{a}_1$ and can, of course, always be determined by resolving the numbers into their prime factors and thus finding out which is divisible by $\mathfrak{a}_1$. It can, however, usually be determined with much less work from the fact that in determining which of these numbers is divisible by $\mathfrak{a}_1$, it is helpful to observe that, if $\mathfrak{a}_1$ be divisible by $\mathfrak{p}^r$ but not by $\mathfrak{p}^{r+1}$, where $n[\mathfrak{p}]=p$, and if α be one of the numbers satisfying 1), and $n[\alpha]$ be divisible by p^r but not by p^{r+1}, α itself not being divisible by p, then if α be divisible by $\mathfrak{p}$, it is divisible by $\mathfrak{p}^r$.

The above method for determining a basis of an ideal $\mathfrak{a}$ depended upon the knowledge of the prime factors of $\mathfrak{a}$. We shall now explain how a basis may be determined without this knowledge and without that of $n[\mathfrak{a}]$, giving therefore incidentally a method for finding $n[\mathfrak{a}]$. We have seen that, if among the prime factors of $\mathfrak{a}$ there occur one or more pairs of conjugate ideals[1], $\mathfrak{a}$ is divisible by a principal ideal (e), where e is a rational integer. Every number, $a_i+b_i\omega$, is therefore a number of (e) and hence is divisible by e. Therefore a_i and b_i must be divisible by e. Conversely, if in every number, $a_i+b_i\omega$, of $\mathfrak{a}$, a_i and b_i, be divisible by e, then $\mathfrak{a}$ is divisible by (e).

Let e be the greatest common divisor of the coefficients, a_i, b_i, in all the numbers defining $\mathfrak{a}$, and let $a_i=er_i$, $b_i=es_i$. Then

$$\mathfrak{a}=\mathfrak{a}_1(e),$$

where $\mathfrak{a}_1$ is the product of prime ideals of the first degree, no two of which are conjugates. We have seen that a canonical basis of $\mathfrak{a}_1$ has the form $a, b+\omega$. Furthermore $\mathfrak{a}_1=(r_1+s_1\omega, \cdots, r_n+s_n\omega)$ and the greatest common divisor of $r_1, \cdots, r_n, s_1, \cdots, s_n$ is 1. By

[1] Of the first degree or one or more of the second degree.

multiplying each number, $r_i + s_i\omega$, defining $\mathfrak{a}_1$, by ω, when $\omega = \sqrt{m}$, and by $\omega - 1$, when $\omega = \frac{1}{2}(1 + \sqrt{m})$, we can introduce into the symbol the numbers, $t_i + r_i\omega$; that is, such that the coefficient of ω is r_i. Since the greatest common divisor of the coefficients, $r_1, \cdots, r_n, s_1, \cdots, s_n$, of ω is 1, we can find rational integers, $u_1, \cdots, u_n, v_1, \cdots, v_n$, such that

$$r_1u_1 + \cdots + r_nu_n + s_1v_1 + \cdots + s_nv_n = 1,$$

and hence can introduce into the symbol a number $b + \omega$; that is, one in which the coefficient of ω is 1. This is evidently one of the desired basis numbers. To find the other number, a, we proceed as follows. Every number in the symbol can be expressed as a linear combination of $b + \omega$ and a rational integer; thus

$$r_1 + s_1\omega = s_1(b + \omega) + r_1 - s_1b = s_1(b + \omega) + c_1,$$

where c_1 is a rational integer. We have therefore

$$c_1 = r_1 + s_1\omega - s_1(b + \omega).$$

Hence we can introduce c_1 into the symbol and omit $r_1 + s_1\omega$. Proceeding in this manner with each of the remaining numbers, we have finally in the symbol only rational integers and $b + \omega$. Let a be the greatest common divisor of these rational integers and $n[b + \omega]$. Evidently we can introduce a into the symbol and omit all of the remaining rational integers ; that is, we have

$$\mathfrak{a}_1 = (a,\ b + \omega).$$

To show that $a,\ b + \omega$ is a basis of $\mathfrak{a}_1$, we must show that any linear combination $a(e_1 + f_1\omega) + (b + \omega)(e_2 + f_2\omega)$ of a and $b + \omega$, where $e_1 + f_1\omega$, $e_2 + f_2\omega$ are any integers of the realm, is expressible as a linear combination $ax + (b + \omega)y$, where x and y are rational integers; that is, we must show that the equation

$$ax + (b + \omega)y = a(e_1 + f_1\omega) + (b + \omega)(e_2 + f_2\omega)$$

is satisfied by integral values of x and y for all integral values of e_1, f_1, e_2, f_2. Multiplying, putting $\omega^2 = m$, or $\omega + \frac{1}{4}(m - 1)$, according as $\omega = \sqrt{m}$, or $\frac{1}{2}(1 + \sqrt{m})$, equating coefficients and making use of the fact that $n[b + \omega]$ is divisible by a, we see easily that this condition is satisfied. Hence $a, b+\omega$ is a canonical basis of $\mathfrak{a}_1$.

It is well to observe that, when an ideal has the form $(a, b+\omega)$, it does not follow necessarily that $a, b+\omega$ is a basis. The necessary and sufficient condition for this is that $n[b+\omega]$ shall be divisible by a.

Ex. 1. Let $\mathfrak{a}=(2)(11)(3, 1+\sqrt{-5})^2(7, 3+\sqrt{-5})$ be the ideal whose basis it is required to determine. We have

$$\mathfrak{a}_1=(3, 1+\sqrt{-5})^2(7, 3+\sqrt{-5}),$$

and

$$n[\mathfrak{a}_1]=63.$$

Hence $63, b+\sqrt{-5}$ is a canonical basis of $\mathfrak{a}_1$, where b is to be determined by the condition

$$b+\sqrt{-5}\equiv 0, \text{ mod } \mathfrak{a}_1.$$

The condition

$$n[b+\sqrt{-5}]\equiv 0, \text{ mod } 63;$$

that is,

$$b^2+5\equiv 0, \text{ mod } 63,$$

gives

$$b=11, -11, 25 \text{ or } -25,$$

and hence as possible basis numbers of $\mathfrak{a}_1$

$$11+\sqrt{-5},\ -11+\sqrt{-5},\ 25+\sqrt{-5},\ -25+\sqrt{-5}.$$

It is easily seen that $11+\sqrt{-5}$ and $-25+\sqrt{-5}$ are not divisible by $(3, 1+\sqrt{-5})$ and hence, of course, are not divisible by $\mathfrak{a}_1$, while of the two numbers $-11+\sqrt{-5}$ and $25+\sqrt{-5}$ remaining, only $-11+\sqrt{-5}$ is divisible by $(7, 3+\sqrt{-5})$.

Hence $-11+\sqrt{-5}$ is the number required, a result easily verified when we see that

$$(-11+\sqrt{-5})=(2, 1+\sqrt{-5})(3, 1+\sqrt{-5})^2(7, 3+\sqrt{-5}).$$

Hence, $63, -11+\sqrt{-5}$ is a basis of $\mathfrak{a}_1$, and $(1386, -242+22\sqrt{-5})$ is a basis representation of $\mathfrak{a}$.

Ex. 2. Let $\mathfrak{a}=(210, 70+70\sqrt{-5}, 90+30\sqrt{-5}, -20+40\sqrt{-5})$ be the ideal whose basis it is required to determine. Using the second method, we have $e=10$ and

$$\mathfrak{a}_1=(21, 7+7\sqrt{-5}, 9+3\sqrt{-5}, -2+4\sqrt{-5}).$$

We see that we can introduce the number $10+\sqrt{-5}$ and have easily

$$\mathfrak{a}_1=(21, 63, 21, 42, 10+\sqrt{-5}).$$

Now 21 is the greatest common divisor of 21, 63, 42 and $n[10+\sqrt{-5}]$, $=105$, and therefore

$$\mathfrak{a}_1=(21, 10+\sqrt{-5}),$$

where $21, 10+\sqrt{-5}$ is a canonical basis. A canonical basis of $\mathfrak{a}$ is evidently $210, 100+10\sqrt{-5}$.

§ 7. Determination of a number α of any ideal $\mathfrak{a}$ such that $(\alpha)/\mathfrak{a}$ is prime to any given ideal $\mathfrak{m}$.

We have proved the existence of such a number and shall now show how it may be determined in any given case, this problem being not only of interest but of considerable importance in the solution of certain problems to be given later. The proof given above of the existence of α furnishes us with a clue to a method for its determination, which we shall illustrate by some examples. As is seen from the above proof, the determination of α in the general case is dependent only upon its determination in the case where $\mathfrak{m}$ is a prime ideal $\mathfrak{p}$.

If $\mathfrak{a}, = (\alpha_1, \alpha_2, \cdots, \alpha_m)$, be any ideal, then some one, α_i, of the numbers $\alpha_1, \alpha_2, \cdots, \alpha_m$,[1] defining $\mathfrak{a}$, which are, of course, all divisible by $\mathfrak{a}$, must be indivisible by $\mathfrak{ap}$; for otherwise, all numbers of $\mathfrak{a}$ would belong to $\mathfrak{ap}$ and $\mathfrak{a}$ be divisible by $\mathfrak{ap}$, which is impossible. This number, α_i, is the required number α. We have, therefore, merely to resolve in turn the numbers defining $\mathfrak{a}$ into their prime ideal factors until we find one which satisfies the required condition.

Consider the realm $k(\sqrt{-5})$ and let

$$\mathfrak{a} = (21, 10 + \sqrt{-5}); \quad \mathfrak{m} = (2, 1 + \sqrt{-5}).$$

Resolving $\mathfrak{a}$ into its prime factors, we have

$$\mathfrak{a} = (3, 1 + \sqrt{-5})(7, 3 + \sqrt{-5}).$$

Proceeding now to resolve in turn the numbers defining $\mathfrak{a}$ into their prime ideal factors, we have evidently

$$(21) = (3)(7) =$$

$$(3, 1 + \sqrt{-5})(3, 1 - \sqrt{-5})(7, 3 + \sqrt{-5})(7, 3 - \sqrt{-5}).$$

We see now that the quotient

$$(21)/\mathfrak{a} = (3, 1 - \sqrt{-5})(7, 3 - \sqrt{-5}),$$

is prime to $(2, 1 + \sqrt{-5})$, and hence 21 is the number, α, required.

[1] We can reduce these always to two but have chosen the more general case so as to show that this reduction is unnecessary.

Also, since

$$(10+\sqrt{-5})=(3,\ 1+\sqrt{-5})(7,\ 3+\sqrt{-5})(\sqrt{-5}),$$

the quotient

$$\frac{(10+\sqrt{-5})}{\mathfrak{a}}=(\sqrt{-5})$$

is seen to be prime to $(2,\ 1+\sqrt{-5})$; hence $10+\sqrt{-5}$ will also serve as α. We could have seen at once that either 21 or $10+\sqrt{-5}$ would serve as the required number, for they are both prime to $(2,\ 1+\sqrt{-5})$, their norms being prime to $n(2,\ 1+\sqrt{-5})$. If $\mathfrak{a}$ be a principal ideal (β) and $\mathfrak{m}$ any ideal, it is evident that the quotient

$$(\beta)/(\beta)=(1)$$

is prime to $\mathfrak{m}$, and hence β is the number, α, required.

To illustrate the determination of α in the general case, let

$$\mathfrak{a}=(21,\ 10+\sqrt{-5}) \text{ and } \mathfrak{m}=(15,\ 5+\sqrt{-5}).$$

Resolving these ideals into their prime ideal factors, we have as above

$$\mathfrak{a}=(3,\ 1+\sqrt{-5})(7,\ 3+\sqrt{-5}),$$

and $$\mathfrak{m}=(3,\ 1-\sqrt{-5})(\sqrt{-5}),$$

the last result being easily obtained by the method employed in the factorization of $\mathfrak{a}$, or by simply observing that each number defining $\mathfrak{m}$ is divisible by $\sqrt{-5}$.

We have found

$$(21)=(3,\ 1+\sqrt{-5})(3,\ 1-\sqrt{-5})(7,\ 3+\sqrt{-5})(7,\ 3-\sqrt{-5}),$$

and $(10+\sqrt{-5})=(3,\ 1+\sqrt{-5})(7,\ 3+\sqrt{-5})(\sqrt{-5})$, and it is well to see whether one of these numbers does not fulfil the conditions demanded of α, this often being the case. Here we see, however, that neither of the quotients,

$$(21)/\mathfrak{a}=(3,\ 1-\sqrt{-5})(7,\ 3-\sqrt{-5}),$$

or $$(10+\sqrt{-5})/\mathfrak{a}=(\sqrt{-5}),$$

is prime to $\mathfrak{m}$, and therefore that neither of the numbers 21 or $10+\sqrt{-5}$ will serve as α. Hence we must proceed to construct α as in the above proof.

We have

$$\mathfrak{a}_1=(3,\ 1+\sqrt{-5})(7,\ 3+\sqrt{-5})(3,\ 1-\sqrt{-5}),$$

$$\mathfrak{a}_2=(3,\ 1+\sqrt{-5})(7,\ 3+\sqrt{-5})(\sqrt{-5}),$$

and it is at once evident that 21 and $10+\sqrt{-5}$ will serve as α_1 and α_2 respectively; for the quotient,

$$(21)/\mathfrak{a}_1=(7,\ 3-\sqrt{-5})$$

is prime to $(\sqrt{-5})$, and

$$(10+\sqrt{-5})/\mathfrak{a}_2=(1)$$

is prime to $(3,\ 1-\sqrt{-5})$.

Hence $\qquad \alpha=21+10+\sqrt{-5}=31+\sqrt{-5}$

is the number required.

This result is easily substantiated by factoring $(31+\sqrt{-5})$ into its prime ideal factors.

We have

$$n(31+\sqrt{-5})=966=2\cdot 3\cdot 7\cdot 23;$$

hence $(31+\sqrt{-5})$ is the product of four ideals whose norms are respectively, 2, 3, 7 and 23. The quotient, $(31+\sqrt{-5})/\mathfrak{a}$, is therefore the product of two ideals whose norms are respectively 2 and 23, and hence is prime to $\mathfrak{m}$, whose factors have the norms 3 and 5. We indeed see easily that

$$(31+\sqrt{-5})=(2,\ 1+\sqrt{-5})(3,\ 1+\sqrt{-5})(7,\ 3+\sqrt{-5})$$
$$(23,\ 8+\sqrt{-5}).$$

§ 8. The ϕ-Function for Ideals.

By $\phi(\mathfrak{m})$, where $\mathfrak{m}$ is any ideal, we denote the number of integers of a complete residue system, mod $\mathfrak{m}$, which are prime to $\mathfrak{m}$; that is, the number of integers in a reduced residue system, mod $\mathfrak{m}$.

Thus, if $\mathfrak{m}=(3, 1+\sqrt{-5})$, taking as a complete residue system, mod $(3, 1+\sqrt{-5})$, the numbers 1, 2, 3, we see that 1 and 2 only are prime to $(3, 1+\sqrt{-5})$, 3 being divisible by it, and hence

$$\phi(3, 1+\sqrt{-5})=2;$$

that is,

$$\phi(3, 1+\sqrt{-5})=n(3, 1+\sqrt{-5})-1.$$

Likewise, if $\mathfrak{m}=(3)=(3, 1-\sqrt{-5})(3, 1+\sqrt{-5})$, taking as a complete residue system, mod (3), the numbers $0, 1, 2, \sqrt{-5}$, $1+\sqrt{-5}$, $2+\sqrt{-5}$, $2\sqrt{-5}$, $1+2\sqrt{-5}$, $2+2\sqrt{-5}$, we see that $1, 2, \sqrt{-5}, 2\sqrt{-5}$ are prime to (3) and hence

$$\phi(3)=4.$$

In particular, we have $\phi(1)=1$.

Ex. 1. Determine $\phi(1+\sqrt{-5})$.
Ex. 2. Determine $\phi(13, 5+\sqrt{-14})$.

THEOREM 9. *If $\mathfrak{p}$ be any prime ideal,*

$$\phi(\mathfrak{p}^e)=n[\mathfrak{p}^e]\left(1-\frac{1}{n[\mathfrak{p}]}\right).$$

By Th. 2 there are in a complete system of incongruent numbers, mod $\mathfrak{p}^e$, exactly $n[\mathfrak{p}^e]/n[\mathfrak{p}]$ that are divisible by $\mathfrak{p}$, and hence $n[\mathfrak{p}^e]-n[\mathfrak{p}^e]/n[\mathfrak{p}]$ that are prime to $\mathfrak{p}^e$. Hence

$$\phi(\mathfrak{p}^e)=n[\mathfrak{p}^e]\left(1-\frac{1}{n[\mathfrak{p}]}\right).$$

Ex. We have

$$\begin{aligned}\phi(3, 1-\sqrt{-14})^3&=n[(3, 1-\sqrt{-14})^3]\left(1-\frac{1}{n(3, 1-\sqrt{-14})}\right)\\&=27(1-\tfrac{1}{3})\\&=18.\end{aligned}$$

The general expression for $\phi(\mathfrak{m})$, where $\mathfrak{m}$ is any ideal, could be deduced by a method very similar to the one first employed in *R*. We shall make use, however, of the second method employed in *R* (Chap. III, § 14), for this was at once applicable in $k(i)$ (Chap. V, § 12), and we shall find the same to be true in the case of ideals. This method depends in *R*, it will be remembered, upon the property of the ϕ-function that, if a be prime to b, then

$$\phi(ab)=\phi(a)\cdot\phi(b).$$

To prove this for ideals we begin by proving the following theorem.

THEOREM 10. *If* $\mathfrak{m}$ *be the product of the ideals* $\mathfrak{a}_1, \mathfrak{a}_2, \cdots, \mathfrak{a}_s$ *that are prime each to each, and* $\alpha_1, \alpha_2, \cdots, \alpha_s$ *any integers of the realm, there exist integers,* ω, *such that*

$$\omega \equiv \alpha_1, \text{ mod } \mathfrak{a}_1, \; \omega \equiv \alpha_2, \text{ mod } \mathfrak{a}_2, \; \cdots, \; \omega \equiv \alpha_s, \text{ mod } \mathfrak{a}_s, \qquad 1)$$

and all these integers are congruent each to each, mod $\mathfrak{m}$.[1]

This theorem is proved most easily by a method analogous to the symmetrical one employed for the corresponding theorems in R and $k(i)$.

Let $$\mathfrak{m}=\mathfrak{a}_1\mathfrak{b}_1=\mathfrak{a}_2\mathfrak{b}_2=\cdots=\mathfrak{a}_s\mathfrak{b}_s.$$

Then $$\mathfrak{b}_1+\mathfrak{b}_2+\cdots+\mathfrak{b}_s=(1),$$

and hence there exist in the ideals $\mathfrak{b}_1, \mathfrak{b}_2, \cdots, \mathfrak{b}_s$ respectively, numbers $\beta_1, \beta_2, \cdots, \beta_s$, such that

$$\beta_1+\beta_2+\cdots+\beta_s=1 \text{ (Chap. XI, Th. 8, Cor.).} \qquad 2)$$

The number

$$\alpha_1\beta_1+\alpha_2\beta_2+\cdots+\alpha_s\beta_s$$

satisfies all of the congruences 1). For example, we have

$$\alpha_1\beta_1+\alpha_2\beta_2+\cdots+\alpha_s\beta_s\equiv\alpha_1, \text{ mod } \mathfrak{a}_1;$$

for, since $\mathfrak{b}_2, \mathfrak{b}_3, \cdots, \mathfrak{b}_s$ are all divisible by $\mathfrak{a}_1$, the numbers $\beta_2, \beta_3, \cdots, \beta_s$ are all divisible by $\mathfrak{a}_1$, and from 2) it follows that

$$\beta_1\equiv 1, \text{ mod } \mathfrak{a}_1.$$

Furthermore, if ω be any number satisfying the congruences 1), we have by multiplying them respectively with $\beta_1, \beta_2, \cdots, \beta_s$,

$$\begin{aligned} \omega\beta_1 &\equiv \alpha_1\beta_1, \text{ mod } \mathfrak{m}, \\ \omega\beta_2 &\equiv \alpha_2\beta_2, \text{ mod } \mathfrak{m}, \\ &\cdots\cdots\cdots \\ \omega\beta_s &\equiv \alpha_s\beta_s, \text{ mod } \mathfrak{m}. \end{aligned} \qquad 3)$$

[1] See Chap. III, § 14, and Chap. V, § 12; also Dirichlet-Dedekind: § 180, II.

Adding together the congruences 3), and making use of 2), we have

$$\omega \equiv \alpha_1\beta_1 + \alpha_2\beta_2 + \cdots + \alpha_s\beta_s, \text{ mod } \mathfrak{m}.$$

Hence all numbers satisfying the congruences 1) form a single number class, mod $\mathfrak{m}$.

If we let $\alpha_1, \alpha_2, \cdots, \alpha_s$ run through complete residue systems with respect to the moduli $\mathfrak{a}_1, \mathfrak{a}_2, \cdots, \mathfrak{a}_s$ respectively, the resulting

$$n[\mathfrak{a}_1]n[\mathfrak{a}_2] \cdots n[\mathfrak{a}_s] = n[\mathfrak{m}]$$

values of ω evidently form a complete residue system, mod $\mathfrak{m}$. The necessary and sufficient condition for ω to be prime to $\mathfrak{m}$ is that $\alpha_1, \alpha_2, \cdots, \alpha_s$ be prime respectively to the moduli $\mathfrak{a}_1, \mathfrak{a}_2, \cdots, \mathfrak{a}_s$; for, from the congruences 1) we see that the necessary and sufficient condition that ω be prime to each one of the factors $\mathfrak{a}_1$, $\mathfrak{a}_2$, $\cdots$, $\mathfrak{a}_s$ of $\mathfrak{m}$ is that each α be prime to its $\mathfrak{a}$.

Hence, when $\alpha_1, \alpha_2, \cdots, \alpha_s$ run through reduced residue systems, moduli $\mathfrak{a}_1, \mathfrak{a}_2, \cdots, \mathfrak{a}_s$, respectively, the resulting values of ω form a reduced residue system, mod $\mathfrak{m}$. We have, therefore, at once the following theorem:

THEOREM 11. *If $\mathfrak{a}_1$, $\mathfrak{a}_2$, $\cdots$, $\mathfrak{a}_s$ be ideals prime each to each, then*

$$\phi(\mathfrak{a}_1\mathfrak{a}_2 \cdots \mathfrak{a}_s) = \phi(\mathfrak{a}_1)\phi(\mathfrak{a}_2) \cdots \phi(\mathfrak{a}_s).$$

We can now obtain easily an expression for $\phi(\mathfrak{m})$ when $\mathfrak{m}$ is any ideal whatever.

THEOREM 12. *If $\mathfrak{m}, = \mathfrak{p}_1^{e_1}\mathfrak{p}_2^{e_2} \cdots \mathfrak{p}_r^{e_r}$, be any ideal, where $\mathfrak{p}_1$, $\mathfrak{p}_2$, $\cdots$, $\mathfrak{p}_r$ are the different prime factors of $\mathfrak{m}$, then*

$$\phi(\mathfrak{m}) = n[\mathfrak{m}]\left(1 - \frac{1}{n[\mathfrak{p}_1]}\right)\left(1 - \frac{1}{n[\mathfrak{p}_2]}\right) \cdots \left(1 - \frac{1}{n[\mathfrak{p}_r]}\right)$$

By Th. 11 we have

$$\phi(\mathfrak{m}) = \phi(\mathfrak{p}_1^{e_1})\phi(\mathfrak{p}_2^{e_2}) \cdots \phi(\mathfrak{p}_r^{e_r}),$$

from which by Th. 9 it follows that

$$\phi(\mathfrak{m}) = n[\mathfrak{p}_1^{e_1}]\left(1 - \frac{1}{n[\mathfrak{p}_1]}\right)n[\mathfrak{p}_2^{e_2}]\left(1 - \frac{1}{n[\mathfrak{p}_2]}\right) \cdots n[\mathfrak{p}_r^{e_r}]\left(1 - \frac{1}{n[\mathfrak{p}_r]}\right)$$

Hence by Th. 3

$$\phi(\mathfrak{m}) = n[\mathfrak{m}]\left(1-\frac{1}{n[\mathfrak{p}_1]}\right)\left(1-\frac{1}{n[\mathfrak{p}_2]}\right)\cdots\left(1-\frac{1}{n[\mathfrak{p}_r]}\right)$$

Ex. 1. We have

$$(21,\ 10+\sqrt{-5}) = (3,\ 1+\sqrt{-5})(7,\ 3+\sqrt{-5})$$

and hence

$$\phi(21,\ 10+\sqrt{-5}) = 21(1-\tfrac{1}{3})(1-\tfrac{1}{7}) = 12$$

Ex. 2. Find

$$\phi(6+\sqrt{-14}) \text{ and } \phi(189,\ 77+7\sqrt{-14}).$$

THEOREM 13. *If $\mathfrak{d}$ be any divisor of an ideal $\mathfrak{m}$, and $\mathfrak{m}=\mathfrak{n}\mathfrak{d}$, the number of integers of a complete residue system, mod $\mathfrak{m}$, which have with $\mathfrak{m}$ the greatest common divisor $\mathfrak{d}$ is $\phi(\mathfrak{n})$.*

Since by § 1, ix, if the theorem be true for any particular residue system, mod $\mathfrak{m}$, it is true for all, we may take the system used in Th. 2. We have shown that the integers

$$\delta\nu_1,\ \delta\nu_2,\ \cdots,\ \delta\nu_{n[\mathfrak{n}]}, \qquad 4)$$

where δ is a number of $\mathfrak{d}$ such that $(\delta)/\mathfrak{d}$ is prime to $\mathfrak{n}$, and $\nu_1, \nu_2, \cdots, \nu_{n[\mathfrak{n}]}$ is a complete residue system, mod $\mathfrak{n}$, comprise all and only those integers of a complete residue system, mod $\mathfrak{m}$, which are divisible by $\mathfrak{d}$. Hence the integers of the complete residue system, mod $\mathfrak{m}$, which have with $\mathfrak{m}$ the greatest common divisor $\mathfrak{d}$, are those of the system 4) in which the coefficient of $\mathfrak{d}$ is prime to $\mathfrak{n}$, and these are $\phi(\mathfrak{n})$ in number.

THEOREM 14. *If $\mathfrak{d}_1, \mathfrak{d}_2, \cdots, \mathfrak{d}_n$ be the different divisors of $\mathfrak{m}$, then*

$$\sum_{i=1}^{n}\phi(\mathfrak{d}_i) = n[\mathfrak{m}]$$

Let $\mathfrak{d}_1, \mathfrak{d}_2, \cdots, \mathfrak{d}_n$ be the different divisors of $\mathfrak{m}$, including $\mathfrak{m}$ and (1). Then

$$\mathfrak{m} = \mathfrak{m}_1\mathfrak{d}_1 = \mathfrak{m}_2\mathfrak{d}_2 = \cdots = \mathfrak{m}_n\mathfrak{d}_n.$$

Let

$$\mu_1,\ \mu_2,\ \cdots,\ \mu_{n[\mathfrak{m}]} \qquad 5)$$

be a complete residue system, mod $\mathfrak{m}$, and separate these numbers into as many classes as there are different divisors of $\mathfrak{m}$, putting into one class the $\phi(\mathfrak{m}_1)$ numbers that have with $\mathfrak{m}$ the greatest common divisor $\mathfrak{d}_1$ (Th. 13), into another, the $\phi(\mathfrak{m}_2)$ numbers that have with $\mathfrak{m}$ the greatest common divisor $\mathfrak{d}_2$, etc. It is evident that each of the numbers 5) will be in one and but one of these classes, and hence, since they are $n[\mathfrak{m}]$ in number,

$$\phi(\mathfrak{m}_1)+\phi(\mathfrak{m}_2)+\cdots+\phi(\mathfrak{m}_n)=n[\mathfrak{m}].$$

But $\mathfrak{m}_1, \mathfrak{m}_2, \cdots, \mathfrak{m}_n$ are the different divisors of $\mathfrak{m}$, though in a different order from that of the $\mathfrak{d}$'s. The theorem is therefore proved.

The proof here given of this theorem is, it will be observed, dependent only upon Th. 13. The property of the ϕ-function thus shown completely defines the function and we shall be able to derive from it, as in *R*, the general expression for $\phi(\mathfrak{m})$. From the general expression for $\phi(\mathfrak{m})$ may then be obtained Th. 11. We may also obtain Th. 14 from the general expression for $\phi(\mathfrak{m})$, as in *R*. These two proofs are left to the reader.

THEOREM 15. *If $\mathfrak{m}$ be any ideal other than (1), whose prime factors are $\mathfrak{p}_1, \mathfrak{p}_2, \cdots, \mathfrak{p}_r$, and $\mathfrak{d}$ any divisor of $\mathfrak{m}$ other than $\mathfrak{m}$, and if we separate all ideals of the form*

$$\frac{\mathfrak{m}}{\mathfrak{p}_1\mathfrak{p}_2\cdots\mathfrak{p}_i},$$

no $\mathfrak{p}$ being repeated, into two classes, I and II, putting in class I those such that $\mathfrak{m}$ is divided by none or by the product of an even number of the $\mathfrak{p}$'s, and in class II those such that $\mathfrak{m}$ is divided by the product of an odd number of the $\mathfrak{p}$'s, then exactly as many ideals of the one class are divisible by $\mathfrak{d}$ as of the other.

We see that the positive and negative terms of the developed product[1]

$$\mathfrak{m}\left(1-\frac{1}{\mathfrak{p}_1}\right)\left(1-\frac{1}{\mathfrak{p}_2}\right)\cdots\left(1-\frac{1}{\mathfrak{p}_r}\right)$$

coincide respectively with the ideals of classes I and II; that is,

[1] No meaning of addition or subtraction is to be abscribed to the + or − sign attached to these terms, it being simply observed that all the terms in the developed product are ideals, to some of which the sign + is attached and to others the sign —.

denoting by $\Sigma\mathfrak{m}_1$, $\Sigma\mathfrak{m}_2$ respectively the sums[1] of the ideals of these classes, we have

$$\mathfrak{m}\left(1-\frac{1}{\mathfrak{p}_1}\right)\left(1-\frac{1}{\mathfrak{p}_2}\right)\cdots\left(1-\frac{1}{\mathfrak{p}_r}\right)=\Sigma\mathfrak{m}_1-\Sigma\mathfrak{m}_2.$$

Let $$\mathfrak{m}=\mathfrak{p}_1^{e_1}\mathfrak{p}_2^{e_2}\cdots\mathfrak{p}_r^{e_r}.$$

We shall prove the theorem first for the case in which

$$e_1=e_2=\cdots=e_r=1;$$

that is, $\mathfrak{m}$ is not divisible by a higher power than the first of any prime ideal.

Put $$\mathfrak{p}_1\mathfrak{p}_2\cdots\mathfrak{p}_r=\mathfrak{a}.$$

We have

$$\mathfrak{a}\left(1-\frac{1}{\mathfrak{p}_1}\right)\left(1-\frac{1}{\mathfrak{p}_2}\right)\cdots\left(1-\frac{1}{\mathfrak{p}_r}\right)=(\mathfrak{p}_1-1)(\mathfrak{p}_2-1)\cdots(\mathfrak{p}_r-1)$$
$$=\Sigma\mathfrak{a}_1-\Sigma\mathfrak{a}_2,$$

where $\Sigma\mathfrak{a}_1$, $\Sigma\mathfrak{a}_2$ have meanings corresponding to those of $\Sigma\mathfrak{m}_1$, $\Sigma\mathfrak{m}_2$.

If now $\mathfrak{b}$ be any divisor of $\mathfrak{a}$ other than $\mathfrak{a}$, the number of $\mathfrak{a}_1$ terms which are divisible by $\mathfrak{b}$ is exactly equal to the number of $\mathfrak{a}_2$ terms which are divisible by $\mathfrak{b}$; for, if we put

$$\mathfrak{a}=\mathfrak{b}\mathfrak{g}_1\mathfrak{g}_2\cdots\mathfrak{g}_s,$$

where $\mathfrak{g}_1, \mathfrak{g}_2, \cdots, \mathfrak{g}_s$ are those prime factors of $\mathfrak{a}$ which do not divide $\mathfrak{b}$, then the $\mathfrak{a}_1$'s and $\mathfrak{a}_2$'s, which are divisible by $\mathfrak{b}$ are respectively the positive and negative terms of the developed product

$$\mathfrak{b}(\mathfrak{g}_1-1)(\mathfrak{g}_2-1)\cdots(\mathfrak{g}_s-1). \qquad 6)$$

Moreover, since $\mathfrak{b}\neq\mathfrak{a}$, there is at least one prime ideal which divides $\mathfrak{a}$ but not $\mathfrak{b}$; that is, there is at least one $\mathfrak{g}$.

Hence there are always exactly as many positive as negative terms in the developed product 6), and consequently as many $\mathfrak{a}_1$'s

[1] This sum is to be understood in a purely formal sense as merely the aggregate of the ideals of the class connected by + signs, and has, of course, no connection with the notation for the greatest common divisor given on p. 311.

as $\mathfrak{a}_2$'s divisible by $\mathfrak{b}$. The theorem is therefore proved when $\mathfrak{m}$ is not divisible by a higher power than the first of any prime ideal.

We proceed now to prove the theorem for the general case.

Letting $\mathfrak{a}$, $\mathfrak{a}_1$, $\mathfrak{a}_2$ retain the meaning assigned above, we have

$$\mathfrak{m} = \mathfrak{p}_1^{e_1-1}\mathfrak{p}_2^{e_2-1}\cdots\mathfrak{p}_r^{e_r-1}\cdot\mathfrak{p}_1\mathfrak{p}_2\cdots\mathfrak{p}_r = \mathfrak{n}\mathfrak{a},$$

and it is evident that the ideals $\mathfrak{m}_1$, $\mathfrak{m}_2$ coincide respectively with the products $\mathfrak{n}\mathfrak{a}_1$, $\mathfrak{n}\mathfrak{a}_2$.

Let now $\mathfrak{d}$ be any divisor of $\mathfrak{m}$ other than $\mathfrak{m}$ and let $\mathfrak{g}$ be the greatest common divisor of the two ideals

$$\mathfrak{d} = \mathfrak{g}\mathfrak{b}, \text{ and } \mathfrak{n} = \mathfrak{g}\mathfrak{c}.$$

We see that $\mathfrak{b}$ is a divisor of $\mathfrak{a}$, for $\mathfrak{c}$ is prime to $\mathfrak{b}$, and $\mathfrak{c}\mathfrak{a}$ is divisible by $\mathfrak{b}$, since

$$\frac{\mathfrak{c}\mathfrak{a}}{\mathfrak{b}} = \frac{\mathfrak{g}\mathfrak{c}\mathfrak{a}}{\mathfrak{g}\mathfrak{b}} = \frac{\mathfrak{n}\mathfrak{a}}{\mathfrak{d}} = \frac{\mathfrak{m}}{\mathfrak{d}}, \qquad 7)$$

and $\mathfrak{m}$ is divisible by $\mathfrak{d}$.

From 7) it follows, since $\mathfrak{c}$ is prime to $\mathfrak{b}$, that, if $\mathfrak{d} = \mathfrak{m}$, then $\mathfrak{c} = (1)$ and $\mathfrak{b} = \mathfrak{a}$. Conversely, if $\mathfrak{b} = \mathfrak{a}$, and hence is divisible by all prime factors of $\mathfrak{m}$, then $\mathfrak{c}$, since it is a divisor of $\mathfrak{m}$ but prime to $\mathfrak{b}$, must be (1) and hence $\mathfrak{d} = \mathfrak{m}$.

Excluding therefore the case $\mathfrak{d} = \mathfrak{m}$, so that we have always $\mathfrak{b} \neq \mathfrak{a}$, there are among the ideals $\mathfrak{a}_1$ exactly as many that are divisible by $\mathfrak{b}$ as there are among the ideals $\mathfrak{a}_2$.

Since, moreover, the necessary and sufficient condition that an ideal

$$\mathfrak{m}_1 = \mathfrak{n}\mathfrak{a}_1 = \mathfrak{g}\mathfrak{c}\mathfrak{a}_1,$$

or

$$\mathfrak{m}_2 = \mathfrak{n}\mathfrak{a}_2 = \mathfrak{g}\mathfrak{c}\mathfrak{a}_2,$$

shall be divisible by $\mathfrak{d}, = \mathfrak{g}\mathfrak{b}$, is that $\mathfrak{a}_1$ or $\mathfrak{a}_2$ shall be divisible by $\mathfrak{b}$, there are exactly as many of the ideals $\mathfrak{m}_1$ divisible by $\mathfrak{d}$ as of the ideals $\mathfrak{m}_2$. The theorem is therefore proved.

This theorem and proof is interesting as illustrating once more how exactly everything concerning rational integers that involves no property other than that of divisibility, can be carried over to the general realm in terms of ideals.

As in the case of rational integers, the following theorem can be deduced from the one just proved.

THEOREM 16. a. *If $f(\mathfrak{m})$ and $F(\mathfrak{m})$ be two functions of any ideal $\mathfrak{m}$ that are connected by the relation*

$$\Sigma f(\mathfrak{d}) = F(\mathfrak{m}), \qquad 8)$$

where $\mathfrak{d}$ runs through all divisors of $\mathfrak{m}$, including $\mathfrak{m}$, then

$$f(\mathfrak{m}) = \Sigma F(\mathfrak{m}_1) - \Sigma F(\mathfrak{m}_2), \qquad 9)$$

where $\mathfrak{m}_1$, $\mathfrak{m}_2$ run through the values defined in the last theorem.

b. *If $f(\mathfrak{m})$ and $F(\mathfrak{m})$ be connected by the relation*

$$\Pi f(\mathfrak{d}) = \Pi F(\mathfrak{m}), \qquad 10)$$

then

$$f(\mathfrak{m}) = \frac{\Pi F(\mathfrak{m}_1)}{\Pi F(\mathfrak{m}_2)}. \qquad 11)$$

To prove a) it is sufficient to observe that, if $\mathfrak{d}_1$ be any divisor of $\mathfrak{m}$ other than $\mathfrak{m}$, it is a divisor of exactly as many of the $\mathfrak{m}_1$'s as of the $\mathfrak{m}_2$'s (Th. 15), and hence when in 9) we replace the F's by their values in terms of the f's from 8), $f(\mathfrak{d}_1)$ will occur exactly as often with the plus sign as with the minus sign. Hence all terms in the second member of 9) will cancel with the exception of $f(\mathfrak{m})$, which occurs but once. The proof of b) is similar and will be left to the reader.

From Th. 16, a, we can easily obtain by the aid of Th. 14 the general expression for $\phi(\mathfrak{m})$.

From Th. 14 we have

$$\Sigma\phi(\mathfrak{d}) = n[\mathfrak{m}],$$

where $\mathfrak{d}$ runs through all divisors of $\mathfrak{m}$. Applying Th. 16, a, we have

$$f(\mathfrak{m}) = \phi(\mathfrak{m}), \quad F(\mathfrak{m}) = n[\mathfrak{m}],$$

and hence

$$\phi(\mathfrak{m}) = \Sigma n[\mathfrak{m}_1] - \Sigma n[\mathfrak{m}_2].$$

Since, moreover,

$$\Sigma\mathfrak{m}_1 - \Sigma\mathfrak{m}_2 = \mathfrak{m}\left(1 - \frac{1}{\mathfrak{p}_1}\right)\left(1 - \frac{1}{\mathfrak{p}_2}\right)\cdots\left(1 - \frac{1}{\mathfrak{p}_r}\right),$$

and, if

$$\mathfrak{m}_i = \frac{\mathfrak{m}}{\mathfrak{p}_1\mathfrak{p}_2 \cdots \mathfrak{p}_i},$$

then

$$n[\mathfrak{m}_i] = \frac{n[\mathfrak{m}]}{n[\mathfrak{p}_1]n[\mathfrak{p}_2]\cdots n[\mathfrak{p}_i]},$$

we have

$$\Sigma n[\mathfrak{m}_1] - \Sigma n[\mathfrak{m}_2] = n[\mathfrak{m}]\left(1 - \frac{1}{n[\mathfrak{p}_1]}\right)\left(1 - \frac{1}{n[\mathfrak{p}_2]}\right)\cdots\left(1 - \frac{1}{n[\mathfrak{p}_r]}\right),$$

and hence

$$\phi(\mathfrak{m}) = n[\mathfrak{m}]\left(1 - \frac{1}{n[\mathfrak{p}_1]}\right)\left(1 - \frac{1}{n[\mathfrak{p}_2]}\right)\cdots\left(1 - \frac{1}{n[\mathfrak{p}_r]}\right).$$

Summing up what has been learned concerning the ϕ-function for ideals, we see that, exactly as in the case of the corresponding function in R, the function possesses the two properties:

i. $\phi(\mathfrak{a}\mathfrak{b}) = \phi(\mathfrak{a})\cdot\phi(\mathfrak{b})$ where $\mathfrak{a}$ is prime to $\mathfrak{b}$.

ii. $\Sigma\phi(\mathfrak{d}) = n[\mathfrak{m}]$, where $\mathfrak{d}$ runs through all divisors of $\mathfrak{m}$; and that either one of these properties completely defines the function, and from it may be deduced the general expression for $\phi(\mathfrak{m})$ and the other properties, or we may as in R derive the general expression for the function directly from its definition, and then from it get i and ii.

The conception of ϕ-functions of higher order and the theorems relating to them which hold for rational integers (Chap. III, § 6) can be at once extended to ideals.

§ 9. Residue Systems Formed by Multiplying the Numbers of a Given System by an Integer Prime to the Modulus.

THEOREM 17. *If* $\mu_1, \mu_2, \cdots, \mu_{n[\mathfrak{m}]}$ *be a complete residue system, mod* $\mathfrak{m}$, *and* α *any integer prime to* $\mathfrak{m}$, *then* $\alpha\mu_1, \alpha\mu_2, \cdots, \alpha\mu_{n[\mathfrak{m}]}$ *is also a complete residue system, mod* $\mathfrak{m}$.

The integers $\alpha\mu_1, \alpha\mu_2, \cdots, \alpha\mu_{n[\mathfrak{m}]}$ are incongruent each to each, mod $\mathfrak{m}$, for from

$$\alpha\mu_i \equiv \alpha\mu_j, \text{ mod } \mathfrak{m}$$

it would follow that, since α is prime to $\mathfrak{m}$,

$$\mu_i \equiv \mu_j, \text{ mod } \mathfrak{m},$$

which is contrary to the hypothesis that $\mu_1, \mu_2, \cdots, \mu_{n[\mathfrak{m}]}$ form a complete residue system, mod $\mathfrak{m}$. The integers $\alpha\mu_1, \alpha\mu_2, \cdots, \alpha\mu_{n[\ ]}$ are, moreover, $n[\mathfrak{m}]$ in number. They form, therefore, a complete residue system, mod $\mathfrak{m}$.

COR. *If* $\rho_1, \rho_2, \cdots, \rho_{\phi(\mathfrak{m})}$ *be a reduced residue system, mod* $\mathfrak{m}$, *and* α *be prime to* $\mathfrak{m}$, *then* $\alpha\rho_1, \alpha\rho_2, \cdots, \alpha\rho_{\phi(\mathfrak{m})}$ *is also a reduced residue system, mod* $\mathfrak{m}$; for $\alpha\rho_1, \alpha\rho_2, \cdots, \alpha\rho_{\phi(\mathfrak{m})}$ are incongruent each to each, mod $\mathfrak{m}$, prime to $\mathfrak{m}$, and $\phi(\mathfrak{m})$ in number.

Ex. Since $1, 2, 3, \sqrt{-5}, 1+\sqrt{-5}, 2+\sqrt{-5}, 2\sqrt{-5}, 1+2\sqrt{-5}, 2+2\sqrt{-5}$ constitute a complete residue system, mod (3), and $\sqrt{-5}$ is prime to (3), $\sqrt{-5}, 2\sqrt{-5}, 3\sqrt{-5}, -5, -5+\sqrt{-5}, -5+2\sqrt{-5}, -10, -10+\sqrt{-5}, -10+2\sqrt{-5}$ is also a complete residue system, mod (3).

Likewise since $1, 2, \sqrt{-5}, 2\sqrt{-5}$ is a reduced residue system, mod (3), $\sqrt{-5}, 2\sqrt{-5}, -5, -10$ is also a reduced residue system, mod (3).

If $\mathfrak{p}$ be any prime ideal and α an integer prime to $\mathfrak{p}$, it is evident from the above that there exists an integer α_1 such that

$$\alpha\alpha_1 \equiv 1, \text{ mod } \mathfrak{p}.$$

We call α_1 the *reciprocal of* α, *mod* $\mathfrak{p}$.

§ 10. The Analogue for Ideals of Fermat's Theorem.

The following theorem is for ideals the exact analogue of what Fermat's Theorem, as generalized by Euler, is for rational integers. The similarity in the proofs of the two theorems should be noticed.

THEOREM 18. *If* $\mathfrak{m}$ *be any ideal and* α *any integer prime to* $\mathfrak{m}$, *then*

$$\alpha^{\phi(\mathfrak{m})} \equiv 1, \text{ mod } \mathfrak{m}.$$

Let

$$\rho_1, \rho_2, \cdots, \rho_{\phi(\mathfrak{m})} \qquad 1)$$

be a reduced residue system, mod $\mathfrak{m}$. Then, since

$$\alpha\rho_1, \alpha\rho_2, \cdots, \alpha\rho_{\phi(\mathfrak{m})} \qquad 2)$$

is also a reduced residue system, mod $\mathfrak{m}$, each number of 2) is congruent, mod $\mathfrak{m}$, to some number of 1); that is,

$$\left.\begin{aligned} \alpha\rho_1 &\equiv \rho_{j_1} \\ \alpha\rho_2 &\equiv \rho_{j_2} \\ \vdots\quad & \quad\vdots \\ \alpha\rho_{\phi(\mathfrak{m})} &\equiv \rho_{j_{\phi(\mathfrak{m})}} \end{aligned}\right\}, \text{mod } \mathfrak{m}, \qquad 3)$$

where

$$\rho_{j_1},\ \rho_{j_2},\ \cdots,\ \rho_{j_{\phi(\mathfrak{m})}},$$

are the numbers 1), though perhaps in a different order.

Multiplying the congruences 3) together, we have

$$\alpha^{\phi(\mathfrak{m})}\cdot\rho_1\rho_2\cdots\rho_{\phi(\mathfrak{m})} \equiv \rho_{j_1}\rho_{j_2}\cdots\rho_{j_{\phi(\mathfrak{m})}}, \text{ mod } \mathfrak{m},$$

from which, since $\rho_1\rho_2\cdots\rho_{\phi(\mathfrak{m})}$ is prime to $\mathfrak{m}$, it follows that,

$$\alpha^{\phi(\mathfrak{m})} \equiv 1, \text{ mod } \mathfrak{m}.$$

Ex. Let $\mathfrak{m} = (3+\sqrt{-5})$, and $\alpha = 3$. We see that (3) is prime to $(3+\sqrt{-5})$ and that $\phi(3+\sqrt{-5}) = 6$; whence

$$3^6 \equiv 1, \text{ mod } (3+\sqrt{-5}),$$

for 3^6-1, $=728$, is divisible by $n[(3+\sqrt{-5})]$, $=14$, and hence by $(3+\sqrt{-5})$.

Cor. 1. *If $\mathfrak{p}$ be a prime ideal, and α an integer not divisible by $\mathfrak{p}$, then*

$$\alpha^{n[\mathfrak{p}]-1} \equiv 1, \text{ mod } \mathfrak{p}.$$

This is the exact analogue of Fermat's Theorem for rational integers

Cor. 2. *If $\mathfrak{p}$ be any prime ideal, and α any integer, then*

$$\alpha^{n[\mathfrak{p}]} \equiv \alpha, \text{ mod } \mathfrak{p}.$$

§ 11. Congruences of Condition.

Just as in the rational realm we have so far considered congruences that may be compared to algebraic identities, the values of all the quantities involved being given and the congruences expressing simply the fact that the difference of the two numbers is a number of the ideal that is the modulus, or, in other words, this difference considered as a principal ideal is divisible by the modulus.

We shall now, as in the rational realm, consider congruences that hold only when special values are given to certain of the quantities; that is, the values of these "unknown" quantities are to be determined by the condition imposed by the congruence.

To develop the theory of congruences of condition for ideal moduli it is necessary to introduce the conception of the congruence of two polynomials with respect to an ideal modulus; thus,

If $f(x_1, x_2, \cdots, x_n)$ be a polynomial in the n undetermined quantities $x_1, x_2, \cdots, x_n$ with coefficients which are integers of $k(\sqrt{m})$ and $\mathfrak{m}$ be any ideal of $k(\sqrt{m})$, we say that $f(x_1, x_2, \cdots, x_n)$ is identically congruent to 0 with respect to the modulus $\mathfrak{m}$, if all its coefficients be divisible by $\mathfrak{m}$.[1]

This relation is expressed symbolically by

$$f(x_1, x_2, \cdots, x_n) \equiv 0, \text{ mod } \mathfrak{m}.$$

Two polynomials, $f(x_1, x_2, \cdots, x_n)$ and $\phi(x_1, x_2, \cdots, x_n)$, are said to be identically congruent to each other, mod $\mathfrak{m}$, if their difference be identically congruent to 0, mod $\mathfrak{m}$, or, what is the same thing, if the coefficients of corresponding terms in the two polynomials be congruent, mod $\mathfrak{m}$; that is, in symbols

$$f(x_1, x_2, \cdots, x_n) \equiv \phi(x_1, x_2, \cdots, x_n), \text{ mod } \mathfrak{m},$$

if $$f(x_1, x_2, \cdots, x_n) - \phi(x_1, x_2, \cdots, x_n) \equiv 0, \text{ mod } \mathfrak{m}.$$

For example; we have

$$(1 + 3\sqrt{-5})x^2 + 5xy + 7y^2 + 1 + 2\sqrt{-5} \equiv$$
$$(8 + 3\sqrt{-5})x^2 + (2 - \sqrt{-5})xy + 2, \text{ mod } (7, 3 + \sqrt{-5}).$$

If $$f(x_1, x_2, \cdots, x_n) \equiv \phi(x_1, x_2, \cdots, x_n), \text{ mod } \mathfrak{m}, \qquad 1)$$

and $\alpha_1, \alpha_2, \cdots, \alpha_n$ be any n integers of the realm, then evidently

$$f(\alpha_1, \alpha_2, \cdots, \alpha_n) \equiv \phi(\alpha_1, \alpha_2, \cdots, \alpha_n), \text{ mod } \mathfrak{m}. \qquad 2)$$

If, however, 1) does not hold, then 2) does not hold in general[2] for every set of integers $\alpha_1, \alpha_2, \cdots, \alpha_n$.

[1] It will be understood throughout this discussion that the coefficients of a polynomial are integers of some certain quadratic realm and that the modulus is an ideal of this realm.

[2] For an exception see § 13.

The demand that $x_1, x_2, \cdots, x_n$ shall have such values and only such that 2) will hold is expressed by writing

$$f(x_1, x_2, \cdots, x_n) \equiv \phi(x_1, x_2, \cdots, x_n), \text{ mod } \mathfrak{m}. \qquad 3)$$

Any set of integers satisfying 2) is called a *solution* of 3). The determination of all such sets, or the proof that none exists, is called *solving the congruence* 3). We call 3) a *congruence of condition.*

If $\alpha_1, \alpha_2, \cdots, \alpha_n$ and $\beta_1, \beta_2, \cdots, \beta_n$ be two sets of n integers each and

$$\left.\begin{array}{c} \alpha_1 \equiv \beta_1 \\ \alpha_2 \equiv \beta_2 \\ \vdots \quad \vdots \\ \alpha_n \equiv \beta_n \end{array}\right\}, \text{ mod } \mathfrak{m}, \qquad 4)$$

then by § 1, v,

$$f(\alpha_1, \alpha_2, \cdots, \alpha_n) \equiv f(\beta_1, \beta_2, \cdots, \beta_n), \text{ mod } \mathfrak{m},$$

and $$\phi(\alpha_1, \alpha_2, \cdots, \alpha_n) \equiv \phi(\beta_1, \beta_2, \cdots, \beta_n), \text{ mod } \mathfrak{m}.$$

Hence if $\alpha_1, \alpha_2, \cdots, \alpha_n$ be a solution of 3), $\beta_1, \beta_2, \cdots, \beta_n$ is also a solution. Two solutions so related are, however, looked upon as identical. In order that two solutions be different it is necessary and sufficient that the n relations 4) shall not hold simultaneously.

It is evident from the above that in order to solve any congruence, as 3), it is sufficient to substitute for the unknowns the $(n[\mathfrak{m}])^n$ sets of values obtained by putting for each unknown the $n[\mathfrak{m}]$ numbers of a complete residue system, mod $\mathfrak{m}$, and observe which values of $f(x_1, x_2, \cdots, x_n)$ so obtained are congruent to the corresponding values of $\phi(x_1, x_2, \cdots, x_n)$, mod $\mathfrak{m}$.

There being only a finite number, $(n[\mathfrak{m}])^n$, of possible solutions, we can by this process always completely solve any given congruence.

If the congruence have the form

$$f(x_1, x_2, \cdots, x_n) \equiv 0, \text{ mod } \mathfrak{m},$$

and $\alpha_1, \alpha_2, \cdots, \alpha_n$ be a solution, then $f(x_1, x_2, \cdots, x_n)$ is said to be *zero, mod* $\mathfrak{m}$, for these values of $x_1, x_2, \cdots, x_n$.

Ex. The solutions of the congruence

$$(3+\sqrt{-5})x^2+xy+2\equiv 0, \bmod (3, 1+\sqrt{-5}),$$

are easily seen to be

$$x\equiv 1, y\equiv -1, \quad \text{and} \quad x\equiv -1, y\equiv 1, \bmod (3, 1+\sqrt{-5}).$$

§ 12. Equivalent Congruences.

Two congruences,

$$f_1(x_1, x_2, \cdots, x_n)\equiv f_2(x_1, x_2, \cdots, x_n), \bmod \mathfrak{m}, \qquad 1)$$

$$\phi_1(x_1, x_2, \cdots, x_n)\equiv \phi_2(x_1, x_2, \cdots, x_n), \bmod \mathfrak{m}, \qquad 2)$$

are said to be equivalent when every solution of the first is a solution of the second and every solution of the second is a solution of the first.

All that is said in Chap. III, § 10, regarding congruences in R applies equally to congruences with ideal moduli in any realm $k(\sqrt{m})$.

We have two transformations which lead to equivalent congruences; first, if 1) be the given congruence and

$$F_1(x_1, x_2, \cdots, x_n)\equiv F_2(x_1, x_2, \cdots, x_n), \bmod \mathfrak{m}, \qquad 3)$$

be any identical congruence, mod $\mathfrak{m}$, in $x_1, x_2, \cdots, x_n$, we can add 3) member by member to 1), obtaining

$$f_1(x_1, x_2, \cdots, x_n)+F_1(x_1, x_2, \cdots, x_n)\equiv f_2(x_1, x_2, \cdots, x_n) + F_2(x_1, x_2, \cdots, x_n), \bmod \mathfrak{m},$$

a congruence equivalent to 1).

By means of this transformation we can transpose any term with its sign changed, from one member of a congruence to the other and can thus reduce any congruence, as 1), to an equivalent congruence of the form

$$f(x_1, x_2, \cdots, x_n)\equiv 0, \bmod \mathfrak{m},$$

whose second member is 0. We shall hereafter assume the congruences with which we deal to have been reduced to this form.

We may also by this transformation reduce the coefficients of $f(x_1, x_2, \cdots, x_n)$ to their smallest possible absolute values, mod $\mathfrak{m}$, and thus lessen the labor of solving the congruences. In particular we can remove those terms whose coefficients are divisible by $\mathfrak{m}$. If $\mathfrak{m}$ be such that a complete residue system, mod $\mathfrak{m}$, can be constructed entirely of rational integers, all coefficients of $f(x_1, x_2, \cdots, x_n)$ can be replaced by rational integers. Using then this residue system for substitution the work becomes greatly simplified, especially when we remember that $n[a]$ divisible by $n[\mathfrak{m}]$ is a *sufficient* as well as necessary condition that a shall be divisible by $\mathfrak{m}$, if a be a rational integer.

Ex. The congruence

$$(4+3\sqrt{-5})x^2+(1-\sqrt{-5})xy+(3+7\sqrt{-5})y^2+17+4\sqrt{-5}\equiv 0,$$
$$\text{mod } (7,\ 3+\sqrt{-5}), \qquad 4)$$

is equivalent to the congruence

$$2x^2+4xy+3y^2+5\equiv 0, \text{ mod } (7,\ 3+\sqrt{-5}).$$

This is equivalent to adding to 4) member by member the identical congruence

$$(-2-3\sqrt{-5})x^2+(3+\sqrt{-5})xy-7\sqrt{-5}y^2-12-4\sqrt{-5}\equiv 0,$$
$$\text{mod } (7,\ 3+\sqrt{-5}),$$

$-2-3\sqrt{-5}$, $3+\sqrt{-5}$, $-7\sqrt{-5}$, and $-12-4\sqrt{-5}$ being all divisible by $(7,\ 3+\sqrt{-5})$.

A second transformation which leads to an equivalent congruence is the multiplication of both members of the congruence by any integer, α, prime to the modulus; that is, the congruences

$$f(x_1, x_2, \cdots, x_n)\equiv 0, \text{ mod } \mathfrak{m},$$

and

$$\alpha f(x_1, x_2, \cdots, x_n)\equiv 0, \text{ mod } \mathfrak{m},$$

where α is prime to $\mathfrak{m}$, are equivalent.

Conversely, we may divide all the coefficients of a congruence by any integer prime to the modulus, obtaining an equivalent congruence

Ex. The congruences

$$(3+3\sqrt{-5})x^2+9x-6-15\sqrt{-5}\equiv 0, \text{ mod } (3+\sqrt{-5}),$$
$$(1+\sqrt{-5})x^2+3x-2-5\sqrt{-5}\equiv 0, \text{ mod } (3+\sqrt{-5}),$$

are equivalent, since (3) is prime to $(3+\sqrt{-5})$.

As a special case of the *multiplication transformation*, as we shall call the second of the above transformations, we have the multiplication of the congruence by -1; that is, *the change of sign of each of its coefficients.*

§ 13. Congruences in One Unknown with Ideal Moduli.

The general congruence in one unknown has the form

$$f(x) = \alpha_0 x^n + \alpha_1 x^{n-1} + \cdots + \alpha_n \equiv 0, \text{ mod } \mathfrak{m}, \qquad 1)$$

where $\alpha_0, \alpha_1, \cdots, \alpha_n$ are algebraic integers of any realm k, $\mathfrak{m}$ an ideal of this realm, and n a positive rational integer.

If ρ be an integer of k such that

$$f(\rho) \equiv 0, \text{ mod } \mathfrak{m},$$

ρ is called a *root* of 1).

The same analogies that existed in the rational realm in the case of congruences with one unknown when the modulus is a prime are easily seen to exist for prime ideal moduli, and their absence in the case of composite ideal moduli is equally marked.

The reason is, of course, that just as in R the product of two integers is divisible by a prime number when and only when one of the integers is divisible by the prime, so the product of two integers, that is, two principal ideals, is divisible by a prime ideal when and only when one of the integers (that is, one of the principal ideals) is divisible by the prime ideal. Furthermore, we have the same difference in the case of congruences with prime ideal moduli between saying that all the coefficients are divisible by the modulus and that the congruence is satisfied by every value of the unknown; for example, as is easily seen from Fermat's Theorem as extended to ideals, the congruence

$$x^{n[\mathfrak{p}]} - x \equiv 0, \text{ mod } \mathfrak{p},$$

where $\mathfrak{p}$ is a prime ideal, is satisfied by every integer of the realm, but its coefficients are not all divisible by $\mathfrak{p}$.

Before taking up the general congruence in one unknown with ideal modulus, we shall consider that of the first degree. We give first two simple examples of congruences of higher degree.

Ex. 1. Let

$$(5+\sqrt{-5})x^2 + (1+\sqrt{-5})x + 8 + 3\sqrt{-5} \equiv 0, \text{ mod } (3, 1+\sqrt{-5}), \qquad 2)$$

be the given congruence. We observe first that

$$1+\sqrt{-5}\equiv 0,\ \text{mod}\ (3,\ 1+\sqrt{-5}),$$
$$5+\sqrt{-5}\equiv 1,\ \text{mod}\ (3,\ 1+\sqrt{-5}),$$
$$8+3\sqrt{-5}\equiv 2,\ \text{mod}\ (3,\ 1+\sqrt{-5}),$$

and hence 2) reduces to

$$x^2+2\equiv 0,\ \text{mod}\ (3,\ 1+\sqrt{-5}).$$

Substituting the numbers, 0, 1, 2, which constitute a complete residue system, mod $(3,\ 1+\sqrt{-5})$, we have

$$2=2\not\equiv 0,\ \text{mod}\ (3,\ 1+\sqrt{-5}).$$
$$1+2=3\equiv 0,\ \text{mod}\ (3,\ 1+\sqrt{-5}).$$
$$4+2=6\equiv 0,\ \text{mod}\ (3,\ 1+\sqrt{-5}).$$

The congruence has therefore the two roots 1 and 2.

Ex. 2. The congruence

$$(5-6\sqrt{-5})x^2+7x+1\equiv 0,\ \text{mod}\ (1-\sqrt{-5}),$$

is equivalent to the congruence

$$-x^2+x+1\equiv 0,\ \text{mod}\ (1-\sqrt{-5}), \qquad 3)$$

since

$$5-6\sqrt{-5}\equiv -1,\ \text{mod}\ (1-\sqrt{-5}),$$

and

$$7\equiv 1,\ \text{mod}\ (1-\sqrt{-5}),$$

Substituting the numbers 0, 1, 2, 3, 4, 5, of a complete residue system, mod $(1-\sqrt{-5})$, in 3), we see that the congruence has no roots.

§ 14. The General Congruence of First Degree with One Unknown.

That there is always one and only one integer, ξ, of a complete residue system, mod $\mathfrak{m}$, that satisfies the congruence

$$\alpha x\equiv\beta,\ \text{mod}\ \mathfrak{m}, \qquad 1)$$

where α and β are integers, $\mathfrak{m}$ any ideal and α prime to $\mathfrak{m}$, is evident; for, if ξ run through a complete residue system, mod $\mathfrak{m}$, then one and only one of the resulting products, $\alpha\xi_i$, is congruent to β, mod $\mathfrak{m}$ (Th. 17). Hence 1) has one and only one root, ξ_i. We proceed now with the discussion of the general congruence of the form 1), removing the restriction α prime to $\mathfrak{m}$.

A necessary condition that the congruence shall have a solution is evidently, from (§ 1, ix), that β shall be divisible by the greatest common divisor, $\mathfrak{d}$, of α and $\mathfrak{m}$. We shall see that this condition is, as in the corresponding cases in R and $k(i)$, also sufficient, and that, if it be satisfied, the congruence has exactly $n[\mathfrak{d}]$ roots, incongruent, mod $\mathfrak{m}$.

To show this, let

$$\mathfrak{m} = \mathfrak{m}_1\mathfrak{d},$$

and take as a complete residue system, mod $\mathfrak{m}$, the $n[\mathfrak{m}_1]n[\mathfrak{d}]$, $= n[\mathfrak{m}]$, integers

$$\rho\delta_r + \mu_s \begin{cases} r = 1, 2, \cdots, n[\mathfrak{d}] \\ s = 1, 2, \cdots, n[\mathfrak{m}_1] \end{cases} \qquad 2)$$

where ρ is a number of $\mathfrak{m}_1$ such that $(\rho)/\mathfrak{m}_1$ is prime to $\mathfrak{d}$, and

$$\delta_1, \delta_2, \cdots, \delta_{n[\mathfrak{d}]}, \quad \mu_1, \mu_2, \cdots, \mu_{n[\mathfrak{m}_1]},$$

are complete residue systems with respect to the moduli $\mathfrak{d}$ and $\mathfrak{m}_1$ respectively.

We shall show that, if (β) be divisible by the greatest common divisor of (α) and $\mathfrak{m}$, exactly $n[\mathfrak{d}]$ of the numbers 2) satisfy 1).

Let $\rho\delta_h + \mu_i$ be one of the integers 2).

Since $\alpha\rho$ is divisible by $\mathfrak{m}$, we have by substitution in 1), as the necessary and sufficient condition that $\rho\delta_h + \mu_i$ shall satisfy 1),

$$\alpha\mu_i \equiv \beta, \text{ mod } \mathfrak{m}.$$

But since $(\alpha)/\mathfrak{d}$ is prime to $\mathfrak{m}$, the numbers

$$\alpha\mu_1, \alpha\mu_2, \cdots, \alpha\mu_{n[\mathfrak{m}_1]} \qquad 3)$$

are all and only those numbers of a complete residue system, mod $\mathfrak{m}$, which are divisible by $\mathfrak{d}$ (Th. 2).

But β is divisible by $\mathfrak{d}$. Hence there is one and only one of the integers 3) to which β is congruent, mod $\mathfrak{m}$.

Let this integer be $\alpha\mu_i$.

It is evident that of the integers 2)

$$\rho\delta_1 + \mu_i, \rho\delta_2 + \mu_i, \cdots, \rho\delta_{n[\mathfrak{d}]} + \mu_i,$$

satisfy the congruence 1), and are the only ones that do so. They are, moreover, $n[\mathfrak{d}]$ in number. Hence the congruence 1) has exactly $n[\mathfrak{d}]$ roots that are incongruent, mod $\mathfrak{m}$.

In particular, when $\mathfrak{d} = (1)$, that is, when α is prime to $\mathfrak{m}$, the congruence has, as we have already seen, one and only one root, all other integers satisfying it being congruent to this single one, mod $\mathfrak{m}$. In this case by means of Fermat's Theorem for ideals, we can find, as in the analogous case in the rational realm, a general expression for the root of the congruence

$$\alpha x \equiv \beta, \text{ mod } \mathfrak{m}, \qquad 4)$$

where α is prime to $\mathfrak{m}$, and $\mathfrak{m}$ is any ideal.

Since α is prime to $\mathfrak{m}$, we have

$$\alpha^{\phi(\mathfrak{m})} \equiv 1, \text{ mod } \mathfrak{m},$$

and hence

$$\beta\alpha^{\phi(\mathfrak{m})} \equiv \beta, \text{ mod } \mathfrak{m},$$

or

$$\alpha\beta\alpha^{\phi(\mathfrak{m})-1} \equiv \beta, \text{ mod } \mathfrak{m}.$$

Hence $\beta\alpha^{\phi(\mathfrak{m})-1}$ is the root of the congruence 4).

The most obvious method of solving any given congruence, and one always applicable, is to substitute in turn the numbers of a complete residue system with respect to the modulus, thus determining all the roots, if any exist, or proving the non-existence of a root. This is usually the easiest method when the norm of the modulus, $\mathfrak{m}$, is small, and especially when the numbers $1, \cdots, n[\mathfrak{m}] - 1$ constitute a complete residue system, mod $\mathfrak{m}$.

This method has already been used in § 13, Exs. 1 and 2. We shall further illustrate it and also the method depending on Fermat's Theorem on the congruence

$$5x \equiv 1 + \sqrt{-5}, \text{ mod } (7, 3 + \sqrt{-5}), \qquad 5)$$

The numbers 0, 1, 2, 3, 4, 5, 6 constitute a complete residue system, mod $(7, 3 + \sqrt{-5})$, substituting them in turn, we have

$$\left.\begin{array}{l} 0 - (1 + \sqrt{-5}) = -1 - \sqrt{-5} \not\equiv 0 \\ 5 - (1 + \sqrt{-5}) = 4 - \sqrt{-5} \equiv 0 \\ 10 - (1 + \sqrt{-5}) = 9 - \sqrt{-5} \not\equiv 0 \\ 15 - (1 + \sqrt{-5}) = 14 - \sqrt{-5} \not\equiv 0 \\ 20 - (1 + \sqrt{-5}) = 19 - \sqrt{-5} \not\equiv 0 \\ 25 - (1 + \sqrt{-5}) = 24 - \sqrt{-5} \not\equiv 0 \\ 30 - (1 + \sqrt{-5}) = 29 - \sqrt{-5} \not\equiv 0 \end{array}\right\}, \text{ mod } (7, 3 + \sqrt{-5}), \qquad \begin{array}{r} 6) \\ 7) \\ 8) \\ 9) \\ 10) \\ 11) \\ 12) \end{array}$$

all of which results, except 7) and 11), follow at once from the fact that $n[-1-\sqrt{-5}], =6$, $n[9-\sqrt{-5}], =86$, $n[14-\sqrt{-5}], =201$, $n[19-\sqrt{-5}], =366$, and $n[29-\sqrt{-5}], =846$, are none of them divisible by $n(7, 3+\sqrt{-5}), =7$, and hence none of the numbers, $-1-\sqrt{-5}$, $9-\sqrt{-5}$, $14-\sqrt{-5}$, $19-\sqrt{-5}$, and $29-\sqrt{-5}$ can be divisible by $(7, 3+\sqrt{-5})$.

To obtain 7), we observe that $n[4-\sqrt{-5}], =21$, is divisible by $n(7, 3+\sqrt{-5})$, and therefore $4-\sqrt{-5}$ may be divisible by $(7, 3+\sqrt{-5})$. This is seen to be the case since

$$7-(3+\sqrt{-5})=4-\sqrt{-5}.$$

Hence 1 is a root of 5).

To obtain 11), we proceed exactly as with 7) and find that the condition $n[24-\sqrt{-5}]$ divisible by $n(7, 3+\sqrt{-5})$, which is necessary in order that $24-\sqrt{-5}$ shall be divisible by $(7, 3+\sqrt{-5})$, is satisfied, but that the equation

$$7x+(3+\sqrt{-5})y=24-\sqrt{-5}$$

gives as values for x and y

$$x=\frac{27}{7},\quad y=-1.$$

These not being both integral, $24-\sqrt{-5}$ is not divisible by $(7, 3+\sqrt{-5})$.

This last result could have been obtained also by showing that

$$(7, 3+\sqrt{-5}, 24-\sqrt{-5})=(1).$$

This method is, in general, if α be any integer and $\mathfrak{b}, =(\beta_1, \beta_2)$, any ideal, to show that α is not divisible by $\mathfrak{b}$, it is sufficient to show that the ideal $(\beta_1, \beta_2, \alpha)$ contains a rational integer smaller than any in $\mathfrak{b}$.

If we had noticed originally that, since $5=-(\sqrt{-5})^2$, and $(7, 3+\sqrt{-5})$ is prime to $\sqrt{-5}$, the congruence has one and only one root, the work, after finding that 1 was a root, would have been unnecessary. It was given in full to illustrate this most primitive but fundamental method of solution, which is entirely independent of the above discussion.

We shall illustrate now upon the same congruence the method dependent upon Fermat's Theorem.

Since 5 is prime to $(7, 3+\sqrt{-5})$, and $\phi(7, 3+\sqrt{-5})=6$, we see that $(1+\sqrt{-5})5^5$ is the root of 5). To show that

$$(1+\sqrt{-5})5^5\equiv 1, \text{ mod } (7, 3+\sqrt{-5}),$$

we observe that

$$1+\sqrt{-5}\equiv -2, \text{ mod } (7, 3+\sqrt{-5}),$$

and

$$5\equiv -2, \text{ mod } (7, 3+\sqrt{-5}),$$

and hence

$$(1+\sqrt{-5})5^5\equiv(-2)(-2)^5\equiv 64\equiv 1, \text{ mod } (7, 3+\sqrt{-5}).$$

The solution of a congruence of the form 1) where α is not prime to $\mathfrak{m}$ is perhaps most conveniently accomplished by means of the method suggested by the general discussion of this case. We shall illustrate this by two examples.

Ex. 2.

$$2x \equiv 7, \text{ mod } (1+\sqrt{-5}).$$

The greatest common divisor of (2) and $(1+\sqrt{-5})$ is seen to be $(2, 1+\sqrt{-5})$, that does not divide (7). Hence the congruence has no root.

Ex. 3.

$$2x \equiv 1-\sqrt{-5}, \text{ mod } (1+\sqrt{-5}). \qquad 13)$$

Since $(1-\sqrt{-5})$ is divisible by $(2, 1+\sqrt{-5})$, the greatest common divisor of (2) and $(1+\sqrt{-5})$, the congruence has $n(2, 1+\sqrt{-5}), =2$, roots.

We have

$$\frac{(1+\sqrt{-5})}{(2, 1+\sqrt{-5})} = (3, 1+\sqrt{-5})$$

Taking as a complete residue system, mod $(3, 1+\sqrt{-5})$, the numbers 0, 1, 2, and substituting these numbers in 13), we have

$$\left.\begin{array}{l} 0-(1-\sqrt{-5}) = -1+\sqrt{-5} \not\equiv 0 \\ 2-(1-\sqrt{-5}) = 1+\sqrt{-5} \equiv 0 \\ 4-(1-\sqrt{-5}) = 3+\sqrt{-5} \not\equiv 0 \end{array}\right\}, \text{ mod } (1+\sqrt{-5}).$$

We have therefore, in the notation of the general discussion,

$$\mu_i \equiv 1, \text{ mod } (1+\sqrt{-5}).$$

Since

$$\frac{(3)}{(3, 1+\sqrt{-5})}, = (3, 1-\sqrt{-5}),$$

is prime to $(2, 1+\sqrt{-5})$; we may take $\rho = 3$, and since 0, 1 constitutes a complete residue system, mod $(2, 1+\sqrt{-5})$, we have as the two roots of 13)

$$3 \cdot 0 + 1 = 1, \text{ and } 3 \cdot 1 + 1 = 4.$$

The reader may verify these results, as found in examples 2 and 3, by direct substitution of the numbers of a complete residue system, mod $(1+\sqrt{-5})$.

These two congruences (Exs. 2 and 3) will serve as instructive examples of the dependence of the entire theory of algebraic numbers upon the unique factorization theorem, and the necessity for the introduction of the ideal.

In Ex. 2, 2 and $1+\sqrt{-5}$, considered merely as integers of $k(\sqrt{-5})$, are prime to each other, and, were it not for the failure of the unique factorization theorem in $k(\sqrt{-5})$, we should expect the congruence therefore to have a single root in accordance with the results obtained in R and $k(i)$. Substituting the numbers of a complete residue system, mod $1+\sqrt{-5}$, we find that it has no root.

Likewise in Ex. 3, considering the numbers involved merely as integers of $k(\sqrt{-5})$, we should expect the congruence to have a single root.

Substituting the numbers of a complete residue system, mod $1+\sqrt{-5}$, we find that it has two roots. The reason for these discrepancies is made plain when we resolve 2, 7, $1-\sqrt{-5}$, $1+\sqrt{-5}$, into their prime ideal factors.

§ 15. Divisibility of one Polynomial by another with respect to a Prime Ideal Modulus. Common Divisors. Common Multiples.

If $\mathfrak{p}$ be any prime ideal of a realm k, we have the following definition:

A polynomial, $f(x)$, is said to be divisible with respect to the modulus $\mathfrak{p}$ by a polynomial $\phi(x)$, when there exists a polynomial $Q(x)$ such that

$$f(x) \equiv Q(x)\phi(x), \text{ mod } \mathfrak{p}.$$

We say that $\phi(x)$ and $Q(x)$ are *divisors* or *factors*, mod $\mathfrak{p}$, of $f(x)$, and that $f(x)$ is a *multiple*, mod $\mathfrak{p}$, of $\phi(x)$ and $Q(x)$. The sum of the degrees of the factors of $f(x)$ is evidently equal to the degree of $f(x)$.

The coefficients of $f(x)$, $\phi(x)$ and $Q(x)$ are understood to be integers of k.

Ex. It is easily seen that

$$(4+3\sqrt{-5})x^5-x^4+x^3+\sqrt{-5}x^2+(1+\sqrt{-5})x+2$$
$$\equiv(\sqrt{-5}x^2+(1+\sqrt{-5})x+2)((3+2\sqrt{-5})x^3+1), \text{ mod } (7, 3+\sqrt{-5}).$$

Hence

$$\sqrt{-5}x^2+(1+\sqrt{-5})x+2 \quad \text{and} \quad (3+2\sqrt{-5})x^3+1$$

are divisors, mod $(7, 3+\sqrt{-5})$, of

$$(4+3\sqrt{-5})\,x^5-x^4+x^3+\sqrt{-5}x^2+(1+\sqrt{-5})x+2.$$

We have the same consequences of this definition and the same definitions of *common divisor* and *common multiple* for prime ideal moduli as for rational prime numbers (Chap. III, § 15).

§ 16. Unit and Associated Polynomials with respect to a Prime Ideal Modulus. Primary Polynomials.

We see as in the rational realm that the integers of the realm, not divisible by $\mathfrak{p}$, divide every polynomial with respect to the modulus $\mathfrak{p}$, since they divide 1, mod $\mathfrak{p}$, and that these are the only polynomials having this property.

We call therefore the integers of k, which are not divisible by $\mathfrak{p}$, the *unit polynomials, mod* $\mathfrak{p}$, or briefly *the units, mod* $\mathfrak{p}$.

Since two polynomials that are congruent, mod $\mathfrak{p}$, are considered as identical, we can take as the units, mod $\mathfrak{p}$, the integers of any reduced residue system, mod $\mathfrak{p}$.

Two polynomials which differ only by a unit factor, mod $\mathfrak{p}$, are called *associated polynomials* and are looked upon as identical in all questions of divisibility, mod $\mathfrak{p}$.

Two polynomials that are associated with a third polynomial, mod $\mathfrak{p}$, are associated with each other, mod $\mathfrak{p}$.

Two polynomials that are associated, mod $\mathfrak{p}$, are evidently of the same degree and each is a divisor, mod $\mathfrak{p}$, of the other.

Conversely, if two polynomials be each divisible, mod $\mathfrak{p}$, by the other, they are associated, mod $\mathfrak{p}$.

Two polynomials that have no common factor, mod $\mathfrak{p}$, *other than the units, are said to be prime to each other, mod* $\mathfrak{p}$.

Any polynomial, $f(x)$, has $n(\mathfrak{p})-1$ associates, mod $\mathfrak{p}$. Of these, one and only one has the coefficient of its highest degree 1. This one is called the *primary* associate, mod $\mathfrak{p}$ of $f(x)$. For example, the six polynomials

$$x^3+2x-3,\quad 2x^3+4x-6,\quad 3x^3+6x-2,$$

$$4x^3+\ x-5,\quad 5x^3+3x-1,\quad 6x^3+5x-4,$$

are associated, mod 7, and x^3+2x-3 is the primary one.

§ 17. Prime Polynomials with respect to a Prime Ideal Modulus. Determination of the Prime Polynomials, mod $\mathfrak{p}$, of any Given Degree.

A polynomial that is not a unit, mod $\mathfrak{p}$, *and that has no divisors, mod* $\mathfrak{p}$, *other than its associates and the units, is called a prime polynomial, mod* $\mathfrak{p}$. If it has divisors, mod $\mathfrak{p}$, other than these it is said to be *composite,* mod $\mathfrak{p}$.

We can determine the primary prime polynomials, mod $\mathfrak{p}$, of any given degree, n, by the process employed in the same case in the rational realm; that is, write down all primary polynomials, mod $\mathfrak{p}$, of degree n; then, having determined by multiplying together the primary polynomials, mod $\mathfrak{p}$, of degree less than n, all composite primary polynomials, mod $\mathfrak{p}$, of degree n, we strike them from the list of all primary polynomials, mod $\mathfrak{p}$, of degree n. Those left are evidently the primary prime polynomials, mod $\mathfrak{p}$, of degree n.

§ 18. Division of one Polynomial by another with respect to a Prime Ideal Modulus.

THEOREM 19. *If $f(x)$ be any polynomial and $\phi(x)$ be any polynomial not identically congruent to 0, mod $\mathfrak{p}$, there exists a polynomial $Q(x)$, such that the polynomial*

$$f(x) - Q(x)\phi(x) \equiv R(x), \text{ mod } \mathfrak{p},$$

is of lower degree than $\phi(x)$.

The operation of determining the polynomials $Q(x)$ and $R(x)$ is called dividing $f(x)$ by $\phi(x)$, mod $\mathfrak{p}$. We call $Q(x)$ the quotient and $R(x)$ the remainder. The proof of this theorem is precisely the same as that for the corresponding one in the rational realm.

The conception of the congruence of two polynomials with respect to a double modulus is the same for a prime ideal as for a rational prime number.

§ 19. Unique Factorization Theorem for Polynomials with respect to a Prime Ideal Modulus.

We shall now show that, just as a polynomial whose coefficients are rational integers can be resolved in one and but one way into prime factors with respect to a rational prime modulus, so a polynomial, whose coefficients are integers of any given quadratic[1] realm, can be resolved in one and but one way into prime factors with respect to a prime ideal modulus. The proof will be seen to be identical with that employed for rational numbers. We begin by stating the following theorem, whose truth is evident.

[1] This holds for realms of any degree.

THEOREM 20. *If* $f(x) \equiv Q(x)\phi(x) + R(x)$, *mod* $\mathfrak{p}$, *every polynomial that divides, mod* $\mathfrak{p}$, *both* $f(x)$ *and* $\phi(x)$ *divides both* $\phi(x)$ *and* $R(x)$ *and vice versa; that is, the common divisors, mod* $\mathfrak{p}$, *of* $f(x)$ *and* $\phi(x)$ *are identical with the common divisors, mod* $\mathfrak{p}$, *of* $\phi(x)$ *and* $R(x)$.

THEOREM 21. *If* $f_1(x)$, $f_2(x)$ *be any two polynomials and* $\mathfrak{p}$ *a prime ideal, there exists a common divisor* $D(x)$, *mod* $\mathfrak{p}$, *of* $f_1(x)$, $f_2(x)$, *such that* $D(x)$ *is divisible, mod* $\mathfrak{p}$, *by every common divisor, mod* $\mathfrak{p}$, *of* $f_1(x)$, $f_2(x)$, *and there exist two polynomials,* $\phi_1(x)$, $\phi_2(x)$, *such that*

$$f_1(x)\phi_1(x) + f_2(x)\phi_2(x) \equiv D(x), \text{ mod } \mathfrak{p}.$$

We may evidently assume $f_2(x)$ of degree not higher than $f_1(x)$. Dividing $f_1(x)$ by $f_2(x)$, mod $\mathfrak{p}$, we can find two polynomials, $Q_1(x)$, $f_3(x)$, such that

$$f_1(x) \equiv Q_1(x)f_2(x) + f_3(x), \text{ mod } \mathfrak{p},$$

$f_3(x)$ being of lower degree than $f_2(x)$.

Dividing $f_2(x)$ by $f_3(x)$, mod $\mathfrak{p}$, we have

$$f_2(x) \equiv Q_2(x)f_3(x) + f_4(x), \text{ mod } \mathfrak{p},$$

where $f_4(x)$ is of lower degree than $f_3(x)$, and similarly

$$\left.\begin{array}{l} f_3(x) \equiv Q_3(x)f_4(x) + f_5(x) \\ \quad\vdots \qquad\qquad\qquad \vdots \\ f_{n-2}(x) \equiv Q_{n-2}(x)f_{n-1}(x) + f_n(x) \\ f_{n-1}(x) \equiv Q_{n-1}(x)f_n(x) \end{array}\right\}, \text{ mod } \mathfrak{p},$$

a chain of identical congruences in which we must after a finite number of steps reach one in which the remainder, $f_{n+1}(x)$, is 0, mod $\mathfrak{p}$, since the degrees of that remainder continually decrease.

By Th. 20 the common divisors, mod $\mathfrak{p}$, of $f_n(x)$ and $f_{n-1}(x)$ are identical with those of $f_{n-1}(x)$ and $f_{n-2}(x)$, those of $f_{n-1}(x)$, $f_{n-2}(x)$ with those of $f_{n-2}(x)$, $f_{n-3}(x)$, and finally those of $f_3(x)$, $f_2(x)$ with those of $f_2(x)$, $f_1(x)$.

But $f_n(x)$ is a common divisor, mod $\mathfrak{p}$, of $f_n(x)$ and $f_{n-1}(x)$ and is evidently divisible by every common divisor of $f_n(x)$

and $f_{n-1}(x)$. Hence $f_n(x)$ is the desired common divisor, $D(x)$, mod $\mathfrak{p}$, of $f_1(x)$ and $f_2(x)$.

If now we substitute the value of $f_3(x)$ in terms of $f_1(x)$, $f_2(x)$, obtained from the first of these congruences, in the second and the values of $f_3(x)$ and $f_4(x)$ in terms of $f_1(x)$, $f_2(x)$ in the third and continue this process until the congruence

$$f_{n-2}(x) \equiv Q_{n-2}(x) f_{n-1}(x) + f_n(x), \text{ mod } \mathfrak{p},$$

is reached, we shall obtain a congruence,

$$f_1(x)\phi_1(x) + f_2(x)\phi_2(x) \equiv D(x), \text{ mod } \mathfrak{p},$$

where $\phi_1(x)$, $\phi_2(x)$ are polynomials.

COR. *If $f_1(x)$, $f_2(x)$ be two polynomials prime to each other, mod $\mathfrak{p}$, there exist two polynomials, $\phi_1(x)$, $\phi_2(x)$, such that*

$$f_1(x)\phi_1(x) + f_2(x)\phi_2(x) \equiv 1, \text{ mod } \mathfrak{p}.$$

In this case $D(x)$ is an integer, α, not divisible by $\mathfrak{p}$, and we have

$$f_1(x)\Phi_1(x) + f_2(x)\Phi_2(x) \equiv \alpha, \text{ mod } \mathfrak{p},$$

whence, multiplying by the reciprocal of α, mod $\mathfrak{p}$, we obtain

$$f_1(x)\phi_1(x) + f_2(x)\phi_2(x) \equiv 1, \text{ mod } \mathfrak{p}.$$

THEOREM 22. *If the product of two polynomials, $f_1(x)$, $f_2(x)$, be divisible, mod $\mathfrak{p}$, by a prime polynomial, $P(x)$, at least one of the polynomials $f_1(x)$, $f_2(x)$ is divisible, mod $\mathfrak{p}$, by $P(x)$.*

Let $$f_1(x)f_2(x) \equiv Q(x)P(x), \text{ mod } \mathfrak{p}, \qquad 1)$$

where $Q(x)$ is a polynomial, and assume $f_1(x)$ not divisible, mod $\mathfrak{p}$, by $P(x)$.

Then $f_1(x)$ and $P(x)$ are prime, mod $\mathfrak{p}$, to each other and by Th. 21, Cor. there exist two polynomials, $\phi_1(x)$, $\phi_2(x)$, such that

$$f_1(x)\phi_1(x) + P(x)\phi_2(x) \equiv 1, \text{ mod } \mathfrak{p}. \qquad 2)$$

Multiplying 2) by $f_2(x)$ and making use of 1), we have

$$P(x)[Q(x)\phi_1(x) + f_2(x)\phi_2(x)] \equiv f_2(x), \text{ mod } \mathfrak{p},$$

where $Q(x)\phi_1(x) + f_2(x)\phi_2(x)$ is a polynomial. Hence $f_2(x)$ is divisible, mod $\mathfrak{p}$, by $P(x)$.

COR. 1. *If the product of any number of polynomials be divisible, mod $\mathfrak{p}$, by a prime polynomial, $P(x)$, at least one of the polynomials is divisible, mod $\mathfrak{p}$, by $P(x)$.*

COR. 2. *If neither of two polynomials be divisible, mod $\mathfrak{p}$, by a prime polynomial, $P(x)$, their product is not divisible, mod $\mathfrak{p}$, by $P(x)$.*

THEOREM 23. *A polynomial, $f(x)$, can be resolved, mod $\mathfrak{p}$, in one and but one way into a product of prime polynomials, mod $\mathfrak{p}$.*

The proof of this theorem is identical with the corresponding one in the rational realm.

We can now evidently write any polynomial, $f(x)$, in the form

$$f(x) \equiv \alpha(P_1(x))^{e_1}(P_2(x))^{e_2} \cdots (P_n(x))^{e_n}, \text{ mod } \mathfrak{p},$$

where $P_1(x)$, $P_2(x)$, $\cdots$, $P_n(x)$ are the unassociated prime factors, mod $\mathfrak{p}$, of $f(x)$.

If we take $P_1(x)$, $P_2(x)$, $\cdots$, $P_n(x)$ primary, the resolution is absolutely unique.

The representations of the greatest common divisor and least common multiple, mod $\mathfrak{p}$, of two polynomials are identical with those in the rational realm.

The resolution of any polynomial into its prime factors, mod $\mathfrak{p}$, may be effected by the method employed in the case of rational numbers.

§ 20. The General Congruence of the nth Degree in One Unknown and with Prime Ideal Modulus.

THEOREM 24. *If ρ be a root of the congruence*

$$f(x) = \alpha_0 x^n + \alpha_1 x^{n-1} + \cdots + \alpha_n \equiv 0, \text{ mod } \mathfrak{p}, \qquad 1)$$

$f(x)$ is divisible, mod $\mathfrak{p}$, by $x - \rho$, and conversely, if $f(x)$ be divisible, mod $\mathfrak{p}$, by $x - \rho$, ρ is a root of 1).

Dividing, mod $\mathfrak{p}$, $f(x)$ by $x - \rho$, we have

$$f(x) \equiv (x - \rho)\phi(x) + f(\rho), \text{ mod } \mathfrak{p},$$

whence, since ρ is a root of 1),

$$f(x) \equiv (x - \rho)\phi(x), \text{ mod } \mathfrak{p};$$

that is, $f(x)$ is divisible, mod $\mathfrak{p}$, by $x-\rho$. The converse is evident.

If $f(x)$ be prime, mod $\mathfrak{p}$, the congruence 1) evidently has no roots. The converse is, however, not true; that is, $f(x)$ may be composite, mod $\mathfrak{p}$, but 1) have no roots, for the prime factors of $f(x)$, mod p, may all be of higher degree than the first.

This theorem gives us another method for determining the factors, mod $\mathfrak{p}$, of the first degree of any polynomial in x. Some of these factors may be alike and we are led therefore to say that ρ *is a multiple root of order* e of 1), if $f(x)$ be divisible, mod $\mathfrak{p}$, by $(x-\rho)^e$ but not by $(x-\rho)^{e+1}$.

If, therefore, $\rho_1, \rho_2, \cdots, \rho_m$ be the incongruent roots of 1) of orders $e_1, e_2, \cdots, e_m$ respectively, we have

$$f(x) \equiv (x-\rho_1)^{e_1}(x-\rho_2)^{e_2} \cdots (x-\rho_m)^{e_m} f_1(x), \text{ mod } \mathfrak{p},$$

where $f_1(x)$ is a polynomial having no linear factors, mod $\mathfrak{p}$, and whose degree s is such that

$$e_1 + e_2 + \cdots + e_m + s = n,$$

where n is the degree of $f(x)$.

Counting a multiple root of order e as e roots, we see that 1) has exactly as many roots as $f(x)$ has linear factors, mod $\mathfrak{p}$, and have the following important theorem:

THEOREM 25. *The number of roots of the congruence*

$$f(x) = \alpha_0 x^n + \alpha_1 x^{n-1} + \cdots + \alpha_n \equiv 0, \text{ mod } \mathfrak{p},$$

where $\mathfrak{p}$ *is a prime ideal, is not greater than its degree.*

COR. 1. *If the number of incongruent roots of a congruence with prime ideal modulus be greater than its degree, the congruence is an identical one.*

COR. 2. *If the congruence*

$$f(x) \equiv 0, \text{ mod } \mathfrak{p}, \qquad 2)$$

have exactly as many roots as its degree, and $\phi(x)$ *be a divisor, mod* $\mathfrak{p}$, *of* $f(x)$, *then the congruence*

$$\phi(x) \equiv 0, \text{ mod } \mathfrak{p},$$

has exactly as many roots as its degree; for

$$f(x) \equiv \phi(x) Q(x), \text{ mod } \mathfrak{p},$$

where $Q(x)$ is a polynomial in x, and every root of the congruence 2) is a root of either the congruence

$$\phi(x) \equiv 0, \text{ mod } \mathfrak{p}, \qquad 3)$$

or of the congruence

$$Q(x) \equiv 0, \text{ mod } \mathfrak{p}. \qquad 4)$$

Moreover, the sum of the degrees of 3) and 4) is equal to the degree of 2).

If, therefore, $\phi(x)$ had fewer roots than its degree, then $Q(x)$ must have more roots than its degree, which is impossible.

Hence the corollary.

§ 21. The Congruence $x^{\phi(\mathfrak{m})} - 1 \equiv 0$, mod $\mathfrak{m}$.

Although in the case of congruences of degree higher than the first the theorem just given tells all that we can in general say regarding the number of the roots, still there is, as in the rational realm, one important case in which the number of roots is always exactly equal to the degree of the congruence.

THEOREM 26. *The congruence*

$$x^{\phi(\mathfrak{m})} \equiv 1, \text{ mod } \mathfrak{m}, \qquad 1)$$

has exactly $\phi(\mathfrak{m})$ *roots.*

The $\phi(\mathfrak{m})$ integers of a reduced residue system, mod $\mathfrak{m}$, evidently satisfy 1). Moreover, since by § 1, ix two integers congruent, mod $\mathfrak{m}$, have with $\mathfrak{m}$ the same greatest common divisor and the greatest common divisor of (1) and $\mathfrak{m}$ is (1), every root of 1) must have with $\mathfrak{m}$ the greatest common divisor (1); that is, be prime to $\mathfrak{m}$. Hence the number of roots of 1) is exactly equal to $\phi(\mathfrak{m})$, its degree.

Ex. 1. The congruence

$$x^{\phi(1+\sqrt{-5})} \equiv 1, \text{ mod } (1+\sqrt{-5}),$$

or

$$x^2 \equiv 1, \text{ mod } (1+\sqrt{-5}),$$

has two roots, 1 and 5,
Likewise the congruence

$$x^{\phi(7, 3+\sqrt{-5})} \equiv 1, \text{ mod } (7, 3+\sqrt{-5}),$$

or
$$x^6 \equiv 1, \text{ mod } (7, 3+\sqrt{-5}),$$
has six roots, 1, 2, 3, 4, 5, 6.

Ex. 2. Consider the congruence
$$x^{\phi(2\sqrt{-5}, -5+\sqrt{-5})} \equiv 1, \text{ mod } (2\sqrt{-5}, -5+\sqrt{-5}). \qquad 2)$$
Since
$$(2\sqrt{-5}, -5+\sqrt{-5}) = (\sqrt{-5})(2, 1+\sqrt{-5}),$$
we have
$$\phi(2\sqrt{-5}, -5+\sqrt{-5}) = \phi(\sqrt{-5})\phi(2, 1+\sqrt{-5}) = 4\cdot 1 = 4.$$
Substituting therefore in the congruence
$$x^4 \equiv 1, \text{ mod } (2\sqrt{-5}, -5+\sqrt{-5}),$$
the numbers 0, 1, 2, 3, 4, 5, 6, 7, 8, 9, which form a complete residue system, mod $(2\sqrt{-5}, -5+\sqrt{-5})$, we see that the numbers 1, 3, 7, 9, which form a reduced residue system, mod $(2\sqrt{-5}, -5+\sqrt{-5})$, are the only ones which satisfy the congruence.

COR. *If d be a positive divisor of $\phi(\mathfrak{p})$, the congruence*
$$x^d - 1 \equiv 0, \text{ mod } \mathfrak{p},$$
where $\mathfrak{p}$ is a prime ideal, has exactly d roots.

This follows at once from Th. 25, Cor. 2, since $x^d - 1$ is a divisor, mod $\mathfrak{p}$, of $x^{\phi(\mathfrak{p})} - 1$.

The congruence $x^{n[\mathfrak{p}]} - x \equiv 0$, mod $\mathfrak{p}$, having the $n[\mathfrak{p}]$ roots $\rho_1, \rho_2, \cdots, \rho_{n[\mathfrak{p}]}$ equal in number to its degree, we have the identical congruence
$$x^{n[\mathfrak{p}]} - x \equiv (x-\rho_1)(x-\rho_2)\cdots(x-\rho_{n[\mathfrak{p}]}), \text{ mod } \mathfrak{p}.$$

For example
$$x^7 - x \equiv x(x-1)(x-2)(x-3)(x-4)(x-5)(x-6),$$
$$\text{mod } (7, 3+\sqrt{-5}).$$

§ 22. The Analogue for Ideals of Wilson's Theorem.

The result just obtained gives us a proof of the following theorem:

THEOREM 27. *If $\mathfrak{p}$ be a prime ideal and $\rho_1, \rho_2, \cdots, \rho_{\phi(\mathfrak{p})}$ a reduced residue system, mod $\mathfrak{p}$, then*
$$\rho_1\rho_2\cdots\rho_{\phi(\mathfrak{p})} + 1 \equiv 0, \text{ mod } \mathfrak{p}.$$

Since the congruence
$$x^{\phi(\mathfrak{p})} - 1 \equiv 0, \text{ mod } \mathfrak{p},$$

has exactly $\phi(\mathfrak{p})$ roots, $\rho_1, \rho_2, \cdots, \rho_{\phi(\mathfrak{p})}$, we have by § 21

$$x^{\phi(\mathfrak{p})} - 1 \equiv (x-\rho_1)(x-\rho_2)\cdots(x-\rho_{\phi(\mathfrak{p})}), \text{ mod } \mathfrak{p}.$$

Putting $x=0$, we have

$$-1 \equiv (-\rho_1)(-\rho_2)\cdots(-\rho_{\phi(\mathfrak{p})}), \text{ mod } \mathfrak{p},$$

whence, since $\phi(\mathfrak{p})$ is even, except when $n[\mathfrak{p}]=2$,

$$\rho_1\rho_2\cdots\rho_{\phi(\mathfrak{p})}+1 \equiv 0, \text{ mod } \mathfrak{p},$$

which evidently holds also when $n[\mathfrak{p}]=2$.

Ex. Let $\mathfrak{p}=(7, 3+\sqrt{-5})$; then 1, 2, 3, 4, 5, 6 is a reduced residue system, mod $(7, 3+\sqrt{-5})$, and we have

$$1\cdot 2\cdot 3\cdot 4\cdot 5\cdot 6+1=721\equiv 0, \text{ mod } (7, 3+\sqrt{-5}).$$

§ 23. Common Roots of Two Congruences.

The common roots of two congruences

$$f_1(x)\equiv 0, \text{ mod } \mathfrak{p}, \text{ and } f_2(x)\equiv 0, \text{ mod } \mathfrak{p},$$

are evidently the roots of the congruence

$$\phi(x)\equiv 0, \text{ mod } \mathfrak{p},$$

where $\phi(x)$ is the greatest common divisor, mod $\mathfrak{p}$, of $f_1(x)$ and $f_2(x)$.

Since the congruence

$$x^{n[\mathfrak{p}]}-x\equiv 0, \text{ mod } \mathfrak{p},$$

has for its roots the numbers of a complete residue system, mod $\mathfrak{p}$, the incongruent roots of any congruence

$$f(x)\equiv 0, \text{ mod } \mathfrak{p},$$

will be the roots of the congruence

$$\phi(x)\equiv 0, \text{ mod } \mathfrak{p},$$

where $\phi(x)$ is the greatest common divisor, mod $\mathfrak{p}$, of $x^{n[\mathfrak{p}]}-x$ and $f(x)$.

This gives us another method of determining all the incongruent roots of any given congruence with prime modulus.

§ 24. Determination of the Multiple Roots of a Congruence with Prime Ideal Modulus.

The multiple roots of the congruence

$$f(x) \equiv 0, \text{ mod } \mathfrak{p}, \qquad 1)$$

may be determined just as in the case of rational integers. Let $P(x)$ be a prime polynomial, mod $\mathfrak{p}$, and let $f(x)$ be divisible, mod $\mathfrak{p}$, by $[P(x)]^e$ but not by $[P(x)]^{e+1}$; then

$$f(x) \equiv [P(x)]^e \phi(x), \text{ mod } \mathfrak{p},$$

or, what is the same thing,

$$f(x) = [P(x)]^e \phi(x) + F(x), \qquad 2)$$

where $F(x)$ and $\phi(x)$ are polynomials in x, with coefficients which are integers of the realm k, to which $\mathfrak{p}$ and the coefficients of $f(x)$ belong, and $F(x)$ is identically 0, mod $\mathfrak{p}$.

Differentiating 2), we have

$$f'(x) = [P(x)]^{e-1}[eP'(x)\phi(x) + P(x)\phi'(x)] + F'(x),$$

where $P'(x)$, $\phi'(x)$ and $F'(x)$ are polynomials in x with coefficients which are integers of k, and $F'(x)$ is identically 0, mod $\mathfrak{p}$, for all coefficients of $F(x)$ being divisible by $\mathfrak{p}$, all coefficients of $F'(x)$ are divisible by $\mathfrak{p}$. Hence

$$f'(x) \equiv [P(x)]^{e-1}\phi_1(x), \text{ mod } \mathfrak{p},$$

where $\phi_1(x)$ is a polynomial in x, with coefficients which are integers of k, and is, moreover, not divisible, mod $\mathfrak{p}$, by $P(x)$, for

$$\phi_1(x) = eP'(x)\phi(x) + P(x)\phi'(x),$$

where $P'(x)$ is of lower degree than $P(x)$ and $\phi(x)$ is prime, mod $\mathfrak{p}$, to $P(x)$. Therefore $f'(x)$ is divisible, mod $\mathfrak{p}$, by the prime factor $P(x)$ exactly once less often than $f(x)$.

In particular, if $f(x)$ be divisible, mod $\mathfrak{p}$, by $(x-\rho)^e$ but not by $(x-\rho)^{e+1}$, then $f'(x)$ is divisible, mod $\mathfrak{p}$, by $(x-\rho)^{e-1}$ but not by $(x-\rho)^e$.

Hence the theorem:

THEOREM 28. *If the congruence*

$$f(x) \equiv 0, \text{ mod } \mathfrak{p},$$

have a multiple root, ρ, of order e, the congruence

$$f'(x) \equiv 0, \text{ mod } \mathfrak{p},$$

has the multiple root ρ of order e — 1.

If the greatest common divisor, mod $\mathfrak{p}$, of $f(x)$ and $f'(x)$ be $\phi(x)$, then the roots of the congruence

$$\phi(x) \equiv 0, \text{ mod } \mathfrak{p}, \qquad 3)$$

if it have any, will be the multiple roots of 1) and each root of 3) will occur once oftener as a root of 1) than as a root of 3).

It may happen, of course, that $f(x)$ and $f'(x)$ have a common divisor, $\phi(x)$, mod $\mathfrak{p}$, and yet 1) has no multiple roots. In this case the repeated prime factors, mod $\mathfrak{p}$, of $f(x)$ are of degree higher than the first, and $\phi(x)$, therefore, contains no factor of the first degree, mod $\mathfrak{p}$.

§ 25. Solution of Congruences in One Unknown and with Composite Modulus.

The solution of a congruence of the form

$$f(x) = a_0x^n + a_1x^{n-1} + \cdots + a_n \equiv 0, \text{ mod } \mathfrak{m}, \qquad 1)$$

where

$$\mathfrak{m} = \mathfrak{m}_1\mathfrak{m}_2 \cdots \mathfrak{m}_t,$$

$\mathfrak{m}_1, \mathfrak{m}_2, \cdots, \mathfrak{m}_t$ being ideals prime each to each, can be reduced to the solution of the series of t congruences

$$\left.\begin{aligned} f(x) &\equiv 0, \text{ mod } \mathfrak{m}_1, \\ f(x) &\equiv 0, \text{ mod } \mathfrak{m}_2, \\ &\vdots \\ f(x) &\equiv 0, \text{ mod } \mathfrak{m}_t. \end{aligned}\right\} \qquad 2)$$

Every root of 1) is evidently a root of each of the congruences 2), and conversely any integer, ρ, of the realm which is simultaneously a root of each of the congruences 2) is a root of 1), for if the integer $f(\rho)$ be divisible by each of the ideals $\mathfrak{m}_1, \mathfrak{m}_2, \cdots, \mathfrak{m}_t$, which are prime each to each, it is divisible by their product.

If therefore $\alpha_1, \alpha_2, \cdots, \alpha_t$ be roots of the congruences 2) and ρ be chosen so that

$$\left.\begin{array}{l}\rho \equiv \alpha_1, \text{ mod } \mathfrak{m}_1,\\ \rho \equiv \alpha_2, \text{ mod } \mathfrak{m}_2,\\ \vdots \quad \vdots \quad \vdots\\ \rho \equiv \alpha_t, \text{ mod } \mathfrak{m}_t,\end{array}\right\} \qquad 3)$$

then ρ is a root of 1).

Since $\mathfrak{m}_1, \mathfrak{m}_2, \cdots, \mathfrak{m}_t$ are prime each to each, it is by Th. 10 always possible to find ρ so as to satisfy the conditions 3).

Let $\beta_1, \beta_2, \cdots, \beta_t$ be auxiliary integers selected as in Th. 10; then

$$\rho \equiv \alpha_1\beta_1 + \alpha_2\beta_2 + \cdots + \alpha_t\beta_t, \text{ mod } \mathfrak{m}, \qquad 4)$$

is a root of 1), and, if the congruences 2) have respectively $l_1, l_2, \cdots, l_t$ incongruent roots, then by Th. 10 1) has $l_1 l_2 \cdots l_t$ incongruent roots, which are obtained by putting for $\alpha_1, \alpha_2, \cdots, \alpha_t$ in 4) respectively the $l_1, l_2, \cdots, l_t$ roots of the congruences 2). In particular, if any one of the congruences 2) have no root, then 1) has no root.

We may now suppose $\mathfrak{m} = \mathfrak{p}_1^{e_1}\mathfrak{p}_2^{e_2} \cdots \mathfrak{p}_r^{e_r}$, where the $\mathfrak{p}$'s are different prime ideals, and show, as in the corresponding case in R (p. 96), that the solution of the congruence $f(x) \equiv 0$, mod $\mathfrak{p}^e$, can be made to depend upon that of $f(x) \equiv 0$, mod $\mathfrak{p}^{e-1}$, and hence eventually upon that of $f(x) \equiv 0$, mod $\mathfrak{p}$, the same method being applicable with slight modifications.

§ 26. Residues of Powers for Ideal Moduli.

If α be prime to the ideal $\mathfrak{m}$, and

$$\beta \equiv \alpha^t, \text{ mod } \mathfrak{m},$$

where t is a positive rational integer, β is said to be a power residue of α with respect to the modulus $\mathfrak{m}$.

For example, since

$$-2\sqrt{-5} \equiv (1 + \sqrt{-5})^3, \text{ mod } (7, 3 + \sqrt{-5}),$$

we say that $-2\sqrt{-5}$ is a power residue of $1 + \sqrt{-5}$, mod $(7, 3 + \sqrt{-5})$. Two power residues of α which are congruent, mod $\mathfrak{m}$, to each other and hence to the same power of α, are looked upon as the same.

A system of integers such that every power residue, mod $\mathfrak{m}$, of α is congruent, mod $\mathfrak{m}$, to one and only one integer of the system is called a complete system of power residues of α, mod $\mathfrak{m}$. These integers may evidently be selected from among the integers of any reduced residue system, mod $\mathfrak{m}$. The following table gives the power residues of all numbers of a reduced residue system, mod $(7, 3+\sqrt{-5})$, the system taken being 1, 2, 3, 4, 5, 6.

$$m = (7, 3+\sqrt{-5})$$

α^0	α^1	α^2	α^3	α^4	α^5	α^6
1	1	1	1	1	1	1
1	2	4	1	2	4	1
1	3	2	6	4	5	1
1	4	2	1	4	2	1
1	5	4	6	2	3	1
1	6	1	6	1	6	1

We ask now what is the smallest value, t_α, of t, greater than 0, for which

$$\alpha^t \equiv 1, \text{ mod } \mathfrak{m}.$$

That such a value of t always exists and is equal to or less than $\phi(\mathfrak{m})$ is evident from Th. 10 by which we have, since α is prime to $\mathfrak{m}$,

$$\alpha^{\phi(\mathfrak{m})} \equiv 1, \text{ mod } \mathfrak{m}.$$

Giving to t_α the above meaning, we say that the integer α *appertains to the exponent* t_α *with respect to the modulus* $\mathfrak{m}$.

We see, by consulting the above table, that 3 and 5 appertain to the exponent 6; that is, $\phi(\mathfrak{m})$, mod $(7, 3+\sqrt{-5})$, that 2 and 4 appertain to the exponent 3, mod $(7, 3+\sqrt{-5})$, and that 6 appertains to the exponent 2, mod $(7, 3+\sqrt{-5})$.

It is evident that, if $\alpha \equiv \beta$, mod $\mathfrak{m}$, then α and β appertain to the same exponent, mod $\mathfrak{m}$. Hence to find the exponents to which all integers appertain, mod $\mathfrak{m}$, it is only necessary to examine the numbers of a reduced residue system, mod $\mathfrak{m}$.

THEOREM 29. *If the integer α appertain to the exponent t_α, mod $\mathfrak{m}$, then the t_α powers of α,*

$$1, \alpha, \alpha^2, \cdots, \alpha^{t_\alpha - 1}, \tag{1}$$

are incongruent each to each, mod $\mathfrak{m}$.

Let α^s, α^{s+r} be any two of the numbers 1).

If

$$\alpha^{s+r} \equiv \alpha^s, \text{ mod } \mathfrak{m}, \tag{2}$$

then, since α is prime to $\mathfrak{m}$,

$$\alpha^r \equiv 1, \text{ mod } \mathfrak{m}. \tag{3}$$

But r is less than t_α and 3) is therefore impossible, since α appertains to t_α.

Hence 2) is impossible.

THEOREM 30. *If α appertain to the exponent t_α, mod $\mathfrak{m}$, any two powers of α with positive exponents are congruent or incongruent, mod $\mathfrak{m}$, according as their exponents are congruent or incongruent, mod t_α.*

Let $\alpha^{s_1}, \alpha^{s_2}$ be any two powers of α, s_1, s_2 being positive rational integers, and let

$$s_1 = q_1 t_\alpha + r_1, \quad s_2 = q_2 t_\alpha + r_2,$$

where q_1, q_2 are positive rational integers and

$$0 \leqq r_1 < t_\alpha, \quad 0 \leqq r_2 < t_\alpha, \quad r_1 \geqq r_2. \tag{4}$$

If

$$\alpha^{q_1 t_\alpha + r_1} \equiv \alpha^{q_2 t_\alpha + r_2}, \text{ mod } \mathfrak{m}, \tag{5}$$

then

$$\alpha^{r_1} \equiv \alpha^{r_2}, \text{ mod } \mathfrak{m}, \tag{6}$$

and hence, since α is prime to $\mathfrak{m}$,

$$\alpha^{r_1 - r_2} \equiv 1, \text{ mod } \mathfrak{m}.$$

But from 4) we have $0 \leqq r_1 - r_2 < t_\alpha$, whence, since α appertains to t_α, mod $\mathfrak{m}$,

$$r_1 = r_2. \tag{7}$$

Therefore

$$s_1 \equiv s_2, \text{ mod } t_\alpha, \tag{8}$$

is a necessary condition that we shall have

$$\alpha^{s_1} \equiv \alpha^{s_2}, \text{ mod } \mathfrak{m}. \tag{9}$$

Moreover, from 8) follow in turn 7), 6) and 5). Hence 8) is also a sufficient condition for the existence of 9).

We have therefore

$$\left.\begin{array}{llll} \alpha^0 & \equiv \alpha^{t_a} & \equiv \alpha^{2t_a} & \equiv \cdots \\ \alpha & \equiv \alpha^{t_a+1} & \equiv \alpha^{2t_a+1} & \equiv \cdots \\ \vdots & \vdots & \vdots & \\ \alpha^{t_a-1} & \equiv \alpha^{2t_a-1} & \equiv \alpha^{3t_a-1} & \equiv \cdots \end{array}\right\} \text{mod } \mathfrak{m};$$

that is, the same law of periodicity holds for power residues with respect to ideal moduli as in the case of rational integers.

This can be verified by an examination of the table (p. 393), where we see, for example, that 2 appertains to the exponent 3, mod $(7, 3+\sqrt{-5})$, and that

$$\left.\begin{array}{l} 2^0 \equiv 2^3 \equiv 2^6 \equiv \cdots \\ 2 \equiv 2^4 \equiv 2^7 \equiv \cdots \\ 2^2 \equiv 2^5 \equiv 2^8 \equiv \cdots \end{array}\right\} \text{mod } (7, 3+\sqrt{-5}),$$

and

$$\left.\begin{array}{l} 0 \equiv 3 \equiv 6 \equiv \cdots \\ 1 \equiv 4 \equiv 7 \equiv \cdots \\ 2 \equiv 5 \equiv 8 \equiv \cdots \end{array}\right\} \text{mod } 3.$$

THEOREM 31. *The exponent, t_a, to which an integer, α, appertains with respect to the modulus $\mathfrak{m}$, is always a divisor of $\phi(\mathfrak{m})$.*

Since $$\alpha^{\phi(\mathfrak{m})} \equiv 1 \equiv \alpha^0, \text{ mod } \mathfrak{m},$$

we have by Th. 30 $$\phi(\mathfrak{m}) \equiv 0, \text{ mod } t_a.$$

THEOREM 32. *If two integers, α_1, α_2, appertain, mod $\mathfrak{m}$, to two exponents, t_1, t_2, which are prime to each other, then their product, $\alpha_1\alpha_2$, appertains, mod $\mathfrak{m}$, to the exponent, t_1t_2.*

Let $\alpha_1\alpha_2$ appertain to the exponent t, then

$$(\alpha_1\alpha_2)^t \equiv 1, \text{ mod } \mathfrak{m}. \qquad 10)$$

Raising both members of 10) to the t_1th power, we have

$$\alpha_1^{t_1t}\alpha_2^{t_1t} \equiv 1, \text{ mod } \mathfrak{m}.$$

But $$\alpha_1^{t_1t} \equiv 1, \text{ mod } \mathfrak{m},$$

and hence $$\alpha_2^{t_1t} \equiv 1, \text{ mod } \mathfrak{m}.$$

Therefore, since α_2 appertains to the exponent t_2, mod $\mathfrak{m}$, t_1t must be a multiple of t_2, whence, since t_1, t_2 are prime to each other, it follows that t is a multiple of t_2.

In like manner we can show that t is a multiple of t_1.

Therefore, t being a multiple of both t_1 and t_2, is a multiple of their product, t_1t_2.

Hence the smallest possible value of t for which 1) holds is t_1t_2.

Therefore, $\alpha_1\alpha_2$ appertains to the exponent t_1t_2, mod $\mathfrak{m}$.

Ex. We see from the table (p. 393) that 2 and 6 appertain, mod $(7, 3+\sqrt{-5})$, respectively to the exponents 3 and 2, and that their product, 12, $\equiv 5$, mod $(7, 3+\sqrt{-5})$, appertains to the exponent 6, mod $(7, 3+\sqrt{-5})$.

Limiting ourselves now to the case in which the modulus is a prime ideal $\mathfrak{p}$, we ask whether there are integers appertaining to every positive divisor of $\phi(\mathfrak{p})$, and, if so, how many?

An examination of the table will show us how matters stand when $\mathfrak{p} = (7, 3+\sqrt{-5})$.

We have $\phi(7, 3+\sqrt{-5}) = 6$, and the positive divisors of 6 are 1, 2, 3 and 6.

To 1 appertains the single integer 1.

To 2 appertains the single integer 6.

To 3 appertain two integers, 2 and 4.

To 6 appertain two integers, 3 and 5.

THEOREM 33. *To every positive divisor, t, of $\phi(\mathfrak{p})$ there appertain $\phi(t)$ integers with respect to the modulus $\mathfrak{p}$.*

Assume that to every positive divisor, t, of $\phi(\mathfrak{p})$ there appertains at least one integer, α. We shall show that, if this assumption be true, there appertain to t $\phi(t)$ integers; that is, to every positive divisor, t, of $\phi(\mathfrak{p})$ there appertains either $\phi(t)$[1] integers or no integer.

Let $\psi(t)$ denote the number of integers appertaining to t. Each of the integers

$$\alpha^0 = 1, \alpha, \alpha^2, \cdots, \alpha^{t-1}, \tag{11}$$

is a root of the congruence

$$\xi^t \equiv 1, \text{ mod } \mathfrak{p}; \tag{12}$$

for, if α^r be any one of these integers, then

$$(\alpha^r)^t = (\alpha^t)^r \equiv 1, \text{ mod } \mathfrak{p},$$

[1] We consider t simply as a rational integer, and $\phi(t)$ is to be understood in this sense.

since $$\alpha^t \equiv 1, \text{ mod } \mathfrak{p}.$$

The integers 11) are, moreover, incongruent each to each, mod $\mathfrak{p}$ (Th. 29), and being t in number, are, therefore, all the roots of 12), since 12) cannot have more than t incongruent roots (Th. 25, Cor. 2). But every integer appertaining to t must evidently be a root of 12) and we need look, therefore, only among the integers 11) to find all the integers belonging to t.

Let α^r be as before any one of the integers 11).

If α^r appertain to t we must have $\alpha^r, \alpha^{2r}, \cdots, \alpha^{(t-1)r}$ all incongruent to 1, mod $\mathfrak{p}$.

By Th. 30 the necessary and sufficient condition for this is

$$ir \not\equiv 0, \text{ mod } t, \tag{13}$$

where i runs through the values $1, 2, \cdots, t-1$.

It is easily seen that the necessary and sufficient condition that 13) shall hold is that r shall be prime to t. Hence the necessary and sufficient condition that any one α^r of the integers 11) shall appertain to t is that its exponent r shall be prime to t.

This condition is fulfilled by $\phi(t)$ of the integers 11), and we have proved therefore that

$$\psi(t) = \text{either } \phi(t) \text{ or } 0.$$

We shall now prove that the latter case can never occur.

We separate the $\phi(\mathfrak{p})$ integers of a reduced residue system, mod $\mathfrak{p}$, into classes according to the divisor of $\phi(\mathfrak{p})$ to which they appertain; that is, if $t_1, t_2, \cdots, t_n$ be the positive divisors of $\phi(\mathfrak{p})$ we put in one class the $\psi(t_1)$ integers of the above system that appertain to t_1, in another class the $\psi(t_2)$ integers that appertain to t_2, etc. It is evident that no integer can belong to two different classes and that every integer of this system must belong to some one of these classes.

The integers of a reduced residue system, mod $\mathfrak{p}$, being $\phi(\mathfrak{p})$ in number, we have, therefore

$$\psi(t_1) + \psi(t_2) + \cdots + \psi(t_n) = \phi(\mathfrak{p}).$$

But, considering $\phi(\mathfrak{p})$ simply as an integer of R, we have also (Chap. III, Th. 6)

$$\phi(t_1) + \phi(t_2) + \cdots + \phi(t_n) = \phi(\mathfrak{p}).$$

Hence

$$\psi(t_1)+\psi(t_2)+\cdots+\psi(t_n)=\phi(t_1)+\phi(t_2)+\cdots+\phi(t_n). \quad 14)$$

Since, however, every term in the first member of 14) is equal either to the corresponding term in the second member or to 0, and hence, if even a single term in the first member of 14) were 0, 14) would not hold, no term in the first member of 14) is 0.

Therefore $$\psi(t)=\phi(t).$$

An examination of the table (p. 393) will illustrate this.

§ 27. Primitive Numbers with respect to a Prime Ideal Modulus.[1]

Among the integers of a reduced remainder system, mod $\mathfrak{p}$, there are, we have seen, $\phi(\phi(\mathfrak{p}))$ that belong to the exponent $\phi(\mathfrak{p})$. These integers are caller *primitive numbers with respect to the modulus* $\mathfrak{p}$, or briefly, *primitive numbers,* mod $\mathfrak{p}$.

From the table (p. 393) we see that 3 and 5 are primitive numbers with respect to the modulus $(7, 3+\sqrt{-5})$. If ρ be a primitive number, mod $\mathfrak{p}$, the $\phi(\mathfrak{p})$ powers of ρ,

$$\rho^0=1, \rho^1, \rho^2, \rho^3, \cdots, \rho^{\phi(\mathfrak{p})-1},$$

form a reduced residue system, mod $\mathfrak{p}$. This is for many purposes an extremely useful way of representing such a system.

We can determine a primitive number, mod $\mathfrak{p}$, by the method used (Chap. III, § 33) to determine a primitive root of a rational prime.

We can prove Wilson's Theorem for an ideal modulus by the aid of such a reduced residue system, just as the original theorem was proved for rational integers (Chap. III, § 29).

It will be noticed that the primitive numbers, mod $\mathfrak{p}$, play exactly the same role with regard to $\mathfrak{p}$ that the primitive roots of a rational prime, p, do with regard to p. It would seem desirable to have the nomenclatures the same, but those employed are the usual ones. It would, perhaps, be best to use the term primitive number instead of primitive root in the case of rational integers.

§ 28. Indices.

If $$\alpha\equiv\rho^i, \text{ mod } \mathfrak{p},$$

[1] See Hilbert: Bericht, § 9.

where ρ is a primitive number, mod $\mathfrak{p}$, and i be one of the numbers $0, 1, 2, \cdots, \phi(\mathfrak{p})-1$, i is said to be the index of α to the base ρ with respect to the modulus $\mathfrak{p}$.

The relation between an integer and its index, which was seen in R to be similar to that of a number to its logarithm, is evidently the same in the case of ideals. It can be shown exactly as in R that, if ρ be any primitive number, mod $\mathfrak{p}$, α, β any integers of the realm, and m a positive rational integer, we have the following relations.

i. *The index of the product of two integers is congruent to the sum of the indices of the factors, mod $\phi(\mathfrak{p})$, that is;*

$$\text{ind}_\rho(\alpha\beta) \equiv \text{ind}_\rho \alpha + \text{ind}_\rho \beta, \text{ mod } \phi(\mathfrak{p}).$$

ii. *The index of the mth power of an integer is congruent to m times the index of the integer, mod $\phi(\mathfrak{p})$, that is;*

$$\text{ind}_\rho \alpha^m \equiv m \,\text{ind}_\rho \alpha, \text{ mod } \phi(\mathfrak{p}).$$

We observe that in every system

$$\text{ind}_\rho 1 = 0.$$

By means of the following tables we can illustrate the use of indices for an ideal modulus. Table A gives for the modulus $(7, 3+\sqrt{-5})$ the index to the base 3 of each integer of a reduced residue system, and Table B gives the residue corresponding to any index to the same base and modulus.

It is evident that two integers congruent to each other, mod $\mathfrak{p}$, have the same index in any system of indices, mod $\mathfrak{p}$.

A.

Residue	1	2	3	4	5	6
Index	0	2	1	4	5	3

B.

Index	0	1	2	3	4	5
Residue	1	3	2	6	4	5

To pass from an index system with the base ρ_1 to one with the base ρ_2, the modulus being $\mathfrak{p}$, we find as in R that

$$\text{ind}_{\rho_2} \alpha \equiv \text{ind}_{\rho_1} \alpha \cdot \text{ind}_{\rho_2} \rho_1, \ \text{mod}\ \phi(\mathfrak{p});$$

that is, to obtain the system with base ρ_2 from one with base ρ_1, we multiply each index of the latter system by $\text{ind}_{\rho_2}\rho_1$, the smallest positive residues, mod $\phi(\mathfrak{p})$, of these products bring the required system to the base ρ_2.

In particular, if $\alpha = \rho_2$, we have

$$\text{ind}_{\rho_1} \rho_2 \cdot \text{ind}_{\rho_2} \rho_1 \equiv 1, \ \text{mod}\ \phi(\mathfrak{p}).$$

Ex. To obtain for the modulus $(7, 3+\sqrt{-5})$ a system of indices to the base 5 from one of the base 3 we have first to find $\text{ind}_5 3$. From the relation just given

$$\text{ind}_3 5 \cdot \text{ind}_5 3 \equiv 1, \ \text{mod}\ 6,$$

whence from Table A it follows that

$$5\ \text{ind}_5 3 \equiv 1, \ \text{mod}\ 6,$$

and therefore

$$\text{ind}_5 3 = 5.$$

Multiplying by 5 each index to the base 2 and taking the least positive residues, mod 6, of these products, we obtain for the modulus $(7, 3+\sqrt{-5})$ the following table of indices to the base 5.

Residue	1	2	3	4	5	6
Index	0	4	5	2	1	3

§ 29. Solution of Congruences by Means of Indices.

As in R, the solution of any congruence of the form

$$\alpha x \equiv \beta, \ \text{mod}\ \mathfrak{p}, \qquad 1)$$

where α is not divisible by $\mathfrak{p}$, can be effected by means of a table of indices for the modulus $\mathfrak{p}$; for from 1) it follows that

$$\text{ind}\,\alpha + \text{ind}\,x \equiv \text{ind}\,\beta, \ \text{mod}\ \phi(\mathfrak{p}),$$

which gives

$$\text{ind}\,x \equiv \text{ind}\,\beta - \text{ind}\,\alpha, \ \text{mod}\ \phi(\mathfrak{p}),$$

from which x can be determined.

Ex. 1. From the congruence

$$(2+\sqrt{-5})x \equiv -1+3\sqrt{-5}, \bmod (7, 3+\sqrt{-5}),$$

we obtain $\text{ind}_3\ (2+\sqrt{-5}) + \text{ind}_3\ x \equiv \text{ind}_3\ (-1+3\sqrt{-5})$, mod 6; that is, since

$$2+\sqrt{-5} \equiv 6, \bmod (7, 3+\sqrt{-5}),$$

and

$$-1+3\sqrt{-5} \equiv 4, \bmod (7, 3+\sqrt{-5}),$$

$$3+\text{ind}_3\ x \equiv 4, \bmod 6,$$

or

$$\text{ind}_3\ x = 1,$$

whence

$$x \equiv 3, \bmod (7, 3+\sqrt{-5}).$$

The solution of the congruence

$$\alpha x^n \equiv \beta, \bmod \mathfrak{p}, \qquad 2)$$

where α is not divisible by $\mathfrak{p}$, can be reduced by the use of indices to the solution of a congruence of the first degree, mod $\phi(\mathfrak{p})$.

From 2) it follows that

$$\text{ind}\,\alpha + n\,\text{ind}\,x \equiv \text{ind}\,\beta, \bmod \phi(\mathfrak{p}),$$

and hence

$$n\,\text{ind}\,x \equiv \text{ind}\,\beta - \text{ind}\,\alpha, \bmod \phi(\mathfrak{p}), \qquad 3)$$

which is a congruence of the first degree in the unknown x. Moreover, n, ind x, ind β, ind α and $\phi(\mathfrak{p})$ are evidently to be regarded merely as integers of R. Hence by § 14 the necessary and sufficient condition that 3) shall be solvable, is that ind β — ind α shall be divisible by the greatest common divisor, d, of n and $\phi(\mathfrak{p})$, and, if this condition be satisfied, 3) has $|d|$ roots.

To these $|d|$ values of ind x correspond $|d|$ values of x satisfying 2) and incongruent, mod $\mathfrak{p}$. These are the roots of 2). We see therefore that by the use of a table of indices we can reduce the solution of both 1) and 2) to the solution of congruences between rational integers.

Ex. 2. Consider the congruence

$$(1+\sqrt{-5})x^4 \equiv -\sqrt{-5}, \bmod (7, 3+\sqrt{-5}), \qquad 4)$$

where $1+\sqrt{-5}$ is not divisible by $(7, 3+\sqrt{-5})$.

$\text{ind}_3\ (1+\sqrt{-5}) + 4\ \text{ind}_3\ x \equiv \text{ind}_3 - \sqrt{-5}$, mod 6; that is, since

$$1+\sqrt{-5} \equiv 5, \bmod (7, 3+\sqrt{-5}),$$

and

$$-\sqrt{-5} \equiv 3, \text{ mod } (7, 3+\sqrt{-5}),$$

using table A,

$$5+4 \text{ ind}_3\, x \equiv 1, \text{ mod } 6$$

or

$$4 \text{ ind}_3\, x \equiv 2, \text{ mod } 6. \qquad 5)$$

Since the greatest common divisor, 2, of 6 and 4 divides 2, the congruence 5) has two roots which are easily found to be 2 and 5.

Hence we have

$$\text{ind}_3\, x = 2 \text{ or } 5,$$

and therefore

$$x \equiv 2 \text{ or } 5, \text{ mod } (7, 3+\sqrt{-5}).$$

These results are easily verified by substitution in 4). We obtain

$$(1+\sqrt{-5})2^4 \equiv 2+2\sqrt{-5} \equiv -\sqrt{-5}, \text{ mod } (7, 3+\sqrt{-5}),$$

and

$$(1+\sqrt{-5})5^4 \equiv 2+2\sqrt{-5} \equiv -\sqrt{-5}, \text{ mod } (7, 3+\sqrt{-5}).$$

Ex. 3. The congruence

$$(1+\sqrt{-5})x^4 \equiv 2, \text{ mod } (7, 3+\sqrt{-5}),$$

has no roots, since the congruence

$$\text{ind}_3\, (1+\sqrt{-5}) + 4 \text{ ind}_3\, x \equiv \text{ind}_3\, 2, \text{ mod } 6,$$

or

$$4 \text{ ind}_3\, x \equiv 3, \text{ mod } 6,$$

has no roots, the greatest common divisor, 2, of 4 and 6 not dividing 3.

Ex. 4. Construct a table of indices to the base 10 for the modulus $(23, 8+\sqrt{-5})$ and solve by its aid the congruence

$$(2+3\sqrt{-5})x^5 \equiv -\sqrt{-5}, \text{ mod } (23, 8+\sqrt{-5}).$$

Ex. 5. Show that the congruence

$$(1+\sqrt{-5})x^4 \equiv 15, \text{ mod } (23, 8+\sqrt{-5})$$

has no root.

The congruence $x^n \equiv \beta$, mod $\mathfrak{p}$, where $\mathfrak{p}$ is a prime ideal, can be treated as was the corresponding congruence in R (Chap. III, § 34), and a criterion for its solvability given analogous to Euler's. The general congruence of the 2d degree in one unknown can be discussed and the first part of the theory of quadratic residues for ideal moduli developed as in R, Legendre's symbol being replaced by $\left(\frac{\alpha}{\mathfrak{p}}\right)$, where α is an integer and $\mathfrak{p}$ a prime ideal of $k(\sqrt{m})$ (see Sommer: Vorlesungen über Zahlentheorie, pp. 92–98).

The reader should work out the above. It is evident from the nature of an ideal that no direct reciprocal relation can exist between α and $\mathfrak{p}$, such as that between two rational primes as expressed by the quadratic reciprocity law. A discussion of the reciprocity laws in the higher realms is beyond the scope of this book; for them the reader may consult Hilbert: Bericht, and Math. Ann., Vol. 51; Sommer: V. ü. Z., Fünfter Abschnitt.

CHAPTER XIII.

THE UNITS OF THE GENERAL QUADRATIC REALM.

§ 1. Definition.

The units of any quadratic realm are those integers of the realm which divide every integer of the realm. For purposes of investigation they may be defined as follows:

i. *The divisors of 1 and hence those integers whose reciprocals are integers.*

ii. *Those integers whose norms are* ± 1.

These two definitions are easily seen to coincide; for, if ϵ be a unit of $k(\sqrt{m})$, we have from i

$$\epsilon\alpha = 1, \qquad 1)$$

where α is an integer of $k(\sqrt{m})$.

From 1) it follows that

$$n[\epsilon]n[\alpha] = 1,$$

and hence $$n[\epsilon] = \pm 1;$$

that is, ii is a consequence of i.

Likewise, if ϵ be a unit of $k(\sqrt{m})$, we have from ii

$$\epsilon\epsilon' = \pm 1,$$

where ϵ' is the conjugate of ϵ and therefore an integer of $k(\sqrt{m})$.

Therefore ϵ is a divisor of 1, and hence i is a consequence of ii. It follows from the above definition that *if each of two integers, α, β, divide the other, their quotient is a unit;* for, if

$$\alpha/\beta = \gamma,$$

γ and $1/\gamma$ are both integers; hence γ is a unit by i. In particular, the quotient of two units is a unit. In investigating the units of the general quadratic realm, we shall distinguish two cases according as the realm is imaginary or real.

§ 2. **Units of an Imaginary Quadratic Realm.**

The fact that the norms of all the integers of an imaginary quadratic realm are positive will enable us to determine the units of such a realm.

Let m be a positive integer containing no squared factor; then $k(\sqrt{-m})$ is an imaginary quadratic realm, and we have seen that all imaginary quadratic realms will be obtained if m take all positive values.

Let $\epsilon, = x + y\omega$, be a unit of $k(\sqrt{-m})$, 1, ω being a basis of the realm.

We have

$$n[\epsilon] = (x + y\omega)(x + y\omega') = 1, \qquad 1)$$

the value -1 being impossible, since the realm is imaginary.

We have now to see for what rational integral values of x and y 1) holds, and to do so must distinguish two cases.

i. When $-m \equiv 2$ or 3, mod 4, and hence $\omega = \sqrt{-m}$. Then

$$n[\epsilon] = (x + y\sqrt{-m})(x - y\sqrt{-m}) = x^2 + my^2 = 1.$$

If $m > 1$, it follows that $y = 0$ and $x = \pm 1$, and hence $\epsilon = \pm 1$.

If $m = 1$, we have the realm $k(i)$ whose units we have found to be ± 1, $\pm i$.

ii. When $-m \equiv 1$, mod 4, and hence $\omega = (1 + \sqrt{-m})/2$. Then

$$n[\epsilon] = \left(x + y\frac{1 + \sqrt{-m}}{2}\right)\left(x + y\frac{1 - \sqrt{-m}}{2}\right)$$

$$= \left(x + \frac{y}{2}\right)^2 + \frac{my^2}{4} = 1.$$

If $m > 4$, it follows that $y = 0$ and $x = \pm 1$, and hence

$$\epsilon = \pm 1.$$

If $m = 3$ we have the realm $k(\sqrt{-3})$ whose units we have found to be ± 1, $\pm[(1 \pm \sqrt{-3})/2]$. We see, therefore, *that $k(i)$ has the four units ± 1, $\pm i$, and $k(\sqrt{-3})$ the six units ± 1, $\pm[(1 \pm \sqrt{-3})/2]$, and that all other imaginary quadratic realms have only the two units ± 1.*

§ 3. Units of a Real Quadratic Realm.

The determination of the units of a real quadratic realm is much more difficult. We shall see that, as in the realm $k(\sqrt{2})$, the units of such a realm are infinite in number and can all be expressed as powers of a single unit called the fundamental unit. To show this we shall need the two following theorems, the first of which, due to Minkowski, is of great importance in the theory of numbers.

THEOREM I. *If* $\alpha_1 x + \beta_1 y$, $\alpha_2 x + \beta_2 y$ *be two homogeneous linear forms with real coefficients whose determinant*

$$\delta = \begin{vmatrix} \alpha_1 & \beta_1 \\ \alpha_2 & \beta_2 \end{vmatrix}$$

is not 0, *there exist two rational integers,* x_0, y_0, *not both zero such that*

$$|\alpha_1 x_0 + \beta_1 y_0| \leqq |\sqrt{\delta}|,$$

and

$$|\alpha_2 x_0 + \beta_2 y_0| \leqq |\sqrt{\delta}|.$$ [1]

If we put

$$\left.\begin{aligned} \xi &= \alpha_1 x + \beta_1 y \\ \eta &= \alpha_2 x + \beta_2 y \end{aligned}\right\} \qquad 1)$$

then

$$x = \frac{\beta_2}{\delta}\xi - \frac{\beta_1}{\delta}\eta,$$

$$y = -\frac{\alpha_2}{\delta}\xi + \frac{\alpha_1}{\delta}\eta,$$

or

$$\left.\begin{aligned} x &= A_1\xi + B_1\eta \\ y &= A_2\xi + B_2\eta \end{aligned}\right\} \qquad 2)$$

Putting

$$\begin{vmatrix} A_1 & B_1 \\ A_2 & B_2 \end{vmatrix} = \Delta$$

we see that $\Delta\delta = 1$.

If now we can find two quantities, ξ_0, η_0, such that

$$|\xi_0| \leqq 1/|\sqrt{\Delta}| \text{ and } |\eta_0| \leqq 1/|\sqrt{\Delta}|,$$

[1] Minkowski: Geometrie der Zahlen, p. 104. Hilbert: Bericht, Hülfsatz 6.

and such that the corresponding values x_0, y_0 of x and y are rational integers, then x_0 and y_0 are the required values of x and y.

For, if
$$x_0 = A_1\xi_0 + B_1\eta_0,$$
and
$$y_0 = A_2\xi_0 + B_2\eta_0,$$
then
$$\xi_0 = \alpha_1 x_0 + \beta_1 y_0,$$
$$\eta_0 = \alpha_2 x_0 + \beta_2 y_0,$$
and hence, since
$$|\xi_0| \leqq |\sqrt{\delta}| \text{ and } |\eta_0| \leqq |\sqrt{\delta}|,$$
we have
$$|\alpha_1 x_0 + \beta_1 y_0| \leqq |\sqrt{\delta}|$$
$$|\alpha_2 x_0 + \beta_2 y_0| \leqq |\sqrt{\delta}|.$$

To prove our theorem it will be sufficient therefore to show that two quantities, ξ_0, η_0, exist which satisfy the conditions
$$|\xi_0| \leqq 1/|\sqrt{\Delta}|; \quad |\eta_0| \leqq 1/|\sqrt{\Delta}|,$$
and such that
$$x_0 = A_1\xi_0 + B_1\eta_0,$$
$$y_0 = A_2\xi_0 + B_2\eta_0,$$
are rational integers, where A_1, A_2, B_1, B_2 are real and
$$\Delta = \begin{vmatrix} A_1 & B_1 \\ A_2 & B_2 \end{vmatrix} \neq 0.$$

In the proof of the theorem we shall prove first the case in which α_1, α_2, β_1, β_2 are rational and integral, then that in which the coefficients are rational and finally require merely that they be real. In the first two cases the theorem will be proved in its original form, in the last case in the equivalent form given above.

The proof in the second case will depend directly upon the truth of the theorem for the first case, and that in the third case upon case two.

i. Let α_1, α_2, β_1, β_2 be rational integers.

We shall need a theorem concerning binary linear forms.

Calling a binary linear form $a_1x + b_1y$, where a_1, b_1 are rational integers, for the sake of brevity a form, and two such forms a form system, we say that a form $c_1x + d_1y$ is reducible to o by the form system $a_1x + b_1y$, $a_2x + b_2y$, if

$$c_1x + d_1y = g_1(a_1x + b_1y) + g_2(a_2x + b_2y),$$

where g_1, g_2 are rational integers.

Two forms are reducible to one another by a given form system if their difference is reducible to o by this system.

Two form systems are said to be *equivalent* if every form that is reducible to o by either one of the systems is also reducible to o by the other system.

The analogy to the basis of an ideal is at once evident, for, if $\mathfrak{a}_1 = (a_1\omega_1 + b_1\omega_2,\ a_2\omega_1 + b_2\omega_2)$ be an ideal, where $a_1\omega_1 + b_2\omega_2$, $a_2\omega_1 + b_2\omega_2$ is a basis, then an integer, $c_1\omega_1 + d_1\omega_2$, is a number of the ideal if

$$c_1\omega_1 + d_1\omega_2 = g_1(a_1\omega_1 + b_1\omega_2) + g_2(a_2\omega_1 + a_2\omega_2),$$

where g_1, g_2 are rational integers. Thus the reducibility of a form to o by a given form system corresponds to a number belonging to an ideal.

We can show exactly as in the case of a canonical basis of an ideal (Chap. XI, Th. 1) that among the form systems equivalent to a given system there is one, Ax, $Bx + Cy$, such that among all forms of the form ax, reducible to o by the given system, Ax is that one in which a is smallest in absolute value, and among those of the form $bx + cy$ reducible to o by the given system, $Bx + Cy$, is one of these in which c is smallest in absolute value. We can then show that, if two form systems be equivalent, the absolute values of the determinants of their coefficients are equal (see Chap. XI, Th. 1, Cor.).

It will now be evident that to say in the case of forms that two forms are reducible to one another by a given form system is the same as saying in the case of an ideal that two integers are congruent with respect to this ideal, for in the former case the difference of the two forms is reducible to o by the given system while in the latter the difference of the two integers is a number of the ideal.

The statement in the one case that there are exactly

$$\begin{Vmatrix} a_1 & b_1 \\ a_2 & b_2 \end{Vmatrix}$$

forms, no two of which are reducible to one another by the form system a_1x+b_1y, a_2x+b_2y, is the same as the statement in the other case that there are exactly

$$\begin{Vmatrix} a_1 & b_1 \\ a_2 & b_2 \end{Vmatrix}$$

integers which are incongruent each to each with respect to the ideal $(a_1\omega_1+a_2\omega_2,\ b_1\omega_1+b_2\omega_2)$, and may be proved similarly (see Chap. XII, Th. 1).

We observe now that $|\delta|$ is equal to one of the square numbers

$$1,\ 4,\ 9,\ 16,\ 25,\ \cdots,\ r^2,\ (r+1)^2,\ \cdots,$$

or lies between two of them.

Let $$r^2 \leqq |\delta| < (r+1)^2,$$

and form the $(r+1)^2$ forms

$$ax+by \begin{cases} a=0,1,2,\cdots,r, \\ b=0,1,2,\cdots,r. \end{cases} \qquad 3)$$

Since there are only $|\delta|$ forms, no two of which are reducible to one another by means of the form system $\alpha_1x+\beta_1y$, $\alpha_2x+\beta_2y$, at least two of the forms 3) are reducible to one another by this system.

Let these two forms be a_ix+b_iy and a_jx+b_jy.

Then

$$a_ix+b_iy=a_jx+b_jy+c(\alpha_1x+\beta_1y)+d(\alpha_2x+\beta_2y);$$

that is,

$$(a_i-a_j)x+(b_i-b_j)y=(\alpha_1c+\alpha_2d)x+(\beta_1c+\beta_2d)y,$$

and hence $$\alpha_1c+\alpha_2d=a_i-a_j,$$

$$\beta_1c+\beta_2d=b_i-b_j.$$

Since $|a_i - a_j|$ and $|b_i - b_j| \leqq r$, they are both $\leqq |\sqrt{\delta}|$; hence c and d are the required values of x and y.

ii. Let $\alpha_1, \alpha_2, \beta_1, \beta_2$ be rational fractions.

Let their least common denominator be g. Then $g\alpha_1, g\alpha_2, g\beta_1, g\beta_2$ are rational integers.

By case i we can find two rational integers, x_0, y_0, such that

$$|g\alpha_1 x_0 + g\beta_1 y_0| \leqq |\sqrt{\delta g^2}|,$$
$$|g\alpha_2 x_0 + g\beta_2 y_0| \leqq |\sqrt{\delta g^2}|. \qquad 4)$$

On dividing both members of 4) by g we get

$$|\alpha_1 x_0 + \beta_1 y_0| \leqq |\sqrt{\delta}|,$$
$$|\alpha_2 x_0 + \beta_2 y_0| \leqq |\sqrt{\delta}|.$$

Hence x_0 and y_0 are the required values of x and y.

iii. Let $\alpha_1, \alpha_2, \beta_1, \beta_2$ be any real numbers.

We shall prove the theorem in its second form; that is, that if A_1, A_2, B_1, B_2 be any real numbers, such that the determinant,

$$\begin{vmatrix} A_1 & B_1 \\ A_2 & B_2 \end{vmatrix} = \Delta$$

is not zero, there exist two numbers, ξ_0, η_0, satisfying the conditions

$$|\xi_0| \leqq 1/|\sqrt{\Delta}|, \quad |\eta_0| \leqq 1/|\sqrt{\Delta}|,$$

and such that

$$x_0 = A_1\xi_0 + B_1\eta_0,$$
$$y_0 = A_2\xi_0 + B_2\eta_0,$$

are rational integers.

Let A_1, A_2, B_1, B_2 be defined respectively by the rational fundamental series

$$\left.\begin{matrix} a_1, a_2, a_3, \cdots \\ b_1, b_2, b_3, \cdots \\ a_1', a_2', a_3', \cdots \\ b_1', b_2', b_3', \cdots \end{matrix}\right\} \qquad 5)$$

that is,

$$\left.\begin{matrix} A_1 = \lim\limits_{n \doteq \infty} a_n, & B_1 = \lim\limits_{n \doteq \infty} b_n \\ A_2 = \lim\limits_{n \doteq \infty} a_n', & B_2 = \lim\limits_{n \doteq \infty} b_n' \end{matrix}\right\} \qquad 6)$$

Let

$$\Delta_n = \begin{vmatrix} a_n & b_n \\ a'_n & b'_n \end{vmatrix},$$

where a_n, b_n, a_n', b_n' are the nth terms of the above series. then

$$\lim_{n \doteq \infty} \Delta_n = \lim_{n \doteq \infty} a_n \cdot \lim_{n \doteq \infty} b_n' - \lim_{n \doteq \infty} a_n' \cdot \lim_{n \doteq \infty} b_n,$$

$$= A_1 B_2 - A_2 B_1 = \Delta.$$

We observe now that in the series

$$\Delta_1,\ \Delta_2,\ \Delta_3,\ \cdots, \tag{7}$$

though some of the terms may be 0, the number of such terms is always finite; that is, from some ith term onward no Δ is 0; for otherwise, $\lim_{n \doteq \infty} \Delta_n$ would not exist or else would be 0.

Since now the terms 5) are all rational numbers, and Δ_i and all succeeding Δ's are different from 0, we can find by case ii for every set, a_{i+p}, b_{i+p}, a'_{i+p}, b'_{i+p} of $(i+p)$th terms of the series 5), two numbers, ξ_{i+p}, η_{i+p}, such that

$$|\xi_{i+p}| \leqq 1/|\sqrt{\Delta_{i+p}}|, \quad |\eta_{i+p}| \leqq 1/|\sqrt{\Delta_{i+p}}|, \tag{8}$$

and that

$$a_{i+p}\xi_{i+p} + b_{i+p}\eta_{i+p},$$

$$a'_{i+p}\xi_{i+p} + b'_{i+p}\eta_{i+p},$$

are rational integers.

From 8) it is evident that the absolute values of the terms of the series

$$\xi_i,\ \xi_{i+1},\ \xi_{i+2},\ \cdots,$$

$$\eta_i,\ \eta_{i+1},\ \eta_{i+2},\ \cdots,$$

have an upper limit, for no term of the series

$$|\Delta_i|,\ |\Delta_{i+1}|,\ |\Delta_{i+2}|,\ \cdots,$$

is 0, and $\lim_{n \doteq \infty} \Delta_n = \Delta \neq 0$, whence the terms of this series have a lower limit.

Let this upper limit of the absolute values of the ξ's and η's be k.

Consider a system of rectangular axes and construct a square with the origin as center, its sides equal to $2k$ and parallel to the axes.

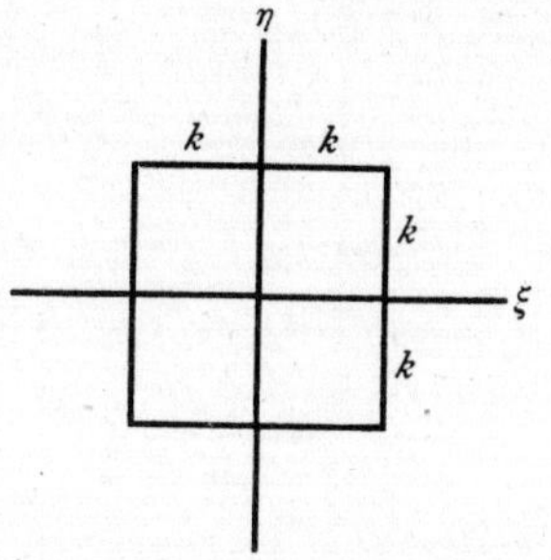

If now we consider ξ_{i+p}, η_{i+p} as the abscissa and ordinate respectively of a point, we may represent each pair of numbers ξ_{i+p}, η_{i+p} $(p=0, 1, 2, \cdots)$ by a point.

All these points will be within or on the boundary drawn as above.

Since there are infinitely many points (ξ_{i+p}, η_{i+p}) within or on this boundary they will have at least one limiting point within or on the boundary. Let the coördinates of this point (or, if there be more than one, of any particular one) be ξ_0, η_0.

There will be certain series of the points (ξ_{i+p}, η_{i+p}) which approach and remain arbitrarily close to (ξ_0, η_0) as p is indefinitely increased.

If $(\xi_{i+p'}, \eta_{i+p'})$ denote such a series, where p' represents only those values of p which gives this series, we have

$$\xi_0 = \lim_{p' \doteq \infty} \xi_{i+p'}, \quad \eta_0 = \lim_{p' \doteq \infty} \eta_{i+p'}.$$

Then

$$\lim_{p' \doteq \infty} (a_{i+v'}\xi_{i+p'} + b_{i+p'}\eta_{i+p'}) = A_1\xi_0 + B_1\eta_0,$$

$$\lim_{p' \doteq \infty} (a'_{i+p'}\xi_{i+p'} + b'_{i+p'}\eta_{i+p'}) = A_2\xi_0 + B_2\eta_0.$$

But all terms of the series

$$a_{i+p'}\xi_{i+p'} + b_{i+p'}\eta_{i+p'},$$

and

$$a'_{i+p'}\xi_{i+p'} + b'_{i+p'}\eta_{i+p'},$$

are rational integers.

Hence their limits, $A_1\xi_0 + B_1\eta_0$ and $A_2\xi_0 + B_2\eta_0$, are rational integers. Therefore ξ_0 and η_0 are the required numbers, and the theorem is proved in its second form. It holds therefore in its original form.

From the above theorem we have at once the following theorem:

THEOREM 2. *If $\alpha_1 x + \beta_1 y$, $\alpha_2 x + \beta_2 y$ be two homogeneous linear forms with real coefficients, whose determinant*

$$\begin{vmatrix} \alpha_1 & \beta_1 \\ \alpha_2 & \beta_2 \end{vmatrix} = \delta$$

is not 0, and κ, κ_λ be any two positive quantities such that

$$\kappa\kappa_\lambda = |\delta|,$$

there exist rational integers x_0, y_0, not both 0, such that

$$|\alpha_1 x_0 + \beta_1 y_0| \leqq \kappa,$$
$$|\alpha_2 x_0 + \beta_2 y_0| \leqq \kappa_\lambda.$$ [1]

Given the two forms

$$\frac{\alpha_1}{\kappa}x + \frac{\beta_1}{\kappa}y, \qquad \frac{\alpha_2}{\kappa_\lambda}x + \frac{\beta_2}{\kappa_\lambda}y,$$

whose determinant is not zero, there exist by Th. 1 two rational integers, x_0, y_0, not both 0, such that

$$\left|\frac{\alpha_1}{\kappa}x_0 + \frac{\beta_1}{\kappa}y_0\right| \leqq 1,$$
$$\left|\frac{\alpha_2}{\kappa_\lambda}x_0 + \frac{\beta_2}{\kappa_\lambda}y_0\right| \leqq 1,$$

and hence

$$|\alpha_1 x_0 + \beta_1 y_0| \leqq \kappa,$$
$$|\alpha_2 x_0 + \beta_2 y_0| \leqq \kappa_\lambda.$$

From this theorem we obtain at once the following theorem, which is necessary for the investigation concerning the units of a real quadratic realm as well as interesting on its own account.

[1] Hilbert: Bericht, Hülfsatz 7.

THEOREM 3. *There are in every real quadratic realm an infinite number of integers, the absolute value of whose norms* $\leqq |\sqrt{d}|$.

i. The existence of at least one such integer is seen at once. For, if 1, ω be a basis of the realm,

$$x + y\omega, \quad x + y\omega'$$

are two linear forms whose determinant

$$\begin{vmatrix} 1 & \omega \\ 1 & \omega' \end{vmatrix} = \omega' - \omega = \sqrt{d} \neq 0,$$

and making use of Th. 2 and putting

$$\kappa = \kappa_1, \quad \kappa_\lambda = |\sqrt{d}|/\kappa_1,$$

where $\kappa_1 > 0$, we see that there exist two rational integers, x_1, y_1, which are not both 0, and which are such that

$$|x_1 + y_1\omega| \leqq \kappa_1,$$
$$|x_1 + y_1\omega'| \leqq |\sqrt{d}|/\kappa_1,$$

and hence

$$|(x_1 + y_1\omega)(x_1 + y_1\omega')| \leqq |\sqrt{d}|;$$

that is,

$$|n[x_1 + y_1\omega]| \leqq |\sqrt{d}|.$$

Therefore the realm contains at least one integer, $\alpha_1, = x_1 + y_1\omega$, the absolute value of whose norm is less than or equal to $|\sqrt{d}|$.

To show that there are an infinite number of such integers we proceed as follows:

To prove the existence in the realm of an integer, $\alpha_2, = x_2 + y_2\omega$, that is different from $\pm\alpha_1$, and such that

$$|n[\alpha_2]| \leqq |\sqrt{d}|,$$

we have only so to choose κ_1 that from the condition

$$|\alpha_2| \leqq \kappa_1$$

it will necessarily follow that

$$\alpha_2 \neq \pm\alpha_1.$$

This may be effected in infinitely many ways, a simple one being to take for κ_1 some positive quantity $\kappa_2 < |\alpha_1|$; for example, $|\alpha_1/2|$, for then from

$$|\alpha_2| \leqq \kappa_2 < |\alpha_1|$$

it follows that

$$|\alpha_2| < |\alpha_1|,$$

whence

$$\alpha_2 \neq \pm \alpha_1.$$

Since by Th. 2 there exist two rational integers, x_2, y_2, which are not both 0 and which are such that

$$|x_2 + y_2\omega| \leqq \kappa_2,$$
$$|x_2 + y_2\omega'| \leqq |\sqrt{d}|/\kappa_2,$$

it follows that there is in the realm an integer, $\alpha_2, = x_2 + y_2\omega$, different from $\pm \alpha_1$, and such that

$$|n[\alpha_2]| \leqq |\sqrt{d}|.$$

To prove the existence in the realm of a third integer, α_3, different from $\pm \alpha_1$ and $\pm \alpha_2$ and such that

$$|n[\alpha_3]| \leqq |\sqrt{d}|,$$

we have only to put for κ in the inequality a positive quantity κ_3 less than $|\alpha_2|$, when it is at once evident that such an integer exists; for from

$$|\alpha_3| \leqq \kappa_3 < |\alpha_2| < |\alpha_1|$$

it follows that $\alpha_3 \neq \pm \alpha_2$, and $\alpha_3 \neq \pm \alpha_1$.

Continuing in this manner we can prove the existence in the realm of as many such integers as we choose. They are, therefore, infinite in number.

Ex. We shall illustrate the above theorem by showing that we can actually find in $k(\sqrt{7})$ as many integers as we please, the absolute values of whose norms are less than or equal to $|\sqrt{28}|$, d being in $k(\sqrt{7})$ equal to 28.

Following the method employed in the proof, we let $\alpha_1, = x_1 + y_1\sqrt{7}$, be any integer satisfying the required condition and κ_1 be any positive quantity, say 2.

We have to determine x, y so that

$$|\alpha_1| \leqq \frac{|\sqrt{28}|}{2}, \quad |\alpha_1'| \leqq 2 \qquad 9)$$

We may assume without loss of generality that x_1, y_1 have the same sign, for, this assumption being made and $\sqrt{7}$ being taken positive,

$$|x_1+y_1\sqrt{7}|>|x_1-y_1\sqrt{7}|,$$

otherwise not, and the most favorable way in which the conditions 9) can be imposed is $|x_1+y_1\sqrt{7}|\leqq$ the larger of the two quantities κ_1 and $|\sqrt{d}|/\kappa_1$, here $|\sqrt{28}|/2$, $|x_1-y_1\sqrt{7}|\leqq$ the smaller of the two quantities κ_1 and $|\sqrt{d}|/\kappa_1$, here 2. Making this assumption, the conditions which x_1, y_1 must satisfy are

$$|x_1+y_1\sqrt{7}|\leqq\sqrt{7}, \tag{10}$$

$$|x_1-y_1\sqrt{7}|\leqq 2. \tag{11}$$

The further assumption x_1, y_1 positive, which may evidently be made without loss of generality, will simplify the work.

Doing this, we see that, since x_1 and y_1 have the same sign, from 10)

$$x_1=0, \quad y_1=1$$

or

$$x_1=1, \quad y_1=0$$

or

$$x_1=2, \quad y_1=0.$$

But it is evident from 11) that of the three values only those pairs in which $y_1=0$ are admissible; hence

$$x_1+y_1\sqrt{7}=1 \text{ or } 2.$$

The only integers of $k(\sqrt{7})$ which satisfy the condition 9) are therefore ± 1, ± 2. The absolute values of the norms of 1, -1, 2, and -2 are evidently all less than $|\sqrt{28}|$.

To find another integer α_2, $=x_2+y_2\sqrt{7}$, the absolute value of whose norm is less than $|\sqrt{28}|$, we proceed as in the proof of Th. 3 and let $\kappa_2=|\alpha_1/2|$, where α_1 is any one of the integers 1, -1, 2 or -2, say 2; that is, we have now to determine x_2, y_2 so that

$$|x_2+y_2\sqrt{7}|\leqq\sqrt{28}, \tag{12}$$

$$|x_2-y_2\sqrt{7}|\leqq 1, \tag{13}$$

where x_2, y_2 are assumed to be both positive. Since x_2, y_2 have the same sign and the value 0 for α_2 is excluded, we see from 12) that

$$x_2=0, \quad y_2=1 \text{ or } 2,$$

or

$$x_2=1 \text{ or } 2, \quad y_2=1,$$

or

$$x_2=1, 2, 3, 4, 5, \quad y_2=0;$$

but 13) excludes all these values except

$$x_2=2, \quad y_2=1$$

and

$$x_2=1, \quad y_2=0.$$

The last set gives $\alpha_2=1$, an integer already found, but the other gives $2+\sqrt{7}$, a new integer satisfying the conditions 12) and 13), and hence one the absolute value of whose norm is less than $|\sqrt{28}|$, but $(2+\sqrt{7})/2$ can not be taken as κ_3 since it is greater than $\kappa_2=1$.

We shall take $2-\sqrt{7}$, the conjugate of $2+\sqrt{7}$, as α_3, a new integer such that $|n[2-\sqrt{7}]|=3<|\sqrt{28}|$, and $|(2-\sqrt{7})/2|<\kappa_2$. If now we put $\kappa_3=|(2-\sqrt{7})/2|$, and proceed as before, we can find an integer α_3 such that

$$|n[\alpha_3]|<|\sqrt{28}|, \text{ and } \alpha_3 \neq \pm\alpha_2, \ \alpha_3 \neq \pm\alpha_1.$$

We obtain $5-2\sqrt{7}$ and $8-3\sqrt{7}$, satisfying the required conditions. Continuing in this manner, we can find as many integers as we please satisfying the required conditions.

THEOREM 4. *If κ be any positive constant, there exist only a finite number of algebraic integers of the second degree such that they and their conjugates are simultaneously less than κ in absolute value.*[1]

Let α be an integer of the second degree such that

$$|\alpha|<\kappa, \quad |\alpha'|<\kappa. \qquad 14)$$

Let
$$x^2+a_1x+a_2=0$$

be the irreducible rational equation of which α and α' are the roots. We have

$$a_1=-(\alpha+\alpha'), \quad a_2=\alpha\alpha',$$

hence
$$|a_1|=|\alpha+\alpha'|, \quad |a_2|=|\alpha\alpha'|.$$

But
$$|\alpha+\alpha'|<2\kappa, \quad |\alpha\alpha'|<\kappa^2,$$

hence
$$|a_1|<2\kappa, \quad |a_2|<\kappa^2. \qquad 15)$$

It is evident that only a finite number of rational integers can satisfy the condition 15); hence there are only a finite number of equations of the second degree whose roots satisfy 14). There are, therefore, only a finite number of integers of the second degree satisfying 14). This theorem, it will be observed, is proved not for a single quadratic realm but for the integers of all quadratic realms taken together.

Moreover, it will be noticed that not all the roots of these equations satisfy 14) but that among their roots are all the integers of the second degree that satisfy 14). See Ex. § 4.

[1] Hilbert: Bericht, Satz 43.

THEOREM 5. *There exists in every real quadratic realm a unit, ϵ, different from ± 1, and such that every unit, η, of the realm has the form*

$$\eta = \pm \epsilon^m,$$

where m is a positive or negative rational integer, or 0.[1]

The proof of this theorem may be conveniently divided into the following four parts:

i. *Every real quadratic realm contains an infinite number of integers, $\alpha_1, \alpha_2, \alpha_3, \cdots$, the absolute values of whose norms are less than or equal to $|\sqrt{d}|$.*

ii. *A quadratic realm, whether real or imaginary, contains only a finite number of ideals whose norms are less than $|\sqrt{d}|$, and hence the infinite series of integers, $\alpha_1, \alpha_2, \alpha_3, \cdots$, considered as principal ideals, $(\alpha_1), (\alpha_2), (\alpha_3), \cdots$, give only a finite number of different principal ideals, whence it follows that the integers, $\alpha_1, \alpha_2, \alpha_3, \cdots$, must fall into a finite number of classes, each containing an infinite number of integers which differ from each other only by unit factors, and hence there are in every real quadratic realm an infinite number of units different from ± 1.*

iii. *Infinitely many of these units of a real quadratic realm are greater than 1; among these there is a smallest one, ϵ.*

iv. *Every unit, η, of the realm has the form*

$$\eta = \pm \epsilon^m,$$

where m is a positive or negative integer, or 0.

Having already proved i, we begin with ii.

ii. We obtain all prime ideals whose norms are less than $|\sqrt{d}|$ by resolving all positive rational primes less than $|\sqrt{d}|$ into their prime ideal factors.

There are evidently only a finite number of such prime ideals. By multiplying these prime ideals together we obtain all ideals whose norms are less than $|\sqrt{d}|$. These ideals are evidently also finite in number. Hence among the infinite system of principal ideals

$$(\alpha_1), (\alpha_2), (\alpha_3), \cdots \qquad 16)$$

[1] See Hilbert: Bericht. Satz 47.

whose norms $\leqq |\sqrt{d}|$, at least one ideal must be repeated an infinite number of times.

Let the infinitely many ideals

$$(\alpha_{i_1}), (\alpha_{i_2}), (\alpha_{i_3}),$$

taken from the system 16) be the same. Then each one of the integers

$$\alpha_{i_1}, \alpha_{i_2}, \alpha_{i_3}, \cdots, \qquad 17)$$

must be divisible by every other one; that is, we have

$$\alpha_{i_1} = \beta \alpha_{i_2},$$

and

$$\gamma \alpha_{i_1} = \alpha_{i_2},$$

where β and γ are integers.

Hence β and γ are units (§ 1), and are, moreover, different from ± 1, since we may assume that no two of the integers 17), as $\alpha_{i_1}, \alpha_{i_2}$, are so related that

$$\alpha_{i_1} = \pm \alpha_{i_2}.$$

Furthermore, the number of such units is infinite; for

$$\alpha_{i_1} = \delta \alpha_{i_3},$$

where δ is a unit, and if $\beta = \pm \delta$, then $\alpha_{i_2} = \pm \alpha_{i_3}$, which is impossible.

Hence the quotients obtained by dividing each of the integers 17) by α_{i_1} constitute an infinite system of units,

$$\eta_1, \eta_2, \cdots,$$

such that we never have

$$\eta_i = \pm \eta_j.$$

iii. There are in the realm an infinite number of units which are > 1; for from each one of the units, $\eta_1, \eta_2, \cdots$, as η_i, we can derive such a unit, since one of the integers,

$$\eta_i, \ -\eta_i, \ 1/\eta_i, \text{ or } -1/\eta_i,$$

all of which are units, must be such a unit. Among this infinite system of units greater than 1 there is a smallest one; for, if η_i

be a unit greater than 1, there are by Th. 4 only a finite number of integers, α, of the realm such that

$$|\alpha| < \eta_\iota; \quad |\alpha'| < \eta_\iota;$$

and hence only a finite number of units, η, such that

$$|\eta| < \eta_\iota; \quad |\eta'| < \eta_\iota. \qquad 18)$$

But if η be any unit greater than 1 but less than η_ι, we have from

$$\eta\eta' = \pm 1,$$

$$\eta|\eta'| = 1,$$

and hence

$$|\eta'| < 1 < \eta_\iota;$$

that is, η must satisfy 18).

There are, therefore, only a finite number of units, η, such that

$$1 < \eta < \eta_\iota;$$

and hence there is among them a smallest one, which is, of course, the smallest of all those units of the realm that are greater than 1. Denote this unit by ϵ.

iv. It is evident that the units

$$\cdots, \pm\epsilon^{-2}, \pm\epsilon^{-1}, \pm\epsilon^{0}, \pm\epsilon^{1}, \pm\epsilon^{2}, \cdots, \qquad 19)$$

are all different; for from

$$\epsilon^m = \pm\epsilon^n, \quad m > n,$$

it would follow that

$$\epsilon^{m-n} = \pm 1,$$

which is impossible, since $\epsilon \neq \pm 1$, and none of the numbers of the realm are imaginary.

We shall now show that the system 19) comprises all units of the realm.

Let ξ be any positive unit greater than or less than 1; then ξ will lie between two consecutive, positive or negative powers of ϵ, or else be equal to a power of ϵ; that is, we can determine an integer, n, positive, or negative, such that

$$\epsilon^n \leqq \xi < \epsilon^{n+1}.$$

Let $$\xi/\epsilon^n = \xi_1;$$

then ξ_1 is a unit, and we have

$$1 \leqq \xi_1 < \epsilon$$

But we cannot have

$$1 < \xi_1 < \epsilon,$$

for ϵ is the smallest unit greater than 1. Hence

$$\xi_1 = 1;$$

and therefore $$\xi = \epsilon^n.$$

When n is positive the units are greater than 1, and when n is negative they are all positive but less than 1; $n = 0$ gives $\xi = 1$. By letting n take all rational integers from $-\infty$ to $+\infty$ we thus obtain all positive units of the realm.

Now let ξ be a negative unit; then $-\xi$ is a positive unit, and we have

$$-\xi = \epsilon^n;$$

hence $$\xi = -\epsilon^n.$$

Every unit, ξ, therefore, of a real quadratic realm has the form

$$\xi = \pm \epsilon^n,$$

where n is a positive or negative rational integer, or 0, and ϵ is the smallest unit of the realm > 1.

This unit ϵ is called the *fundamental unit* of the realm.

§ 4. Determination of the Fundamental Unit.

If in any quadratic realm $k(\sqrt{m})$ any unit, η, be known, we can at once obtain a unit greater than 1; for one of the four units,

$$\eta, \ -\eta, \ 1/\eta \text{ or } -1/\eta,$$

has this property.

Denote that one of these four units which is greater than 1 by η_1. We have now to determine whether there are any units in the realm which are greater than 1 but less than η_1, and, if there be any such units, to find the smallest of them.

Th. 4 enables us to do this; for by the method employed in the proof we can find the rational integral equations finite in number, among whose roots are the integers α of the second degree finite in number, such that

$$|\alpha| < \eta_1; \quad |\alpha'| < \eta_1. \qquad 1)$$

Among these integers will be included all units, ξ, such that

$$1 < \xi < \eta_1, \qquad 2)$$

for we have seen that from 2) and

$$\xi\xi' = \pm 1,$$

it follows that

$$|\xi| < \eta_1; \quad |\xi'| < \eta_1.$$

Since we wish to find only those units which satisfy 1), and the last term of the irreducible rational equation satisfied by an integer of the second degree is the norm of the integer, we may make the last term of each of our equations ± 1.

Writing down, therefore, all irreducible equations of the form

$$x^2 + ax \pm 1 = 0, \qquad 3)$$

where a is a rational integer, such that

$$|a| < 2\eta_1,$$

and solving these equations, we obtain all units which satisfy 1), not only of the realm under discussion but of all real quadratic realms.

If there be any unit of the realm under discussion which is greater than 1 but less than η_1, it will be found among these.

Ex. Let the realm under discussion be $k(\sqrt{5})$. Since

$$n[2+\sqrt{5}] = -1$$

$2+\sqrt{5}$ is a unit of $k(\sqrt{5})$. Moreover $2+\sqrt{5} > 1$.

To determine those units of $k(\sqrt{5})$ that are greater than 1 but less than $2+\sqrt{5}$, if any exist, we write down all irreducible equations of the form 3), in which $|a| < 2(2+\sqrt{5})$. We need only write those in which a is negative since the change of sign of a merely changes the signs of the roots.

We have, therefore, as the equations among whose roots will be found the unit sought for, if it exist,

$$\begin{array}{ll} x^2-x+1=0 & x^2-x-1=0 \\ x^2-2x+1=0 & x^2-2x-1=0 \\ x^2-3x+1=0 & x^2-3x-1=0 \\ x^2-4x+1=0 & x^2-4x-1=0 \\ x^2-5x+1=0 & x^2-5x-1=0 \\ x^2-6x+1=0 & x^2-6x-1=0 \\ x^2-7x+1=0 & x^2-7x-1=0 \\ x^2-8x+1=0 & x^2-8x-1=0 \end{array}$$

Solving these equations, we obtain four units of $k(\sqrt{5})$ which are greater than 1, $\frac{1}{2}(1+\sqrt{5})$, $\frac{1}{2}(3+\sqrt{5})$; $2+\sqrt{5}$ and $\frac{1}{2}(7+3\sqrt{5})$, and of them evidently $\frac{1}{2}(1+\sqrt{5})$ is the smallest and hence the fundamental unit.

The foregoing determination of the fundamental unit of a real quadratic realm depended upon the supposition that some unit of the realm was known. To find some unit of the realm we may proceed as follows, the method being that used in Th. 5 to show the existence in such a realm of a unit different from ± 1.

Let $k(\sqrt{m})$ be the realm.

Determine first how many different ideals have their norms less than $|\sqrt{d}|$. This is easily done by factoring all rational primes less than $|\sqrt{d}|$ and forming all products of these ideals, such that the norms of these products are less than $|\sqrt{d}|$. Suppose that there are m different ideals whose norms are less than $|\sqrt{d}|$.

Find now $m+1$ integers whose norms are less than $|\sqrt{d}|$, which can be done by the method used in the proof of Th. 3. The quotient of some pair of these integers whose norms have the same absolute value must be a unit.

This method of determining the fundamental unit may be shortened by observing that, if $c+d\sqrt{m}$ be the fundamental unit of $k(\sqrt{m})$, where c and d are either rational integers or rational fractions whose numerators are odd and denominators 2, then c and d are both positive, and hence no equation of the form 3), where $|a|>2c$, can have as a root a unit of the realm greater than 1 and less than $c+d\sqrt{m}$. Therefore the fundamental unit is a root of the first equation among the equations

3), arranged in ascending values of $|a|$, whose roots are units of $k(\sqrt{m})$. From this, we see that, in the example above, it was unnecessary to proceed further after finding $\frac{1}{2}(1+\sqrt{5})$ as a root of

$$x^2 - x - 1 = 0.$$

The number of equations to be examined may also be reduced by observing that we must have

$$a^2 + 4 \equiv 0, \text{ mod } m,$$

if an equation, whose last term is -1, is to have as a root a unit of $k(\sqrt{m})$. If m be divisible by a prime, p, of the form $4n-1$, this relation is evidently impossible, for it requires that -1 shall be a quadratic residue of p. *Hence the fundamental unit of $k(\sqrt{m})$ can not have -1 as norm, if m be divisible by a prime of the form $4n-1$.*

§ 5. Pell's Equation.

It will be at once recognized that the determination of the units of a real quadratic realm, $k(\sqrt{m})$, is equivalent to solving Pell's Equation:

$$x^2 - my^2 = \pm 1, \text{ where } m \equiv 2 \text{ or } 3, \text{ mod } 4,$$

and $$x^2 - my^2 = \pm 4,$$

or $$x^2 - my^2 = \pm 1, \text{ where } m \equiv 1, \text{ mod } 4;$$

furthermore the smallest solution will give the fundamental unit.

The general problem of determining an integer with given norm, H, of which the above is a particular case, is evidently equivalent to solving

$$x^2 - my^2 = H.$$

The following theorems relating to Pell's Equation are taken from Chrystal's Algebra, Part II, p. 450, and the reader is referred to this work for their proof and for the complete discussion of this subject.[1] Confining ourselves now to solutions in which x and y are prime to each other, for, if x and y have a common factor r, then r^2 must be a factor of H and we can reduce the

[1] See also H. J. S. Smith: pp. 192–200.

equation to $x'^2 - my'^2 = H'$, where $H' = H/r^2$, and limiting our discussion to the case $|H| < |\sqrt{m}|$, we have the following theorem:

THEOREM 6. *The equation*

$$x^2 - my^2 = \pm H$$

where m and H are positive integers and m is not a perfect square, admits of an infinite number of solutions provided its right-hand side occurs among the quantities $(-1)^n M_n$ belonging to the development of $\sqrt{m}$ as a simple continued fraction, where M_n is the $(n+1)^{th}$ rational divisor, and all these solutions are $x = p_n$, $y = q_n$, where p_n/q_n is the nth convergent in the development of $\sqrt{m}$.

COR 1. *The equation*

$$x^2 - my^2 = 1 \qquad 1)$$

where m is positive and not a perfect square always admits of an infinite number of integral solutions, all of which are furnished by the penultimate convergents in the successive or alternate periods of $\sqrt{m}$.

COR 2. *The equation*

$$x^2 - my^2 = -1 \qquad 2)$$

where m is positive and not a perfect square admits of an infinite number of integral solutions, provided there be an odd number of quotients in the period of $\sqrt{m}$, and all these solutions are furnished by the penultimate convergents in the alternate periods of $\sqrt{m}$.

If there be an even number of quotients in the period of $\sqrt{m}$ the equation has no integral solution.

If p, q be the first solution of 1) or 2), we have

$$x + y\sqrt{m} = (p \pm q\sqrt{m})^n,$$

where n takes all positive values, or all odd positive integral values. Then the resulting values of x, y are all solutions of 1) or 2) respectively.

For the discussion of the equation

$$x^2 - my^2 = \pm H.$$

where H is greater than $\sqrt{m}$, the reader is referred to Chrystal's Algebra, Part II, p. 454.

The following examples will illustrate these theorems:

Ex. 1. Determine the fundamental unit of $k(\sqrt{7})$. We must solve $x^2 - 7y^2 = -1$, if possible, and if not possible, then $x^2 - 7y^2 = 1$.

Expanding $\sqrt{7}$ in a continued fraction we have

$$\sqrt{7} = 2 + \frac{1}{1+}\,\frac{1}{1+}\,\frac{1}{1+}\,\frac{1}{4+}\,\frac{1}{1+}\,\frac{1}{1+}\,\frac{1}{1+}\,\frac{1}{4+}\cdots$$

which gives the following table, where, as in Chrystal, n is number of convergent, a_n the nth partial quotient, p_n the numerator of the nth convergent, q_n the denominator of the nth convergent, M_n the $(n+1)$th rational divisor.

n	a_n	p_n	q_n	M_n
1	2	2	1	3
2	1	3	1	2
3	1	5	2	3
4	1	8	3	1
5	4	37	14	3

There being an even number, 4, of quotients in the period of $\sqrt{7}$, the equation $x^2 - 7y^2 = -1$ has no solution (Th. 6, Cor. 2); that is, the realm $k(\sqrt{7})$ has no unit with negative norm. We observe, however, that the penultimate convergent, 8/3, in the period of $\sqrt{7}$ gives

$$8^2 - 7\cdot 3^2 = 1, \qquad \text{(Th. 6, Cor. 1.)}$$

that is, $8+3\sqrt{7}$, $8-3\sqrt{7}$, $-8+3\sqrt{7}$ and $-8-3\sqrt{7}$ are units of $k(\sqrt{7})$, $8+3\sqrt{7}$ being the fundamental unit. This can be verified by the method of the previous section.

Ex. 2. Determine the fundamental unit of $k(\sqrt{17})$. Expanding $\sqrt{17}$ in a continued fraction, we have

$$\sqrt{17} = 4 + \frac{1}{8+}\,\frac{1}{8+}\cdots$$

which gives the table, there being only one quotient in the period of $\sqrt{17}$.

n	a_n	p_n	q_n	M_n
1	4	4	1	1
2	8	33	8	1

Hence the equations

$$x^2 - 17y^2 = -4 \text{ and } x^2 - 17y^2 = 4$$

have no solution, but the equation

$$x^2-17y^2=-1$$

has the solutions $x=\pm 4$, $y=\pm 1$, and $4+\sqrt{17}$ is seen to be the fundamental unit. This can be verified by seeing that among the roots of the equations

$$x^2-ax\pm 1=0$$

where $|a|<2(4+\sqrt{17})$, the only unit of $k(\sqrt{17})$, which is greater than 1, is $4+\sqrt{17}$.

Ex. 3. Find the fundamental units of the realms $k(\sqrt{10})$, $k(\sqrt{11})$ and $k(\sqrt{21})$.

CHAPTER XIV.

THE IDEAL CLASSES OF A QUADRATIC REALM.

§ 1. Equivalence of Ideals.[1]

We have seen (Chap. XI, Th. 5) that in any quadratic realm, $k(\sqrt{m})$, there exists for every ideal $\mathfrak{a}$ an ideal $\mathfrak{m}$, such that the product $\mathfrak{a}\mathfrak{m}$ is a principal ideal.

Attention was also called to the evident fact that although the particular ideal which was shown to have the desired property was the conjugate $\mathfrak{a}'$ of $\mathfrak{a}$, all ideals of the form $\mathfrak{a}'(\gamma)$, where (γ) is any principal ideal, have this property.

Since, moreover, if $\mathfrak{a}$ and $\mathfrak{b}$ be any two ideals, there exists in $\mathfrak{a}$ a number α such that $(\alpha)/\mathfrak{a}$ is prime to $\mathfrak{b}$ (Chap. XI, Th. 11), it is evident that there is an infinite number of ideals each one prime to all the others and each such that its product by $\mathfrak{a}$ is a principal ideal; for, if α_1 be any number of $\mathfrak{a}$, then

$$(\alpha_1)=\mathfrak{a}\mathfrak{a}_1,$$

where $\mathfrak{a}_1$ is an ideal having the desired property. By the above theorem there exists in $\mathfrak{a}$ a number α_2 such that

$$(\alpha_2)=\mathfrak{a}\mathfrak{a}_2,$$

where $\mathfrak{a}_2$ is prime to $\mathfrak{a}_1$ and is evidently an ideal having the desired property. In like manner there exists in $\mathfrak{a}$ a number α_3 such that

$$(\alpha_3)=\mathfrak{a}\mathfrak{a}_3,$$

where $\mathfrak{a}_3$ is an ideal having the desired property and prime to $\mathfrak{a}_1\mathfrak{a}_2$, and hence to each of them.

Proceeding in this manner, it is evident that an infinite number of ideals exist each of which is prime to all of the others and such that, when multiplied by $\mathfrak{a}$, the product is a principal ideal.

[1] Hilbert: Bericht, Cap. VII.

We see, therefore, that the ideal $\mathfrak{m}$ need not contain $\mathfrak{a}'$ as a factor; for example,

$$(2,\ 1+\sqrt{-5})(3,\ 1+\sqrt{-5})=(1+\sqrt{-5}),$$

$$(2,\ 1+\sqrt{-5})(3,\ 1-\sqrt{-5})=(1-\sqrt{-5}),$$

where $(3,\ 1+\sqrt{-5})$ and $(3,\ 1-\sqrt{-5})$ are prime to $(2,\ 1-\sqrt{-5})$ and to each other.

From the fact that infinitely many ideals give, when multiplied by one and the same ideal, products which are principal ideals, we are led to the introduction of the idea of the equivalence of ideals, which is defined as follows:

Two ideals, $\mathfrak{a}$ and $\mathfrak{b}$, are said to be equivalent if an ideal $\mathfrak{m}$ exists such that the products $\mathfrak{am}$ and $\mathfrak{bm}$ are both principal ideals.

The equivalence of $\mathfrak{a}$ and $\mathfrak{b}$ is expressed symbolically by writing

$$\mathfrak{a}\sim\mathfrak{b};$$

that they are not equivalent by writing

$$\mathfrak{a}\nsim\mathfrak{b}.$$

For example, as we have seen above, the product of each of the ideals $(3,\ 1+\sqrt{-5})$ and $(3,\ 1-\sqrt{-5})$ by the ideal $(2,\ 1+\sqrt{-5})$ is a principal ideal; hence $(3,\ 1+\sqrt{-5})$ is equivalent to $(3,\ 1-\sqrt{-5})$, or in symbols

$$(3,\ 1+\sqrt{-5})\sim(3,\ 1-\sqrt{-5}).$$

Likewise, since the product of $(2,\ 1+\sqrt{-5})$ by itself is a principal ideal, $(2,\ 1+\sqrt{-5})$ is equivalent to each of the two ideals $(3,\ 1+\sqrt{-5})$ and $(3,\ 1-\sqrt{-5})$.

As an example from another realm $k(\sqrt{-17})$, we see that

$$(3,\ 1+\sqrt{-17})\sim(11,\ 4-\sqrt{-17}),$$

for it can be easily shown that

$$(11,\ 4+\sqrt{-17})(11,\ 4-\sqrt{-17})=(11),$$

and $$(11,\ 4+\sqrt{-17})(3,\ 1+\sqrt{-17})=(4+\sqrt{-17}).$$

If $$\mathfrak{a}\sim\mathfrak{b},$$

then by the definition there exists an ideal $\mathfrak{c}$, such that

$$\mathfrak{ac}=(\mu),$$

$$\mathfrak{bc}=(\nu).$$

Multiplying these equations respectively by $\mathfrak{b}$ and $\mathfrak{a}$, we have

$$\mathfrak{abc} = (\mu)\mathfrak{b} = (\nu)\mathfrak{a};$$

that is, if $\mathfrak{a} \sim \mathfrak{b}$, there exist two integers, μ and ν, such that

$$(\nu)\mathfrak{a} = (\mu)\mathfrak{b}.$$

Furthermore, if $\mathfrak{a}$ and $\mathfrak{b}$ be any two ideals and there exist two integers, μ and ν, such that

$$(\nu)\mathfrak{a} = (\mu)\mathfrak{b}, \qquad 1)$$

then

$$\mathfrak{a} \sim \mathfrak{b};$$

for let $\mathfrak{m}$ be any ideal such that the product $\mathfrak{am}$ is a principal ideal (γ), then multiplying 1) by $\mathfrak{m}$, we have

$$(\nu)\mathfrak{am} = (\nu\gamma) = (\mu)\mathfrak{bm}.$$

But, if the product of a principal ideal and another ideal be a principal ideal, the second ideal must be a principal ideal also. Hence $\mathfrak{bm}$ is a principal ideal and consequently

$$\mathfrak{a} \sim \mathfrak{b}.$$

We may therefore define the equivalence of two ideals as follows, this definition being, as shown above, exactly equivalent to the former one:

Two ideals, $\mathfrak{a}$ and $\mathfrak{b}$, are equivalent if two integers, α and β, exist such that

$$\mathfrak{a}(\beta) = \mathfrak{b}(\alpha).$$[1]

For example, we have

$$(1-\sqrt{-5})(3,\ 1+\sqrt{-5}) = (1+\sqrt{-5})(3,\ 1-\sqrt{-5}),$$

whence it follows that

$$(3,\ 1+\sqrt{-5}) \sim (3,\ 1-\sqrt{-5}).$$

We shall use both of these definitions of equivalence, each having some advantages of its own.

Equivalences between ideals obey the following laws:

i. If $\mathfrak{a} \sim \mathfrak{b}$ and $\mathfrak{b} \sim \mathfrak{c}$, 2)

[1] Hilbert: Bericht, p. 223.

then $$\mathfrak{a} \sim \mathfrak{c},$$

for from 2) it follows that there exist integers α, β, γ, δ, such that

$$\mathfrak{a}(\beta) = \mathfrak{b}(\alpha) \text{ and } \mathfrak{b}(\delta) = \mathfrak{c}(\gamma),$$

and hence, multiplying these equations respectively by (δ) and (α),

$$\mathfrak{a}(\beta\delta) = \mathfrak{c}(\alpha\gamma),$$

Therefore $$\mathfrak{a} \sim \mathfrak{c}.$$

ii. If $$\mathfrak{a} \sim \mathfrak{b} \text{ and } \mathfrak{c} \sim \mathfrak{d}, \qquad 3)$$

then $$\mathfrak{ac} \sim \mathfrak{bd},$$

for from 3) it follows that there exist integers α, β, γ, δ, such that

$$\mathfrak{a}(\beta) = \mathfrak{b}(\alpha) \text{ and } \mathfrak{c}(\delta) = \mathfrak{d}(\gamma),$$

and hence $$\mathfrak{ac}(\beta\delta) = \mathfrak{bd}(\alpha\gamma).$$

Therefore $$\mathfrak{ac} \sim \mathfrak{bd}.$$

If $$\mathfrak{a} \sim \mathfrak{b},$$

then from ii it follows immediately that

$$\mathfrak{a}^n \sim \mathfrak{b}^n,$$

where n is any positive rational integer.

The original definition of equivalence given above is that used by Dedekind, the second is equivalent to the following, which is given by Hilbert and Weber:

Every number of a realm, κ, not an integer, can be represented as the quotient of two integers; that is,

$$\kappa = \alpha/\beta.$$

If now we look upon α and β as principal ideals and remove all factors common to (α) and (β), we have

$$(\alpha)/(\beta) = \mathfrak{a}/\mathfrak{b},$$

a representation that is evidently unique. For example, let

$$\kappa = \frac{1+\sqrt{-5}}{1-\sqrt{-5}}.$$

We have

$$\frac{(1+\sqrt{-5})}{(1-\sqrt{-5})}=\frac{(2,\ 1+\sqrt{-5})(3,\ 1+\sqrt{-5})}{(2,\ 1+\sqrt{-5})(3,\ 1-\sqrt{-5})}=\frac{(3,\ 1+\sqrt{-5})}{(3,\ 1-\sqrt{-5})}.$$

If inversely the quotient $\mathfrak{a}/\mathfrak{b}$ of two ideals, $\mathfrak{a}$ and $\mathfrak{b}$, where $\mathfrak{a}$ and $\mathfrak{b}$ may or may not have a common factor, is equal to the quotient of two principal ideals, (α) and (β); that is, if

$$\mathfrak{a}/\mathfrak{b}=(\alpha)/(\beta),$$

and hence may be taken to represent in the above sense a number, $\kappa=\alpha/\beta$, then we say that $\mathfrak{a}$ is equivalent to $\mathfrak{b}$.

For some purposes it is useful to define the equivalence of ideals in a narrower manner, considering $\mathfrak{a}$ equivalent to $\mathfrak{b}$ when and only when a number, κ, *whose norm is positive* exists such that

$$\kappa=\mathfrak{a}/\mathfrak{b};$$

that is, when two integers, α and β, *whose norms have the same sign,* exist such that

$$(\beta)\mathfrak{a}=(\alpha)\mathfrak{b}.$$

This definition of equivalence will evidently be essentially different from the original one when and only when the realm contains *no unit whose norm is negative.* In quadratic realms this will always be the case except when the realm is real and the norm of the fundamental unit is -1.

In general this definition of equivalence is identical with the original one in all realms of odd degree.

Examples. Show that the following equivalences hold

1) $(23,\ 8-\sqrt{-5})\sim(7,\ 3+\sqrt{-5})$,

2) $(7,\ 1+\sqrt{-13})\sim(2,\ 1+\sqrt{-13})$,

3) $\left(2,\ \frac{1+\sqrt{-31}}{2}\right)^3\sim(1)$,

4) $(2,\ \sqrt{-10})\sim(5,\ \sqrt{-10})$,

5) $(3,\ 1-\sqrt{-14})^2\sim(2,\ \sqrt{-14})$,

6) $(5,\ 1+\sqrt{26})\sim(2,\ \sqrt{26})$,

§ 2. Ideal Classes.

Since, if two ideals, $\mathfrak{a}_1$, $\mathfrak{a}_2$, be equivalent to an ideal $\mathfrak{a}$, they are equivalent to each other (§ 1, i), the ideals of a realm can be separated into classes by putting two ideals into the same or different classes according as they are or are not equivalent to each other.

The system of ideals composing such a class has the property that every ideal in it is equivalent to every other one and that it consists of the totality of all ideals which are equivalent to any one of the ideals composing the class.

Such a class is called an *ideal class* and is denoted by a Latin capital letter.

Any ideal $\mathfrak{a}$ of a class A, may evidently be taken as the representative of the class, and the class is completely determined by $\mathfrak{a}$.

The class composed of all principal ideals and as whose representative we can take (1), is called the *principal* class and is denoted by 1.

If $\mathfrak{a}_1$, $\mathfrak{a}_2$ be any two ideals of the class A, and $\mathfrak{b}_1$, $\mathfrak{b}_2$ be any two ideals of the class B, then since from

$$\mathfrak{a}_1 \sim \mathfrak{a}_2,$$

and

$$\mathfrak{b}_1 \sim \mathfrak{b}_2,$$

it follows that

$$\mathfrak{a}_1\mathfrak{b}_1 \sim \mathfrak{a}_2\mathfrak{b}_2 \ (\S 1, \text{ii}),$$

it is evident that all ideals of the form $\mathfrak{a}\mathfrak{b}$, where $\mathfrak{a}$ and $\mathfrak{b}$ are any ideals of the classes A and B respectively, belong to a single class, C, which class can, however, contain infinitely many ideals other than the products $\mathfrak{a}\mathfrak{b}$.

The ideal class C is called the *product of the ideal classes A and B* and we write

$$C = AB.$$

For example, we have

$$(3,\ 1+\sqrt{-5})(2,\ 1+\sqrt{-5}) = (1+\sqrt{-5}),$$

whence it follows that the product of the classes of $(3,\ 1+\sqrt{-5})$ and $(2,\ 1+\sqrt{-5})$ is the principal class. But $(3,\ 1+\sqrt{-5})$ and $(2,\ 1+\sqrt{-5})$ belong to the same class, A. Hence we have $A^2 = 1$.

The product of any ideal class A by the principal class is A; that is,

$$A \cdot 1 = A.$$

Inversely from $$AB = B$$

it follows evidently that $$A = 1.$$

In the multiplication of ideal classes it is evident from the definition of the product of two classes that the commutative and associative laws hold; that is,

$$AB = BA$$

and $$AB \cdot C = A \cdot BC.$$

We see, therefore, that in the formation of the product of any number of classes, $A_1, A_2, \cdots, A_m$, the order in which the classes are taken will make no difference in the final result, which we denote by $A_1 A_2 \cdots A_m$.

If $\mathfrak{a}_1, \mathfrak{a}_2, \cdots, \mathfrak{a}_m$ be any representatives of the classes $A_1, A_2, \cdots, A_m$, then $\mathfrak{a}_1 \mathfrak{a}_2 \cdots \mathfrak{a}_m$ is a representative of the class $A_1 A_2 \cdots A_m$.

If each of the m factors is the class, A, then the product is called the mth power of A and is denoted by A^m.

We have $$A^1 = A$$

and $$A^0 = 1.$$

THEOREM 1. *For every ideal class A there exists one and only one ideal class B such that the product AB is the principal class.*[1]

Let $\mathfrak{a}$ be any ideal of the class A and α any number of $\mathfrak{a}$. Then

$$\mathfrak{a}\mathfrak{b} = (\alpha), \qquad 1)$$

where $\mathfrak{b}$ is an ideal whose class we denote by B. Then from 1) it follows that

$$AB = 1. \qquad 2)$$

If now a class C other than B exist such that

$$AC = 1, \qquad 3)$$

[1] Hilbert: Bericht, Satz 45.

we have from 2)

$$ABC = C,$$

and hence, making use of 3)

$$B = C.$$

The theorem is therefore proved.

The class B is called the reciprocal class of the class A and is denoted by A^{-1}.

It is evident that inversely A is the reciprocal class of A^{-1}.

Defining further A^{-m} as the reciprocal class of A^m, the following laws are seen to hold for any positive integral rational exponents, r, s.

$$A^r A^s = A^{r+s}, \quad (A^r)^s = A^{rs}, \quad (AB)^r = A^r B^r.$$

THEOREM 2. *If A be any ideal class and $\mathfrak{b}$ any ideal, there exists in A an ideal prime to $\mathfrak{b}$.*[1]

The quotients obtained by dividing each number, α, of an ideal $\mathfrak{a}$ by $\mathfrak{a}$ are evidently ideals that belong to a single class.

Among them can be found an ideal prime to any given ideal $\mathfrak{b}$, for α can be chosen so that $(\alpha)/\mathfrak{a}$ is prime to $\mathfrak{b}$. Hence the theorem.

§ 3. **The Class Number of a Quadratic Realm.**

We shall now show that the number of ideal classes in any given quadratic[2] realm is finite; that is, there exists in every quadratic realm a system of ideals finite in number such that the product of any ideal of the realm by one and only one of these ideals is a principal ideal. Such a system of ideals for a given realm we shall call a *complete system of non-equivalent ideals.*

The number of ideals composing such a system, that is, *the number of ideal classes of the realm* is denoted by h.

To prove that h is finite we need the following theorem:

THEOREM 3. *In every ideal $\mathfrak{a}$ there exists a number α different from 0 and such that*

[1] Dirichlet-Dedekind: p. 579.

[2] This theorem holds for the general realm of the nth degree.

$$|n[\alpha]| \leqq |n[\mathfrak{a}]\sqrt{d}|,$$

where d is the discriminant of the realm.[1]

We shall distinguish two cases according as the realm is real or imaginary.

i. Let $\mathfrak{a}$ be any ideal of a real quadratic realm, k, and

$$\alpha_1 = a_1\omega_1 + a_2\omega_2, \quad \alpha_2 = b_1\omega_1 + b_2\omega_2,$$

a basis of $\mathfrak{a}$, where ω_1, ω_2 is a basis of k. Since α_1, α_2 and their conjugates, α_1', α_2' are real numbers, k being a real realm, $\alpha_1 x + \alpha_2 y$, $\alpha_1' x + \alpha_2' y$ are linear forms with real coefficients, and their determinant can easily be shown to be different from 0. Hence by Minkowski's Theorem (Chap. XIII, Th. 1) there exist rational integers, x_0, y_0, such that

$$\left.\begin{aligned} |\alpha_1 x_0 + \alpha_2 y_0| &\leqq |\sqrt{\alpha_1\alpha_2' - \alpha_2\alpha_1'}| \\ |\alpha_1' x_0 + \alpha_2' y_0| &\leqq |\sqrt{\alpha_1\alpha_2' - \alpha_2\alpha_1'}| \end{aligned}\right\} \qquad 1)$$

It is easily seen that $\alpha, = \alpha_1 x_0 + \alpha_2 y_0$, is the desired number of $\mathfrak{a}$, for if $\alpha = \alpha_1 x_0 + \alpha_2 y_0$, then $\alpha' = \alpha_1' x_0 + \alpha_2' y_0$, and hence from 1)

$$|n[\alpha]| \leqq |\alpha_1\alpha_2' - \alpha_2\alpha_1'|.$$

Moreover,

$$\begin{vmatrix} \alpha_1 & \alpha_2 \\ \alpha_1' & \alpha_2' \end{vmatrix} = \begin{vmatrix} a_1 & a_2 \\ b_1 & b_2 \end{vmatrix} \cdot \begin{vmatrix} \omega_1 & \omega_2 \\ \omega_1' & \omega_2' \end{vmatrix};$$

that is,

$$|\alpha_1\alpha_2' - \alpha_2\alpha_1'| = |n[\mathfrak{a}]\sqrt{d}|,$$

and hence

$$|n[\alpha]| \leqq |n[\mathfrak{a}]\sqrt{d}|.$$

ii. The realm is imaginary.

Let $\qquad \alpha_1 = \rho_1 + i\sigma_1, \quad \alpha_2 = \rho_2 + i\sigma_2,$

where $\rho_1, \rho_2, \sigma_1, \sigma_2$ are real numbers and $i = \sqrt{-1}$, be a basis of $\mathfrak{a}$.

Since $\rho_1, \rho_2, \sigma_1, \sigma_2$ are real numbers, whose determinant is different from 0, there exist by Minkowski's Theorem rational integers, x_0, y_0, such that

$$|\rho_1 x_0 + \rho_2 y_0| \leqq |\sqrt{\rho_1\sigma_2 - \rho_2\sigma_1}|,$$

$$|\sigma_1 x_0 + \sigma_2 y_0| \leqq |\sqrt{\rho_1\sigma_2 - \rho_2\sigma_1}|.$$

[1] Hilbert: Bericht, Satz 46.

We shall show that

$$\alpha = \alpha_1 x_0 + \alpha_2 y_0$$

is the desired number.

We have

$$\alpha = \alpha_1 x_0 + \alpha_2 y_0 = \rho_1 x_0 + \rho_2 y_0 + i(\sigma_1 x_0 + \sigma_2 y_0),$$

$$\alpha' = \alpha_1' x_0 + \alpha_2' y_0 = \rho_1 x_0 + \rho_2 y_0 - i(\sigma_1 x_0 + \sigma_2 y_0),$$

$$n[\alpha] = (\rho_1 x_0 + \rho_2 y_0)^2 + (\sigma_1 x_0 + \sigma_2 y_0)^2,$$

and hence

$$n[\alpha] \leqq 2|\rho_1\sigma_2 - \rho_2\sigma_1|.$$

It is easily seen, moreover, that

$$|\alpha_1\alpha_2' - \alpha_2\alpha_1'| = 2|\rho_1\sigma_2 - \rho_2\sigma_1|,$$

whence

$$n[\alpha] \leqq |\alpha_1\alpha_2' - \alpha_2\alpha_1'|.$$

We have, however, as in i,

$$|\alpha_1\alpha_2' - \alpha_2\alpha_1'| = |n[\mathfrak{a}]\sqrt{d}|,$$

and therefore

$$n[\alpha] \leqq |n[\mathfrak{a}]\sqrt{d}|.$$

THEOREM 4. *There exists in every ideal class of a realm, k, an ideal whose norm does not exceed the absolute value of the square root of the discriminant of k.*[1]

Let A be any ideal class and $\mathfrak{j}$ an ideal of the reciprocal class A^{-1}. By the last theorem there exists in $\mathfrak{j}$ a number, ι, such that

$$|n[\iota]| \leqq |n[\mathfrak{j}]\sqrt{d}|. \qquad 2)$$

But

$$(\iota) = \mathfrak{j}\mathfrak{a}, \qquad 3)$$

where $\mathfrak{a}$ is an ideal belonging to the class reciprocal to A^{-1}; that is, to A.

From 3) it follows that

$$|n[\iota]| = n[\mathfrak{j}]n[\mathfrak{a}],$$

and hence from 2)

$$n[\mathfrak{a}] \leqq |\sqrt{d}|.$$

[1] Hilbert: Bericht, Satz 50.

THEOREM 5. *The number of ideal classes of any realm is finite.*[1]

Since every ideal is a divisor of its norm, we shall by the last theorem obtain at least one representative of each ideal class of any given realm, k; that is, a complete system of non-equivalent ideals, if we resolve into their ideal factors all positive rational integers which are less than $|\sqrt{d}|$, where d is the discriminant of k.

There are evidently only a finite number of rational integers satisfying this condition and each of them is resolvable into only a finite number of ideal factors. The number of ideals of k whose norms are less than $|\sqrt{d}|$ is therefore finite.

Hence the number of ideal classes of k is finite.

The last two theorems enable us to determine the number of ideal classes of any quadratic realm, the method consisting simply in determining into how many classes the finite number of ideals fall, whose norms are less than $|\sqrt{d}|$.[2]

We shall illustrate this method of determining the class number by several examples. This we do the more readily as in the solutions of these examples will be found many of the problems which arise in reckoning with ideals.

Our task then being to ascertain into how many classes the ideals of any given realm, k, fall, whose norms are $\leqq |\sqrt{d}|$, it is evident that this will be accomplished, if we determine into how many classes fall the prime ideals and those of their powers and products whose norms satisfy the given condition.

Having determined the prime ideals whose norms are $\leqq |\sqrt{d}|$ by resolving all rational primes which are $\leqq |\sqrt{d}|$ into their ideal factors, we next determine what equivalences exist between these ideals, including, of course, (1) as a representative of the principal class. The number of classes given by these prime ideals and (1) having been determined, it remains to be ascertained

[1] Hilbert: Bericht, Satz 50.

[2] This method of determining the class number of a realm is applicable to realms of higher degree. See Hilbert: Bericht, p. 226; also "Tafel der Klassenanzahlen für Kubische Zahlkörper" by the author.

whether any powers and products of these prime ideals, the norms of such powers and products being $\leqq|\sqrt{d}|$, give new classes.

The solution of the question whether or no two given ideals are equivalent will be discussed in full in connection with the numerical examples.

THEOREM 6. *If h be the class number of a realm, k, the hth power of every ideal class is the principal class.*[1]

Let A be any ideal class of k.

In the series

$$A, A^2, \cdots, A^r, \cdots,$$

we must have two classes the same, as

$$A^{r+e} = A^r,$$

and hence

$$A^e = 1.$$

If A^e be the lowest power of A which gives the principal class; then the classes

$$A^0 = 1, A, A^2, \cdots, A^{e-1} \qquad 4)$$

are all different.

If B be a class different from all the classes 4), then the classes

$$B, AB, A^2B, \cdots, A^{e-1}B$$

are all different from each other and from each of the classes 4). Continuing this process, we see that h is a multiple of e. But e was the exponent of the lowest power of any class that gives the principal class.

Hence the hth power of every class of k is the principal class.

From this theorem it is evident that the hth power of every ideal is a principal ideal.

Ex. 1. $k(i)$. Basis: $1, i$. $d = -4$.
Each class must contain an ideal whose norm is $\leqq|\sqrt{-4}|$, that is $\leqq 2$. We shall indicate this by writing $n[\mathfrak{a}] \leqq |\sqrt{-4}|$; $n[\mathfrak{a}] = 1$ or 2. We have

$$(2) = (1+i)^2.$$

The only ideals whose norms satisfy the given condition are therefore (1) and $(1+i)$, both of which are principal ideals. There is therefore

[1] Hilbert: Bericht, Satz 51.

only one class, the principal class. Hence $h=1$. Therefore the ordinary unique factorization law holds in $k(i)$, as we have already seen to be the case.

Ex. 2. $k(\sqrt{-3})$. Basis: $1, \frac{1}{2}(1+\sqrt{-3})$. $d=-3$

$$n[\alpha] \leqq |\sqrt{-3}|, \; n[\alpha]=1.$$

The only ideal whose norm satisfies the given condition is (1), hence there is only one class, the principal class; that is,

$$h=1.$$

Ex. 3. $k(\sqrt{2})$. Basis: $1, \sqrt{2}$. $d=8$

$$n[\alpha] \leqq |\sqrt{8}|, \; n[\alpha]=1 \text{ or } 2.$$

We have

$$(2)=(\sqrt{2})^2.$$

The only ideals whose norms satisfy the given condition are (1) and $(\sqrt{2})$, both of which are principal ideals.

Hence

$$h=1.$$

Ex. 4. $k(\sqrt{-5})$. Basis: $1, \sqrt{-5}$. $d=-20$.

$$n[\alpha] \leqq |\sqrt{-20}|, \; n[\alpha]=1, 2, 3, \text{ or } 4.$$

We have

$$(2)=(2, 1+\sqrt{-5})^2,$$

$$(3)=(3, 1+\sqrt{-5})(3, 1-\sqrt{-5}).$$

We have now to determine what equivalences, if any, exist between the ideals (1), $(2, 1+\sqrt{-5})$, $(3, 1+\sqrt{-5})$, $(3, 1-\sqrt{-5})$ and $(2, 1+\sqrt{-5})^2$, these being all the ideals whose norms satisfy the given condition. We see at once that $(2, 1+\sqrt{-5})^2, =(2)$, is a principal ideal and represents therefore with (1), the principal class.

On the other hand, it is easily shown that $(2, 1+\sqrt{-5})$ is a non-principal ideal, for, if it were a principal ideal, there must exist an integer, $\alpha, =x+y\sqrt{-5}$, such that

$$(\alpha)=(2, 1+\sqrt{-5}),$$

and hence

$$n[\alpha]=n(2, 1+\sqrt{-5});$$

that is, two rational integers, x, y, must exist such that

$$x^2+5y^2=2.$$

This is, however, manifestly impossible.

Hence $(2, 1+\sqrt{-5})$ is a non-principal ideal and the representative of a new class, which we shall denote by A.

We have already proved (§ 1) that $(3, 1+\sqrt{-5})$ and $(3, 1-\sqrt{-5})$ are equivalent to $(2, 1+\sqrt{-5})$.

They belong therefore to A, and all ideals of $k(\sqrt{-5})$ fall into two classes, 1 and A. Hence $h=2$. It will be observed that $A^2=1$.

Ex. 5. $k(\sqrt{7})$. Basis: 1, $\sqrt{7}$. $d=28$.

$$n[\alpha] \leqq |\sqrt{28}|, \quad n[\alpha]=1, 2, 3, 4, \text{ or } 5.$$

We have

$$(2)=(2, 1+\sqrt{7})^2$$

$$(3)=(3, 1+\sqrt{7})(3, 1-\sqrt{7})$$

$$(5)=(5).^1$$

The ideals to be considered are therefore (1), $(2, 1+\sqrt{7})$, $(3, 1+\sqrt{7})$, $(3, 1-\sqrt{7})$ and $(2, 1+\sqrt{7})^2$; of these (1) and $(2, 1+\sqrt{7})^2$ belong to the class 1.

We proceed as in the case of $(2, 1+\sqrt{-5})$ in the last example to determine whether $(2, 1+\sqrt{7})$ is or is not a principal ideal. In order that $(2, 1+\sqrt{7})$ may be a principal ideal, it is necessary and sufficient that there exist an integer $\alpha, =x+y\sqrt{7}$, such that

$$|n[\alpha]|=n(2, 1+\sqrt{7});$$

that is, that there exist rational integers x, y, such that

$$x^2-7y^2=2 \text{ or } -2.$$

We see that $x=3$, $y=1$ satisfy this condition.[2] Hence

$$(2, 1+\sqrt{7})=(3+\sqrt{7}),$$

a principal ideal, $3+\sqrt{7}$ being divisible by $(2, 1+\sqrt{7})$, since the latter is the only ideal whose norm is 2. We can in like manner show that $(3, 1+\sqrt{7})$ is a principal ideal, for $x=2$, $y=\pm 1$ satisfy the condition

$$x^2-7y^2=-3$$

whence

$$(3, 1+\sqrt{7})=(2+\sqrt{7}) \text{ or } (2-\sqrt{7}).$$

So far as the task in hand is concerned, it is indifferent to which of the two conjugate principal ideals, $(2+\sqrt{7})$ and $(2-\sqrt{7})$, $(3, 1+\sqrt{7})$ is equal, for all that we need know is that it is a principal ideal, from which it follows at once that $(3, 1-\sqrt{7})$ is a principal ideal, for it belongs to the class reciprocal to that of $(3, 1+\sqrt{7})$ since

$$(3, 1+\sqrt{7})(3, 1-\sqrt{7}) \sim (1).$$

It is easily seen, however, that $2+\sqrt{7}$ is not a number of $(3, 1+\sqrt{7})$ while $2-\sqrt{7}$ does enjoy this property. Hence

$$(3, 1+\sqrt{7})=(2-\sqrt{7}),$$

and

$$(3, 1-\sqrt{7})=(2+\sqrt{7}).$$

All the ideals of $k(\sqrt{7})$ whose norms are $\leqq |\sqrt{d}|$ being principal ideals, we have $h=1$.

[1] This denotes that (5) is a prime ideal.

[2] See also Chap XIII, § 5, Pell's Equation.

We are assisted in determining to which of the classes, 1, A, $A^2, \cdots, A^t$, if any, a given ideal $\mathfrak{j}$ belongs by the following theorem:

THEOREM 7. *If $\mathfrak{a}^t$ be the lowest power of $\mathfrak{a}$ which is a principal ideal, $\mathfrak{a}, \mathfrak{a}^2, \cdots, \mathfrak{a}^t \sim 1$, being representatives of the t classes*

$$A, A^2, \cdots, A^t = 1, \tag{5}$$

and $\mathfrak{j}^s$ the lowest power of an ideal $\mathfrak{j}$ which is a principal ideal, then in order that $\mathfrak{j}$ may belong to one of the classes 5) it is necessary that t shall be divisible by s, and furthermore, if this condition be satisfied and $t = t_1 s$, then $\mathfrak{j}$ can belong to none of the classes 5) except the $\phi(s)$ classes A^i, for which $i = i_1 t_1$, and i_1 is prime to s.

If $$\mathfrak{j} \sim \mathfrak{a}^i,$$

then $$\mathfrak{j}^t \sim \mathfrak{a}^{ti} \sim 1 \sim \mathfrak{j}^s,$$

whence $$t \equiv 0, \text{ mod } s;$$

that is, t divisible by s is a necessary condition that $\mathfrak{j}$ shall belong to one of the classes 5).

Furthermore, if $$\mathfrak{j} \sim \mathfrak{a}^i,$$

then $$\mathfrak{j}^s \sim \mathfrak{a}^{si} \sim 1 \sim \mathfrak{a}^t,$$

whence $$si \equiv 0, \text{ mod } t, = t_1 s,$$

and therefore $$i \equiv 0, \text{ mod } t_1;$$

that is, $$i = i_1 t_1.$$

Then
$$\begin{aligned} \mathfrak{j} &\sim \mathfrak{a}^{i_1 t_1}, \\ \mathfrak{j}^2 &\sim \mathfrak{a}^{2 i_1 t_1}, \\ \vdots\ & \quad \vdots \\ \mathfrak{j}^f &\sim \mathfrak{a}^{f i_1 t_1}, \\ \vdots\ & \quad \vdots \\ \mathfrak{j}^g &\sim \mathfrak{a}^{g i_1 t_1}, \\ \vdots\ & \quad \vdots \\ \mathfrak{j}^s &\sim \mathfrak{a}^{s i_1 t_1} \sim 1, \end{aligned}$$

from which it follows, since no two of the ideals $\mathfrak{j}, \mathfrak{j}^2, \cdots, \mathfrak{j}^s$ are equivalent, that

$$i_1t_1,\ 2i_1t_1,\ \cdots,\ fi_1t_1,\ \cdots,\ gi_1t_1,\ \cdots,\ si_1t_1,$$

must be incongruent each to each, mod t; that is, we must have

$$fi_1t_1 \not\equiv gi_1t_1, \text{ mod } t, = t_1s,$$

where f and g are any two of the integers, 1, 2, $\cdots$, s, different from each other.

Therefore we must have $\quad fi_1 \not\equiv gi_1$, mod s;

that is, the integers $i_1, 2i_1, \cdots, si_1$ must form a complete residue system, mod s, which can be the case only when i_1 is prime to s.

Hence in case $\mathfrak{j}$ should belong to any one of the classes 5) it is possible only to have

$$\mathfrak{j} \sim \mathfrak{a}^{i_1t_1},$$

where $t_1 = t/s$, and i_1 is prime to s.

There are therefore only $\phi(s)$ of the classes 1) to which it is possible for $\mathfrak{j}$ to belong.

Ex. 6. Let $\mathfrak{a}^{24}$ be the lowest power of $\mathfrak{a}$ which is a principal ideal, $\mathfrak{a}, \mathfrak{a}^2, \cdots, \mathfrak{a}^{24} \sim 1$, representing therefore the twenty-four classes

$$A, A^2, \cdots, A^{24} = 1, \tag{6}$$

Let $\mathfrak{j}^6$ be the lowest power of $\mathfrak{j}$ which is a principal ideal.

Since 24 is divisible by 6, it is possible for $\mathfrak{j}$ to belong to $\phi(6) = 2$, of the classes 6). We have $t = 4$, and those of the classes 6) to which it is possible for $\mathfrak{j}$ to belong are A^4 and A^{20}.

By means of Th. 7 we can reduce the labor of determining h; for, if $\mathfrak{a}$ be an ideal satisfying Minkowski's condition, that is, $n[\mathfrak{a}] \leqq |\sqrt{d}|$, and $\mathfrak{a}^t$ the lowest power of $\mathfrak{a}$ that is a principal ideal, then

$$\mathfrak{a}, \mathfrak{a}^2, \cdots, \mathfrak{a}^t \sim 1,$$

are representatives of t ideal classes,

$$A, A^2, \cdots, A^t = 1, \tag{7}$$

and, as we have seen in the last theorem, h is a multiple of t.

Let now N be the number of ideals of the realm that satisfy

Minkowski's condition, n the number of these ideals that belong to one or the other of the classes 7), and c the number of the known classes 7) that have found representatives among the ideals satisfying Minkowski's condition.

The t classes 7) must evidently have representatives among the N ideals satisfying Minkowski's condition, and therefore, since only c of these classes have yet found representatives among these ideals, $t-c$ of the $N-n$ of these ideals whose classes have not yet been determined must belong respectively to the $t-c$ classes whose representatives are missing. We have then as possible representatives of new classes

$$N-n-(t-c) \text{ ideals, and, if}$$

$$N-n-(t-c)<t;$$

that is, if $$N-n+c<2t,$$

it follows, since h must be divisible by t, that

$$h=t.$$

In particular, if $$N<2t,$$

we have at once $$h=t.$$

If $$N-n+c \nless 2t,$$

we must proceed to determine whether some of the remaining ideals belong to the classes 7). Let $\mathfrak{j}$ be one no power of which belongs to one of the classes 7) and let $\mathfrak{j}^s$ be the lowest power of $\mathfrak{j}$ which is a principal ideal.

Then $\mathfrak{j}, \mathfrak{j}^2, \cdots, \mathfrak{j}^{s-1}$ are representatives of the $s-1$ new classes, $B, B^2, \cdots, B^{s-1}$, and there are now in all st known classes

$$\begin{array}{l} 1, A, A^2, \cdots, A^{t-1}, \\ B, BA, BA^2, \cdots, BA^{t-1}, \\ \cdots\cdots\cdots\cdots \\ B^{s-1}, B^{s-1}A, B^{s-1}A^2, \cdots, B^{s-1}A^{t-1}, \end{array} \qquad 8)$$

and h is therefore divisible by st.

If now n and c have their former meaning except that 8) are now the known classes, and if

$$N-n+c<2st,$$

then

$$h=st.$$

If, however,

$$N-n+c \nless 2st,$$

we proceed as before to determine the classes to which the remaining ideals belong, observing always whether

$$N-n+c<2st.$$

If we find one that belongs to none of the classes 8), we proceed as with $\mathfrak{j}$.

Ex. 7. $k(\sqrt{-31})$. Basis: $1, \frac{1+\sqrt{-31}}{2}, d=-31$.

$$n[\mathfrak{a}] \leqq |\sqrt{-31}|; \quad n[\mathfrak{a}]=1, 2, 3, 4 \text{ or } 5.$$

We have

$$(2)=\left(2, \frac{1+\sqrt{-31}}{2}\right)\left(2, \frac{1-\sqrt{-31}}{2}\right),$$

$$(3)=(3),$$

$$(5)=\left(5, \frac{3+\sqrt{-31}}{2}\right)\left(5, \frac{3-\sqrt{-31}}{2}\right).$$

Since

$$x^2+xy+8y^2 \neq 2$$

for any integral values of x and y, there is no integer of $k(\sqrt{-31})$ whose norm is 2. Hence

$$\left(2, \frac{1+\sqrt{-31}}{2}\right) \not\sim (1).$$

We proceed to determine the lowest power of $\left(2, \frac{1+\sqrt{-31}}{2}\right)$ that is a principal ideal.

We have

$$\left(2, \frac{1+\sqrt{-31}}{2}\right)^2=\left(4, \frac{1+\sqrt{-31}}{2}\right) \not\sim (1),$$

since the only integer of $k(\sqrt{-31})$, whose norm is 4, is 2, and, if

$$\left(2, \frac{1+\sqrt{-31}}{2}\right)^2=(2),$$

then

$$\left(2, \frac{1+\sqrt{-31}}{2}\right)=\left(2, \frac{1-\sqrt{-31}}{2}\right),$$

which is impossible.

We have

$$\left(2, \frac{1+\sqrt{-31}}{2}\right)^3 = \left(8, \frac{1+\sqrt{-31}}{2}\right) = \left(\frac{1+\sqrt{-31}}{2}\right) \sim (1),$$

since

$$8 = \frac{1+\sqrt{-31}}{2} \cdot \frac{1-\sqrt{-31}}{2}.$$

Hence we have so far found representatives, 1, $\left(2, \frac{1+\sqrt{-31}}{2}\right)$, and $\left(2, \frac{1+\sqrt{-31}}{2}\right)^2$, $\left(2, \frac{1+\sqrt{-31}}{2}\right)^3 \sim 1$ of three classes 1, A, A^2, $(A^3 = 1)$.

Therefore h is divisible by 3.

Of the eight ideals satisfying Minkowski's condition, (1), $\left(2, \frac{1+\sqrt{-31}}{2}\right)$, $\left(2, \frac{1-\sqrt{-31}}{2}\right)$, (2), $\left(2, \frac{1+\sqrt{-31}}{2}\right)^2$, $\left(2, \frac{1-\sqrt{-31}}{2}\right)^2$, $\left(5, \frac{3+\sqrt{-31}}{2}\right)$ and $\left(5, \frac{3-\sqrt{-31}}{2}\right)$ four belong to these classes and from

$$(2) = \left(2, \frac{1+\sqrt{-31}}{2}\right)\left(2, \frac{1-\sqrt{-31}}{2}\right)$$

we see that $\left(2, \frac{1-\sqrt{-31}}{2}\right)$ belongs to A^2, and hence $\left(2, \frac{1-\sqrt{-31}}{2}\right)^2$ to A.

The inequality $N - n + c < 2t$ is now seen to hold, for we have $N = 8$, $n = 6$, $c = 3$, and $t = 3$, and it is evident that $h = 3$. The classes to which $\left(5, \frac{3+\sqrt{-31}}{2}\right)$ and $\left(5, \frac{3-\sqrt{-31}}{2}\right)$ belong are easily determined, since

$$n\left[\frac{3+\sqrt{-31}}{2}\right] = 10,$$

and $\frac{3+\sqrt{-31}}{2}$ is a number of both $\left(2, \frac{1-\sqrt{-31}}{2}\right)$ and $\left(5, \frac{3+\sqrt{-31}}{2}\right)$, whence

$$\left(\frac{3+\sqrt{-31}}{2}\right) = \left(2, \frac{1-\sqrt{-31}}{2}\right)\left(5, \frac{3+\sqrt{-31}}{2}\right).$$

Therefore $\left(5, \frac{3+\sqrt{-31}}{2}\right)$ belongs to A, and $\left(5, \frac{3-\sqrt{-31}}{2}\right)$ to A^2.

Ex. 8. $k(\sqrt{82})$. Basis: 1, $\sqrt{82}$. $d = 328$.

$n[\alpha] \leqq \sqrt{328}\,|$; $n[\alpha] = 1, 2, 3, 4, 5, 6, 7, 8, 9, 10, 11, 12, 13, 14, 15, 16, 17$, or 18.

We have

$$(2) = (2, \sqrt{82})^2$$
$$(3) = (3, 1+\sqrt{82})(3, 1-\sqrt{82})$$
$$(5) = (5)$$
$$(7) = (7)$$
$$(11) = (11, 4+\sqrt{82})(11, 4-\sqrt{82})$$
$$(13) = (13, 2+\sqrt{82})(13, 2-\sqrt{82})$$
$$(17) = (17).$$

We must now determine whether $(2, \sqrt{82})$ is a principal ideal. To do this we determine whether $k(\sqrt{82})$ contains an integer whose norm is 2; that is whether integral values of x and y can be found satisfying the equation

$$x^2 - 82y^2 = 2. \qquad 9)$$

Using Th. 6, Chap XIII, and developing $\sqrt{82}$ as a continued fraction, we see that

$$\sqrt{82} = 9 + \frac{1}{18+}\frac{1}{18+}\cdots$$

and have

n	a_n	p_n	q_n	M_n
1	9	9	1	1
2	18	163	18	1

From this it is evident that 9) has no solution, and hence that $(2, \sqrt{82})$ is a non-principal ideal.

From this development of $\sqrt{82}$, it is also evident that $k(\sqrt{82})$ contains no integers with norms 3, 5, 6, or 7, and furthermore $9+\sqrt{82}$ is the fundamental unit.[1]

That $k(\sqrt{82})$ contained no integers with norms 5 or 7 was, of course, already shown by the fact (5) and (7) are principal ideals. We have, however, learned, in addition to the fact that $(2, \sqrt{82})$ is a non-principal ideal, that $(3, 1+\sqrt{82})$ and $(3, 1-\sqrt{82})$ are non-principal ideals, since $k(\sqrt{82})$ contains no integer with norm 3, and, moreover, that neither of the products of these last two ideals by $(2, \sqrt{82})$ can be a principal ideal, since $k(\sqrt{82})$ contains no integer with norm 6.

We shall now determine into how many classes the ideals, which have been proved to be non-principal, fall.

We have $(2, \sqrt{82})$ as a representative of a new class, A, and $A^2 = 1$.

Calculate now the norms of a few integers of $k(\sqrt{82})$. We have $n[8+\sqrt{82}] = -18$.

$(8+\sqrt{82})$ is the product of three ideals whose norms are 2, 3 and 3 respectively. Since $8+\sqrt{82}$ is a number of $(3, 1-\sqrt{82})$ and not of $(3, 1+\sqrt{82})$, we must have

$$(8+\sqrt{82}) = (2, \sqrt{82})\ (3, 1-\sqrt{82})^2.$$

[1] Since the norm of the fundamental unit, $9+\sqrt{82}$, of $k(\sqrt{82})$ is -1, the non-existence of an integer with a given positive norm implies the non-existence of an integer with corresponding negative norm.

From which it follows that $(3, 1-\sqrt{82})^2$ belongs to A, and $(3, 1-\sqrt{82})$ gives a new class B. We have $A = B^2$.

But $n[1-\sqrt{82}] = -81 = -3^4$, and $1-\sqrt{82}$ is a number of $(3, 1-\sqrt{82})$ and not of $(3, 1+\sqrt{82})$. Hence

$$(1-\sqrt{82}) = (3, 1-\sqrt{82})^4,$$

and we see that we now have four classes 1, B, B^2, B^3, $(B^4 = 1)$, as representatives of which among the ideals satisfying Minkowski's condition, we may take (1), $(3, 1-\sqrt{82})$, $(2, \sqrt{82})$ and $(3, 1+\sqrt{82})$. We have now $N = 21$, $n = 17$, $c = 4$, and $t = 4$, and hence $N - n + c \not< 2t$; that is, there are four ideals, the factors of (11) and (13), whose classes are yet undetermined and we have found representatives of all of our four known classes. One of these remaining ideals might therefore give a new class and we should have $h = 8$. That h is either 4 or 8, we now know. This is, however, easily settled, for $n[7+\sqrt{82}] = -33$, and $7+\sqrt{82}$ is a number of both $(3, 1+\sqrt{82})$ and $(11, 4-\sqrt{82})$. Hence

$$(7+\sqrt{82}) = (3, 1+\sqrt{82})(11, 4-\sqrt{82}),$$

and $(11, 4-\sqrt{82})$ belongs to the class B. Therefore

$$h = 4.$$

We see that $(11, 4+\sqrt{82})$ belongs to B^3 and from the fact that $n[2+\sqrt{82}] = -78 = -2 \cdot 3 \cdot 13$, we can show easily that $(13, 2+\sqrt{82})$ belongs to B and $(13, 2-\sqrt{82})$ to B^3.

Ex. 9. Show that $h=6$ for $k(\sqrt{-26})$, $h=1$ for $k(\sqrt{-19})$, $h=2$ for $k(\sqrt{15})$, $h=2$ for $k(\sqrt{26})$, $h=4$ for $k(\sqrt{-34})$, $h=6$ for $k(\sqrt{-61})$.

The labor of finding h by this method can be reduced by using another theorem, due also to Minkowski, which gives a smaller limit below which the norms of the representatives of the classes must fall, thus diminishing the number of ideals to be examined. This theorem for the general realm of the nth degree is as follows: *In every ideal class there is an ideal, $\mathfrak{a}$, such that*

$$n[\mathfrak{a}] < \left(\frac{4}{\pi}\right)^r \frac{n!}{n^n} \,|\sqrt{d}\,|,$$

where n is the degree of the realm, d its discriminant, and r the number of pairs of imaginary realms which occur among the conjugate realms, $k, k', \cdots, k^{(n-1)}$.[1]

In a real quadratic realm, we have $n[\mathfrak{a}] < \frac{1}{2}\,|\sqrt{d}\,|$, and in the case of $k(\sqrt{82})$ need, therefore, to examine only those ideals whose norms are less than 10.

It will be noticed that we did find, as representatives of all classes, ideals whose norms satisfied this condition.

[1] Minkowski: Diophantische Approximationen, p. 185. See also "Tafel der Klassenanzahlen für Kubische Zahlkörper" by the author for its application to cubic realms.

For a table giving the class numbers of quadratic realms, their fundamental units and other data, see J. Sommer: Vorlesungen über Zahlentheorie.

This table extends, for imaginary realms, to $m = -97$, and, for real realms, to $m = 101$. This book should be consulted by those who wish to pursue the subject further.

The class number of a realm can also be expressed by means of an infinite series. See Hilbert: Bericht, Cap. VII and § 79; also Dirichlet-Dedekind: § 184.

We shall close this chapter with a theorem that gives important information regarding the class number of a realm in a certain special case. For its proof, we shall need two theorems, the second of which throws additional light upon the question whether the norm of the fundamental unit of a real quadratic realm is 1 or -1.

THEOREM 8. *Every number, α, of a quadratic realm, $k(\sqrt{m})$, whose norm is 1, can be represented as the quotient, γ/γ', of two conjugate integers, γ, γ', of the realm.*[1]

We have seen that α can be put in the form

$$\alpha = \frac{a + b\omega}{c},$$

where $1, \omega$ is a basis of the realm and a, b and c are rational integers. Let $\gamma = x + y\omega$, where x and y are rational integers to be determined, and let the rational equation of which ω is a root be

$$x^2 + ex + f = 0.$$

Put

$$\frac{a + b\omega}{c} = \frac{x + y\omega}{x + y\omega'} \tag{10}$$

Making use of the relations $\omega + \omega' = -e$, and $\omega\omega' = f$, we have from 10), as the equations that x and y must satisfy,

$$\left.\begin{aligned} (a - c)x + (bf - ae)y &= 0, \\ bx - (a + c)y &= 0. \end{aligned}\right\} \tag{11}$$

These equations evidently have a solution different from $x = 0$,

[1] See Hilbert: Bericht, Satz 90.

$y=0$ when and only when the determinant, D, of their coefficients is 0, and, if $D=0$, they have an infinite number of solutions $x=rx_1$, $y=ry_1$, where x_1, y_1 is any particular solution different from 0, 0, and hence have an infinite number of integral solutions, for we can choose r so that rx_1, ry_1 are integers.

We have

$$D=-a^2+abe-b^2f+c^2=-n[\alpha]\cdot c^2+c^2=0,$$

since $n[\alpha]=1$. Hence the equations 11) have an infinite number of integral solutions and the theorem is therefore proved.

As a particular solution of 11), we may take $x=a+c$, $y=b$, all integral solutions then being of the form

$$x=\frac{s(a+c)}{t}, \quad y=\frac{sb}{t},$$

where s and t are rational integers and t a common divisor of $a+c$ and b.

We can, of course, take a, b and c without a common divisor, and then have also a prime to b, since $n[\alpha]=1$.

Ex. Let $\alpha=\dfrac{2+\sqrt{-5}}{3}$. We have $a=2$, $b=1$, $c=3$, and hence

$$\frac{2+\sqrt{-5}}{3}=\frac{5+\sqrt{-5}}{5-\sqrt{-5}}.$$

THEOREM 9. *If the discriminant, d, of a real quadratic realm, $k(\sqrt{m})$, be divisible by a single prime number, the norm of the fundamental unit of the realm is* -1.[1]

In order that d may be divisible by a single prime number, we must have $m=2$, or a prime $\equiv 1$, mod 4.

Let ϵ be the fundamental unit of $k(\sqrt{m})$.

If $n[\epsilon]=1$, by Th. 8 there would exist an integer, γ, of $k(\sqrt{m})$ such that

$$\epsilon=\frac{\gamma}{\gamma'}. \qquad 12)$$

Then from 12) it would follow that

$$(\gamma)=(\gamma'),$$

[1] Hilbert: Bericht, p. 294.

and hence that (γ) is either an ambiguous ideal (p. 347), an ambiguous ideal multiplied by a rational principal ideal (a), or (a). Since, however, d is divisible by the single prime m, the realm contains only one ambiguous prime ideal $(\sqrt{m})$, which is therefore the only ambiguous ideal of the realm. Hence, we must have

$$(\gamma)=(\sqrt{m}),\ (a\sqrt{m})\ \text{or}\ (a),$$

and therefore $\gamma=\eta\sqrt{m},\ \eta a\sqrt{m}$ or ηa,

where η is a unit. But we have then from 12)

$$\epsilon=\frac{\eta\sqrt{m}}{-\eta'\sqrt{m}},\quad \frac{\eta a\sqrt{m}}{-\eta' a\sqrt{m}}\quad \text{or}\quad \frac{\eta a}{\eta' a},$$

and hence $\epsilon=-\eta^2$ or η^2,

from which it would follow that ϵ is not the fundamental unit, as was assumed. Hence the assumption that $n[\epsilon]=1$ is untenable, and the theorem is proved.

The realms $k(\sqrt{2})$, $k(\sqrt{5})$ and $k(\sqrt{17})$, whose fundamental units have been found to be $1+\sqrt{2}$, $\frac{1}{2}(1+\sqrt{5})$ and $4+\sqrt{17}$ respectively, will illustrate the truth of this theorem.

THEOREM 10. *If the discriminant of a quadratic realm, $k(\sqrt{m})$, be divisible by a single prime number, the class number, h, of the realm is odd.*[1]

Assume h to be even. Then there is in the realm certainly one non-principal ideal, $\mathfrak{j}$, whose square is a principal ideal; that is, $\mathfrak{j}^2\sim 1$. But we have also $\mathfrak{j}\mathfrak{j}'\sim 1$, and hence $\mathfrak{j}\sim\mathfrak{j}'$; that is, there exist integers, α, β, of the realm such that

$$(\alpha)\mathfrak{j}=(\beta)\mathfrak{j}'. \qquad 13)$$

From 13) we have $n[(\alpha)]=n[(\beta)]$, whence $\alpha/\beta,=\kappa$, is a number of the realm whose norm is ± 1. When $k(\sqrt{m})$ is imaginary, we have $n[\kappa]=1$, and when $k(\sqrt{m})$ is real and $n[\epsilon]=-1$, where ϵ is the fundamental unit, we have either $n[\kappa]=1$, or $n[\epsilon\kappa]=1$. By Th. 8 we can put $\kappa=\gamma/\gamma'$, or $\epsilon\kappa=\gamma/\gamma'$, according as $n[\kappa]=1$ or -1, γ and γ' being conjugate integers of the realm. In both cases, we have

[1] Hilbert: Bericht, Hülfsatz 13.

$$\frac{(\alpha)}{(\beta)} = \frac{(\gamma)}{(\gamma')},$$

and hence from 13) $(\gamma)\mathfrak{j} = (\gamma')\mathfrak{j}'$, as a consequence of $\mathfrak{j}^2 \sim 1$, where $\mathfrak{j}$ is a non-principal ideal; that is, as a consequence of h even.

Hence $(\gamma)\mathfrak{j}$ is either an ambiguous ideal, an ambiguous ideal multiplied by a rational principal ideal (a), or (a). Since, however, when $m = 2$, or a prime $\equiv 1$, mod 4, the realm contains no ambiguous ideal other than $(\sqrt{m})$ (see proof of Th. 9), and, in the case of $k(i)$, the only ambiguous ideal is $(1+i)$, we see that in all cases $(\gamma)\mathfrak{j}$ must be a principal ideal, and hence $\mathfrak{j}$ a principal ideal. But this renders untenable our assumption that h is even. Hence h is odd.

The realms $k(i)$, $k(\sqrt{-3})$, $k(\sqrt{2})$ and $k(\sqrt{-31})$, whose class numbers were found to be 1, 1, 1 and 3 respectively, will illustrate the truth of this theorem.

It is evident that in determining the class number of a realm, satisfying the conditions of Th. 10, we can use, since h must be odd, instead of the inequality $N - n + c < 2t$, the inequality $N - n + c < 3t$, thus shortening the work still further. Making use of this in Ex. 7, it is unnecessary to determine the class to which belongs $\left(2, \frac{1 - \sqrt{-31}}{2}\right)$.

INDEX.

Numerals refer to pages.